Instructor's Solutions Manual

to accompany

Precalculus

A Graphing Approach

Raymond A. Barnett
Merritt College

Michael R. Ziegler
Marquette University

Karl E. Byleen
Marquette University

Norma James
New Mexico State University

Boston   Burr Ridge, IL   Dubuque, IA   Madison, WI   New York   San Francisco   St. Louis
Bangkok   Bogotá   Caracas   Lisbon   London   Madrid
Mexico City   Milan   New Delhi   Seoul   Singapore   Sydney   Taipei   Toronto

McGraw-Hill Higher Education

A Division of The McGraw-Hill Companies

Instructor's Solutions Manual to accompany
PRECALCULUS: A GRAPHING APPROACH.

This book is printed on acid-free paper.

3 4 5 6 7 8 9 0 QPD/QPD 9 0 3 2

ISBN 0-07-005719-2

www.mhhe.com

Table of Contents

Part 1: Solutions

Part II: Answers

PREFACE

Part I of this manual contains solutions to the even-numbered problems in the exercise sets at the end of each section in the textbook. The solutions to the odd-numbered problems in these exercise sets and to all problems in the chapter review and cumulative review exercise sets can be found in the Student Solutions Manual that accompanies this textbook. Thus, taken together, this manual and the Student Solutions Manual provide solutions to all problems in the textbook.

Part II of this manual contains the answers to all the problems in the textbook in one convenient location.

PART I
SOLUTIONS

CHAPTER 1
Exercise 1-1

2.

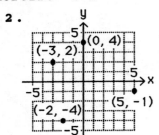

4.

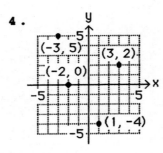

6. $A(0, 3)$, $B(-4, -5)$, $C(4, 1)$, $D(1, -3)$

8. $A(4, 2)$, $B(-2, -4)$, $C(-4, 3)$, $D(5, 0)$

10. $(-5, 4)$, $(6, -1)$

$$d = \sqrt{(x_1 - x_2)^2 + (y_1 - y_2)^2}$$
$$= \sqrt{(-5 - 6)^2 + (4 - (-1))^2}$$
$$= \sqrt{146}$$

12. $(5, -3)$, $(-1, 4)$

$$d = \sqrt{(x_1 - x_2)^2 + (y_1 - y_2)^2}$$
$$= \sqrt{(5 - (-1))^2 + (-3 - 4)^2}$$
$$= \sqrt{85}$$

14. $C(0, 0)$, $r = 5$
$$(x - h)^2 + (y - k)^2 = r^2$$
$$(x - 0)^2 + (y - 0)^2 = 5^2$$
$$x^2 + y^2 = 25$$

16. $C(5, 6)$, $r = 2$
$$(x - h)^2 + (y - k)^2 = r^2$$
$$(x - 5)^2 + (y - 6)^2 = 4$$

18. $C(-5, 6)$, $r = \sqrt{11}$
$$(x - h)^2 + (y - k)^2 = r^2$$
$$(x - (-5))^2 + (y - 6)^2 = (\sqrt{11})^2$$
$$(x + 5)^2 + (y - 6)^2 = 11$$

20. $C(4, -1)$, $r = \sqrt{5}$
$$(x - h)^2 + (y - k)^2 = r^2$$
$$(x - 4)^2 + (y - (-1))^2 = (\sqrt{5})^2$$
$$(x - 4)^2 + (y + 1)^2 = 5$$

22.

x	y
-3	5
-2	4
-1	3
0	2
1	1
2	0
3	-1

24.

x	y
-3	-5
-2	0
-1	3
0	4
1	3
2	0
3	-5

26.

x	y
-3	2.5
-2	4
-1	4.5
0	4
1	2.5
2	0
3	-3.5

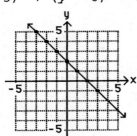

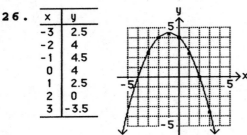

28. (A) 5   (B) -8   (C) 6   (D) -2, 4   (E) -4, 6   (F) -3, 5

30. (A) -3   (B) 1   (C) 4   (D) 3, 6   (E) -6, -4, 2, 7   (F) -5, 2, 7

32.

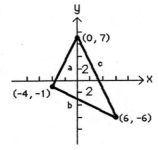

$$c = \sqrt{(0 - 6)^2 + (7 - (-6))^2} = \sqrt{205}$$

$$a = \sqrt{(0 - (-4))^2 + (7 - (-1))^2} = \sqrt{80}$$

$$b = \sqrt{(-4 - 6)^2 + (-1 - (-6))^2} = \sqrt{125}$$

$$c^2 = 205$$

$$a^2 + b^2 = 80 + 125 = 205$$

$$c^2 = a^2 + b^2, \text{ a right triangle}$$

34.

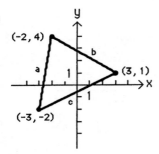

$$a = \sqrt{(-2 - (-3))^2 + (4 - (-2))^2} = \sqrt{37}$$

$$b = \sqrt{(-2 - 3)^2 + (4 - 1)^2} = \sqrt{34}$$

$$c = \sqrt{(3 - (-3))^2 + (1 - (-2))^2} = \sqrt{45}$$

$$p = a + b + c$$

$$= \sqrt{37} + \sqrt{34} + \sqrt{45}$$

$$\approx 18.62$$

36. $y = x^{2/3}$

x	y
−8	4
−1	1
0	0
1	1
8	4

38. $y = x^4$

x	y
−2	16
−1	1
0	0
1	1
2	16

40. $y = \sqrt{5 - x}$

x	y
5	0
1	2
4	1
−4	3

42. $y = x\sqrt{1 + x^2}$

x	y
−3	−9.5
−2	−4.5
−1	−1.4
0	0
1	1.4
2	4.5
3	9.5

44.

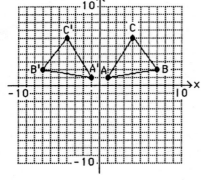

The triangles are mirror images of each other across the y-axis. Changing the sign of the x-coordinate reflects the graph across the y-axis.

46.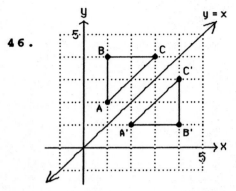

The triangles are mirror images of each other, reflected across the line $y = x$. Reversing the coordinates of each point reflects the graph across the line $y = x$.

48. $(-3, 2)$, $(5, -2)$

$$\left(\frac{x_1 + x_2}{2}, \frac{y_1 + y_2}{2}\right) = \left(\frac{-3 + 5}{2}, \frac{(2 + (-2))}{2}\right) = (1, 0)$$

50. $(-3, 2)$, $(7, -4)$

Center: $\left(\dfrac{-3 + 7}{2}, \dfrac{(2 + (-4))}{2}\right) = (2, -1)$

Diameter: $d = \sqrt{(-3 - 7)^2 + (2 + 4)^2}$

$\qquad\qquad = \sqrt{100 + 36}$

$\qquad\qquad = \sqrt{136}$

$\qquad\qquad = 2\sqrt{34}$

Radius $= \dfrac{d}{2} = \sqrt{34}$

$(x - h)^2 + (y - k)^2 = r^2$
$(x - 2)^2 + (y + 1)^2 = 34$

52. $C(-5, 4)$ through $(2, -3)$

$\qquad (x - h)^2 + (y - k)^2 = r^2$

$\qquad (x - (-5))^2 + (y - 4)^2 = r^2$

$\qquad (x + 5)^2 + (y - 4)^2 = r^2$

at $(2, -3)$: $(2 + 5)^2 + (-3 - 4)^2 = r^2$

$\qquad\qquad\qquad 7^2 + (-7)^2 = r^2$

$\qquad\qquad\qquad 49 + 49 = r^2$

$\qquad\qquad\qquad\qquad 98 = r^2$

$\qquad (x + 5)^2 + (y - 4)^2 = 98$

54. (A) $p = \$5.60$, $q = 3000$ cases

(B) Supply increases by ≈ 300 cases when price increases.

(C) Supply decreases by 400 cases when price decreases.

(D) When the price increases, the supply will increase.

56. (A) 7:00 PM $\approx 60°$ (B) Lowest temperature $44°$ at 5 AM

(C) $52°$ at 9 AM and 10 PM

58. $n = 8 - p$ $4 \leq p \leq 8$
$R = np = (8 - p)p$,
$4 \leq p \leq 8$

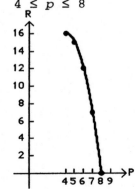

60. $V = 4\sqrt{25 - x^2}$, $-5 \leq x \leq 5$

(A)

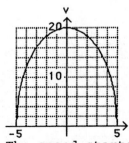

(B) The speed starts at 0 at the bottom of the oscillation and increases to a maximum speed of 20 (at the rest position). It then decreases to 0 at the top of the oscillation.

Exercise 1-2

2. (0, 10) Yes
x: -7 < 0 < 9
y: -4 < 10 < 11

4. (-3, -5) No
-5 is not in -4 < y < 11

6. (-8, 12) No
-8 is not in -7 ≤ x ≤ 9
12 is not in -4 < y < 11

8.

x	-4	0	-2	7	4
y	2	-4	0	-2	3

(A) Xmin = -4, Xmax = 7
    Ymin = -4, Ymax = 3

(B) Enter the values on your graphing calculator. Using the trace button will yield values of $x \approx .117$ apart and values of $y \approx .113$ apart. A rectangle in the plane can have tic marks at whatever intervals you decide.

10. $y = 0.5x$

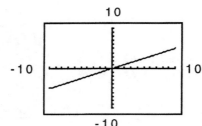

12. $y = 0.3x^2 - 4$

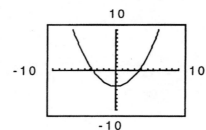

14. $y = -2\sqrt{x + 5}$

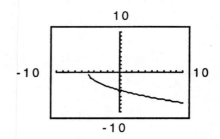

16. $y = 2x^2 + 12x + 5$, $-7 \le x \le 1$

x	-7	-5	-3	-1	1
y	19	-5	-13	-5	19

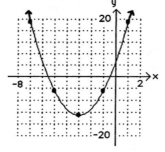

18. $y = \sqrt{8 - 2x}$, $-4 \le x \le 4$

x	-4	-2	0	2	4
y	4	3.5	2.8	2	0

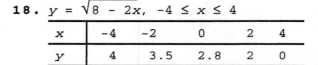

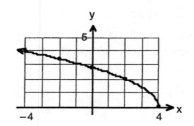

20. $y = 0.5x(x + 3.5)(2.8 - x)$, $-4 \le x \le 4$

x	-4	-2	0	2	4
y	6.8	-7.2	0	4.4	-18

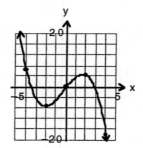

22. $y = 3 + 4\sqrt[3]{x - 4}$; graph y and trace and zoom to each y-value.
(A) (**5.95**, 8)   (B) (**-7.39**, -6)   (C) (**3.58**, 0)

24. $y = 2 - 0.5x - 0.1x^3$; graph y and trace and zoom to each y-value.
(A) (**-3.23**, 7)   (B) (**3.72**, -5)   (C) (**2.11**, 0)

26. $y = x^2 + 2x - 1$:

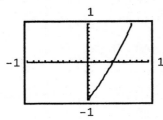 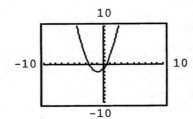 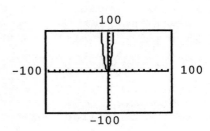

Best view

28. $y = 20x - x^2$:

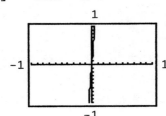 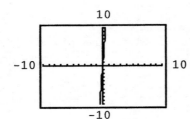 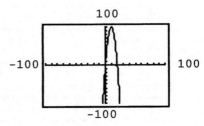

Best view

30. $3x^3 - 7x^2 + 3 = 0$; graph y and zoom and trace to all y-values of 0.
$x \approx -0.59, 0.81, 2.11$

32. $-0.01x^4 + 0.56x^2 - 3 = 0$; graph y and zoom and trace to all y-values of 0.
$x \approx -7.07, -2.45, 2.45, 7.07$

34. $(\sqrt[3]{4}, 4)$ on $y = x^3$. $\sqrt[3]{4} \approx 1.5874$

36. Answers will vary. For example on the TI-83, -4.8 to 14 produces x-values to the nearest tenth.

38. During unrestricted cursor movement, the y-coordinate does not change when the cursor moves left or right. When the cursor moves up or down, the x-coordinate does not change. These coordinates are coordinates of screen pixels. While tracing, the coordinate changes as the graph changes. Tracing produces coordinates on the graph itself.

40. $y = 25 + 50x - 16x^2$

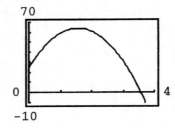

The ball is in the air approximately 3.6 seconds.

42. The base of the box will have dimensions $(9 - 2x)$ inches and $(12 - 2x)$ inches, with height x inches.
$$V = (9 - 2x)(12 - 2x)x$$
$$72 = (9 - 2x)(12 - 2x)x$$
Graph $y = (9 - 2x)(12 - 2x)x$ and trace and zoom to a y-value of 72:
$x \approx 1.06$
$x \approx 2.42$

A 1.06 in. square or a 2.42 in. square can be cut out.
Dimension for smaller square: 1.06" × 9.88" × 6.88"
Dimension for larger square: 2.42" × 7.16" × 4.16"

44. The box will have a base of $(10 - 1.5x)$ inches and $(10 - 2x)$ inches with a height of x inches ($x < 5$ since $10 - 2x > 0$).

$$V = \ell \cdot w \cdot h$$
$$75 = (10 - 1.5x)(10 - 2x)x$$

Graph $y = (10 - 1.5x)(10 - 2x)x$ and trace to a y-value of 75.

$\qquad x \approx 1.21, 2.65$

A 1.21 in. square or a 2.65 in. square can be cut out.
Dimension for smaller square: 1.21" × 7.58" × 8.19"
Dimension for larger square: 2.65" × 4.70" × 6.03"

46. Graph $y = 100 - 0.6\sqrt{x}$, $5{,}000 \le x \le 20{,}000$

(A)

x	11,700	10,000	8,400
y	35	40	45

(B) Demand decreases 1,600 cases when the price increases.

(C) Demand increases 1,700 cases when the price is decreased from \$40 to \$35.

48. $R = xy$ from problem 46.

(A)

y	35	40	45
R	409,500	400,000	378,000

(B) Revenue decreases \$22,000 when the price increases from \$40 to \$45.

(C) Revenue increases \$9,500 when the price decreases from \$40 to \$35.

(D) The company should lower the price \$5 to increase the revenue.

Exercise 1-3

2. A function. Each domain value is associated with a unique (one and only one) range value.

4. Not a function. The domain value -1 is associated with two range values.

6. A function. Each domain value is associated with a unique range value.

8. A function. No two ordered pairs have the same first term.
Domain = {-1, 0, 1, 2}; Range = {4, 3, 2, 1}

10. A function. No two ordered pairs have the same first term.
Domain = {-10, -5, 0, 5, 10}; Range = {0, 5, 10}

12. Not a function. The ordered pairs (1, 1) and (1, 2) as well as (2, 1) and (2, 2), and (3, 1) and (3, 2) have the same first term.

14. Vertical line test is passed, therefore a function.

16. Vertical line test is passed. A function.

18. Vertical line test failed. Not a function.

20. $g(t) = 4 - t$
$g(6) = 4 - 6$
$\qquad = -2$

22. $F(m) = 3m^2 + 2m - 4$
$F(-3) = 3(-3)^2 + 2(-3) - 4$
$F(-3) = 17$

24. $G(u) = u - u^2 \qquad g(t) = 4 - t$
$G(2) = 2 - 2^2 \qquad g(-3) = 4 - (-3)$
$G(2) = -2 \qquad\quad g(-3) = 7$

$G(2) - g(-3) = -2 - 7$
$\qquad\qquad\quad = -9$

26. $G(u) = u - u^2$ $F(m) = 3m^2 + 2m - 4$
    $G(-2) = -2 - (-2)^2$ $F(-1) = 3(-1)^2 + 2(-1) - 4$
    $G(-2) = -6$ $F(-1) = -3$
    $3G(-2) + 2F(-1) = 3(-6) + 2(-3) = -24$

28. $g(t) = 4 - t$ $G(u) = u - u^2$ $f(x) = 3x - 5$
    $g(4) = 4 - 4$ $G(1) = 1 - 1^2$ $f(2) = 3(2) - 5$
    $g(4) = 0$ $G(1) = 0$ $f(2) = 1$

$\dfrac{g(4) \cdot f(2)}{G(1)} = \dfrac{0 \cdot 1}{0}$, undefined.

30. $g(t) = 4 - t$
$\dfrac{g(5) - g(3)}{2} = \dfrac{(4 - 5) - (4 - 3)}{2} = \dfrac{-2}{2} = -1$

32. $f(x) = 1 + 7x - 5x^2$ Domain: all real numbers or $(-\infty, \infty)$

34. $f(x) = \dfrac{x}{x - 3}$, $x - 3 \neq 0$, $x \neq 3$
Domain all real numbers except 3 or $(-\infty, 3) \cup (3, \infty)$

36. $f(x) = 4\sqrt{x} + 3$ Domain: $x \geq 0$ or $[0, \infty)$

38. $f(x) = 2\sqrt{-x} - 1$, $-x \geq 0$ so $x \leq 0$
Domain: $x \leq 0$ or $(-\infty, 0]$

40. $f(x) = \dfrac{x}{x - 2} - \dfrac{3}{x + 3}$; $x - 2 \neq 0$, $x + 3 \neq 0$
Domain: all real numbers except -3 and 2 or $(-\infty, -3) \cup (-3, 2) \cup (2, \infty)$

42. $f(x) = \dfrac{\sqrt{-x}}{x + 4}$; denominator: $x \neq -4$, numerator: $x \leq 0$
Domain: $x \leq 0$, $x \neq -4$ or $(-\infty, -4) \cup (-4, 0]$

44. $f(1) = 5(1)^2 - 6$ **46.** $f(1) = -8 + 5(1) - 2(1)^2$
    $f(2) = 5(2)^2 - 6$ $f(2) = -8 + 5(2) - 2(2)^2$
    $f(3) = 5(3)^2 - 6$ $f(3) = -8 + 5(3) - 2(3)^2$
    $f(x) = 5x^2 - 6$ $f(x) = -8 + 5(x) - 2x^2$

48. $K(r) = 7 - 4r$

$\dfrac{K(1 + h) - K(1)}{h} = \dfrac{7 - 4(1 + h) - (7 - 4(1))}{h}$

$= \dfrac{7 - 4 - 4h - 7 + 4}{h} = \dfrac{-4h}{h}$

$= -4$

50. $P(m) = 2m^2 + 3$

$\dfrac{P(2 + h) - P(2)}{h} = \dfrac{2(2 + h)^2 + 3 - (2(2)^2 + 3)}{h}$

$= \dfrac{2(4 + 4h + h^2) + 3 - 8 - 3}{h}$

$= \dfrac{8 + 8h + 2h^2 - 8}{h} = \dfrac{8h + 2h^2}{h}$

$= 8 + 2h$

52. $D(p) = -3p^2 - 4p + 9$

$$\frac{D(-1 + h) - D(-1)}{h} = \frac{-3(-1 + h)^2 - 4(-1 + h) + 9 - (-3(-1)^2 - 4(-1) + 9)}{h}$$

$$= \frac{-3(1 - 2h + h^2) + 4 - 4h + 9 + 3 - 4 - 9}{h}$$

$$= \frac{-3 + 6h - 3h^2 - 4h + 3}{h}$$

$$= \frac{2h - 3h^2}{h}$$

$$= -3h + 2$$

54. $f(x) = 7x + 5x^3$

56. $G(x) = \sqrt{4 + x^2}$

58. $g(x) = 5x^3 - 8x$; Answers may vary. One possibility:
Function g multiplies the cube of the domain element by 5 and then subtracts the product of 8 and the domain element.

60. $G(x) = \dfrac{x}{3x - 6}$; Answers may vary. One possibility:
Function G divides the domain element by a denominator formed by multiplying the domain element by 3 and subtracting 6.

62. $g(x + h) = 5 - 7(x + h)^2 + 8(x + h)$

$g(x) = 5 - 7x^2 + 8x$

64. $s(x + h) = 2\sqrt[3]{x + h} - 6(x + h) - 5$

$s(x) = 2\sqrt[3]{x} - 6x - 5$

66. $f(x) = -2x + 5$

(A) $$\frac{f(x + h) - f(x)}{h} = \frac{-2(x + h) + 5 - (-2x + 5)}{h}$$

$$= \frac{-2x - 2h + 5 + 2x - 5}{h} = \frac{-2h}{h}$$

$$= -2$$

(B) $$\frac{f(x) - f(a)}{x - a} = \frac{-2x + 5 - (-2a + 5)}{x - a}$$

$$= \frac{-2x + 5 + 2a - 5}{x - a}$$

$$= \frac{-2(x - a)}{x - a}$$

$$= -2$$

68. $f(x) = x^2 + x - 1$

(A) $$\frac{f(x + h) - f(x)}{h} = \frac{(x + h)^2 + (x + h) - 1 - (x^2 + x - 1)}{h}$$

$$= \frac{x^2 + 2xh + h^2 + x + h - 1 - x^2 - x + 1}{h}$$

$$= \frac{2xh + h^2 + h}{h}$$

$$= 2x + h + 1$$

(B) $\dfrac{f(x) - f(a)}{x - a} = \dfrac{x^2 + x - 1 - (a^2 + a - 1)}{x - a}$

$= \dfrac{x^2 + x - 1 - a^2 - a + 1}{x - a}$

$= \dfrac{x^2 + x - a^2 - a}{x - a} = \dfrac{(x^2 - a^2) + (x - a)}{x - a}$

$= \dfrac{(x + a)(x - a) + (x - a)}{(x - a)}$

$= \dfrac{(x - a)(x + a + 1)}{(x - a)}$

$= x + a + 1$

70. $f(x) = -x^2 - 2x - 4$

(A) $\dfrac{f(x + h) - f(x)}{h} = \dfrac{-(x + h)^2 - 2(x + h) - 4 - (-x^2 - 2x - 4)}{h}$

$= \dfrac{-(x^2 + 2xh + h^2) - 2x - 2h - 4 + x^2 + 2x + 4}{h}$

$= \dfrac{-x^2 - 2xh - h^2 - 2h + x^2}{h}$

$= \dfrac{-2xh - h^2 - 2h}{h}$

$= -2x - h - 2$

(B) $\dfrac{f(x) - f(a)}{x - a} = \dfrac{-x^2 - 2x - 4 - (-a^2 - 2a - 4)}{x - a}$

$= \dfrac{-x^2 - 2x - 4 + a^2 + 2a + 4}{x - a}$

$= \dfrac{-x^2 + a^2 - 2x + 2a}{x - a}$

$= \dfrac{-(x - a)(x + a) - 2(x - a)}{x - a}$

$= \dfrac{(x - a)(-(x + a) - 2)}{x - a}$

$= -x - a - 2$

72. $f(x) = x^3 + x$

(A) $\dfrac{f(x + h) - f(x)}{h} = \dfrac{(x + h)^3 + x + h - (x^3 + x)}{h}$

$= \dfrac{x^3 + 3x^2h + 3xh^2 + h^3 + x + h - x^3 - x}{h}$

$= \dfrac{3x^2h + 3xh^2 + h^3 + h}{h}$

$= 3x^2 + 3xh + h^2 + 1$

(B)
$$\frac{f(x) - f(a)}{x - a} = \frac{x^3 + x - (a^3 + a)}{x - a}$$

$$= \frac{x^3 + x - a^3 - a}{x - a}$$

$$= \frac{x^3 - a^3 + x - a}{x - a}$$

$$= \frac{(x - a)(x^2 + ax + a^2) + (x - a)}{(x - a)}$$

$$= \frac{(x - a)(x^2 + ax + a^2 + 1)}{(x - a)}$$

$$= x^2 + ax + a^2 + 1$$

74. $f(x) = \dfrac{x^3 - 1}{x - 1}$

x	y
1.001	3.003
0.999	2.997

$$f(x) = \frac{(x - 1)(x^2 + x + 1)}{x - 1}$$
$$= x^2 + x + 1, \ x \neq 1$$

For $f_1(x) = x^2 + x + 1$
$\quad f_1(1) = 1 + 1 + 1 = 3$

The value would be 3.

76. $S(t) = 10t^2$

(A) $S(8) = 10(8)^2 = 640$
$\quad S(9) = 10(9)^2 = 810$
$\quad S(10) = 10(10)^2 = 1000$
$\quad S(11) = 10(11)^2 = 1210$

(B)
$$\frac{S(11 + h) - S(11)}{h} = \frac{10(11 + h)^2 - 10(11)^2}{h}$$

$$= \frac{10(11^2 + 22h + h^2) - 10(11)^2}{h}$$

$$= \frac{10(11)^2 + 220h + 10h^2 - 10(11)^2}{h}$$

$$= \frac{220h + 10h^2}{h}$$

$$= 220 + 10h$$

(C) $220 + h \rightarrow 220$ as h tends to 0.
This is the speed of the automobile at the instant $t = 11$ sec.

78. $A(x) = 25 - 9x$

(A)
x	0	1	2	3	4	5
$A(x)$	25	16	7	-2	-11	-20

(B) As the altitude increases 1 km, the air temperature decreases by 9°C.

80. $S(x) = 15 + 0.7x$
There is a $15 fixed fee + $0.70 (70¢) for each minute it takes for installation.

82. $I(t) = 1.2 + 0.3t$, 1988: $t = 0$

(A)

t	0	1	2	3	4
Net Income	1.2	1.5	1.8	2.1	2.4
$I(t)$	1.2	1.5	1.8	2.1	2.4

(B)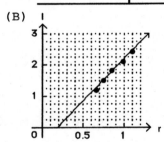

(C) Using the table feature with Tblst = 0 and ΔTbl = 1, then,
1993, $t = 5$:
   $I(5) = \$2.7$ billion
2000, $t = 12$:
   $I(12) = \$4.8$ billion

(D) From 1988 to 1992, the company's income rose at a yearly (linear) rate of 30% (.3t).

84. $I(r) = -.5 + 2.7r$

(A)

r (R&D)	0.66	0.75	0.85	0.99	1.1
Net Income	1.2	1.5	1.8	2.1	2.4
$I(r)$	1.3	1.5	1.8	2.2	2.5

(B)

(C) $I(1.5) = -0.5 + 2.7(1.5) = 3.55$
$\approx \$3.6$ billion

$I(2) = -0.5 + 2.7(2) = \$4.9$ billion

Exercise 1-4

2. For g:
(A) Domain: $(-5, 5]$
(B) Range: $[-4, 4)$
(C) x-intercept(s): 0
(D) y-intercept: 0
(E) Increasing: none
(F) Decreasing: $(-5, 5)$
(G) Constant: none
(H) No points of discontinuity

4. For k:
(A) Domain: $(-\infty, \infty)$
(B) Range: $(-\infty, 3]$
(C) x-intercepts: 0, 4
(D) y-intercepts: 0
(E) Increasing: $(-\infty, 2]$
(F) Decreasing: $[2, \infty)$
(G) Constant: none
(H) No points of discontinuity

6. For q:
(A) Domain: $(-\infty, -3) \cup (-3, \infty)$
(B) Range: $(-\infty, -2) \cup [2, \infty)$
(C) x-intercepts: none
(D) y-intercept: 2
(E) Increasing: $(-\infty, -3) \cup [3, \infty)$
(F) Decreasing: none
(G) Constant: $(-3, 3]$
(H) $x = -3$ is a point of discontinuity

8. $g(x) = 6 - |x - 3|$

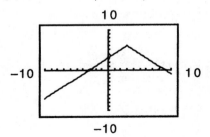

Increasing: $[-10, 3]$
Decreasing: $[3, 10]$
Constant: none

10. $k(x) = |x - 2| - x$

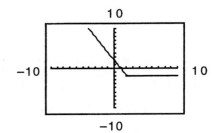

Increasing: none
Decreasing: [-10, 2]
Constant: [2, 10]

12. $h(x) = |x + 5| - |x - 2|$

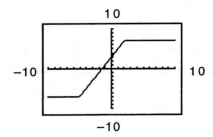

Increasing: [-5, 2]
Decreasing: none
Constant: [-10, -5] ∪ [2, 10]

14. $g(x) = |x + 2| + |x - 4|$

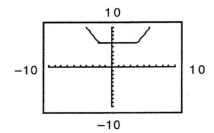

Increasing: [4, 10]
Decreasing: [-10, -2]
Constant: [-2, 4]

16. $S(x) = |x| - |x + 5| - |x - 3|$

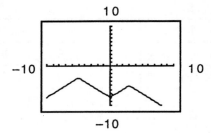

Increasing: [-10, -5] ∪ [0, 3]
Decreasing: [-5, 0] ∪ [3, 10]
Constant: none

18. One possible answer:

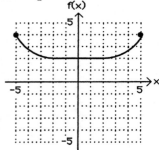

20. One possible answer:

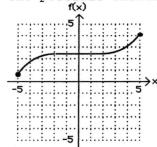

22. One possible answer:

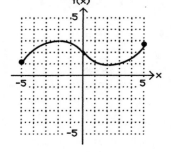

24. Graph $y = 5 - 0.3x^2 - x$
local maximum: (-1.7, 5.8)
x-intercepts: -6.1, 2.7

26. Graph $y = 3x - 8\sqrt{x}$
local minimum: (1.8, -5.3)
x-intercepts: 0, 7.1

28. Graph $y = 2\sqrt[3]{x} - |x| + 2$
local maximum: (0.5, 3.1)
x-intercepts: -0.5, 5.5

30. $f(x) = \begin{cases} x & \text{if } -2 \leq x < 1 \\ -x + 2 & \text{if } 1 \leq x \leq 2 \end{cases}$

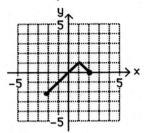

Domain: [-2, 2]; Range: [-2, 1]

32. $f(x) = \begin{cases} 1 & \text{if } -2 \leq x < 2 \\ -3 & \text{if } 2 < x \leq 5 \end{cases}$

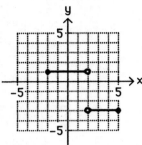

Domain: [-2, 2) ∪ (2, 5]; Range: {-3, 1}
Discontinuous at $x = 2$

34. $f(x) = \begin{cases} -1 - x & \text{if } x \leq 2 \\ 5 - x & \text{if } x > 2 \end{cases}$
Domain: all real numbers
Range: all real numbers
Discontinuous at $x = 2$

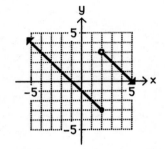

36. $h(x) = \begin{cases} -x^2 - 2 & \text{if } x < 0 \\ x^2 + 2 & \text{if } x > 0 \end{cases}$
Domain: $x \neq 0 \Leftrightarrow (-\infty, 0) \cup (0, \infty)$
Range: $(-\infty, -2) \cup (2, \infty)$
Discontinuous at $x = 0$

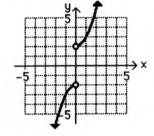

38. $g(x) = -x^2 + 6.9x + 25$
The graph of g increases on [-10, 3.45] to a local maximum value, $f(3.45) \approx 36.90$, and then decreases on [3.45, 10].

40. $k(x) = -x^3 + x^2 + 82x - 25$
The graph of k decreases on [-10, -4.91] to a local minimum value, $f(-4.91) \approx -285.14$, increases on [-4.91, 5.57] to a local maximum value, $f(5.57) \approx 289.96$, and then decreases on [5.57, 10].

42. $q(x) = |x^2 - 2x - 30|$
The graph of q decreases on [-10, -4.57] to a local minimum value, $f(-4.57) \approx 0$, increases on [-4.57, 1] to a local maximum value, $f(1) = 31$, decreases on [1, 6.57] to a local minimum value, $f(6.57) \approx 0$, and then increases on [6.57, 10].

44. One possible answer:

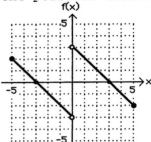

46. One possible answer:

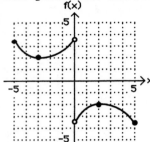

48. One possible answer:

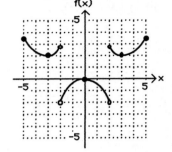

50. $f(x) = \dfrac{4x + 12}{|x + 3|}$

Domain: All real numbers except $x = -3$;
Range: $\{-4, 4\}$ (A set, not an interval);
Discontinuous at $x = -3$

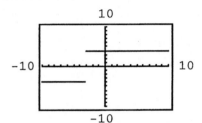

52. $f(x) = x + \dfrac{|2x + 2|}{x + 1}$

Domain: All real numbers except $x = -1$;
Range: $(-\infty, -3) \cup (1, \infty)$;
Discontinuous at $x = -1$

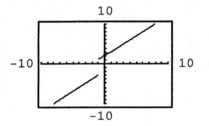

54. $f(x) = |x| + \dfrac{|2x + 4|}{x + 2}$

Domain: All real numbers except $x = -2$;
Range: $(0, \infty)$;
Discontinuous at $x = -2$

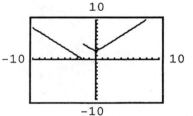

56. $f(x) = \left[\!\left[\dfrac{x}{3} \right]\!\right]$

$$f(x) = \begin{cases} -2 & \text{if } -6 \leq x < -3 \\ -1 & \text{if } -3 \leq x < 0 \\ 0 & \text{if } 0 \leq x < 3 \\ 1 & \text{if } 3 \leq x < 6 \\ 2 & \text{if } 6 \leq x < 9 \end{cases}$$

Domain: all real numbers
Range: all integers
Discontinuous at all integers divisible by 3

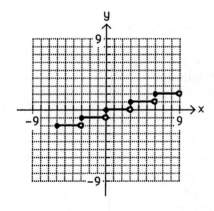

58. $f(x) = [\![2x]\!]$

$$f(x) = \begin{cases} \vdots \\ -2 \text{ if } -1 \le x < -\dfrac{1}{2} \\ -1 \text{ if } -\dfrac{1}{2} \le x < 0 \\ 0 \text{ if } 0 \le x < \dfrac{1}{2} \\ 1 \text{ if } \dfrac{1}{2} \le x < 1 \\ 2 \text{ if } 1 \le x < \dfrac{3}{2} \\ \vdots \end{cases}$$

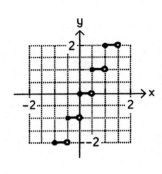

Domain: all real numbers
Range: all integers
Discontinuous at all rational numbers of the form $\dfrac{k}{2}$ where k is an integer.

60. $f(x) = [\![x]\!] - x$

$$f(x) = \begin{cases} \vdots \\ \vdots \\ -2 - x \text{ if } -2 \le x < -1 \\ -1 - x \text{ if } -1 \le x < 0 \\ 0 - x \text{ if } 0 \le x < 1 \\ 1 - x \text{ if } 1 \le x < 2 \\ 2 - x \text{ if } 2 \le x < 3 \\ \vdots \end{cases}$$

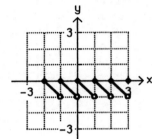

Domain: all real numbers
Range: (-1, 0]
Discontinuous at all integers.

62. (A) One possible answer:

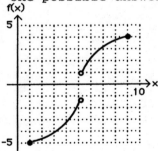

(B) The graph can cross the x axis at most one time.

64. (A) One possible answer:

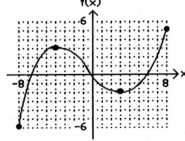

(B) The graph crosses the x-axis three times. Yes, it could cross an infinite number of times. It could not cross fewer than three times.

66. (A) One possible answer:

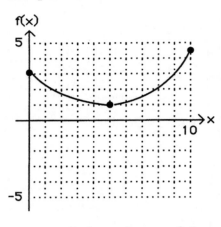

(B) The graph cannot cross the *x* axis.

68. (A) $C(x) = \begin{cases} 4 & 0 < x \le 1 \\ 6 & 1 < x \le 2 \\ 8 & 2 < x \le 3 \\ 10 & 3 < x \le 4 \\ 12 & 4 < x \le 5 \\ 14 & 5 < x \le 6 \end{cases}$

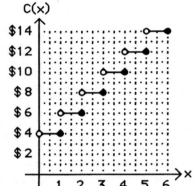

(B) No, since $f(x) \ne C(x)$ at $x = 1, 2, 3, 4, 5,$ or 6

70. $S(x) = \begin{cases} 2x & \text{if } 0 \le x \le 30 \\ 2(30) + 1(x - 30) = x + 30 & \text{if } x > 30 \end{cases}$

No points of discontinuity.
$S(25) = 50$; $S(45) = 75$

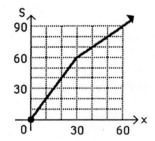

72. $f(x) = 100 \left[\!\left[0.5 + \dfrac{x}{100} \right]\!\right]$

x	40	-40	60	-60	740	750	7,551	-601	-649	-651
$f(x)$	0	0	100	-100	700	800	7,600	-600	-600	-700

$f(x)$ rounds to the nearest hundred.

74. $f(x) = \dfrac{1}{1000} \left[\!\left[0.5 + 1000x \right]\!\right]$

$f(x)$ is a function that rounds real numbers to the nearest thousandth.

76. $P(x) = 38x - 0.035x^2 - 4000$ $0 \le x \le 1700$

(A) $P(100) = -550$ Estimated maximum profit is
$P(200) = 2200$ $6,250 when 500 car seats are sold.
$P(500) = 6250$
$P(600) = 6200$

(B) The maximum profit is \$6,314.29 when 543 car seats are sold.

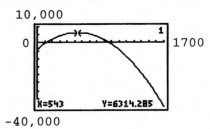

78. $V(x) = 0.5x(40 - 3x)(20 - 2x)$ $0 \le x \le 10$

(A)

x	0	1	2	3	4	5	6	7
$V(x)$	0	333	544	651	672	625	528	399

The estimated maximum volume is 672 in³ when the side of the cut-out square is 4 in.

(B) The maximum volume is approximately 673.84 in³ when the side of the cut-out square is approximately 3.77 in.

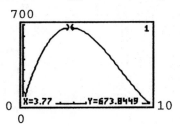

80. $T(x) = 2(20 - x) + 8\sqrt{x^2 + 64}$, $0 \le x \le 20$

(A)

x	0	5	10	5	20
$T(x)$	104	105	122	146	172

The estimated minimal time is 104 minutes when the land portion of the trip is 20 miles.

(B) The minimal time is approximately 102 minutes when the land portion of the trip is approximately 17.9 miles.

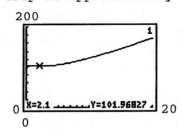

82. $f(x) = 0.33x^2 - 1.3x + 4.8$; 1989: $x = 0$

(A)

x	0	1	2	3	4
Production	4.7	4.1	3.5	3.7	5.0
$f(x)$	4.8	3.8	3.5	3.9	4.9

(B)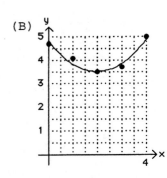

(C) 1994: f(5) ≈ 6.55 million vehicles;
     1995: f(6) ≈ 8.88 million vehicles

(D) From 1989 to 1991, the production
     decreases, with a local minimum occurring
     in 1991. The production then increases.

Exercise 1-5

2. $f(x) = x^5 - x$
$f(-x) = (-x)^5 - (-x)$
$= -x^5 + x$
$-f(x) = -(x^5 - x)$
$= -x^5 + x$
<u>odd</u>: $f(-x) = -f(x)$

4. $h(x) = x^4 - x^2$
$h(-x) = (-x)^4 - (-x)^2$
$= x^4 - x^2$
<u>even</u>: $h(x) = h(-x)$

6. $f(x) = x^5 - 3$
$f(-x) = (-x)^5 - 3$
$= -x^5 - 3$
$-f(x) = -(x^5 - 3)$
$= -x^5 + 3$
<u>neither</u>:
$f(x) \neq f(-x) \neq -f(x)$

8. $P(x) = x^4 - 4$
$P(-x) = (-x)^4 - 4$
$= x^4 - 4$
<u>even</u>: $P(x) = P(-x)$

10. $n(x) = 2x - 3$
$n(-x) = 2(-x) - 3$
$= -2x - 3$
$-n(x) = -(2x - 3)$
$= -2x + 3$
<u>neither</u>: $n(x) \neq n(-x) \neq -n(x)$

12. $g(x) - 1$

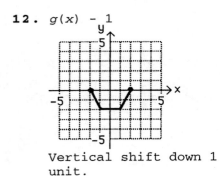

Vertical shift down 1
unit.

14. $f(x) - 1$

Vertical shift down 1
unit.

16. $g(x - 1)$

Horizontal shift right
1 unit.

18. $f(x - 1)$

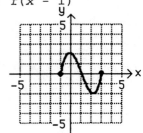

Horizontal shift right
1 unit.

20. $-g(x)$

Reflection about
x-axis.

22. $\frac{1}{2} f(x)$

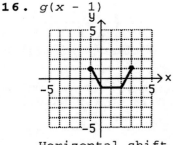

Vertical contraction.

24. The graph of $y = |x|$ is shifted 1 unit to the left; $y = |x + 1|$

26. The graph of $y = \sqrt[3]{x}$ is shifted up 3 units; $y = \sqrt[3]{x} + 3$

28. The graph of $y = \sqrt[3]{x}$ is expanded by a factor of 3: $y = 3\sqrt[3]{x}$

30. The graph of $y = x^2$ is reflected in the x axis; $y = -x^2$

32. $f(x) = x^3$
Shift 5 units right: $g(x) = (x - 5)^3$
Shift 4 units up: $g(x) = (x - 5)^3 + 4$
Graph $y_1 = x^3$, $y_2 = (x - 5)^3 + 4$

34. $f(x) = \sqrt{x}$
Shift 2 units down: $g(x) = \sqrt{x} - 2$
Reflected in the x-axis: $g(x) = -(\sqrt{x} - 2)$
Expanded by a factor of 4: $g(x) = -4(\sqrt{x} - 2)$
Graph $y_1 = \sqrt{x}$, $y_2 = -4(\sqrt{x} - 2)$

36. $f(x) = |x|$
Reflected in the x-axis: $g(x) = -|x|$
Contracted by a factor of 5: $g(x) = -0.5|x|$ or $g(x) = -\frac{1}{2}|x|$
Shifted 3 units to the right: $g(x) = -0.5|x - 3|$
Shifted 4 units up: $g(x) = -0.5|x - 3| + 4$
Graph $y_1 = |x|$, $y_2 = -0.5|x - 3| + 4$

38. $g(x) = (x - 4)^2 - 6$ is the graph of $y = x^2$ shifted 4 units right and 6 units down.

40. $k(x) = -|x + 5|$ is the graph of $y = |x|$ shifted 5 units left and reflected in the x-axis.

42. $g(x) = -2 + \sqrt{x + 3}$ is the graph of $y = \sqrt{x}$ shifted 3 units to the left and 2 units down.

44. $S(x) = -0.5|x|$ is the graph of $y = |x|$ contracted by a factor of 0.5 and reflected in the x-axis.

46. The basic function $y = x^2$ is shifted right 2 units and shifted down 4 units: $y = (x - 2)^2 - 4$.

48. The basic function $y = \sqrt{x}$ is shifted down 2 units: $y = \sqrt{x} - 2$.

50. The basic function $y = |x|$ is shifted left 2 units, up 5 units, and is reflected in the x-axis: $y = 5 - |x + 2|$.

52. The basic function $y = \sqrt[3]{x}$ is shifted right 1 unit, up 2 units and is expanded vertically by a factor of 2: $y = 2\sqrt[3]{x - 1} + 2$.

54. $F1(x) = f(x) + k$ Vertical shift
$F2(x) = F1(-x) = f(-x) + k$ Reflected in the y-axis

$G1(x) = f(-x)$ Reflected in y-axis
$G2(x) = G1(x) + k = f(-x) + k$ Vertical shift

Since $F2 = G2$, order does not matter.

56. $F1(x) = f(x) + k$ Vertical shift
$F2(x) = cF1(x) = cf(x) + ck$ Expansion

$G1(x) = cf(x)$ Expansion
$G2(x) = G1(x) + k = cf(x) + k$ Vertical shift

Since $F2$ and $G2$ are different, order does matter.

58. $F1(x) = f(x - h)$ Horizontal shift
$F2(x) = cF1(x) = cf(x - h)$ Contraction

$G1(x) = cf(x)$ Contraction
$G2(x) = cG1(x) = cf(x - h)$ Horizontal shift

Since $F2 = G2$, order does not matter.

60.

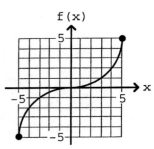

If f is odd, $f(-x) = -f(x)$.

62.

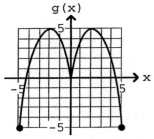

If g is even, $g(x) = g(-x)$.

64. (A) If f is even, $g(x) = xf(x)$ is odd.
example: $f(x) = x^2$, $g(x) = x^3$ (B) If f is odd, $g(x) = xf(x)$ is even.
example: $f(x) = x^3$, $g(x) = x^4$

66. Graph of $f(x)$

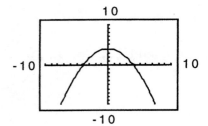

Graph of $|f(x)|$

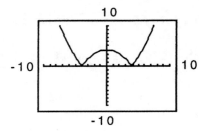

Graph of $-|f(x)|$

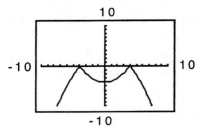

68. Graph of $f(x)$

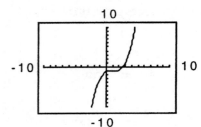

Graph of $|f(x)|$

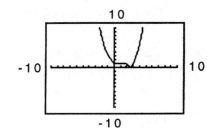

Graph of $-|f(x)|$

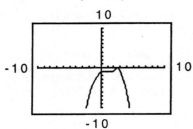

70. For $x \leq 0$ the graph of $-|f(x)|$ is the same as the graph of $f(x)$.
For $x > 0$ the graph of $-|f(x)|$ is the reflected graph of $|f(x)|$ in the x-axis.

72. $F(x) = 0.75f(x)$

$F(x)$ will be the graph of $f(x)$ contracted by a factor of 0.75; that is, all y-values will be multiplied by 0.75, giving the points (200, 30,000), (600, 45,000) and (1000, 90,000).

74. $v = f(x) = C\sqrt{x}$

Wet concrete $y_1 = 3.5\sqrt{x}$ (lowest)

Wet asphalt $y_2 = 4\sqrt{x}$

Dry concrete $y_3 = 5\sqrt{x}$

Dry asphalt $y_4 = 5.5\sqrt{x}$ (highest)

Each graph is an expansion of the graph of $y = \sqrt{x}$.

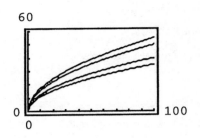

76. $y = 2C - \dfrac{5}{C}x^2$

$y_1 = 2(1) - \dfrac{5}{1}x^2 = 2 - 5x^2$

$y_2 = 2(2) - \dfrac{5}{2}x^2 = 4 - \dfrac{5}{2}x^2$

$y_3 = 2(3) - \dfrac{5}{3}x^2 = 6 - \dfrac{5}{3}x^2$

$y_4 = 2(4) - \dfrac{5}{4}x^2 = 8 - \dfrac{5}{4}x^2$

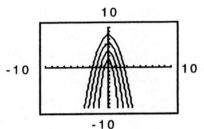

Each graph is a reflection followed by an expansion and then a vertical translation of the graph of $y = x^2$.

78. $V(t) = \dfrac{1}{C^2}(t + 6C)^2$ $0 \le t \le 6|C|$

$y_1 = \dfrac{1}{(-4)^2}(t + 6(-4))^2 = \dfrac{1}{16}(t - 24)^2$

$y_2 = \dfrac{1}{(-5)^2}(t + 6(-5))^2 = \dfrac{1}{25}(t - 30)^2$

$y_3 = \dfrac{1}{(-6)^2}(t + 6(-6))^2 = \dfrac{1}{36}(t - 36)^2$

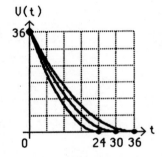

Each graph is a portion of the graph of a horizontal translation followed by a contraction of the graph of $y = t^2$.

CHAPTER 2

Exercise 2-1

2. From the graph, x-intercept = 1
y-intercept = 1
slope = -1

4. From the graph, x-intercept = -1
y-intercept = -3
slope = -3

6. From the graph, x-intercept = 4
y-intercept = -2
slope = $\frac{1}{2}$

8. $y = 5 - 3x^3$; not linear

10. $y = -2 + \sqrt{7}\,x$; linear

12. $y = \frac{3-x}{2} = \frac{3}{2} - \frac{1}{2}x$; linear

14. $y = -\frac{1}{5}(2 - 3x) + \frac{2}{7}(x + 8)$

$= -\frac{2}{5} + \frac{3}{5}x + \frac{2}{7}x + \frac{16}{7}$

$= \left(\frac{3}{5} + \frac{2}{7}\right)x + \left(-\frac{2}{5} + \frac{16}{7}\right)$; linear

16. $y = \frac{2}{3-x}$; not linear

18. $y = -\frac{3}{2}x + 6$

x intercept: $0 = -\frac{3}{2}x + 6$
$0 = -3x + 12$
$3x = 12$
$x = 4$

y intercept: $y = -\frac{3}{2}(0) + 6$
$y = 6$

slope = $m = -\frac{3}{2}$

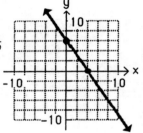

20. $y = \frac{2}{3}x - 3$

x intercept: $0 = \frac{2}{3}x - 3$
$0 = 2x - 9$
$-2x = -9$
$x = \frac{9}{2}$

y intercept: $y = \frac{2}{3}(0) - 3$
$y = -3$

slope = $m = \frac{2}{3}$

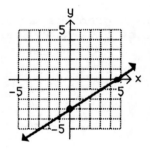

22. $4x + 3y = 24$

x intercept: $4x + 3(0) = 24$
$4x = 24$
$x = 6$

y intercept: $4(0) + 3y = 24$
$3y = 24$
$y = 8$

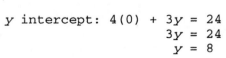

slope: $3y = -4x + 24$
$y = -\frac{4}{3}x + 8$
$m = -\frac{4}{3}$

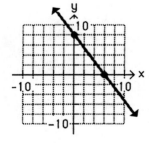

24. $\frac{y}{6} - \frac{x}{5} = 1$

x intercept: $\frac{0}{6} - \frac{x}{5} = 1$ y intercept: $\frac{y}{6} - \frac{0}{5} = 1$

$\qquad\qquad -\frac{1}{5}x = 1$ $\qquad\qquad \frac{1}{6}y = 1$

$\qquad\qquad\quad x = -5$ $\qquad\qquad\quad y = 6$

slope: $\frac{y}{6} = \frac{x}{5} + 1$

$\qquad\quad y = \frac{6}{5}x + 6$

$\qquad\quad m = \frac{6}{5}$

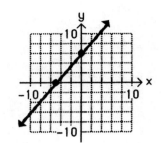

26. $y = -2$,
horizontal line

x intercept: none
y intercept: -2

slope = 0

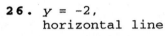
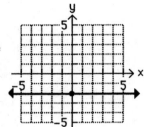

28. $x = 2.5$,
vertical line

x intercept: 2.5
y intercept: none

undefined slope

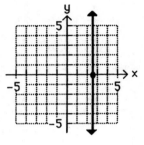

30. $m = -1$, $b = 7$:
$y = mx + b$
$y = -x + 7$

32. $m = \frac{5}{3}$, $b = 6$:

$y = mx + b$

$y = \frac{5}{3}x + 6$

34. Sketch a graph with the given information.
$(2, 0)$; $m = 2$:
$y - y_1 = m(x - x_1)$
$y - 0 = 2(x - 2)$
$\quad y = 2x - 4$

36. Sketch a graph with the given information.

$(-4, -2)$; $m = \frac{1}{2}$:

$y - y_1 = m(x - x_1)$

$y - (-2) = \frac{1}{2}(x - (-4))$

$y + 2 = \frac{1}{2}x + 2$

$\qquad y = \frac{1}{2}x$

38. Sketch a graph with the given information.
$(-3, 4)$, $(6, 1)$:

$m = \frac{y_2 - y_1}{x_2 - x_1}$; $y - y_1 = m(x - x_1)$

$m = \frac{1 - 4}{6 - (-3)}$ $y - 4 = -\frac{1}{3}(x - (-3))$

$m = -\frac{1}{3}$ $y - 4 = -\frac{1}{3}x - 1$

$\qquad\qquad\qquad\qquad y = -\frac{1}{3}x + 3$

40. Sketch a graph with the given information.
$(2, -1)$, $(10, 5)$:

$m = \frac{y_2 - y_1}{x_2 - x_1}$; $y - y_1 = m(x - x_1)$

$m = \frac{5 - (-1)}{10 - 2}$ $y - (-1) = \frac{3}{4}(x - 2)$

$m = \frac{3}{4}$ $y + 1 = \frac{3}{4}x - \frac{3}{2}$

$\qquad\qquad\qquad\qquad y = \frac{3}{4}x - \frac{5}{2}$

42. Sketch a graph with the given information.
$(0, -2)$, $(4, -2)$:

$m = \frac{y_2 - y_1}{x_2 - x_1}$

$m = \frac{-2 - (-2)}{4 - 0}$

$m = 0$, horizontal line
$y = -2$

44. Sketch a graph with the given information.
$(-3, 1)$, $(-3, -4)$:

$$m = \frac{y_2 - y_1}{x_2 - x_1}$$

$$m = \frac{-4 - 1}{-3 - (-3)}$$

$$m = \frac{-5}{0}, \text{ vertical line}$$

$$x = -3$$

46. Sketch a graph with the given information.
$(-4, 0)$, $(0, -5)$:

$$m = \frac{y_2 - y_1}{x_2 - x_1} = \frac{-5 - 0}{0 - (-4)} = -\frac{5}{4}$$

$$y - y_1 = m(x - x_1)$$

$$y - 0 = -\frac{5}{4}(x - (-4))$$

$$y = -\frac{5}{4}x - 5$$

48. $(-4, 0)$; $\parallel$ to $y = -2x + 1$:

$$y = -2x + 1$$
$$m = -2, \parallel m = -2$$

$$y - y_1 = m(x - x_1)$$
$$y - 0 = -2(x - (-4))$$
$$y = -2x - 8$$
$$2x + y = -8$$

50. $(-2, -4)$; $\perp$ to $y = \frac{2}{3}x - 5$

$$y = \frac{2}{3}x - 5; \ m = \frac{2}{3}$$

$$\perp m = -\frac{3}{2}$$

$$y - y_1 = m(x - x_1)$$

$$y - (-4) = -\frac{3}{2}(x - (-2))$$

$$y + 4 = -\frac{3}{2}(x + 2)$$

$$2y + 8 = -3x - 6$$
$$3x + 2y = -14$$

52. parallel to x-axis $\Rightarrow m = 0$
$(7, 3)$ is contained; $y = 3$

54. horizontal $\Rightarrow m = 0$;
$(-2, -3)$ is contained; $y = -3$

56. $3x + 4y = 8$

$$4y = -3x + 8$$

$$y = -\frac{3}{4}x + 2$$

$$m = -\frac{3}{4}$$

$$\parallel m = -\frac{3}{4}$$

$$y - y_1 = m(x - x_1)$$

$$y - 5 = -\frac{3}{4}(x - 3)$$

$$4y - 20 = -3x + 9$$

$$3x + 4y = 29$$

58. $4x + 5y = 0$

$$y = -\frac{4}{5}x$$

$$m = -\frac{4}{5}$$

$$\perp m = \frac{5}{4}$$

$$m = \frac{5}{4}; \ (-2, 4)$$

$$y - y_1 = m(x - x_1)$$

$$y - 4 = \frac{5}{4}(x - (-2))$$

$$4y - 16 = 5x + 10$$

$$5x - 4y = -26$$

60. $$y = -\frac{1}{2}x + b$$

$$m = -\frac{1}{2}$$

y-int = b
Lines will be
parallel.

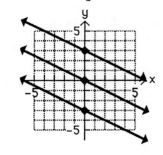

62. $m_{DA} = \frac{2 - (-2)}{0 - (-3)} = \frac{4}{3}$;

$$m_{CB} = \frac{-5 - (-1)}{1 - 4} = \frac{4}{3}$$

Since $m_{DA} = m_{CB} = \frac{4}{3}$,

$DA \parallel CB$.

64. $m_{AD} = \frac{4}{3}$ from problem 62

$m_{DC} = \frac{-5 - (-2)}{1 - (-3)} = -\frac{3}{4}$ from which $m_{AD} \cdot m_{DC} = -1$ which shows $AD \perp DC$.

66.

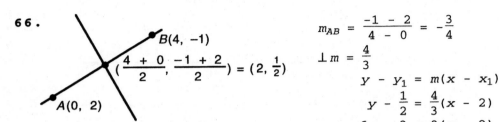

$m_{AB} = \frac{-1 - 2}{4 - 0} = -\frac{3}{4}$

$\perp m = \frac{4}{3}$

$y - y_1 = m(x - x_1)$

$y - \frac{1}{2} = \frac{4}{3}(x - 2)$

$6y - 3 = 8(x - 2)$

$6y - 3 = 8x - 16$

$8x - 6y = 13$

68.

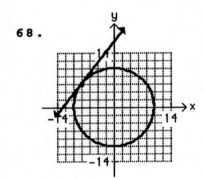

$x^2 + y^2 = 100;\ (-8, 6)$
Find m from the center, $(0, 0)$, to $(-8, 6)$:

$m = \frac{6 - 0}{-8 - 0} = -\frac{3}{4}$

$\perp m = \frac{4}{3}$

$y - y_1 = m(x - x_1)$

$y - 6 = \frac{4}{3}(x - (-8))$

$3y - 18 = 4x + 32$

$4x - 3y = -50$

70.

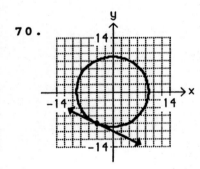

$x^2 + y^2 = 80;\ (-4, -8)$
Find m from the center, $(0, 0)$, to $(-4, -8)$:

$m = \frac{-8 - 0}{-4 - 0} = 2$

$\perp m = -\frac{1}{2}$

$y - y_1 = m(x - x_1)$

$y - (-8) = -\frac{1}{2}(x - (-4))$

$2y + 16 = -x - 4$

$x + 2y = -20$

72.

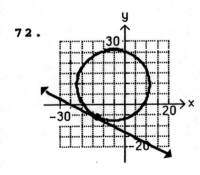

$(x + 5)^2 + (y - 9)^2 = 289;\ (-13, -6)$
center $= (-5, 9)$
radius $= 17$

Find m from the center $(-5, 9)$ to $(-13, -6)$:

$m = \frac{9 - (-6)}{-5 - (-13)} = \frac{15}{8}$

$\perp m = -\frac{8}{15}$

$y - y_1 = m(x - x_1)$

$y - (-6) = -\frac{8}{15}(x - (-13))$

$15y + 90 = -8x - 104$

$8x + 15y = -194$

74. (A) $3x + 4y = 12$ $4x - 3y = 12$

            $4y = -3x + 12$ $-3y = -4x + 12$

              $y = -\dfrac{3}{4}x + 3$ $y = \dfrac{4}{3}x - 4$

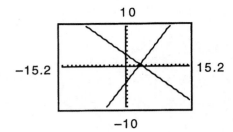

    (B) $2x + 3y = 12$ $3x - 2y = 12$

            $3y = -2x + 12$ $-2y = -3x + 12$

              $y = -\dfrac{2}{3}x + 4$ $y = \dfrac{3}{2}x - 6$

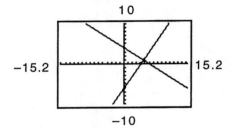

    (C) The lines are perpendicular to each other.

    (D) $Ax + By = C$ $Bx - Ay = C$

            $By = -Ax + C$ $-Ay = -Bx + C$

              $y = -\dfrac{A}{B}x + \dfrac{C}{B}$ $y = \dfrac{B}{A}x - \dfrac{C}{A}$

              $m_1 = -\dfrac{A}{B}$ $m_2 = \dfrac{B}{A}$

         $m_1 \cdot m_2 = -\dfrac{A}{B} \cdot \dfrac{B}{A} = -1$

76. $f(x) = mx + b$, $g(x) = m|x| + b$, $m \neq 0$.
    $f(x)$ is a linear function, increasing when $m > 0$, decreasing when $m < 0$. The graph of $g(x)$ is an absolute value graph which has a V shape. For example, graph $f(x) = 3x + 2$. Then graph $g(x) = 3|x| + 2$. $g(x)$ is never linear as long as $x \in$ Real number.

78.

$$P_3(x_3, mx_3 + b)$$
$$P_2(x_2, mx_2 + b)$$
$$P_1(x_1, mx_1 + b)$$

$$d(P_1, P_2) = \sqrt{(x_2 - x_1)^2 + (mx_2 + b - mx_1 - b)^2}$$

$$d(P_1, P_2) = \sqrt{(x_2 - x_1)^2 + m^2(x_2 - x_1)^2}$$

$$d(P_1, P_2) = (x_2 - x_1)\sqrt{1 + m^2}$$

$$\text{Similarly } d(P_2, P_3) = (x_3 - x_2)\sqrt{1 + m^2}$$

$$d(P_1, P_3) = (x_3 - x_1)\sqrt{1 + m^2}$$

$$d(P_1, P_2) + d(P_2, P_3) = (x_2 - x_1)\sqrt{1 + m^2} + (x_3 - x_2)\sqrt{1 + m^2}$$

$$= (x_3 - x_1)\sqrt{1 + m^2}$$

$$= d(P_1, P_3)$$

which shows that P_1, P_2, P_3 are collinear.

80. (w, s): $(5, 2)$, $(0, 0)$, $m = \dfrac{2}{5} = 0.4$

(A) $s - s_1 = m(w - w_1)$
$\quad\ s - 0 = 0.4(w - 0)$
$\quad\quad\ \ s = 0.4w$

(B) $(w, 3.6)$
$\quad 3.6 = 0.4w$
$\quad\ \ w = 9$ lbs

(C) slope $= 0.4$

82. (C, R): $(20, 33)$, $(60, 93)$

(A)

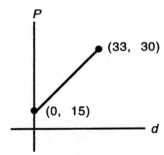

$m = \dfrac{93 - 33}{60 - 20} = 1.5$

$R - 33 = 1.5(C - 20)$

$R - 33 = 1.5C - 30$

$\quad\ \ R = 1.5C + 3, \ (C > 10)$

(B) If $R = 240$: $240 = 1.5C + 3$
$\quad\quad\quad\quad\quad\ \ 237 = 1.5C$
$\quad\quad\quad\quad\quad\quad\ \ C = \$158$

(C) slope $= 1.5$; the retail price rises \$1.50 for each \$1 in cost.

84. (A) $T = 200 + 0.02(200)A$ where $A =$ altitude in thousands of feet.
$\quad\ T = 4A + 200 \ (A \geq 0)$

(B) $T = 4(6.5) + 200$
$\quad\ T = 226$ mph

(C) slope $= 4$ which indicates that true air speed increases 4 mph for each one thousand foot increase in altitude.

86. (A) (d, P): $(0, 15)$, $(33, 30)$

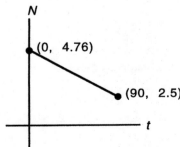

slope $= \dfrac{30 - 15}{33} = \dfrac{5}{11}$

$p - 15 = \dfrac{5}{11}(d - 0)$

$\quad\quad\ p = \dfrac{5}{11}d + 15$

(B) $(d, 40)$: $40 = \dfrac{5}{11}d + 15$
$\quad\quad\quad\quad\quad\ d = 55$ ft.

88. (A) (t, N): $(0, 4.76)$, $(90, 2.5)$ where $t = 0$ at 1900.

slope $= \dfrac{4.76 - 2.5}{0 - 90} = -\dfrac{2.26}{90} = -\dfrac{113}{4500}$

$N - 4.76 = -\dfrac{113}{4500}(t - 0)$

$\quad\quad\quad N = -\dfrac{113}{4500}t + 4.76 \ (t \geq 0)$

(B) $(100, N)$: $N = -\dfrac{113}{4500}(100) + 4.76$
$\quad\quad\quad\quad\quad N \approx 2.25$ people per household

90. (A) $\{50, 70, 130, 150, 200\} \rightarrow L_1$
$\{2250, 3375, 5400, 6125, 8150\} \rightarrow L_2$

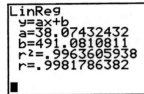

$C(x) = 38x + 491$

(B) The fixed costs are \$491, the variable costs are $38x$, and the cost of producing an additional pair of skates is \$38.

(C)

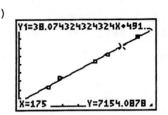

When 175 pairs are produced, the cost is \$7,154.

92. (A) $\{20, 30, 40, 50, 60\} \rightarrow L_1$
$\{11, 22, 29, 37, 44\} \rightarrow L_2$

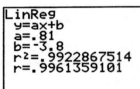

(B) 1932: $x = 32$, $f(32) = 0.81(32) - 3.8$
$= 22.12 \approx 22\%$

1956: $x = 56$, $f(56) = 0.81(56) - 3.8$
$= 41.56 \approx 42\%$

(C) Find x when $f(x) = 100$

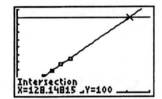

$x \approx 128 \Rightarrow$ The year 2028.
This is unlikely to happen since petroleum supply is limited.

Exercise 2-2

2. $V(x) = 0 : \{a, d\}$

4. $u(x) - v(x) = 0$
$u(x) = v(x) : \{b, e\}$

6. $v(x) \geq 0 : (-\infty, a] \cup [d, \infty)$

8. $v(x) < 0: (a, d)$

10. $5x + 10(x - 2) = 40$
$5x + 10x - 20 = 40$
$15x = 60$
$x = 4$
Graph $y_1 = 5x + 10(x - 2)$;
$y_2 = 40$.
The intersection is at $x = 4$.

12. $5w - (7w - 4) - 2 = 5 - (3w + 2)$
$5w - 7w + 4 - 2 = 5 - 3w - 2$
$-2w + 2 = 3 - 3w$
$w = 1$
Graph $y_1 = 5x - (7x - 4) - 2$;
$y_2 = 5 - (3x + 2)$.
The intersection is at $x = 1$.

14. $\dfrac{x + 3}{4} - \dfrac{x - 4}{2} = \dfrac{3}{8}$
$2(x + 3) - 4(x - 4) = 3$
$2x + 6 - 4x + 16 = 3$
$-2x = -19$
$x = \dfrac{19}{2}$
Graph $y_1 = \dfrac{x + 3}{4} - \dfrac{x - 4}{2}$; $y_2 = \dfrac{3}{8}$.
The intersection is at $x = 9.5$.

16. $4x + 8 \geq x - 1$
$3x \geq -9$
$x \geq -3$; $[-3, \infty)$;

Graph $y_1 = 4x + 8$, $y_2 = x - 1$.
The intersection is at $x = -3$.
$y_1 \geq y_2$ for $x \geq -3$.

18. $-7n \geq 21$

$n \leq -3;\ (-\infty,\ -3]$

$\longleftarrow$ ⟍n
                -3

Graph $y_1 = -7x$, $y_2 = 21$.

The intersection is at $x = -3$.

$y_1 \geq y_2$ for $n \leq -3$.

20. $2 \leq 3m - 7 < 14$

$9 \leq 3m < 21$

$3 \leq m < 7;\ [3,\ 7);$

[———)$\longrightarrow$m
3   7

Graph $y_1 = 2$, $y_2 = 3x - 7$, $y_3 = 14$.

They intersect at $x = 3, 7$.

The inequality is satisfied as above.

22. $|x + 1| = 5$

$x + 1 = \pm 5$

$x = -1 \pm 5$

$x = -6$ or 4

24. $|2w - 9| < 6$

Graph $y_1 = 2x - 9$, $y_2 = 6$.

The intersections are at $x = 1.5,\ 7.5$.

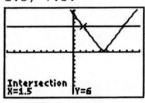

$(1.5,\ 7.5)$

26. $\dfrac{2}{3x} + \dfrac{1}{2} = \dfrac{4}{x} + \dfrac{4}{3}$

$4 + 3x = 24 + 8x$

$5x = -20$

$x = -4$

28. $24 \leq \dfrac{2}{3}(x - 5) < 36$

$72 \leq 2(x - 5) < 108$

$72 \leq 2x - 10 < 108$

$82 \leq 2x < 118$

$41 \leq x < 59$

$[41,\ 59)$

30. $|2s + 3| = 6 - 0.5s$

Graph $y_1 = |2x + 3|$, $y_2 = 6 - 0.5x$

The intersections are at

$s = -6,\ \dfrac{6}{5}\ (1.2).$

32. $|7 - 2x| \geq x - 0.81$

Graph $y_1 = |7 - 2x|$, $y_2 = x - 0.8$.

The intersections are at

$x = 2.6,\ 6.2$.

The inequality is satisfied at

$x \leq 2.6$ or $x \geq 6.2;$

$(-\infty,\ 2.6] \cup [6.2,\ \infty).$

34. $\dfrac{2x}{x + 4} = 7 - \dfrac{6}{x + 4}$, $x \neq -4$

$(x + 4)\left(\dfrac{2x}{x + 4}\right) = (x + 4)\left(7 - \dfrac{6}{x + 4}\right)$

$2x = 7x + 28 - 6$

$-5x = 22$

$x = -\dfrac{22}{5}$

36. $|x + 1| - |x - 2| < 0.4x$

Graph $y_1 = |x + 1| - |x - 2|$,

$y_2 = 0.4x$

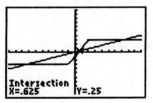

The intersection is at $-7.5, 0.625,$ 7.5.

The inequality is satisfied at

$-7.5 < x < 0.625$ or $x > 7.5$;

$(-7.5,\ 0.625) \cup (7.5,\ \infty).$

38. $F = \dfrac{9}{5}C + 32$

$\dfrac{9}{5}C = F - 32$

$C = \dfrac{5}{9}(F - 32)$

40. $\dfrac{1}{R} = \dfrac{1}{R_1} + \dfrac{1}{R_2}$ for R_1

$RR_1R_2\left(\dfrac{1}{R}\right) = RR_1R_2\left(\dfrac{1}{R_1}\right) + RR_1R_2\left(\dfrac{1}{R_2}\right)$

$R_1R_2 = RR_2 + RR_1$

$R_1R_2 - RR_1 = RR_2$

$R_1(R_2 - R) = RR_2$

$R_1 = \dfrac{RR_2}{R_2 - R_1}$

42.

$A = 2ab + 2ac + 2bc$

$2ac + 2bc = A - 2ab$

$c(2a + 2b) = A - 2ab$

$c = \dfrac{A - 2ab}{2a + 2b}$

44.

$x = \dfrac{3y + 2}{y - 3}$

$x(y - 3) = 3y + 2$

$xy - 3x = 3y + 2$

$xy - 3y = 3x + 2$

$y(x - 3) = 3x + 2$

$y = \dfrac{3x + 2}{x - 3}$

46. $y_1 = |x|$, $y_2 = \sqrt{x^2}$
Graph y_1 and y_2. The graphs are identical for all values of x.

48.   (A) for $abc > 0$ two of three numbers must be negative and one positive or all three must be positive

(B) for $\dfrac{ab}{c} < 0$ two of three numbers must be positive and one negative or all three must be negative

(C) for $\dfrac{a}{bc} > 0$ two of three numbers must be negative and one positive or all three must be positive

(D) for $\dfrac{a^2}{bc} < 0$ a can be either positive or negative, and b and c must have opposite signs

50.   If $u - v = -2$, $u = v + (-2)$, $u < v$ since the difference is less than 0.

52.   If $a > 0$, $b > 0$, and $\dfrac{b}{a} > 1$, then $a < b$ since $\dfrac{b}{a} > 1$.

54.

$0 < |x - 5| < 0.01$ is equivalent to

$0 < |x - 5|$ and $|x - 5| < 0.01$

$|x - 5| > 0$ $-0.01 < x - 5 < 0.01$

$x - 5 < -0$ or $x - 5 > 0$ $4.99 < x < 5.01$

$x < 5$ $x > 5$

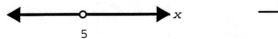

Since both must be true for $0 < |x - 5| < 0.01$ to be true, the graph of the solution is

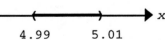

and using interval notation $(4.99, 5) \cup (5, 5.01)$.

56. $0 < |x - 4| < d$ is equivalent to

$$0 < |x - 4| \quad\quad\text{and}\quad\quad |x - 4| < d$$
$$|x - 4| > 0 \quad\quad\quad\quad\quad\quad -d < x - 4 < d$$
$$x - 4 < -0 \text{ or } x - 4 > 0 \quad\quad 4 - d < x < 4 + d$$
$$x < 4 \quad\quad\quad x > 4$$

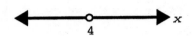 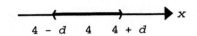

Since both must be true for $0 < |x - 4| < d$ to be true, the graph of the solution is

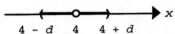

and using interval notation $(4 - d, 4) \cup (4, 4 + d)$.

58. $\dfrac{|x - 1|}{x - 1} = \dfrac{x - 1}{x - 1} = 1$ for $x - 1 > 0$

$\dfrac{|x - 1|}{x - 1} = \dfrac{-(x - 1)}{x - 1} = -1$ for $x - 1 < 0$

$\dfrac{|x - 1|}{x - 1} = \pm 1$

60. (A) earnings = base salary + commission
$$3170 = 1175 + 0.05x$$
$$0.05x = 1995$$
$$x = \$39{,}900 \text{ in sales}$$

(B) $2150 + 0.08(x - 7000) = 1175 + 0.05x$
$$2150 + 0.08x - 560 = 1175 + 0.05x$$
$$0.03x = -415$$

$x = -13{,}833.\overline{3}$ and since sales cannot be negative, earnings will never be the same. Take the first payment method.

62. $|V - 6.94| < 0.02$
$$-0.02 < V - 6.94 < 0.02$$
$$6.92 < V < 6.96$$
$(6.92, \ 6.96)$

64. $C(x) = 550{,}000 + 120x$; $R(x) = 140x$ (B) To break-even, revenue = cost
(A) To make a profit, revenue > cost $140x = 550{,}000 + 120x$
$\quad 140x > 550{,}000 + 120x$ $x = 27{,}500$
$\quad\ 20x > 550{,}000$
$\quad\quad x > 27{,}500$

(C) Answers may vary; but to make a profit, the number sold must be greater than the number to break-even.

66. $C(x) = 660{,}000 + 120x$; $R(x) = 140x$
(A) Answers may vary; but the   (B) $140x > 660{,}000 + 120x$
company could increase the price of $20x > 660{,}000$
each unit, or increase the number of $x > 33{,}000$
units sold.

(C) Refer to #64, $x = 27{,}500$:
$\quad 27{,}500p = 660{,}000 + 120(27{,}500)$
$\quad 27{,}500p = 3{,}960{,}000$
$\quad\quad\quad p = \$144$, new price
Raise the wholesale price from \$140 to \$144 (\$4).

68. $3.65 \times 10^{-3} - 5 \times 10^{-6} \leq N \leq 3.65 \times 10^{-3} + 5 \times 10^{-6}$
$-5 \times 10^{-6} \leq N - 3.65 \times 10^{-3} \leq 5 \times 10^{-6}$
$|N - 3.65 \times 10^{-3}| \leq 5 \times 10^{-6}$

70. Let B = benefit reduction and E = earnings.
$13,000 \leq E \leq 16,000$
$13,000 - 8,880 \leq E - 8,880 \leq 16,000 - 8,880$
$4,120 \leq E - 8,880 \leq 7,120$
$\frac{1}{3}(4,120) \leq \frac{1}{3}(E - 8,880) \leq \frac{1}{3}(7,120)$
$1,373.33 \leq B \leq 2,373.33$

72. $C = \frac{5}{9}(F - 32)$, $20 < C < 30$

$20 < \frac{5}{9}(F - 32) < 30$

$36 < F - 32 < 54$
$68°F < F < 86°F$

74. (A) $V = V_S + (0.03A)V_S = V_S(1 + 0.03A)$

(B) $V = 120(1 + 0.03(6.4))$
$V = 143.04 \approx 143$ mph

(C) $125 = V(1 + 0.03(8.5))$
$V \approx 99.6$ mph

(D) $155 = 135(1 + 0.03(A))$
$1 + 0.03A = \frac{155}{135}$
$0.03A = \frac{155}{135} - 1$
$A = \frac{\frac{155}{135} - 1}{0.03}$
$A \approx 4.94$

The mountain resort has an altitude of 4,940 ft.

Exercise 2-3

2. $g(x) = -x^2 - 2x - 3$
$g(x) = -(x^2 + 2x + 1) - 3 + 1$
$g(x) = -(x + 1)^2 - 2$

4. $k(x) = x^2 - 4x + 4$
$k(x) = (x - 2)^2$

6. $n(x) = -x^2 - 2x + 3$
$n(x) = -(x^2 + 2x + 1) + 3 + 1$
$n(x) = -(x + 1)^2 + 4$

8. $g(x) = -x^2 - 2x - 3 = -(x + 1)^2 - 2$ [#2]

The graph of $g(x)$ is the graph of $y = x^2$ reflected in the x-axis, shifted to the left 1 unit, and down 2 units.

10. $k(x) = x^2 - 4x + 4 = (x - 2)^2$ [#4]

The graph of $k(x)$ is the graph of $y = x^2$ shifted to the right 2 units.

12. $n(x) = -x^2 - 2x + 3 = -(x + 1)^2 + 4$ [#6]

The graph of $n(x)$ is the graph of $y = x^2$ reflected in the x-axis, shifted to the left 1 unit, and up 4 units.

14. $f(x) = (x - 2)^2 + 1$

16. $n(x) = -(x + 1)^2 + 4$

18. $g(x) = -(x + 1)^2 - 2$

20. $f(x) = 3x^2 + 24x + 30$

$f(x) = 3(x^2 + 8x + 16) + 30 - 48$

$f(x) = 3(x + 4)^2 - 18$

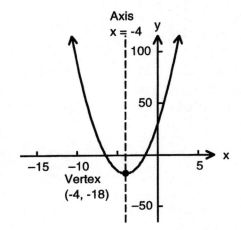

22. $f(x) = -x^2 + 10x - 30$

$f(x) = -(x^2 - 10x + 25) - 30 + 25$

$f(x) = -(x - 5)^2 - 5$

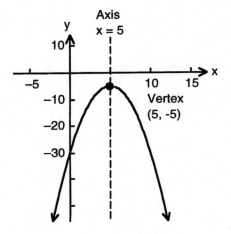

24. $f(x) = 0.4x^2 + 4x + 4$

$f(x) = 0.4(x^2 + 10x + 25) + 4 - 10$

$f(x) = 0.4(x + 5)^2 - 6$

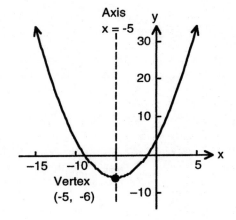

26. $f(x) = 5x^2 + 29x - 17$

$f(x) = 5\left(x^2 + \dfrac{29}{5}x + \dfrac{841}{100}\right) - 17 - \dfrac{841}{20}$

$f(x) = 5\left(x + \dfrac{29}{10}\right)^2 - \dfrac{1181}{20}$

$f(x) = 5(x + 2.9)^2 - 59.05$

Increasing: $[-2.9, \infty]$

Decreasing: $(-\infty, -2.9]$

Range: $[-59.05, \infty)$

28. $f(x) = -8x^2 - 20x + 16$

$f(x) = -8\left(x^2 + \dfrac{5}{2}x + \dfrac{25}{16}\right) + 16 + \dfrac{25}{2}$

$f(x) = -8\left(x + \dfrac{5}{4}\right)^2 + \dfrac{57}{2}$

$f(x) = -8(x + 1.25)^2 + 28.5$

Increasing: $(-\infty, -1.25]$

Decreasing: $[-1.25, \infty)$

Range: $(-\infty, 28.5]$

30. $y = a(x - h)^2 + k$

Vertex at $(-2, -4)$:

$y = a(x + 2)^2 - 4$

Through $(-1, -1)$:

$-1 = a(-1 + 2)^2 - 4$

$3 = a(1)^2$

$a = 3$

$y = 3(x + 2)^2 - 4$

$y = 3(x^2 + 4x + 4) - 4$

$y = 3x^2 + 12x + 8$

32. $y = a(x - h)^2 + k$

Vertex at (3, 3):

$y = a(x - 3)^2 + 3$

Through (0, 0):

$0 = a(0 - 3)^2 + 3$

$-3 = a(9)$

$a = -\dfrac{1}{3}$

$y = -\dfrac{1}{3}(x - 3)^2 + 3$

$y = -\dfrac{1}{3}(x^2 - 6x + 9) + 3$

$y = -\dfrac{1}{3}x^2 + 2x - 3 + 3$

$y = -\dfrac{1}{3}x^2 + 2x$

34. $y = a(x - h)^2 + k$

Vertex at (-2, -12):

$y = a(x + 2)^2 - 12$

Through (-4, 0):

$0 = a(-4 + 2)^2 - 12$

$12 = a(-2)^2$

$a = 3$

$y = 3(x + 2)^2 - 12$

$y = 3(x^2 + 4x + 4) - 12$

$y = 3x^2 + 12x$

36. $y = a(x - h)^2 + k$

Vertex at (5, 8):

$y = a(x - 5)^2 + 8$

Through (0, -2):

$-2 = a(0 - 5)^2 + 8$

$-10 = 25a$

$a = -\dfrac{2}{5} = -0.4$

$y = -0.4(x - 5)^2 + 8$

$y = -0.4(x^2 - 10x + 25) + 8$

$y = -0.4x^2 + 4x - 10 + 8$

$y = -0.4x^2 + 4x - 2$

38. $y = a(x - h)^2 + k$

Vertex at (6, -40):

$y = a(x - 6)^2 - 40$

Through (3, 50):

$50 = a(3 - 6)^2 - 40$

$90 = 9a$

$a = 10$

$y = 10(x - 6)^2 - 40$

$y = 10(x^2 - 12x + 36) - 40$

$y = 10x^2 - 120x + 360 - 40$

$y = 10x^2 - 120x + 320$

40. $y = x^2 - 5x$

For example:

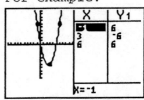 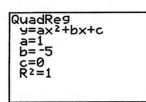

The quadratic regression model should be the same as the original quadratic equation.

42. $f(x) = -(x - 2)^2 + k$, opens downward.

If $k = 0$, the vertex is (2, 0), an x-intercept, so there is only one x-intercept.

If $k < 0$, the vertex is below the x-axis, so there are no x-intercepts.

If $k > 0$, the vertex is above the x-axis, so there will be 2 x-intercepts.

For $f(x) = a(x - h)^2 + k$, $a < 0$, the results will be the same.

44. $x^2 + y^2 - 2x - 10y = 55$

$(x^2 - 2x + 1) + (y^2 - 10y + 25) = 55 + 1 + 25$

$(x - 1)^2 + (y - 5)^2 = 81$

Center: (1, 5), radius: 9

46. $x^2 + y^2 - 4x + 12y = 24$
$(x^2 - 4x + 4) + (y^2 + 12y + 36) = 24 + 4 + 36$
$(x - 2)^2 + (y + 6)^2 = 64$
Center: $(2, -6)$, radius: 8

48. $f(x) = ax^2 + bx + c,\ a \neq 0$

$$f(x) = a\left(x^2 + \frac{b}{a}x + \frac{b^2}{4a^2}\right) + c - \frac{b^2}{4a}$$

$$f(x) = a\left(x + \frac{b}{2a}\right)^2 + \frac{4ac - b^2}{4a}$$

(A) The axis of symmetry: $x = -\dfrac{b}{2a}$ (B) The vertex: $\left(-\dfrac{b}{2a},\ \dfrac{4ac - b^2}{4a}\right)$

(C) The maximum value: $\dfrac{4ac - b^2}{4a},\ a < 0$

The minimum value: $\dfrac{4ac - b^2}{4a},\ a > 0$

50. $f(x) = 9 - x^2;\ (-2,\ 5),\ (4,\ -7)$
$m = \dfrac{5 - (-7)}{-2 - 4} = \dfrac{12}{-6} = -2$
$y - y_1 = m(x - x_1)$
$y - 5 = -2(x + 2)$
$y - 5 = -2x - 4$
$\quad\ \ y = -2x + 1$

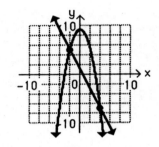

52. $f(x) = x^2 + 2x - 6;\ (2,\ f(2)),\ (2 + h,\ f(2 + h))$
$f(2) = 4 + 4 - 6 = 2$
$f(2 + h) = (2 + h)^2 + 2(2 + h) - 6$
$\qquad\qquad = 4 + 4h + h^2 + 4 + 2h - 6$
$\qquad\qquad = h^2 + 6h + 2$

(A) $m = \dfrac{f(2) - f(2 + h)}{2 - (2 + h)}$

$\quad\ = \dfrac{2 - (h^2 + 6h + 2)}{-h}$

$\quad\ = \dfrac{-h^2 - 6h}{-h} = h + 6$

(B) $h = 1$: $1 + 6 = 7$
$h = 0.1$: $0.1 + 6 = 6.1$
$h = 0.01$: $0.01 + 6 = 6.01$
$h = 0.001$: $0.001 + 6 = 6.001$
The slope appears to be approaching 6.

54. $x + y = 60$
$y = 60 - x$

Product: $xy = x(60 - x)$
$\qquad\qquad = -x^2 + 60x$
$\qquad\qquad = -(x^2 - 60x + 900) + 900$
$\qquad\qquad = -(x - 30)^2 + 900$
Vertex of parabola: $(30,\ 900)$

Maximum product is 900 when both numbers are 30. There is no minimum since the graph of the function opens downward.

56. Perimeter: $x + 50 + x + 2y = 140$
$$2y = 90 - 2x$$
$$y = 45 - x$$

(A) Area $= (x + 50)y$
$$A(x) = (x + 50)(45 - x)$$
$$A(x) = -x^2 - 5x + 2250$$
domain: $0 \le x \le 45$

(B) $A(x) = -\left(x^2 + 5x + \dfrac{25}{4}\right) + 2250 + \dfrac{25}{4}$
$$A(x) = -\left(x + \dfrac{5}{2}\right)^2 + \dfrac{9025}{4}$$
vertex: $\left(-\dfrac{5}{2}, \dfrac{9025}{4}\right)$

Maximum area occurs at $x = -2.5$, which is not in the domain, so $x = 0$.

(C) Dimensions: 50 ft × 45 ft

58. Maximum at (4.5, 324) through (0, 0).

(A) $d(t) = a(t - h)^2 + k$
$d(t) = a(t - 4.5)^2 + 324$
$(0, 0)$: $0 = a(0 - 4.5)^2 + 324$
$0 = 20.25a + 324$
$-20.25a = 324$
$a = -16$
$d(t) = -16(t - 4.5)^2 + 324$
$d(t) = -16(t^2 - 9t + 20.25) + 324$
$d(t) = -16t^2 + 144t - 324 + 324$
$d(t) = -16t^2 + 144t; \quad 0 \le t \le 9$

(B) Find $(x, 250)$:
Graph $y_1 = -16t^2 + 1.44t$;
$y_2 = 250$.

The intersection is at $t \approx 2.35$ sec, 6.65 sec.

60. (A) $d(x) = a(x - h)^2 + k$
Let the center of the bridge be the origin of the coordinate system. Then the vertex is at $(0, 10)$.
$$d(x) = ax^2 + 10$$
$(100, 60)$: $60 = a(10,000) + 10$
$50 = 10,000a$
$a = 0.005$
$d(x) = 0.005x^2 + 10; \quad 10 \le d \le 60$

(B) The center cable is 10 feet long. The next 2 cables occur at $x = \pm 25$:
$$d(25) = 0.005(25)^2 + 10 = 13.125$$
The next 2 cables occur at $x = \pm 50$;
$$d(50) = 0.005(50)^2 + 10 = 22.5$$
The next 2 cables occur at $x = \pm 75$:
$$d(75) = 0.005(75)^2 + 10 = 38.125$$
The sum of the 7 cables is 157.5 feet:
$$10 + 2(13.125) + 2(22.5) + 2(38.125)$$

62. $R(x) = -.3228219836x^2 + 640.014462x - 16529.02301$
$C(x) = 85.79752367x + 118,918.4268$

(A) $P(x) = R(x) - C(x)$
$$50,000 = -.3228219836x^2 + 554.2169383x - 135447.4498$$

Graph $y_1 = 50,000$; $y_2 = P(x)$.
They intersect at $x = 455.42627, 1261.3618$, so ≈ 455 mowers and 1261 mowers.

(B) On the graph of $y_2 = P(x)$ find the vertex (maximum): (858.37, 102,420.81).
Approximately 858 lawnmowers with a profit of \$102,421.

64. $\{0, 5, 10, 15, 20, 25, 30\} \rightarrow L_1$
$\{52, 66, 73, 80, 83, 74, 76\} \rightarrow L_2$

(A)
```
QuadReg
y=ax²+bx+c
a=-.0704761905
b=2.814285714
c=52.69047619
```

(B) Graph the regression equation (A) in y_1 and $y_2 = 52$. They intersect at $x = 40.17629$. Forty years from 1960 would be 2000.

Exercise 2-4

2. $(3 + i) + (4 + 2i) = 3 + i + 4 + 2i$
$= 3 + 4 + i + 2i$
$= 7 + 3i$

4. $(6 - 2i) + (8 - 3i) = 6 - 2i + 8 - 3i$
$= 6 + 8 - 2i - 3i$
$= 14 - 5i$

6. $(9 + 8i) - (5 + 6i) = 9 + 8i - 5 - 6i$
$= 9 - 5 + 8i - 6i$
$= 4 + 2i$

8. $(8 - 4i) - (11 - 2i) = 8 - 4i - 11 + 2i$
$= 8 - 11 - 4i + 2i$
$= -3 - 2i$

10. $6 + (3 - 4i) = 6 + 3 - 4i$
$= 9 - 4i$

12. $(3i)(8i) = 24i^2$
$= -24$
or $-24 + 0i$

14. $-2i(5 - 3i) = -10i + 6i^2$
$= -10i - 6$
$= -6 - 10i$

16. $(-2 - 3i)(3 - 5i) = -6 + 10i - 9i + 15i^2$
$= -6 + i - 15$
$= -21 + i$

18. $(3 + 2i)(2 - i) = 6 - 3i + 4i - 2i^2$
$= 6 + i + 2$
$= 8 + i$

20. $(5 + 3i)(5 - 3i) = 5^2 - (3i)^2$
$= 25 - 9i^2$
$= 25 + 9$
$= 34$ or $34 + 0i$

22. $\dfrac{1}{3 - i} = \dfrac{1}{3 - i} \cdot \dfrac{3 + i}{3 + i}$
$= \dfrac{3 + i}{9 - i^2}$
$= \dfrac{3 + i}{9 + 1}$
$= \dfrac{3}{10} + \dfrac{1}{10}i$

24. $\dfrac{2 - i}{3 + 2i} = \dfrac{2 - i}{3 + 2i} \cdot \dfrac{3 - 2i}{3 - 2i}$
$= \dfrac{6 - 7i + 2i^2}{9 - 4i^2}$
$= \dfrac{6 - 7i - 2}{9 + 4}$
$= \dfrac{4 - 7i}{13}$
$= \dfrac{4}{13} - \dfrac{7}{13}i$

26. $\dfrac{15 - 3i}{2 - 3i} = \dfrac{15 - 3i}{2 - 3i} \cdot \dfrac{2 + 3i}{2 + 3i}$

$\qquad = \dfrac{30 + 39i - 9i^2}{4 - 9i^2}$

$\qquad = \dfrac{30 + 39i + 9}{4 + 9}$

$\qquad = \dfrac{39}{13} + \dfrac{39}{13}i$

$\qquad = 3 + 3i$

28. $(3 - \sqrt{-4}) + (-8 + \sqrt{-25}) = (3 - i\sqrt{4}) + (-8 + i\sqrt{25})$

$\qquad\qquad = 3 - 2i - 8 + 5i$

$\qquad\qquad = -5 + 3i$

30. $(-2 - \sqrt{-36}) - (4 + \sqrt{-49}) = -2 - 6i - 4 - 7i$

$\qquad\qquad\qquad = -6 - 13i$

32. $(2 - \sqrt{-1})(5 + \sqrt{-9}) = (2 - i)(5 + 3i)$

$\qquad\qquad = 10 + i - 3i^2$

$\qquad\qquad = 10 + i + 3$

$\qquad\qquad = 13 + i$

34. $\dfrac{6 - \sqrt{-64}}{2} = \dfrac{6 - 8i}{2}$

$\qquad\qquad = 3 - 4i$

36. $\dfrac{1}{3 - \sqrt{-16}} = \dfrac{1}{3 - 4i} \cdot \dfrac{3 + 4i}{3 + 4i}$

$\qquad = \dfrac{3 + 4i}{9 + 16}$

$\qquad = \dfrac{3}{25} + \dfrac{4}{25}i$

38. $\dfrac{1}{3i} = \dfrac{1}{3i} \cdot \dfrac{i}{i}$

$\qquad = \dfrac{i}{3i^2}$

$\qquad = -\dfrac{1}{3}i$

$\qquad$ or $0 - \dfrac{1}{3}i$

40. $\dfrac{2 - i}{3i} = \dfrac{2 - i}{3i} \cdot \dfrac{i}{i}$

$\qquad = \dfrac{2i - i^2}{3i^2}$

$\qquad = \dfrac{2i + 1}{-3}$

$\qquad = -\dfrac{1}{3} - \dfrac{2}{3}i$

42. $(2 - i)^2 + 3(2 - i) - 5 = 4 - 4i + i^2 + 6 - 3i - 5$

$\qquad\qquad = 5 - 7i - 1$

$\qquad\qquad = 4 - 7i$

44. $g(x) = -x^2 + 4x - 5$

(A) If $x = 2 + i$ then $g(x) = -(2 + i)^2 + 4(2 + i) - 5$

$\qquad\qquad\qquad = -(4 + 4i + i^2) + 8 + 4i - 5$

$\qquad\qquad\qquad = -(3 + 4i) + 3 + 4i$

$\qquad\qquad\qquad = 0$

(B) No real zeros, no x-intercepts. Vertex at $(1, -2)$ and parabola opens downward.

$\qquad$ If $x = 2 - i$ then $g(x) = -(2 - i)^2 + 4(2 - i) - 5$

$\qquad\qquad\qquad = -(4 - 4i + i^2) + 8 - 4i - 5$

$\qquad\qquad\qquad = -(3 - 4i) + 3 - 4i$

$\qquad\qquad\qquad = 0$

46. $i^{21} = i^{20} \cdot i \qquad\qquad i^{43} = i^{40} \cdot i^3 \qquad\qquad i^{52} = (i^4)^{13}$

$\quad\quad = (i^4)^5 \cdot i \qquad\qquad = (i^4)^{10} \cdot (-i) \qquad = (1)^{13}$

$\quad\quad = (1)^5 \cdot i \qquad\qquad = (1)^{10} \cdot (-i) \qquad = 1$

$\quad\quad = i \qquad\qquad\qquad = -i$

48. $3x + (y - 2)i = (5 - 2x) + (3y - 8)i$ equate real and imaginary parts:

$3x = 5 - 2x$ $y - 2 = 3y - 8$

$5x = 5$ $2y = 6$

$x = 1$ $y = 3$

50. $\dfrac{(2 + x) + (y + 3)i}{1 - i} = -3 + i$

Multiply both sides by $(1 - i)$:

$(2 + x) + (y + 3)i = (-3 + i)(1 - i)$

$(2 + x) + (y + 3)i = -3 + 3i + i - i^2$

$(2 + x) + (y + 3)i = -2 + 4i$

$2 + x = -2$ $y + 3 = 4$

$x = -4$ $y = 1$

52. $(3 - i)z + 2 = i$

$\qquad (3 - i)z = -2 + i$

$\qquad\qquad z = \dfrac{-2 + i}{3 - i} \cdot \dfrac{3 + i}{3 + i}$

$\qquad\qquad\quad = \dfrac{-6 + i + i^2}{9 - i^2}$

$\qquad\qquad\quad = \dfrac{-7 + i}{10}$

$\qquad\qquad\quad = -0.7 + 0.1i$

54. $(2 - i)z + (1 - 4i) = (-1 + 3i)z + 4 + 2i$

$\qquad 2z - iz + 1 - 4i = -z + 3iz + 4 + 2i$

$\qquad\qquad 3z - 4iz = 3 + 6i$

$\qquad\qquad z(3 - 4i) = 3 + 6i$

$\qquad\qquad\qquad z = \dfrac{3 + 6i}{3 - 4i} \cdot \dfrac{3 + 4i}{3 + 4i}$

$\qquad\qquad\qquad\quad = \dfrac{9 + 30i + 24i^2}{9 - 16i^2}$

$\qquad\qquad\qquad\quad = \dfrac{-15 + 30i}{25}$

$\qquad\qquad\qquad\quad = -\dfrac{15}{25} + \dfrac{30}{25}i$

$\qquad\qquad\quad$ or $\;-0.6 + 1.2i$

56. $\dfrac{1}{i} = \dfrac{1}{\sqrt{-1}} = \dfrac{\sqrt{1}}{\sqrt{-1}} = \sqrt{\dfrac{1}{-1}} = \sqrt{-1} = i$

The property for radicals, $\dfrac{\sqrt{a}}{\sqrt{b}} = \sqrt{\dfrac{a}{b}}$, is true for real numbers, but is not true

for complex numbers; so $\dfrac{\sqrt{1}}{\sqrt{-1}} \neq \sqrt{\dfrac{1}{-1}}$.

Correctly worked: $\dfrac{1}{i} \cdot \dfrac{i}{i} = \dfrac{i}{i^2} = \dfrac{i}{-1} = -i$

58. $(a + bi) - (c + di) = a + bi - c - di$

$\qquad\qquad\qquad\qquad\quad = (a - c) + (b - d)i$

60. $(u - vi)(u + vi) = u^2 + v^2$

$\qquad$ or $(u^2 + v^2) + 0i$

62. $\dfrac{a + bi}{c + di} = \dfrac{a + bi}{c + di} \cdot \dfrac{c - di}{c - di}$

$\qquad\qquad = \dfrac{ac + (bc - ad)i - bdi^2}{c^2 - d^2i^2}$

$\qquad\qquad = \dfrac{(ac + bd) + (bc - ad)i}{c^2 + d^2}$

$\qquad\qquad = \dfrac{ac + bd}{c^2 + d^2} + \dfrac{(bc - ad)}{c^2 + d^2}i$

64. $i^{4k+1} = i^{4k} \cdot i^1$

$\qquad\quad = (i^4)^k \cdot i$

$\qquad\quad = (1)^k \cdot i$

$\qquad\quad = i$

66. Show $(-3 + 2i)$ is a square root of $5 - 12i$:
$$(-3 + 2i)^2 = 9 - 12i + 4i^2 = 5 - 12i$$

Show $(3 - 2i)$ is a square root of $5 - 12i$:
$$(3 - 2i)^2 = 9 - 12i + 4i^2 = 5 - 12i$$

68. Find $\sqrt{2i}$:

Let $(a + bi)^2 = 2i$
$$a^2 + 2abi + b^2i^2 = 2i$$
$$a^2 - b^2 + 2abi = 0 + 2i$$

Equate real and imaginary parts:

$a^2 - b^2 = 0$	$2abi = 2i$
$(a - b)(a + b) = 0$	$ab = 1$
$a = b, -b$	$a = \dfrac{1}{b}$

Then $\quad b = \dfrac{1}{b} \quad$ or $\quad -b = \dfrac{1}{b}$

$$(b^2) = 1$$
$$b = \pm 1$$

If $b = 1$, $a = 1$, so 1 square root is $1 + i$.
If $b = -1$, $a = -1$, so 1 square root is $-1 - i$.

70. $T_n = i^2 + i^4 + i^6 + \dots + i^{2n}$, $n \geq 1$.
If $n = 2$: $T_2 = i^2 + i^4 = -1 + 1 = 0$
If $n = 3$: $T_3 = i^2 + i^4 + i^6 = -1 + 1 - 1 = -1$
If $n = 4$: $T_4 = i^2 + i^4 + i^6 + i^8 = -1 + 1 - 1 + 1 = 0$
If n is even, $T_n = 0$.
If n is odd, $T_n = -1$.

72. Theorem: The complex numbers are commutative under multiplication.

statement	reason
1. $(a + bi)(c + di) = (ac - bd) + (ad + bc)i$	1. def. of multiplication
2. $ = (ca - db) + (da + cb)i$	2. commutative $(\cdot)$
3. $ = (c + di)(a + bi)$	3. def. of multiplication

74. The sum of a complex number and its conjugate is a real number.

$$z + \bar{z} = (x + yi) + (x - iy)$$
$$= x + yi + x - iy$$
$$= 2x, \text{ a real number}$$

76. The conjugate of the conjugate of a complex number is the complex number.

$$\bar{\bar{z}} = \overline{(\overline{x + yi})} = \overline{(x - yi)} = (x + yi) = z$$

78. The conjugate of the difference of 2 complex numbers is equal to the difference of the conjugate of the 2 complex numbers.

$$\overline{z - w} = \overline{(x + yi) - (u + vi)}$$
$$= \overline{x - u + yi - vi}$$
$$= x - u - yi + vi$$
$$= x - yi - u + vi$$
$$= \bar{z} - (u - vi)$$
$$= \bar{z} - \bar{w}$$

80. The conjugate of the quotient of 2 complex numbers is equal to the quotient of the conjugate of the 2 complex numbers.

$$\overline{\left(\frac{z}{w}\right)} = \overline{\left(\frac{x+yi}{u+vi}\right)} = \overline{\left(\frac{x+yi}{u+vi}\cdot\frac{u-vi}{u-vi}\right)}$$

$$= \overline{\left(\frac{(xu+vy)+(yu-xv)i}{u^2+v^2}\right)}$$

$$= \overline{\left(\frac{xu+vy}{u^2+v^2}+\frac{(yu-xv)}{u^2+v^2}i\right)}$$

$$= \frac{xu+vy}{u^2+v^2}+\frac{xv-yu}{u^2+v^2}i \qquad (1)$$

$$\frac{\overline{z}}{\overline{w}} = \frac{x-yi}{u-vi}\cdot\frac{u+vi}{u+vi}$$

$$= \frac{(xu+vy)+(xv-yu)i}{u^2+v^2}$$

$$= \frac{xu+vy}{u^2+v^2}+\frac{xv-yu}{u^2+v^2}i \qquad (2)$$

comparison of (1) and (2) shows $\overline{\left(\frac{z}{w}\right)} = \frac{\overline{z}}{\overline{w}}$

Exercise 2-5

2.
$$3A^2 = -12A$$
$$3A^2 + 12A = 0$$
$$3A(A+4) = 0$$
$$3A = 0,\ A+4 = 0$$
$$A = 0 \qquad A = -4$$

4.
$$16x^2 + 8x = -1$$
$$16x^2 + 8x + 1 = 0$$
$$(4x+1)(4x+1) = 0$$
$$4x+1 = 0$$
$$4x = -1$$
$$x = -\frac{1}{4}$$

6.
$$8 - 10x = 3x^2$$
$$3x^2 + 10x - 8 = 0$$
$$(3x-2)(x+4) = 0$$
$$3x-2 = 0,\ x+4 = 0$$
$$3x = 2 \qquad x = -4$$
$$x = \frac{2}{3}$$

8.
$$y^2 - 45 = 0$$
$$y^2 = 45$$
$$y = \pm\sqrt{45}$$
$$y = \pm 3\sqrt{5}$$

10.
$$x^2 + 16 = 0$$
$$x^2 = -16$$
$$x = \pm\sqrt{-16}$$
$$x = \pm 4i$$

12. $4x^2 - 9 = 0$
$$x^2 = \frac{9}{4}$$
$$x = \pm\frac{3}{2}$$

14. $16a^2 + 9 = 0$
$$a^2 = -\frac{9}{16}$$
$$a = \pm\sqrt{-\frac{9}{16}}$$
$$a = \pm\frac{3}{4}i$$

16. $(m-3)^2 = 25$
$$m - 3 = \pm 5$$
$$m = 3 \pm 5$$
$$m = -2,\ 8$$

18. $(t+1)^2 = -9$
$$t + 1 = \pm 3i$$
$$t = -1 \pm 3i$$

20. $x^2 - 6x - 3 = 0$

$x = \dfrac{-(-6) \pm \sqrt{(-6)^2 - 4(1)(-3)}}{2(1)}$

$x = \dfrac{6 \pm \sqrt{48}}{2} = \dfrac{6 \pm 4\sqrt{3}}{2}$

$x = 3 \pm 2\sqrt{3}$

22. $y^2 + 3 = 2y$

$y^2 - 2y + 3 = 0$

$y = \dfrac{-(-2) \pm \sqrt{(-2)^2 - 4(1)(3)}}{2(1)}$

$y = \dfrac{2 \pm \sqrt{-8}}{2} = \dfrac{2 \pm 2i\sqrt{2}}{2}$

$y = 1 \pm i\sqrt{2}$

24. $2m^2 + 3 = 6m$

$2m^2 - 6m + 3 = 0$

$m = \dfrac{-(-6) \pm \sqrt{(-6)^2 - 4(2)(3)}}{2(2)}$

$m = \dfrac{6 \pm \sqrt{12}}{4} = \dfrac{6 \pm 2\sqrt{3}}{4}$

$m = \dfrac{3 \pm \sqrt{3}}{2}$

26. $7x^2 + 6x + 4 = 0$

$x = \dfrac{-6 \pm \sqrt{6^2 - 4(7)(4)}}{2(7)}$

$x = \dfrac{-6 \pm \sqrt{-76}}{14} = \dfrac{-6 \pm 2i\sqrt{19}}{14}$

$x = \dfrac{-3 \pm i\sqrt{19}}{7}$

$x = -\dfrac{3}{7} \pm \dfrac{\sqrt{19}}{7}i$

28. $x^2 + x < 12$

Graph $y_1 = x^2 + x$, $y_2 = 12$

Intersection at $x = -4, 3$

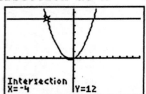

$x^2 + x - 12 < 0$ on $(-4, 3)$; $-4 < x < 3$.

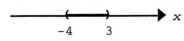

30. $x^2 + 7x + 10 > 0$

Graph $y_1 = x^2 + 7x + 10$

Zeros at $-5, -2$

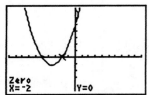

$x^2 + 7x + 10 > 0$ on $(-\infty, -5) \cup (-2, \infty)$; $x < -5$ or $x > -2$.

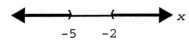

32. $x^2 + 6x \geq 0$

Graph $y_1 = x^2 + 6x$

Zeros at $-6, 0$

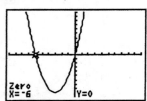

$x^2 + 6x \geq 0$ on $(-\infty, -6] \cup [0, \infty)$; $x \leq -6$ or $x \geq 0$.

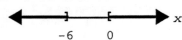

34. $x^2 \leq 4x$

Graph $y_1 = x^2$, $y_2 = 4x$

Intersection at $x = 0, 4$

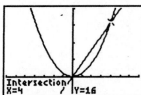

$x^2 - 4x \leq 0$ on $[0, 4]$; $0 \leq x \leq 4$.

36.
$$y^2 - 10y - 3 = 0$$
$$y^2 - 10y + 25 = 3 + 25$$
$$(y - 5)^2 = 28$$
$$y - 5 = \pm\sqrt{28}$$
$$y = 5 \pm 2\sqrt{7}$$

Graph $y_1 = x^2 - 10x - 3$
Zeros at ≈ -0.2915, 10.2915.

38.
$$2d^2 - 4d + 1 = 0$$
$$d^2 - 2d + \frac{1}{2} = 0$$
$$d^2 - 2d + 1 = -\frac{1}{2} + 1$$
$$(d - 1)^2 = \frac{1}{2}$$
$$d - 1 = \pm\sqrt{\frac{1}{2}}$$
$$d = 1 \pm \frac{\sqrt{2}}{2}$$
$$= \frac{2 \pm \sqrt{2}}{2}$$

Graph $y_1 = 2x^2 - 4x + 1$
Zeros at ≈ 0.2929, 1.7071

40.
$$3x^2 + 5x - 4 = 0$$
$$x^2 + \frac{5}{3}x - \frac{4}{3} = 0$$
$$x^2 + \frac{5}{3}x + \frac{25}{36} = \frac{4}{3} + \frac{25}{36}$$
$$\left(x + \frac{5}{6}\right)^2 = \frac{73}{36}$$
$$x + \frac{5}{6} = \pm\sqrt{\frac{73}{36}}$$
$$x = -\frac{5}{6} \pm \frac{\sqrt{73}}{6}$$
$$= \frac{-5 \pm \sqrt{73}}{6}$$

Graph $y_1 = 3x^2 + 5x - 4$
Zeros at ≈ -2.257, 0.591

42.
$$9x^2 + 9x = 4$$
$$9x^2 + 9x - 4 = 0$$
$$(3x + 4)(3x - 1) = 0$$
$$3x + 4 = 0 \quad 3x - 1 = 0$$
$$3x = -4 \quad\quad 3x = 1$$
$$x = -\frac{4}{3} \quad\quad x = \frac{1}{3}$$

Graph $y_1 = 9x^2 + 9x$, $y_2 = 4$

Intersection at $x = -\frac{4}{3}, \frac{1}{3}$

44.
$$x^2 + 2x = 2$$
$$x^2 + 2x + 1 = 2 + 1$$
$$(x + 1)^2 = 3$$
$$x + 1 = \pm\sqrt{3}$$
$$x = -1 \pm \sqrt{3}$$

Graph $y_1 = x^2 + 2x$, $y_2 = 2$
Intersection at $x \approx -2.732$, 0.732

46. $a^2 + b^2 = c^2$ for a:
$$a^2 = c^2 - b^2$$
$$a = \sqrt{c^2 - b^2}$$

48. $A = P(1 + r)^2$ for r:
$$(1 + r)^2 = \frac{A}{P}$$
$$1 + r = \sqrt{\frac{A}{P}}$$
$$r = \sqrt{\frac{A}{P}} - 1$$

50. Graph $y_1 = 0.61x^2 - 4.28x + 2.93 < 0$

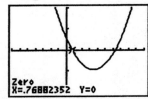

Zeros at $x \approx 6.25$, 0.77
$0.61x^2 - 4.28x + 2.93 < 0$ on
$0.77 < x < 6.25$

52. Graph $y_1 = 5.13x^2 + 7.27x - 4.32 \geq 0$

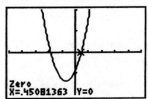

Zeros at $x \approx -1.87$, 0.45
$5.13x^2 + 7.27x - 4.32 \geq 0$ on
$x \leq -1.87$ or $x \geq 0.45$

54. $g(x) = \sqrt{4 - x^2}$
Domain: $4 - x^2 \geq 0$
Graph $y_1 = 4 - x^2$
Zeros at $x = \pm 2$
Domain: $[-2, 2]$

56. $\sqrt[6]{3x^2 - 7x - 6}$
Domain: $3x^2 - 7x - 6 \geq 0$
Graph $y_1 = \sqrt[6]{3x^2 - 7x - 6}$
Zeros at $x = -\dfrac{2}{3},\ 3$
Domain: $\left(-\infty,\ -\dfrac{2}{3}\right] \cup [3,\ \infty)$

58. $G(x) = \dfrac{1}{\sqrt{8x - x^2 - 14}}$
Domain: $8x - x^2 - 14 > 0$
Graph $y_1 = 8x - x^2 - 14$
Zeros at $x \approx 2.586,\ 5.414$
Solving for x using the quadratic formula:
$$x = \frac{-8 \pm \sqrt{8}}{-2} = 4 \pm \sqrt{2}$$
Domain: $(4 - \sqrt{2},\ 4 + \sqrt{2})$

60. Solving $x^2 - 2x + c = 0$ with the quadratic formula gives $x = 1 \pm \sqrt{1 - c}$.
For $1 - c > 0 \Leftrightarrow c < 1$, two distinct real roots.
For $1 - c = 0 \Leftrightarrow c = 1$, one real root (a double root).
For $1 - c < 0 \Leftrightarrow c > 1$, two complex roots (conjugates).

62. $ax^2 + bx + c \leq 0$, given distinct real roots r_1 and r_2 with $r_1 < r_2$
For $a > 0$, the solution set is $[r_1,\ r_2]$.
For $a < 0$, the solution set is $(-\infty,\ r_1] \cup [r_2,\ \infty)$.

64. $ax^2 + bx + c < 0$, given one (double) real root r.
For $a > 0$, the solution set is $\varnothing$, the empty set.
For $a < 0$, the solution set is $(-\infty,\ r) \cup (r,\ \infty)$.

66. Answers may vary. One example is $x^2 < 0$ whose solution set is the empty set.

68. $x^2 - 7ix - 10 = 0$
$$x = \frac{7i \pm \sqrt{49i^2 - 4(-10)}}{2}$$
$$= \frac{7i \pm 3i}{2} = \frac{4i}{2},\ \frac{10i}{2} = 2i,\ 5i \quad (0 + 2i,\ 0 + 5i)$$

70.
$$x^2 = 2ix - 3$$
$$x^2 - 2ix + 3 = 0$$
$$(x - 3i)(x + i) = 0$$
$$x - 3i = 0,\ x + i = 0$$
$$x = 3i \qquad x = -i$$
$$(0 + 3i) \qquad (0 - i)$$

72.
$$x^4 - 1 = 0$$
$$(x^2 - 1)(x^2 + 1) = 0$$
$$(x - 1)(x + 1)(x - i)(x + i) = 0$$
$$x - 1 = 0,\ x + 1 = 0,\ x - i = 0,\ x + i = 0$$
$$x = 1 \qquad x = -1 \qquad x = i \qquad x = -i$$

74. No. Complex roots to quadratics with real coefficients occur in conjugate pairs.

76. $ax^2 + bx + c = 0$, r_1 and r_2 are the 2 roots,

$$x = \frac{-b \pm \sqrt{b^2 - 4ac}}{2a}$$

$$r_1 + r_2 = \frac{-b + \sqrt{b^2 - 4ac}}{2a} + \frac{-b - \sqrt{b^2 - 4ac}}{2a}$$

$$= \frac{-b + \sqrt{b^2 - 4ac} - b - \sqrt{b^2 - 4ac}}{2a}$$

$$= \frac{-2b}{2a}$$

$$= -\frac{b}{a}$$

78. The step $(a - b)^2 = (b - a)^2$
$\qquad\qquad a - b = b - a$ is incorrect.
If $A^2 = B^2$, it may or may not follow that $A = B$.

80. Let x be the number:

$$x + x = x^2$$
$$x^2 = 2x$$
$$x^2 - 2x = 0$$
$$x(x - 2) = 0$$
$$x = 0, \; x - 2 = 0$$
$$x = 2$$

82. Let x be the first number, then $x + 1$ is the next consecutive integer.

$$x(x + 1) = 600$$
$$x^2 + x - 600 = 0$$
$$(x - 24)(x + 25) = 0$$
$$x = 24, \; x = -25 \text{ (discard, not positive)}$$
$$x + 1 = 25$$

The two consecutive integers are 24 and 25.

84. $P(x) = R(x) - C(x)$
$\qquad = (10x - 0.05x^2) - (200 + 2.25x)$
$\qquad = -0.05x^2 + 7.75x - 200$

$\quad P(x) \geq 60$:
$\qquad -0.05x^2 + 7.75x - 200 \geq 60$

Graph $y_1 = P(x)$, $y_2 = 60$.
Intersection at ≈ 49.105, 105.89
Production levels: $50 \leq x \leq 106$

86. $d(t) = 176 - 16t^2$

(A) Domain will occur from time 0 to the time when the projectile hits the ground. Graph $y_1 = d(t)$. The zeros are at $t = 0$, 11.
Domain: [0, 11]

(B) Graph $y_1 = d(t)$, $y_2 = 200$. The intersection is at $t \approx 1.29$, 9.71.

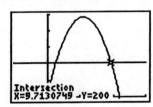

Intersection
X=9.7130749 ⌐Y=200

The projectile will be more than 200 feet above the ground for
$1.29 < t < 9.71$, or (1.29, 9.71).

88. No, the walkway in problem 87 requires $(30 \times 20) - 400 = 600 - 400 = 200$ ft^2.

$$(30 \times 20) - (30 - 2x)(20 - 2x) = 160$$
$$600 - (600 - 60x - 40x + 4x^2) = 160$$
$$-4x^2 + 100x = 160$$
$$-4x^2 + 100x - 160 = 0$$
$$x^2 - 25x + 40 = 0$$
$$x = 23.28, \; 1.72; \text{ discard 23.28 since}$$
$$\text{it is too large.}$$

The width will be 1.72 feet.

90. $A = \frac{1}{2} bh = \frac{1}{2} (5)(4) = 10$

The small isosceles triangle at the top has base w and altitude $4 - h$. It is similar to the large triangle. Using Euclid's theorem:

$$\frac{4 - h}{4} = \frac{w}{5}$$
$$5(4 - h) = 4w$$
$$20 - 5h = 4w$$
$$-5h = 4w - 20$$
$$h = -0.8w + 4$$

(A) $A_{door} = wh$
$\quad A(w) = w(-0.8w + 4)$
$\quad\quad\quad = -0.8w^2 + 4w,\ 0 \leq w \leq 5$

(B) $-0.8w^2 + 4w \geq 4.2$
Graph $y_1 = -0.8x^2 + 4x$, $y_2 = 4.2$
Intersection at $x = 1.5$, 3.5
The inequality is satisfied for
$1.5 \leq w \leq 3.5$.

(C) $h = -0.8w + 4 \geq 2$
$\quad -0.8w + 4 \geq 2$
$\quad\quad -0.8w \geq -2$
$\quad\quad\quad w \leq 2.5$

This restricts w to $0 \leq w \leq 2.5$.

92. let x = length of straightaways and
$\quad\quad y$ = radius of semicircles, then

(1) $2x + 2\pi y = \frac{1}{4}$ mile = 1320 ft

$\quad\quad x + \pi y = 660 \quad\quad$ and
(2) $\pi y^2 + 2yx = 100{,}000$

Solving (1) for x gives $x = 660 - \pi y$ and substitution of this result into (2) yields
$$\pi y^2 + 2y(660 - \pi y) = 100{,}000$$
$$\pi y^2 + 1320y - 2\pi y^2 = 100{,}000$$
$$-\pi y^2 + 1320y = 100{,}000$$
$$\pi y^2 - 1320y + 100{,}000 = 0$$

which may be solved using the quadratic formula to give
$\quad\quad y = 321.0102612 \quad$ and
$\quad\quad y = 99.15878857$
$y = 321$ is rejected since it gives a negative value for x
$y = 99.158\ldots$ gives $x = 660 - \pi y = 348.4834783$

summary: straightaways: 348 ft
$\quad\quad\quad\quad\quad$ diameter = $2y$ = 198 ft

Exercise   2-6

2. $\sqrt{25} = \pm 5$. False: $\sqrt{25} = 5$ since it is the principal square root.

4. $(\sqrt{x - 1})^2 + 1 = x$. True: $(\sqrt{x - 1})^2 + 1 = x - 1 + 1 = x$.

6. If $x^{1/3} = 2$, then $x = 8$. True, since $8^{1/3} = (2^3)^{1/3} = 2$.

8. $\sqrt[4]{x - 3} = 2$
$x - 3 = 16$
$x = 19$

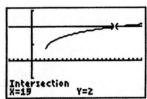

10.
$m - 13 = \sqrt{m + 7}$
$m^2 - 26m + 169 = m + 7$
$m^2 - 27m + 162 = 0$
$(m - 18)(m - 9) = 0$
$m = 18 \qquad m = 9$, reject,
does not check

 , $m = 18$

12. $3 + \sqrt{2x - 1} = 0$
$\sqrt{2x - 1} = -3$
no solution, $\sqrt{2x - 1} \geq 0$

14.
$\sqrt{3w - 2} - \sqrt{w} = 2$
$\sqrt{3w - 2} = \sqrt{w} + 2$
$3w - 2 = w + 4\sqrt{w} + 4$
$2w - 6 = 4\sqrt{w}$
$w - 3 = 2\sqrt{w}$
$w^2 - 6w + 9 = 4w$
$w^2 - 10w + 9 = 0$
$(w - 9)(w - 1) = 0$
$w = 9 \qquad w = 1$, reject, does not check

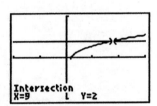

16.
$x^4 - 7x^2 - 18 = 0$
$(x^2 - 9)(x^2 + 2) = 0$
$(x - 3)(x + 3)(x^2 + 2) = 0$
$x - 3 = 0, \ x + 3 = 0, \ x^2 + 2 = 0$
$x = 3 \qquad x = -3 \qquad x^2 = -2$
$x = \pm i\sqrt{2}$

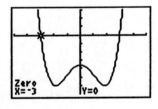

18. $x = \sqrt{5x^2 + 9}$
$x^2 = 5x^2 + 9$
$-4x^2 = 9$
$x^2 = -\dfrac{9}{4}$
$x = \pm\dfrac{3}{2} i$

20. $x^{2/3} - 3x^{1/3} - 10 = 0$

Let $u = x^{1/3}$:
$u^2 - 3u - 10 = 0$
$(u - 5)(u + 2) = 0$
$u = 5 \qquad u = -2$
$x^{1/3} = 5 \qquad x^{1/3} = -2$
$x = 5^3 = 125, \ x = -2^3 = -8$

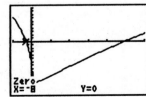

22. $(x^2 + 2x)^2 - (x^2 + 2x) = 6$
Let $u = x^2 + 2x$:

$$u^2 - u = 6$$
$$u^2 - u - 6 = 0$$
$$(u - 3)(u + 2) = 0$$
$$u = 3 \qquad u = -2$$

$$x^2 + 2x = 3 \qquad\qquad x^2 + 2x = -2$$
$$x^2 + 2x - 3 = 0 \qquad x^2 + 2x + 2 = 0$$

$$(x - 1)(x + 3) = 0 \qquad\qquad x = \frac{-2 \pm \sqrt{2^2 - 4(1)(2)}}{2(1)} = \frac{-2 \pm \sqrt{-4}}{2}$$

$$x = 1 \qquad x = -3 \qquad\qquad x = \frac{-2 \pm 2i}{2}$$

$$x = -1 \pm i$$

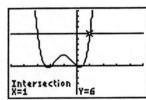

24. $\sqrt{3t + 4} + \sqrt{t} = -3$, no solution. $\sqrt{3t + 4} \geq 0$ and $\sqrt{t} \geq 0$ and two non-negatives can never add to give a negative.

26. $\sqrt{2x - 1} - \sqrt{x - 4} = 2$

$$\sqrt{2x - 1} = \sqrt{x - 4} + 2$$
$$2x - 1 = x - 4 + 4\sqrt{x - 4} + 4$$
$$x - 1 = 4\sqrt{x - 4}$$
$$x^2 - 2x + 1 = 16(x - 4)$$
$$x^2 - 18x + 65 = 0$$
$$(x - 5)(x - 13) = 0$$
$$x = 5 \qquad x = 13$$

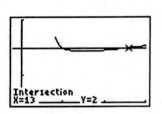

28. $\sqrt{3x + 6} - \sqrt{x + 4} = \sqrt{2}$

$$\sqrt{3x + 6} = \sqrt{2} + \sqrt{x + 4}$$
$$3x + 6 = 2 + 2\sqrt{2(x + 4)} + x + 4$$
$$2x = 2\sqrt{2x + 8}$$
$$x = \sqrt{2x + 8}$$
$$x^2 = 2x + 8$$
$$x^2 - 2x - 8 = 0$$
$$(x - 4)(x + 2) = 0$$
$$x = 4 \qquad x = -2, \text{ reject, does not check}$$

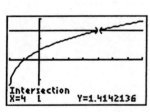

30. $6x - \sqrt{4x^2 - 20x + 17} = 15$

$$6x - 15 = \sqrt{4x^2 - 20x + 17}$$
$$36x^2 - 180x + 225 = 4x^2 - 20x + 17$$
$$32x^2 - 160x + 208 = 0$$
$$2x^2 - 10x + 13 = 0$$

$$x = \frac{10 \pm \sqrt{100 - 4(2)(13)}}{4}$$

$$x = \frac{10 \pm 2i}{4}$$

$$x = \frac{5}{2} \pm \frac{1}{2}i$$

32. $6x^{-2} - 5x^{-1} - 6 = 0$

Let $u = x^{-1}$ $\left(\dfrac{1}{x}\right)$:

$$6u^2 - 5u - 6 = 0$$
$$(3u + 2)(2u - 3) = 0$$
$$u = -\frac{2}{3} \qquad u = \frac{3}{2}$$
$$x^{-1} = -\frac{2}{3} \qquad x^{-1} = \frac{3}{2}$$
$$x = -\frac{3}{2} \qquad x = \frac{2}{3}$$

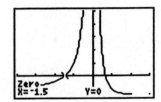

34. $4x^{-4} - 17x^{-2} + 4 = 0$

Let $u = x^{-2}$ $\left(\dfrac{1}{x^2}\right)$:

$$4u^2 - 17u + 4 = 0$$
$$(4u - 1)(u - 4) = 0$$
$$u = \frac{1}{4} \qquad u = 4$$
$$\frac{1}{x^2} = \frac{1}{4} \qquad \frac{1}{x^2} = 4$$
$$x^2 = 4 \qquad x^2 = \frac{1}{4}$$
$$x = \pm 2 \qquad x = \pm\frac{1}{2}$$

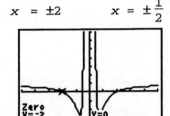

36. $4x^{-1} - 9x^{-1/2} + 2 = 0$

Let $u = x^{-1/2}$ $\left(\dfrac{1}{\sqrt{x}}\right)$:

$$4u^2 - 9u + 2 = 0$$
$$(4u - 1)(u - 2) = 0$$
$$u = \frac{1}{4} \qquad u = 2$$
$$\frac{1}{\sqrt{x}} = \frac{1}{4} \qquad \frac{1}{\sqrt{x}} = 2$$
$$\sqrt{x} = 4 \qquad 2\sqrt{x} = 1$$
$$x = 16 \qquad \sqrt{x} = \frac{1}{2}$$
$$x = \frac{1}{4}$$

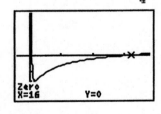

38. $(x - 3)^4 + 3(x - 3)^2 = 4$

Let $u = (x - 3)^2$

$$u^2 + 3u - 4 = 0$$
$$(u + 4)(u - 1) = 0$$
$$u = -4 \qquad u = 1$$
$$(x - 3)^2 = -4 \qquad (x - 3)^2 = 1$$
$$x - 3 = \pm 2i \qquad x - 3 = \pm 1$$
$$x = 3 \pm 2i, \qquad x = 4, 2$$

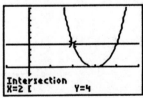

40. $\sqrt{2x + 3} - \sqrt{x - 2} = \sqrt{x + 1}$

$$2x + 3 - 2\sqrt{(2x + 3)(x - 2)} + x - 2 = x + 1$$
$$2x = 2\sqrt{2x^2 - x - 6}$$
$$4x^2 = 8x^2 - 4x - 24$$
$$x^2 = 2x^2 - x - 6$$
$$x^2 - x - 6 = 0$$
$$(x - 3)(x + 2) = 0$$
$$x - 3 = 0, \; x + 2 = 0$$
$$x = 3 \qquad x = -2, \text{ reject, does not check}$$

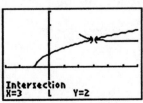

42. $4m^{-2} = 2 + m^{-4}$

$m^{-4} - 4m^{-2} + 2 = 0$

Let $u = m^{-2}$ $\left(\dfrac{1}{m^2}\right)$:

$u^2 - 4u + 2 = 0$

$u = \dfrac{4 \pm \sqrt{8}}{2} = \dfrac{4 \pm 2\sqrt{2}}{2} = 2 \pm \sqrt{2}$

$\dfrac{1}{m^2} = 2 + \sqrt{2}$ $\qquad\qquad$ $\dfrac{1}{m^2} = 2 - \sqrt{2}$

$m^2 = \dfrac{1}{2 + \sqrt{2}} \cdot \dfrac{2 - \sqrt{2}}{2 - \sqrt{2}}$ $\qquad$ $m^2 = \dfrac{1}{2 - \sqrt{2}} \cdot \dfrac{2 + \sqrt{2}}{2 + \sqrt{2}}$

$m^2 = \dfrac{2 - \sqrt{2}}{2}$ $\qquad\qquad$ $m^2 = \dfrac{2 + \sqrt{2}}{2}$

$m = \pm\sqrt{\dfrac{2 - \sqrt{2}}{2}}$ $\qquad\qquad$ $m = \pm\sqrt{\dfrac{2 + \sqrt{2}}{2}}$

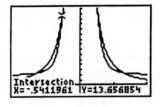

Intersection
X=-.5411961 Y=13.656854

44. $y - 6 + \sqrt{y} = 0$

$\sqrt{y} = 6 - y$

Squaring: $\qquad y = 36 - 12y + y^2$

$y^2 - 13y + 36 = 0$

$(y - 9)(y - 4) = 0$

$y = 9 \qquad y = 4 \qquad$ 9 is rejected since it does not check

$y - 6 + \sqrt{y} = 0 \qquad$ let $u = \sqrt{y}$, then $u^2 = y$

Substitution: $u^2 - 6 + u = 0$

$u^2 + u - 6 = 0$

$(u - 2)(u + 3) = 0$

$u = 2 \qquad\qquad u = -3$

$y = u^2 = 2^2 \qquad\qquad y = u^2 = (-3)^2$

$y = 4$, as before $\qquad y = 9$, reject as before

46. $x = 15 - 2\sqrt{x}$

Squaring: $x - 15 = -2\sqrt{x}$

$x^2 - 30x + 225 = 4x$

$x^2 - 34x + 225 = 0$

$(x - 9)(x - 25) = 0$

$x = 9 \qquad\qquad x = 25$, reject, does not check

$x = 15 - 2\sqrt{x}$; let $u = \sqrt{x}$, $u^2 = x$

Substitution: $u^2 = 15 - 2u$

$u^2 + 2u - 15 = 0$

$(u + 5)(u - 3) = 0$

$u = -5 \qquad u = 3; \qquad u^2 = 9$

$u^2 = 25 \qquad\qquad\qquad x = 9$ as before

$x = 25$, reject as before

48. $3\sqrt{x - 1} = 0.05x + 2.9$

Algebraically: $9(x - 1) = 0.0025x^2 + 0.29x + 8.41$

$9x - 9 = 0.0025x^2 + 0.29x + 8.41$

$0 = 0.0025x^2 - 8.71x + 17.41$

Using the quadratic formula,

$x = \dfrac{8.71 \pm \sqrt{75.69}}{0.005} = 2, 3482$

Graphically:

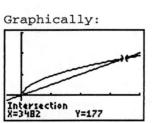

Intersection
X=3482   Y=177

$x = 2, 3482$

50. $x^{-2/5} - 3x^{-1/5} + 1 = 0$

Algebraically: Let $u = x^{-1/5}$ $\left(\dfrac{1}{\sqrt[5]{x}}\right)$

$$u^2 - 3u + 1 = 0$$

$$u = \frac{3 \pm \sqrt{9-4}}{2} = \frac{3 \pm \sqrt{5}}{2}$$

$$\frac{1}{\sqrt[5]{x}} = \frac{3 \pm \sqrt{5}}{2}$$

$$\sqrt[5]{x} = \frac{2}{3 \pm \sqrt{5}}$$

$$x = \left(\frac{2}{3 \pm \sqrt{5}}\right)^5 \approx 0.008131,\ 122.991869$$

Graphically:

Zero
X=122.99187   Y=0

$x \approx 0.008131,\ 122.991869$

52. Let the dimensions of an individual box be x and y, then

(1) $x^2 + y^2 = 6^2$ using the Pythagorean Theorem and noting that the box diagonal is a radius = 6

(2) $xy = 15$

Solving (2) for y gives $y = \dfrac{15}{x}$ and substitution into (1) yields

$$x^2 + \left(\frac{15}{x}\right)^2 = 36$$

$$x^2 + \frac{225}{x^2} = 36$$

$$x^4 + 225 = 36x^2$$

$$x^4 - 36x^2 + 225 = 0$$

Using the quadratic formula,

$x^2 \approx 8.050125629,\ 27.94987437$

$x \approx 2.83727,\ 5.28676$

$y = \dfrac{15}{x} \approx 5.28676,\ 2.83727$

To one decimal place the dimensions are 5.3 in by 2.8 in. Note that using $x^2 = 8.05012562$ or $x = 2.837274331$ gives the same dimensions for the boxes.

54.

$$\pi r\sqrt{r^2 + h^2} = S$$

$$\pi r\sqrt{r^2 + 10^2} = 125$$

$$\pi^2 r^2 (r^2 + 100) = 15625$$

$\pi^2 r^4 + 100\pi^2 r^2 - 15625 = 0$ which may be solved using the quadratic formula

$r^2 = 13.8994796$ from which

$r = 3.73$ cm to two decimal places.

CHAPTER 3

Exercise 3-1

2. $g(x) = -ax^4$ is graph (a).   **4.** $k(x) = -ax^5$ is graph (b).

6. $f(x)$ could be a third degree polynomial.

8. $g(x)$ is not a polynomial.

10.
$$y + 3 \overline{)\,y^2 + 0y - 9\,}$$

$$\frac{y - 3 \qquad\qquad R = 0}{}$$

$$\underline{y^2 + 3y}$$
$$-3y - 9$$
$$\underline{-3y - 9}$$
$$0$$

12.
$$3x + 2 \overline{)\,12x^2 + 11x - 2\,}$$

$$4x + 1 \qquad\qquad R = -4$$

$$\underline{12x^2 + 8x}$$
$$3x - 2$$
$$\underline{3x + 2}$$
$$-4$$

14.
$$a + 3 \overline{)\,a^3 + 0a^2 + 0a + 27\,}$$

$$a^2 - 3a + 9 \qquad\qquad R = 0$$

$$\underline{a^3 + 3a^2}$$
$$-3a^2 + 0a + 27$$
$$\underline{-3a^2 - 9a}$$
$$9a + 27$$
$$\underline{9a + 27}$$
$$0$$

16.
$$x - 3 \overline{)\,x^3 + 0x^2 - x + 3\,}$$

$$x^2 + 3x + 8 \qquad\qquad R = 27$$

$$\underline{x^3 - 3x^2}$$
$$3x^2 - x + 3$$
$$\underline{3x^2 - 9x}$$
$$8x + 3$$
$$\underline{8x - 24}$$
$$27$$

18.

	1	3	-3
		3	18
3$\rfloor$	1	6	15

from which

$$(x^2 + 3x - 3) \div (x - 3) = x + 6 + \frac{15}{x - 3}$$

20.

	2	7	-5
		-8	4
-4$\rfloor$	2	-1	-1

from which

$$(2x^2 + 7x - 5) \div (x + 4) = 2x - 1 + \frac{-1}{x + 4}$$

22.

	1	2	-3	-4
		-2	0	6
-2$\rfloor$	1	0	-3	2

from which

$$(x^3 + 2x^2 - 3x - 4) \div (x + 2) = x^2 - 3 + \frac{2}{x + 2}$$

24.

	4	10	-8
		-12	6
-3$\rfloor$	4	-2	-2

$$P(-3) = -2$$

26.

	2	-12	-1	30
		10	-10	-55
5$\rfloor$	2	-2	-11	-25

$$P(5) = -25$$

28.

	1	5	-13	0	-30
		-7	14	-7	49
-7$\rfloor$	1	-2	1	-7	19

$$P(-7) = 19$$

30.

5	0	-2	0	-3
	5	5	3	3

1⟌5   5   3   3   0 $5x^3 + 5x^2 + 3x + 3$, R = 0

32.

1	0	0	0	-16
	2	4	8	16

2⟌1   2   4   8   0 $x^3 + 2x^2 + 4x + 8$, R = 0

34.

1	-3	-5	6	-3
	4	4	-4	8

4⟌1   1   -1   2   5 $x^3 + x^2 - x + 2$, R = 5

36.

4	20	-24	0	-3	-13	30
	-24	24	0	0	18	-30

-6⟌4   -4   0   0   -3   5   0 $4x^5 - 4x^4 - 3x + 5$, R = 0

38.

2	-5	6	3
	1	-2	2

$\frac{1}{2}$⟌2   -4   4   5 $2x^2 - 4x + 4$, R = 5

40.

3	-1	1	2
	-2	2	-2

$-\frac{2}{3}$⟌3   -3   3   0 $3x^2 - 3x + 3$, R = 0

42.

4	-3	5	7	-6
	2.8	-0.14	3.402	7.2814

0.7⟌4   -0.2   4.86   10.402   1.2814

$4x^3 - 0.2x^2 + 4.86x + 10.402$, R = 1.2814

44.

7	-1	3	-2	0	-5
	-6.3	6.57	-8.613	9.5517	-8.59653

-0.9⟌7   -7.3   9.57   -10.613   9.5517   -13.59653

$7x^4 - 7.3x^3 + 9.57x^2 - 10.613x + 9.5517$, R = -13.59653

46. $P(x) = x^3 + 2x^2 - 5x - 3$

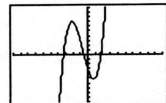

$-10 \leq x \leq 10$
$-10 \leq y \leq 10$

(A) left: $P(x) \to -\infty$ as $x \to \infty$
     right: $P(x) \to \infty$ as $x \to \infty$
     3 possible intercepts, 2 local extrema

(B) x-intercepts: -3.25, -0.52, 1.77
     local maximum at (-2.12, 7.06)
     local minimum at (0.79, -5.21)

48. $P(x) = -x^3 - 3x^2 + 4x - 4$

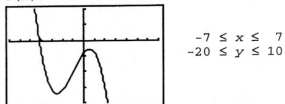

$-7 \leq x \leq 7$
$-20 \leq y \leq 10$

(A) left: $P(x) \to \infty$ as $x \to -\infty$
    right: $P(x) \to -\infty$ as $x \to \infty$
    3 possible intercepts, 2 local extrema

(B) x-intercept: -4.18
    local minimum at $(-2.53, -17.13)$
    local maximum at $(0.53, -2.87)$

50. $P(x) = -x^4 + 6x^2 - 3x - 16$

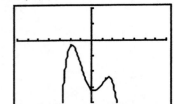

$-7 \leq x \leq 7$
$-20 \leq y \leq 10$

(A) left: $P(x) \to -\infty$ as $x \to -\infty$
    right: $P(x) \to -\infty$ as $x \to \infty$
    4 possible intercepts, 3 local extrema

(B) x-intercept: none
    local maximum at $(-1.85, -1.63)$
    local minimum at $(0.26, -16.38)$
    local maximum at $(1.59, -11.99)$

52. $P(x)$ is a 4th degree polynomial with no x-intercepts. For example,
$P(x) = x^4 + 1$. See also #50.

54. $P(x)$ is a 4th degree polynomial with no turning points. No such polynomial exists. Since both left and right end behavior are the same, there must be at least one turning point.

56.

$$
\begin{array}{r}
4x^2 - 2x - 1 \\
6x^2 + 3x + 5 \overline{\smash{\big)}\ 24x^4 + 0x^3 + 8x^2 - 13x - 7} \\
\underline{24x^4 + 12x^3 + 20x^2} \\
-12x^3 - 12x^2 - 13x - 7 \\
\underline{-12x^3 - 6x^2 - 10x} \\
-6x^2 - 3x - 7 \\
\underline{-6x^2 - 3x - 5} \\
-2
\end{array}
$$

$4x^2 - 2x - 1$, R $= -2$

58.

$$
\begin{array}{r|rrrr}
 & 1 & -2 & 1 & -2 \\
 & & 0 - i & -1 + 2i & 2 \\
\hline
i & 1 & -2 - i & 0 + 2i & 0
\end{array}
$$

$(x^3 - 2x^2 + x - 2) \div (x + i) = x^2 + (-2 - i)x + 2i$, R $= 0$

60. $P(x) = x^2 - 4ix - 13$

(A) $P(5 + 6i)$:

```
                  -4i      -13
            5 + 6i     13 + 40i
5 + 6i | 1   5 + 2i        [40i]
```

(B) $P(1 + 2i)$:

```
                  -4i      -13
            1 + 2i        5
1 + 2i | 1   1 - 2i        [-8]
```

(C) $P(3 + 2i)$:

```
                  -4i      -13
            3 + 2i        13
3 + 2i | 1   3 - 2i         [0]
```

(D) $P(-3 + 2i)$:

```
                  -4i      -13
            -3 + 2i        13
-3 + 2i | 1  -3 - 2i         [0]
```

62. $P(x) = 40 + 70x + 18x^2 + x^3$

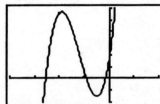

$-20 \leq x \leq 10$
$-50 \leq y \leq 150$

x-intercepts: -12.76, -4.55, -0.69
local maximum at (-9.56, 142.16)
local minimum at (-2.44, -38.16)

64. $P(x) = -0.01x^3 + 2.8x - 3$

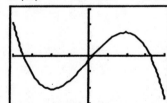

$-20 \leq x \leq 20$
$-30 \leq y \leq 30$

x-intercepts: -17.25, 1.08, 16.17
local minimum at (-9.66, -21.03)
local maximum at (9.66, 15.03)

66. $P(x) = 0.1x^4 + 0.2x^3 - 19x^2 + 17x + 100$

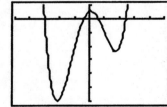

$-25 \leq x \leq 25$
$-1200 \leq y \leq 200$

x-intercepts: -15.07, -1.89, 2.92, 12.04
local minimum at (-10.73, -1191.45)
local maximum at (0.45, 103.82)
local minimum at (8.77, -485.79)

68. $P(x) = x^4 + 20x^3 + 118x^2 + 178x + 79$

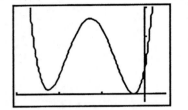

$-12 \le x \le 2$
$-25 \le y \le 300$

x-intercepts: -1, -0.97
local minimum at $(-8.98, 15.98)$
local maximum at $(-5.03, 264.03)$
local minimum at $(-0.98, -0.02)$

70. (A) Using synthetic division to divide $P(x) = a_3x^3 + a_2x^2 + a_1x + a_0$ by $x - r$:

$$\begin{array}{c|cccc}
 & a_3 & a_2 & a_1 & a_0 \\
 & & a_3r & a_2r + a_3r^2 & a_1r + a_2r^2 + a_3r^3 \\
\hline
r & a_3 & a_2 + a_3r & a_1 + a_2r + a_3r^2 & a_0 + a_1r + a_2r^2 + a_3r^3
\end{array}$$

from which $a_3x^2 + (a_2 + a_3r)x + a_1 + a_2r + a_3r^2$ is the quotient and
$\qquad a_0 + a_1r + a_2r^2 + a_3r^3$ is the remainder.

Using the long-division algorithm:

$$
\begin{array}{r}
a_3x^2 + (a_2 + a_3r)x + (a_1 + a_2r + a_3r^2) \\
x - r \overline{)\, a_3x^3 + a_2x^2 + a_1x + a_0 } \\
\underline{a_3x^3 - a_3rx^2} \\
(a_2 + a_3r)x^2 + a_1x + a_0 \\
\underline{(a_2 + a_3r)x^2 - (a_2 + a_3r)rx} \\
(a_1 + a_2r + a_3r^2)x + a_0 \\
\underline{(a_1 + a_2r + a_3r^2)x - (a_1 + a_2r + a_3r^2)r} \\
a_0 + (a_1 + a_2r + a_3r^2)r
\end{array}
$$

from which $a_3x^2 + (a_2 + a_3r)x + (a_1 + a_2r + a_3r^2)$ is the quotient and
$\qquad a_0 + a_1r + a_2r^2 + a_3r^3$ is the remainder.

Summary: both methods give the same results.

(B) $P(r) = a_3r^3 + a_2r^2 + a_1r + a_0 =$ remainder

72. $\quad P(x) = 3x^4 + x^3 - 10x^2 + 5x - 2$
$\qquad\quad = (3x + 1)x^3 - 10x^2 + 5x - 2$
$\qquad\quad = [(3x + 1)x - 10]x^2 + 5x - 2$
$\qquad\quad = \{[(3x + 1)x - 10]x + 5\}x - 2$
$\;\;P(-2) = -12 \qquad$ [calc: $-2 \to x$; type in nested $P(x)$]
$\;\;P(1.3) = -1.6347 \qquad$ [calc: $1.3 \to x$; type in nested $P(x)$]

74. $C(x) = 10,000 + 90x$; $R(x) = px = 0.0004x^3 - x^2 + 569x$

(A) $P(x) = R(x) - C(x)$
$\qquad\quad = 0.0004x^3 - x^2 + 569x - (10,000 + 90x)$
$\qquad\quad = 0.0004x^3 - x^2 + 479x - 10,000$

(B) Graph $P(x)$ in the window $[0, 2000]$ by $[-5000, 75000]$. Find the y-value of the local maximum: 54565.602 at $x = 289.93863$.

The number of air conditioners: 290

The price of 290: $0.0004(290)^2 - 290 + 569 \approx 312.64 \approx \$313$

The maximum profit: $\$54,566$

76. $V = \ell wh$

   (A) $V(x) = (2 + 2x)(2 + 2x)(3 + 2x) - (2)(2)(3)$
       $V(x) = (2 + 2x)^2(3 + 2x) - 12$

   (B) If $V(x) = 0.1$ ft^3: $0.1 = (2 + 2x)^2(3 + 2x) - 12$
       Graph $y_1 = 0.1$, $y_2 = V(x)$. The graphs intersect at $x \approx 0.0031$ feet.

78. (A)
```
CubicReg
 y=ax³+bx²+cx+d
 a=.0726666667
 b=.179047619
 c=10.82619048
 d=141.5952381
```
(B) 1995, $x = 35$: Graph y and find the value of y at $x = 35$.
    $y \approx 3855.4286 \approx \$3855$

80. (A)
```
CubicReg
 y=ax³+bx²+cx+d
 a=-3.313131ᴇ-4
 b=.019974026
 c=-.220981241
 d=2.709090909
```
(B) 1995, $x = 45$: Graph y and find the value of y at $x = 45$.
    $y \approx 3.02143 \approx 3.0$ divorces/1000 population

Exercise 3-2

2. $P(x) = (x - 5)(x + 7)^2$
       $= (x - (+5))(x - (-7))^2$

zero	multiplicity
5	1
-7	2

degree of $P(x) = 1 + 2 = 3$

4. $P(x) = 5(x - 2)^3(x + 3)^2(x - 1)$
       $= 5(x - (2))^3(x - (-3))^2(x - (1))$

zero	multiplicity
2	3
-3	2
1	1

degree of $P(x) = 3 + 2 + 1 = 6$

6. Given -2 (mult 3), 1 (mult 2): $P(x) = (x + 2)^3(x - 1)^2$,
    degree of $P(x) = 3 + 2 = 5$

8. Given $\frac{1}{3}$ (mult 2), $5 + \sqrt{7}$, $5 - \sqrt{7}$: $P(x) = \left(x - \frac{1}{3}\right)^2 (x - (5 + \sqrt{7}))(x - (5 - \sqrt{7}))$,
    degree of $P(x) = 2 + 1 + 1 = 4$

10. Given $i\sqrt{3}$ (mult 2), $-i\sqrt{3}$ (mult 2), 4 (mult 3):
    $P(x) = (x - i\sqrt{3})^2(x + i\sqrt{3})^2(x - 4)^3$, degree of $P(x) = 2 + 2 + 3 = 7$

12. Zeros: -2, -1, 1, 3: $P(x) = (x + 2)(x + 1)(x - 1)(x - 3)$, degree 4

14. Zeros: -3, 1 (mult 2): $P(x) = (x + 3)(x - 1)^2$, degree 3

16. Zeros: -2 (mult 2), 0, 2 (mult 2): $P(x) = (x + 2)^2 \cdot x \cdot (x - 2)^2$, degree 5

18. $P(x) = x^{18} - 1$
    $P(-1) = (-1)^{18} - 1 = 0 \Rightarrow$ yes; $x + 1$ is a factor of $x^{18} - 1$.

20. $P(x) = 3x^4 - 2x^3 + 5x - 6$
    $P(1) = 3(1)^4 - 2(1)^3 + 5(1) - 6 = 0 \Rightarrow$ yes; $x - 1$ is a factor of $P(x)$.

22. $P(x) = x^3 + 3x^2 - 6x - 8$; $b = -8$, $c = 1$
factors of b: ± 1, ± 2, ± 4, ± 8
factors of c: ± 1
$\dfrac{b}{c}$: ± 1, ± 2, ± 4, ± 8 are possible rational zeros

24. $P(x) = 2x^3 + x^2 - 4x - 3$
$b = -3$, $c = 2$
factors of b: ± 1, ± 3
factors of c: ± 1, ± 2
$\dfrac{b}{c}$: ± 1, ± 3, $\pm\dfrac{1}{2}$, $\pm\dfrac{3}{2}$

26. $P(x) = 2x^3 - 9x^2 + 14x - 5$
$b = -5$, $c = 2$
factors of b: ± 1, ± 5
factors of c: ± 1, ± 2
$\dfrac{b}{c}$: ± 1, ± 5, $\pm\dfrac{1}{2}$, $\pm\dfrac{5}{2}$

28. $P(x) = x^3 - 4x^2 - 3x + 18$;
3 a double zero

```
       1   -4   -3    18
            3   -3   -18
   3 | 1   -1   -6     0
            3    6
   3 | 1    2    0   ⇒ x + 2
```

$P(x) = (x - 3)(x - 3)(x + 2)$

30. $P(x) = x^4 + 2x^2 + 1$;
i is a double zero

```
       1    0    2    0    1
            i   -1    i   -1
   i | 1    i    1    i    0
            i   -2   -i
   i | 1   2i   -1    0   ⇒ x² + 2ix - 1
```

$x = \dfrac{-2i \pm \sqrt{4i^2 - 4(-1)}}{2}$

$= \dfrac{-2i \pm \sqrt{0}}{2} = -i$ (double zero)

$P(x) = (x - i)(x - i)(x + i)(x + i)$

32. $P(x) = 3x^3 - 10x^2 + 31x + 26$; $-\dfrac{2}{3}$ is a zero

```
           3   -10    31    26
               -2      8   -26
  -2/3 | 3   -12    39     0   ⇒ 3x² - 12x + 39
```

$P(x) = \left(x + \dfrac{2}{3}\right)(3x^2 - 12x + 39)$

$P(x) = 3\left(x + \dfrac{2}{3}\right)(x^2 - 4x + 13)$

$x = \dfrac{4 \pm \sqrt{16 - 4(13)}}{2}$

$= \dfrac{4 \pm \sqrt{-36}}{2}$

$= \dfrac{4 \pm 6i}{2} = 2 \pm 3i$

$P(x) = 3\left(x + \dfrac{2}{3}\right)(x - (2 + 3i))(x - (2 - 3i))$

$P(x) = (3x + 2)(x - 2 - 3i)(x - 2 + 3i)$

34. $2x^3 - 10x^2 + 12x - 4 = 0$

Possible rational zeros, $\dfrac{b}{c} = \pm 1,\ \pm 2,\ \pm 4,\ \pm\dfrac{1}{2}$

Graph $y = 2x^3 - 10x^2 + 12x - 4$.

y appears to have a zero at $x = 1$:

$$
\begin{array}{r|rrrr}
 & 2 & -10 & 12 & -4 \\
 &   & 2 & -8 & 4 \\
\hline
1 & 2 & -8 & 4 & 0 \\
\end{array}
$$

$2x^2 - 8x + 4 = 0$

$x^2 - 4x + 2 = 0$

$$x = \frac{4 \pm \sqrt{16 - 8}}{2} = \frac{4 \pm 2\sqrt{2}}{2} = 2 \pm \sqrt{2}$$

The roots are $1,\ 2 \pm \sqrt{2}$.

36. $x^4 - 4x^2 - 4x - 1 = 0$

Possible rational zeros, $\dfrac{b}{c} = \pm 1$

Graph $y = x^4 - 4x^2 - 4x - 1$.

y appears to have a double zero at $x = -1$:

$$
\begin{array}{r|rrrrr}
 & 1 & 0 & -4 & -4 & -1 \\
 &   & -1 & 1 & 3 & 1 \\
\hline
-1 & 1 & -1 & -3 & -1 & 0 \\
 &   & -1 & 2 & 1 & \\
\hline
-1 & 1 & -2 & -1 & 0 & \\
\end{array}
$$

$x^2 - 2x - 1 = 0$

$$x = \frac{2 \pm \sqrt{4 + 4}}{2} = \frac{2 \pm 2\sqrt{2}}{2} = 1 \pm \sqrt{2}$$

The roots are -1 (mult 2), $1 \pm \sqrt{2}$.

38. $x^4 - 2x^2 - 16x - 15 = 0$

Possible rational zeros, $\dfrac{b}{c} = \pm 1,\ \pm 3,\ \pm 5,\ \pm 15$

Graph $y = x^4 - 2x^2 - 16x - 15$.

y appears to have zeros at -1 and 3:

$$
\begin{array}{r|rrrrr}
 & 1 & 0 & -2 & -16 & -15 \\
 &   & -1 & 1 & 1 & 15 \\
\hline
-1 & 1 & -1 & -1 & -15 & 0 \\
 &   & 3 & 6 & 15 & \\
\hline
3 & 1 & 2 & 5 & 0 & \\
\end{array}
$$

$x^2 + 2x + 5 = 0$

$$x = \frac{-2 \pm \sqrt{4 - 20}}{2} = \frac{-2 \pm 4i}{2} = -1 \pm 2i$$

The roots are $-1,\ 3,\ -1 \pm 2i$.

40. $2x^5 + x^4 - 6x^3 - 3x^2 - 8x - 4 = 0$

Possible rational zeros, $\dfrac{b}{c} = \pm1,\ \pm2,\ \pm4,\ \pm\dfrac{1}{2}$

Graph $y = 2x^5 + x^4 - 6x^3 - 3x^2 - 8x - 4 = 0$.

y appears to have zeros at -2, $-\dfrac{1}{2}$, and 2:

```
        2    1   -6   -3   -8   -4
            -4    6    0    6    4
  -2 | 2   -3    0   -3   -2    0
             4    2    4    2
   2 | 2    1    2    1    0
            -1    0   -1
 -.5 | 2    0    2    0
```

$$2x^2 + 2 = 0$$
$$x^2 = -1$$
$$x = \pm i$$

The roots are ±2, $-\dfrac{1}{2}$, $\pm i$.

42. $P(x) = x^3 - 7x^2 + 36$

Possible rational zeros, $\dfrac{b}{c} = \pm1,\ \pm2,\ \pm3,\ \pm4,\ \pm6,\ \pm9,\ \pm12,\ \pm18,\ \pm36$

Graph $P(x)$; the zeros appear to be -2, 3, 6:

```
        1   -7    0    36
            -2   18   -36
  -2 | 1   -9   18     0
```

$$x^2 - 9x + 18 = 0$$
$$(x - 3)(x - 6) = 0$$
$$x = 3,\ 6$$

The zeros are -2, 3, 6.

44. $P(x) = x^4 + \dfrac{7}{6}x^3 - \dfrac{7}{3}x^2 - \dfrac{5}{2}x$

$6P(x) = 6x^4 + 7x^3 - 14x^2 - 15x$

Possible rational zeros, $\dfrac{b}{c} = \pm1,\ \pm3,\ \pm5,\ \pm15,\ \pm\dfrac{1}{2},\ \pm\dfrac{3}{2},\ \pm\dfrac{5}{2},\ \pm\dfrac{15}{2},\ \pm\dfrac{1}{3},\ \pm\dfrac{5}{3},$

$$\pm\dfrac{1}{6},\ \pm\dfrac{5}{6}$$

Graph $P(x)$; -1, 0, and $\dfrac{3}{2}$ and $-\dfrac{5}{3}$ appear to be zeros of $P(x)$:

```
         6    7   -14   -15    0
             -6    -1    15    0
  -1 | 6    1   -15     0    0
              9    15    0
 3/2 | 6   10     0    0
```

$$6x^2 + 10x + 0 = 0 \Rightarrow x(6x + 10) = 0$$
$$x = 0, \qquad x = -\dfrac{5}{3}$$

The zeros are $-\dfrac{5}{3}$, -1, 0, $\dfrac{3}{2}$.

46. $P(x) = x^4 - \dfrac{13}{4}x^2 - \dfrac{5}{2}x - \dfrac{1}{4}$

$4P(x) = 4x^4 - 13x^2 - 10x - 1$

Possible rational zeros, $\dfrac{b}{c} = \pm1,\ \pm\dfrac{1}{2},\ \pm\dfrac{1}{4}$

Graph $P(x)$; -1 appears to be a zero of multiplicity 2:

```
        4      0     -13    -10    -1
              -4      4      9      1
  -1│   4     -4     -9     -1      0

              -4      8      1
  -1│   4     -8     -1      0
```

$4x^2 - 8x - 1 = 0$

$x = \dfrac{8 \pm \sqrt{64 + 16}}{8} = \dfrac{8 \pm \sqrt{80}}{8} = \dfrac{8 \pm 4\sqrt{5}}{8} = 1 \pm \dfrac{\sqrt{5}}{2}$

The zeros are -1 (mult 2), $1 \pm \dfrac{\sqrt{5}}{2}$.

48. $P(x) = 2x^5 - 3x^4 - 6x^3 + 23x^2 - 26x + 10$

Possible rational zeros, $\dfrac{b}{c} = \pm1,\ \pm2,\ \pm5,\ \pm10,\ \pm\dfrac{1}{2},\ \pm\dfrac{5}{2}$

Graph $P(x)$; $-\dfrac{5}{2}$ (mult 1) and 1 (mult 2) appear to be zeros:

```
            2     -3     -6     23    -26     10
                 -5     20    -35     30    -10
  -5/2│   2     -8     14    -12      4      0

                  2     -6      8     -4
      1│   2     -6      8     -4      0

                  2     -4      4
      1│   2     -4      4      0
```

$2x^2 - 4x + 4 = 0$

$x^2 - 2x + 2 = 0$

$x = \dfrac{2 \pm \sqrt{4 - 8}}{2} = \dfrac{2 \pm 2i}{2} = 1 \pm i$

The zeros are $-\dfrac{5}{2}$, 1 (mult 2), $1 \pm i$.

50. $P(x) = 6x^3 - 17x^2 - 4x + 3$

Possible rational zeros, $\dfrac{b}{c} = \pm1,\ \pm3,\ \pm\dfrac{1}{2},\ \pm\dfrac{3}{2},\ \pm\dfrac{1}{3},\ \pm\dfrac{1}{6}$

```
        6    -17     -4      3
             18      3     -3
  3│   6      1     -1      0     (x - 3) is a factor
```

$6x^2 + x - 1 = 0$

$(3x - 1)(2x + 1) = 0$

$P(x) = (x - 3)(3x - 1)(2x + 1)$

52. $P(x) = x^3 - 8x^2 + 17x - 4$ Possible rational zeros, $\frac{b}{c} = \pm 1,\ \pm 2,\ \pm 4$

$$
\begin{array}{r|rrrr}
 & 1 & -8 & 17 & -4 \\
 &   & 4 & -16 & 4 \\
\hline
4 & 1 & -4 & 1 & 0
\end{array}
$$
  $(x - 4)$ is a factor

$$x^2 - 4x + 1 = 0$$

$$x = \frac{4 \pm \sqrt{16 - 4}}{2} = \frac{4 \pm 2\sqrt{3}}{2} = 2 \pm \sqrt{3}$$

$$P(x) = (x - 4)(x - (2 + \sqrt{3}))(x - (2 - \sqrt{3}))$$

54. $P(x) = 2x^4 + 3x^3 - 4x^2 - 3x + 2$ Possible rational zeros, $\frac{b}{c} = \pm 1,\ \pm 2,\ \pm \frac{1}{2}$

$$
\begin{array}{r|rrrrr}
 & 2 & 3 & -4 & -3 & 2 \\
 &   & -4 & 2 & 4 & -2 \\
\hline
-2 & 2 & -1 & -2 & 1 & 0
\end{array}
$$
  $(x + 2)$ is a factor

$$
\begin{array}{r|rrrr}
 &   & -2 & 3 & -1 \\
\hline
-1 & 2 & -3 & 1 & 0
\end{array}
$$
  $(x + 1)$ is a factor

$$2x^2 - 3x + 1 = 0$$
$$(2x - 1)(x - 1) = 0 \qquad\qquad P(x) = (x + 2)(x + 1)(2x - 1)(x - 1)$$

56. $[x - (2 - 3i)][x - (2 + 3i)] = x^2 - (2 + 3i)x - (2 - 3i)x + (2 - 3i)(2 + 3i)$

$$= x^2 - 2x - 3ix - 2x + 3ix + 4 - 9i^2$$

$$= x^2 - 4x + 13$$

58. $[x - (5 + 2i)][x - (5 - 2i)] = x^2 - (5 - 2i)x - (5 + 2i)x + (5 + 2i)(5 - 2i)$

$$= x^2 - 5x + 2ix - 5x - 2ix + 25 - 4i^2$$

$$= x^2 - 10x + 29$$

60. $(x - bi)(x + bi) = x^2 - b^2i^2 = x^2 + b^2$

62. $P(x) = x^3 + x^2 - 4x + 6$, $1 + i$ is a zero $\Rightarrow$ $1 - i$ is a zero.

$(x - (1 + i))(x - (1 - i)) = x^2 - 2x + 2$ is a factor.

$$
\begin{array}{r}
x + 3 \\
x^2 - 2x + 2\overline{\smash)x^3 + x^2 - 4x + 6} \\
\underline{x^3 - 2x^2 + 2x} \\
3x^2 - 6x + 6 \\
\underline{3x^2 - 6x + 6} \\
0
\end{array}
$$
from which $x + 3$ is a factor, -3 is a zero.

zeros: $1 - i,\ 1 + i,\ -3$

64. $P(x) = x^3 + 2x^2 + 16x + 32$; $4i$ is a zero $\Rightarrow$ $-4i$ is a zero.

$(x - 4i)(x + 4i) = x^2 + 16$ is a factor.

$$
\begin{array}{r}
x + 2 \\
x^2 + 16 \overline{\smash{\big)}\ x^3 + 2x^2 + 16x + 32} \\
\underline{x^3 \qquad\quad + 16x} \\
2x^2 \qquad\quad + 32 \\
\underline{2x^2 \qquad\quad + 32} \\
0
\end{array}
$$

$\Rightarrow x + 2$ is a factor

-2 is a zero

zeros: $\pm 4i$, -2

66. $P(x) = x^4 - 2x^3 + 7x^2 - 18x - 18$; $-3i$ is a zero $\Rightarrow$ $3i$ is a zero.

$(x - 3i)(x + 3i) = x^2 + 9$ is a factor.

$$
\begin{array}{r}
x^2 - 2x - 2 \\
x^2 + 9 \overline{\smash{\big)}\ x^4 - 2x^3 + 7x^2 - 18x - 18} \\
\underline{x^4 \qquad\quad + 9x^2} \\
-2x^3 - 2x^2 - 18x - 18 \\
\underline{-2x^3 \qquad\quad - 18x} \\
-2x^2 \qquad\quad - 18 \\
\underline{-2x^2 \qquad\quad - 18} \\
0
\end{array}
$$

$\Rightarrow x^2 - 2x - 2$ is a factor

$x^2 - 2x - 2 = 0$ may be solved using the quadratic formula to obtain $x = 1 \pm \sqrt{3}$

zeros: $\pm 3i$, $1 \pm \sqrt{3}$

68. Let $P(x) = x^2 - 12$: ± 1, ± 2, ± 3, ± 4, ± 6, ± 12 are possible rational zeros, none of which give $P(x) = 0 \Rightarrow P(x)$ has no rational zeros. But $\pm \sqrt{12}$ are zeros of $P(x)$ which implies $\sqrt{12}$ is not rational.

70. Let $P(x) = x^5 - 8$: ± 1, ± 2, ± 3, ± 4, ± 8 are possible rational zeros, none of which give $P(x) = 0 \Rightarrow P(x)$ has no rational zeros. But $\sqrt[5]{8}$ is a zero of $P(x)$ which implies $\sqrt[5]{8}$ is not rational.

72. $P(x) = 2x^3 - 9x^2 - 2x + 30$

Possible rat'l zeros, $\dfrac{b}{c} = \pm 1$, ± 2, ± 3, ± 5, ± 6, ± 10, ± 15, ± 30, $\pm \dfrac{1}{2}$, $\pm \dfrac{3}{2}$, $\pm \dfrac{5}{2}$, $\pm \dfrac{15}{2}$

Graph $P(x)$; $\dfrac{5}{2}$ appears to be a zero.

$$
\begin{array}{r|rrrr}
& 2 & -9 & -2 & 30 \\
& & 5 & -10 & -30 \\
\hline
\frac{5}{2} & 2 & -4 & -12 & 0
\end{array}
$$

$2x^2 - 4x - 12 = 0$

$x^2 - 2x - 6 = 0$

$x = \dfrac{2 \pm \sqrt{4 + 24}}{2} = \dfrac{2 \pm 2\sqrt{7}}{2} = 1 \pm \sqrt{7}$ Zeros: $\dfrac{5}{2}$, $1 \pm \sqrt{7}$

74. $P(x) = 6x^4 + 35x^3 + 2x^2 - 233x - 360$

Possible rational zeros, $\dfrac{b}{c}$ = ± all factors of 360 ÷ all factors of 6.

Graph $P(x)$; $-\dfrac{9}{2}$ and $\dfrac{8}{3}$ appear to be zeros.

$$
\begin{array}{r|rrrrr}
 & 6 & 35 & 2 & -233 & -360 \\
 & & -27 & -36 & 153 & 360 \\
\hline
-\dfrac{9}{2} & 6 & 8 & -34 & -80 & 0 \\
 & & 16 & 64 & 80 \\
\hline
\dfrac{8}{3} & 6 & 24 & 30 & 0
\end{array}
$$

$$6x^2 + 24x + 30 = 0$$
$$x^2 + 4x + 5 = 0$$

$$x = \frac{-4 \pm \sqrt{16 - 20}}{2} = \frac{-4 \pm 2i}{2} = -2 \pm i$$

Zeros: $-\dfrac{9}{2}$, $\dfrac{8}{3}$, $-2 \pm i$

76. $P(x) = x^5 - 6x^4 + 6x^3 + 28x^2 - 72x + 48$

Possible rational zeros, $\dfrac{b}{c}$ = ±1, ±2, ±3, ±4, ±6, ±8, ±12, ±16, ±24, ±48.

Graph $P(x)$; 2 appears to be a zero of odd multiplicity.

$$
\begin{array}{r|rrrrrr}
 & 1 & -6 & 6 & 28 & -72 & 48 \\
 & & 2 & -8 & -4 & 48 & -48 \\
\hline
2 & 1 & -4 & -2 & 24 & -24 & 0 \\
 & & 2 & -4 & -12 & 24 \\
\hline
2 & 1 & -2 & -6 & 12 & 0 \\
 & & 2 & 0 & -12 \\
\hline
2 & 1 & 0 & -6 & 0
\end{array}
$$

$$x^2 - 6 = 0$$
$$x^2 = 6$$
$$x = \pm\sqrt{6}$$

Zeros: 2 (mult 3), $\pm\sqrt{6}$

78. $x^3 - 8 = 0$

(A) There are 3 cube roots of 8.

(B)
$$
\begin{array}{r|rrrr}
 & 1 & 0 & 0 & -8 \\
 & & 2 & 4 & 8 \\
\hline
2 & 1 & 2 & 4 & 0
\end{array}
$$

$$x^2 + 2x + 4 = 0$$

$$x = \frac{-2 \pm \sqrt{4 - 16}}{2} = \frac{-2 \pm 2i\sqrt{3}}{2} = -1 \pm i\sqrt{3}$$

80. If P is a polynomial function with real coefficients of degree n, with n even, then the maximum number of times the graph of $y = P(x)$ can cross the x-axis is n with all roots real and the minimum number is 0 with all roots complex.

82. Let $H(x) = P(x) - Q(x)$, then deg $H \le n$ which means H can have at most n zeros. But since $P(x) = Q(x)$ for more than n values of x, $H(x) = 0$ for more than n values ($\Rightarrow H$ has more than n zeros). This is a contradiction unless $H(x) = 0 \Rightarrow P(x) - Q(x) = 0$ or $P(x) = Q(x)$. They would be identities.

84. $V_a = 1 \cdot 1 \cdot 2 = 2$
   $V_b = (1 + x)(1 + x)(2 + x)$
   $6(2) = (1 + x)(1 + x)(2 + x)$

Graph $y_1 = 12$, $y_2 = V_b$. The graphs intersect at $x = 1$.
The sides should be increased by 1 foot.

86. $\ell = 10 - 2x$, $w = 8 - 2x$
   $V(x) = (10 - 2x)(8 - 2x)x$
   $48 = (10 - 2x)(8 - 2x)x$

Graph $y_1 = 48$, $y_2 = V(x)$. The graphs intersect at $x = 1$, 2, and 6.
Discard 6 since $8 - 2(6) < 0$.
The square can be 1 ft $\times$ 1 ft or 2 ft $\times$ 2 ft.

Exercise 3-3

Note: For the synthetic division tables in this section, enter the coefficients of
$P(x) \to L_1$ *and use the SYNDIV program.*

2. There is at least one x-intercept in each of the intervals $(-8, -2)$, $(2, 4)$,
and $(4, 9)$.

4. There is at least one x-intercept in each of the intervals $(-1, 0)$, $(0, 2)$, and
$(2, 5)$.

6. $P(x) = x^3 - 12x^2 + 44x - 49$; $\{1, -12, 44, -49\} \to L_1$, program SYNDIV:

	1	-12	44	-49
2	1	-10	24	-1
3	1	-9	17	2
4	1	-8	12	-1
6	1	-6	8	-1
7	1	-5	9	14

The last column, $P(x)$, changes sign for the
following intervals: $(2, 3)$, $(3, 4)$ and
$(6, 7)$, so there are zeros in each of these
intervals.

8. $P(x) = x^3 + x^2 - 4x - 3$

	1	1	-4	-3
-3	1	-2	2	-9
-2	1	-1	-2	1
-1	1	0	-4	1
0	1	1	-4	-3
1	1	2	-2	-5
2	1	3	2	1
3	1	4	8	21

The last column, $P(x)$, changes signs, so
there are zeros in each of the intervals:
$(-3, -2)$, $(-1, 0)$, and $(1, 2)$.

10. $P(x) = x^3 - 4x^2 + 4$

		1	-4	0	4
	-2	1	-6	12	-20
Lower bound:	-1	1	-5	5	-1
	0	1	-4	0	4
	1	1	-3	-3	1
	2	1	-2	-4	-4
	3	1	-1	-3	-5
Upper bound:	4	1	0	0	4

12. $P(x) = x^4 - 4x^3 + 6x^2 - 4x - 7$

		1	-4	6	-4	-7
	-2	1	-6	18	-40	73
Lower bound:	-1	1	-5	11	-15	8
	0	1	-4	6	-4	-7
	1	1	-3	3	-1	-8
	2	1	-2	2	0	-7
	3	1	-1	3	5	8
Upper bound:	4	1	0	6	20	73

14. $P(x) = x^5 - 3x^4 + 3x^2 + 2x - 1$

		1	-3	0	3	2	-1
Lower bound:	-1	1	-4	4	-1	3	-4
	0	1	-3	0	3	2	-1
	1	1	-2	-2	1	3	2
	2	1	-1	-2	-1	0	-1
Upper bound:	3	1	0	0	3	11	32

16. $P(x) = x^3 + x^2 - 4x - 1$

(A)

		1	1	-4	-1
LB:	-3	1	-2	2	-7
	-2	1	-1	-2	3
	-1	1	0	-4	3
	0	1	1	-4	-1
	1	1	2	-2	-3
UB:	2	1	3	2	3

Real zeros in (-3, -2), (-1, 0) and (1, 2).

(B)
```
RIGHT BOUND: 2
          ⟨1 2⟩
        ⟨1.5 2⟩
     ⟨1.5 1.75⟩
   ⟨1.625 1.75⟩
  ⟨1.6875 1.75⟩
⟨1.6875 1.71875⟩
```

Using the BISECT program,
5 additional intervals.
$x \approx 1.7$

18. $P(x) = x^3 - 3x^2 - x - 2$

(A)

		1	-3	-1	-2
	-2	1	-5	9	-20
LB:	-1	1	-4	3	-5
	0	1	-3	-1	-2
	1	1	-2	-3	-5
	2	1	-1	-3	-8
	3	1	0	-1	-5
UB:	4	1	1	3	10

Real zeros in (3, 4).

(B)
```
              ⟨3 4⟩
            ⟨3 3.5⟩
         ⟨3.25 3.5⟩
        ⟨3.375 3.5⟩
       ⟨3.4375 3.5⟩
  ⟨3.4375 3.46875⟩
⟨3.453125 3.468…⟩
```

Using the BISECT program,
6 additional intervals.
$x \approx 3.5$

20. $P(x) = x^4 - x^3 - 9x^2 + 9x + 4$

(A)

	1	-1	-9	9	4
-4	1	-5	11	-35	144
LB: -3	1	-4	3	0	4
-2	1	-3	-3	15	-26
-1	1	-2	-7	16	-12
0	1	-1	-9	9	4
1	1	0	-9	0	4
2	1	1	-7	-5	-6
3	1	2	-3	0	4
UB: 4	1	3	3	21	88

Real zeros in (-3, -2), (-1, 0), (1, 2), and (2, 3).

(B)

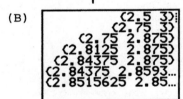

```
            (2  3)
          (2.5  3)
         (2.75  3)
     (2.75  2.875)
   (2.8125  2.875)
  (2.84375  2.875)
 (2.859375  2.875)
```

Using the BISECT program,
6 additional intervals.
$x \approx 2.9$

22. $P(x) = x^4 - 3x^3 - x^2 + 3x + 3$

(A)

	1	-3	-1	3	3
LB: -1	1	-4	3	0	3
0	1	-3	-1	3	3
1	1	-2	-3	0	3
2	1	-1	-3	-3	-3
3	1	0	-1	0	3
UB: 4	1	1	3	15	63

Real zeros in (1, 2) and (2, 3).

(B)

```
          (2.5  3)
         (2.75  3)
     (2.75  2.875)
   (2.8125  2.875)
  (2.84375  2.875)
 (2.84375  2.8593…
 (2.8515625  2.85…
```

Using the BISECT program,
7 additional intervals.
$x \approx 2.9$

24. $P(x) = x^3 + 3x^2 + 4x + 5$

(A)

	1	3	4	5
LB: -3	1	0	4	-7
-2	1	1	2	1
-1	1	2	2	3
0	1	3	4	5
UB: 1	1	4	8	13

Real zeros in (-3, -2).

(B) Use either the BISECT program or locate the zero on the graph of
$P(x)$: $x \approx -2.21$.

26. $P(x) = x^4 - x^3 - 8x^2 - 12x - 25$

(A)

		1	-1	-8	-12	-25
LB: -3		1	-4	4	-24	47
-2		1	-3	-2	-8	-9
-1		1	-2	-6	-6	-19
0		1	-1	-8	-12	-25
1		1	0	-8	-20	-45
2		1	1	-6	-24	-73
3		1	2	-2	-18	-79
4		1	3	4	4	-9
UB: 5		1	4	12	48	215

(B) Use either the BISECT program or locate the zeros on the graph of $P(x)$: $x \approx -2.29, 4.07$.

28. $P(x) = x^5 - x^4 - 2x^2 - 4x - 5$

(A)

		1	-1	0	-2	-4	-5
LB: -1		1	-2	2	-4	0	-5
0		1	-1	0	-2	-4	-5
1		1	0	0	-2	-6	-11
2		1	1	2	2	0	-5
UB: 3		1	2	6	16	44	127

(B) Use either the BISECT program or locate the zero on the graph of $P(x)$: $x \approx 2.12$.

30. $P(x) = x^5 - 2x^4 - 6x^2 - 9x + 10$

(A)

		1	-2	0	-6	-9	10
LB: -2		1	-4	8	-22	35	-60
-1		1	-3	3	-9	0	10
0		1	-2	0	-6	-9	10
1		1	-1	-1	-7	-16	-6
2		1	0	0	-6	-21	-32
UB: 3		1	1	3	3	0	10

(B) Use either the BISECT program or locate the zeros on the graph of $P(x)$: $x \approx -1.35, 0.72, 2.92$.

32. $P(x) = (x - 1)^2 (x - 2)(x - 3)^4$
Yes, since $x = 2$ has multiplicity of one, the graph will cross the x-axis at $x = 2$ (end behavior: $P(x) \to -\infty$ as $x \to -\infty$, $P(x) \to \infty$ as $x \to \infty$).

34. $P(x) = (x - 1)^2 (x - 2)(x - 3)^4$
Use the maximum routine at $x = 1$. Use the minimum routine at $x = 3$. All calculators can use the zero routine at $x = 2$ (some calculators can use the zero routine for all three).

36. $P(x) = x^4 + 4x^3 - 4x^2 - 16x + 16$
Graph $P(x)$ and use the minimum routine for both zeros.
Zeros: -3.24 (double) and 1.24 (double)

38. $P(x) = x^5 - 6x^4 + 2x^3 + 28x^2 - 15x + 2$
Graph $P(x)$; use the zero routine for $x = 2$, and the minimum routine for the other zeros.
Zero: -2 (simple), 0.27 (double), and 3.73 (double)

40. $P(x) = x^5 + 12x^4 + 47x^3 + 56x^2 - 15.75x + 1$
Graph $P(x)$; use the maximum routine for $x = -4.12$, the zero routine for $x = -4$, and the minimum routine for $x = 0.12$.
Zeros: -4.12 (double), -4 (simple), 0.12 (double)

42. $P(x) = x^3 - 37x^2 + 70x - 20$
(A)

	1	-37	70	-20
10	1	-27	-200	-2020
20	1	-17	-270	-5420
30	1	-7	-140	-4220
40	1	3	190	7580
-10	1	-47	540	-5420

40 and -10 are the smallest positive integer multiple of 10 and largest negative integer multiple of 10 that, by Theorem 2, are upper and lower bounds, respectively, for the real zeros of $P(x)$.

(B) 0.35, 1.63, and 35.02 are the real zeros to two places.

44. $P(x) = x^4 - 12x^3 - 425x^2 + 7000$
(A)

	1	-12	-425	0	7,000	
10	1	-2	-445	-4450	-37,500	
20	1	8	-265	-5300	-99,000	
30	1	18	115	3450	110,500	30 is an upper bound
-10	1	-22	-205	2050	-13,500	
-20	1	-32	215	-4300	93,000	-20 is a lower bound

30 and -20 are the smallest positive integer multiple of 10 and largest negative integer multiple of 10 that, by Theorem 2, are upper and lower bounds, respectively, for the real zeros of $P(x)$.

(B) -14.70, -4.46, 3.92, and 27.25 are the real zeros of $P(x)$ to two decimal places.

46. $P(x) = x^4 - 5x^3 - 50x^2 - 500x + 7000$
(A)

	1	-5	-50	-500	7,000	
10	1	5	0	-500	2,000	
20	1	15	250	4500	97,000	20 is an upper bound
-10	1	-15	100	-1500	22,000	-10 is a lower bound

20 and -10 are the smallest positive integer multiple of 10 and largest negative integer multiple of 10 that, by Theorem 2, are upper and lower bounds, respectively, for the real zeros of $P(x)$.

(B) There are no real zeros.

48. $P(x) = 9x^4 + 120x^3 - 3083x^2 - 25,674x - 48,400$
(A)

	9	120	-3083	-25,674	-48,400	
10	9	210	-983	-35,504	-403,440	
20	9	300	2917	32,666	604,920	20 is an upper bound
-10	9	30	-3383	8,156	-129,960	
-20	9	-60	-1883	11,986	-288,120	
-30	9	-150	1417	-68,184	1,997,120	-30 is a lower bound

20 and -30 are the smallest positive integer multiple of 10 and largest negative integer multiple of 10 that, by Theorem 2, are upper and lower bounds, respectively, for the real zeros of $P(x)$.

(B) -23.22, -3.67 (double zero), and 17.22 are the real zeros of $P(x)$ to two decimal places.

50. $P(x) = 0.1x^5 + 0.7x^4 - 18.775x^3 - 340x^2 - 1645x - 2450$

(A)

	0.1	0.7	-18.775	-340	-1645	-2,450	
10	0.1	1.7	-1.775	-357.75	-5222.5	-54,675	
20	0.1	2.7	35.225	364.5	5645	110,450	20 is an upper bound
-10	0.1	-0.3	-15.775	-182.25	177.5	-4,225	
-20	0.1	-1.3	7.225	-484.5	8045	-163,350	-20 is a lower bound

20 and -20 are the smallest positive integer multiple of 10 and largest negative integer multiple of 10 that, by Theorem 2, are upper and lower bounds, respectively, for the real zeros of $P(x)$.

(B) -3.50 (even multiplicity) and 17.69 (odd multiplicity) are the real zeros of $P(x)$ to two decimal places.

[In graphing $y_1 = (x + 3.50)^2 (x - 17.69)^3$ and $y_2 = (x + 3.50)^4 (x - 17.69)$, y_2 is the best fit but the correct answer is $x = -3.50$ (double), 17.69 (simple) with 2 non-real zeros.]

52. $y = x^2$; all points 1 unit away from (2, 1).

$$d = \sqrt{(x - x_1)^2 + (y - y_1)^2}$$
$$1 = \sqrt{(x - 2)^2 + (y - 1)^2}$$
$$1 = (x - 2)^2 + (x^2 - 1)^2$$
$$1 = x^2 - 4x + 4 + x^4 - 2x^2 + 1$$
$$0 = x^4 - x^2 - 4x + 4$$

Graph $y_1 = x^4 - x^2 - 4x + 4$. The zeros are at $x = 1$ and $x = 1.315$. The points are (1, 1) and (1.315, 1.729).

54. $\ell = \dfrac{40 - 3x}{2}$, $w = 20 - 2x$, $h = x$

$V = \ell wh$

$V(x) = (20 - 1.5x)(20 - 2x)x$

$x(400 - 40x - 30x + 3x^2) = 500$

$3x^3 - 70x^2 + 400x - 500 = 0$

Graph $y_1 = 3x^3 - 70x^2 + 400x - 500$. The zeros are at $x \approx 1.741$ and $x \approx 6.234$. The values of x that would result in a box with a volume of 50 cubic inches are 1.741 inches and 6.234 inches.

56. $V = x^2 y = 2$

$y = \dfrac{2}{x^2}$

tape = 20.5 ft - 6 inches = 20.5 ft - .5 ft = 20 ft.

length of tape = $(4x) + (2x + 2y) + (2x + 2y) = 20$

$8x + 4y = 20$

$8x + 4\left(\dfrac{2}{x^2}\right) = 20$

$8x^3 + 8 = 20x^2$

$8x^3 - 20x^2 + 8 = 0$

Graph $y_1 = 8x^3 - 20x^2 + 8$. The zeros are at $x \approx -0.57$ (discard), 0.758, and 2.313.

at $x = 0.758$, $y = \dfrac{2}{(0.758)^2} = 3.481$

at $x = 2.313$, $y = \dfrac{2}{(2.313)^2} = 0.374$

The dimensions are 0.758 × 0.758 × 3.481 feet or 2.313 × 2.313 × 0.374 feet.

Exercise   3-4

2. $k(x) = \dfrac{4 - 2x}{x + 2}$ **4.** $f(x) = \dfrac{2x - 4}{x + 2}$

6. $g(x) = \dfrac{3x + 6}{x - 1}$

Domain: all x except 1 or $(-\infty, 1) \cup (1, \infty)$

$3x + 6 = 0$

$\quad 3x = -6$

$\quad\ x = -2,\ x$ intercept

8. $k(x) = \dfrac{x^2 - 36}{x^2 - 25}$

Domain: all x except ± 5 or $(-\infty, -5) \cup (-5, 5) \cup (5, \infty)$

$x^2 - 36 = 0$

$\quad x^2 = 36$

$\quad\ x\ = \pm 6,\ x$ intercepts

10. $s(x) = \dfrac{x^2 + x - 12}{x^2 + x - 6} = \dfrac{(x + 4)(x - 3)}{(x + 3)(x - 2)}$

Domain: all x except -3 and 2 or $(-\infty, -3) \cup (-3, 2) \cup (2, \infty)$

$(x + 4)(x - 3) = 0$

x intercepts: -4, 3

12. $G(x) = \dfrac{x^2}{x^2 + 16}$

Domain: all real numbers

$(x^2 + 16 = 0 \Rightarrow x^2 = -16$ which never happens$)$

x intercept: 0

14. $h(x) = \dfrac{3x}{x + 5}$

vertical asymptote: $d(x) = 0$ at $x = -5$

horizontal asymptote: $y = 3$, $n(x)$ and $d(x)$ have same degree

$(y = \dfrac{3}{1} = 3)$

16. $r(x) = \dfrac{5x^2 - 7x}{2x^2 - 50}$

vertical asymptote: $2x^2 - 50 = 0$

$\quad\quad\quad\quad\quad\quad\quad 2x^2 = 50$

$\quad\quad\quad\quad\quad\quad\quad\ x^2 = 25$

$\quad\quad\quad\quad\quad\quad\quad\ x = \pm 5$

horizontal asymptote: $y = \dfrac{5}{2}$ since $n(x)$ and $d(x)$ have same degree

18. $q(x) = \dfrac{5x^4}{2x^2 + 3x - 2} = \dfrac{5x^4}{(2x - 1)(x + 2)}$

vertical asymptote: $x = \dfrac{1}{2}$ and $x = -2$

deg $n(x) = 4 >$ deg $d(x) \Rightarrow$ no horizontal asymptote

20. $g(x) = \dfrac{3x}{x^4 + 2x^2 + 1}$

no vertical asymptote since $x^4 + 2x^2 + 1 > 0$ for all x

horizontal asymptote: $y = 0$, deg $n(x) <$ deg $d(x)$

22. $g(x) = \dfrac{1}{x+3} = \dfrac{n(x)}{d(x)}$

$n(x)$ has no zeros: no x intercept

$g(0) = \dfrac{1}{3}$: y intercept

$d(x) = x + 3 = 0$
  $x = -3$: vertical asymptote

deg $n(x)$ < deg $d(x)$ $\Rightarrow$ horizontal asymptote: x-axis

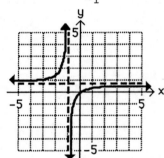

24. $f(x) = \dfrac{3x}{x-3} = \dfrac{n(x)}{d(x)}$

$n(x) = 3x = 0$
  $x = 0$: x intercept

$f(0) = \dfrac{3(0)}{0-3} = 0$: y intercept

$d(x) = x - 3 = 0$
  $x = 3$: vertical asymptote

deg $n(x)$ = deg $d(x)$ $\Rightarrow$ horizontal asymptote: $y = \dfrac{a_1}{b_1} = 3$

26. $p(x) = \dfrac{3x}{4x+4} = \dfrac{n(x)}{d(x)}$

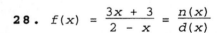

$n(x) = 3x = 0$
  $x = 0$: x intercept

$f(0) = \dfrac{3(0)}{4(0)+4} = 0$: y intercept

$d(x) = 4x + 4 = 0$
        $x = -1$: vertical asymptote

deg $n(x)$ = deg $d(x)$: $y = \dfrac{a_1}{b_1} = \dfrac{3}{4}$ horizontal asymptote

28. $f(x) = \dfrac{3x+3}{2-x} = \dfrac{n(x)}{d(x)}$

$n(x) = 3x + 3 = 0$
          $x = -1$: x intercept

$f(0) = 1.5$: y intercept

$d(x) = 2 - x = 0$
          $x = 2$: vertical asymptote

deg $n(x)$ = deg $d(x)$: horizontal asymptote: $y = -3$

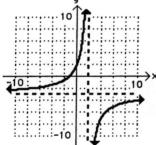

30. $f(x) = \dfrac{x^2+1}{x^2} = \dfrac{n(x)}{d(x)}$

$n(x) = x^2 + 1 = 0$ has no real solutions;
no x intercepts

$f(0) = 1/0$ is undefined; no y intercept

$d(x) = x^2 = 0$
        $x = 0$: vertical asymptote

deg $n(x)$ = deg $d(x)$ $\Rightarrow$ $y = 1$: horizontal asymptote

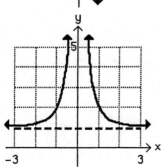

32. $g(x) = \dfrac{6}{x^2 - x - 6} = \dfrac{n(x)}{d(x)} = \dfrac{6}{(x - 3)(x + 2)}$

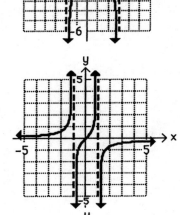

$n(x) = 6 = 0$ has no real solutions $\Rightarrow$ no x intercepts

$f(0) = -1$: y intercept

$d(x) = 0$ for $x = 3$, $x = -2$: vertical asymptotes

deg $n(x)$ < deg $d(x) \Rightarrow y = 0$ (x-axis): vertical asymptote

34. $p(x) = \dfrac{x}{1 - x^2} = \dfrac{n(x)}{d(x)} = \dfrac{x}{(1 - x)(1 + x)}$

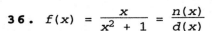

$n(x) = x = 0$: x intercept
$p(0) = 0$: y intercept
$d(x) = 0$ for $x = \pm 1$: vertical asymptotes

deg $n(x)$ < deg $d(x) \Rightarrow y = 0$ (x-axis): horizontal asymptote

36. $f(x) = \dfrac{x}{x^2 + 1} = \dfrac{n(x)}{d(x)}$

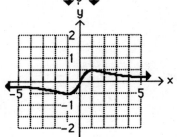

$n(x) = x = 0$: x intercept
$f(0) = 0$: y intercept
$d(x) = 0$ has no real solutions $\Rightarrow$ no vertical asymptotes
deg $n(x)$ < deg $d(x) \Rightarrow y = 0$: horizontal asymptote

38. $f(x) = \dfrac{7x^2}{(2x - 3)^2} = \dfrac{7x^2}{4x^2 - 12x + 9} = \dfrac{n(x)}{d(x)}$

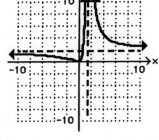

$n(x) = 7x^2 = 0$
$\quad\quad x = 0$: x intercept

$f(0) = 0$: y intercept

$d(x) = (2x - 3)^2 = 0$
$\quad\quad x = \dfrac{3}{2}$: vertical asymptote

deg $n(x)$ = deg $d(x) \Rightarrow y = \dfrac{a_2}{b_2} = \dfrac{7}{4}$: horizontal asymptote

40. $f(x) = \dfrac{x^2 + 6x + 8}{x^2 - x - 2} = \dfrac{(x + 2)(x + 4)}{(x - 2)(x + 1)} = \dfrac{n(x)}{d(x)}$

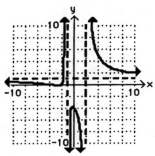

$n(x) = 0 \Rightarrow x = -2, -4$: x intercepts
$f(0) = -4$: y intercept

$d(x) = 0 \Rightarrow x = 2$, $x = -1$: vertical asymptotes

deg $n(x)$ = deg $d(x) \Rightarrow y = 1$: horizontal asymptote

42. The maximum number of vertical asymptotes is 2, as in $f(x) = \dfrac{x^2}{x^2 - 1}$, and the minimum number is 0, as in $f(x) = \dfrac{x^2}{x^2 + 1}$.

44. $g(x) = \dfrac{3x^2}{x + 2} = \dfrac{n(x)}{d(x)}$

$d(x) = x + 2 = 0$
   $x = -2$: vertical asymptote

$$\begin{array}{r}
3x - 6 \\
x + 2 \overline{\smash{\big)}\, 3x^2 } \\
\underline{3x^2 + 6x } \\
-6x \\
\underline{-6x - 12} \\
12
\end{array}$$

$\Rightarrow g(x) = 3x - 6 + \dfrac{12}{x + 2}$
from which
$y = 3x - 6$ is an oblique asymptote

46. $q(x) = \dfrac{x^5}{x^3 - 8} = \dfrac{n(x)}{d(x)}$

$d(x) = x^3 - 8 = 0$
      $x = 2$: vertical asymptote

$\deg n(x) > \deg d(x) \Rightarrow$ no horizontal asymptotes
$\deg n(x) > \deg d(x) + 1 \Rightarrow$ no oblique asymptotes

48. $s(x) = \dfrac{-3x^2 + 5x + 9}{x} = \dfrac{n(x)}{d(x)}$

$d(x) = x = 0$: vertical asymptote

$\dfrac{-3x^2 + 5x + 9}{x} = -3x + 5 + \dfrac{9}{x}$ from which

       $y = -3x + 5$: oblique asymptote

50. $f(x) = \dfrac{2x}{\sqrt{x^2 - 1}} \to 2$ as $x \to \infty$

$f(x) = \dfrac{2x}{\sqrt{x^2 - 1}} \to -2$ as $x \to -\infty$

$y = \pm 2$ are horizontal asymptotes

52. $f(x) = \dfrac{3\sqrt{x^2 + 1}}{x - 1} \to 3$ as $x \to \infty$

$f(x) = \dfrac{3\sqrt{x^2 + 1}}{x - 1} \to -3$ as $x \to -\infty$

$y = \pm 3$ are horizontal asymptotes

54. $g(x) = \dfrac{x^2 - 1}{x} = \dfrac{n(x)}{d(x)}$

$n(x) = x^2 - 1 = 0$
      $x = \pm 1$: x intercepts

$g(0) = \dfrac{-1}{0}$ undefined: no y intercept

$d(x) = x = 0$: vertical asymptote

$g(x) = x - \dfrac{1}{x} \Rightarrow y = x$: oblique asymptote

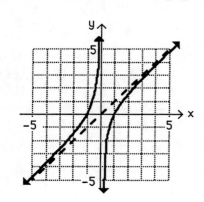

56. $h(x) = \dfrac{x^2 + x - 2}{2x - 4} = \dfrac{n(x)}{d(x)} = \dfrac{(x - 1)(x + 2)}{2(x - 2)}$

$n(x) = (x - 1)(x + 2) = 0$

$\qquad\qquad x = 1, -2: x$ intercepts

$h(0) = \dfrac{1}{2}: y$ intercept

$d(x) = 2(x - 2) = 0$

$\qquad\qquad x = 2:$ vertical asymptote

$$\begin{array}{r} \frac{1}{2}x + \frac{3}{2} \\ 2x - 4 \overline{\smash{\big)}\ x^2 + x - 2} \\ \underline{x^2 - 2x} \\ 3x - 2 \\ \underline{3x - 6} \\ 4 \end{array}$$

$\Rightarrow h(x) = \dfrac{1}{2}x + \dfrac{3}{2} + \dfrac{4}{2x - 4}$

from which

$y = \dfrac{1}{2}x + \dfrac{3}{2}:$ oblique asymptote

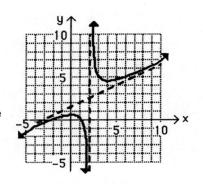

58. $G(x) = \dfrac{x^4 + 1}{x^3} = \dfrac{n(x)}{d(x)}$

$n(x) = x^4 + 1 = 0$ has no real solutions $\Rightarrow$ no x intercepts

$G(0) = \dfrac{1}{0}$ undefined $\Rightarrow$ no y intercepts

$d(x) = x^3 = 0$

$\qquad x = 0$ vertical asymptote

$G(x) = x + \dfrac{1}{x^3}$ from which $y = x:$ oblique asymptote

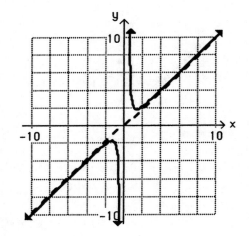

60. $f(x) = \dfrac{x^5}{x^2 + 1}$

$$\begin{array}{r} x^3 - x \\ x^2 + 1 \overline{\smash{\big)}\ x^5} \\ \underline{x^5 + x^3} \\ -x^3 \\ \underline{-x^3 - x} \\ +x \end{array}$$

$f(x) = p(x) + \dfrac{q(x)}{d(x)}$

$f(x) = \dfrac{x^5}{x^2 + 1} = x^3 - x + \dfrac{x}{x^2 + 1} \Rightarrow p(x) = x^3 - x$

As $x \to \infty$, both $f(x)$ and $p(x) \to \infty$. As $x \to -\infty$, both $f(x)$ and $p(x) \to -\infty$. They have the same end behavior.

62. $f(x) = \dfrac{x^5}{x^3 - 1}$

$$
x^3 - 1 \,\overline{\big)\, x^5 \phantom{{}- x^2}} \quad\begin{array}{c} x^2 \\ \end{array}
$$

$$
\begin{array}{r}
x^5 - x^2 \\ \hline
x^2
\end{array}
$$

$f(x) = p(x) + \dfrac{q(x)}{d(x)}$

$f(x) = \dfrac{x^5}{x^2 + 1} = x^2 + \dfrac{x^2}{x^3 - 1} \Rightarrow p(x) = x^2$

As $x \to \infty$, both $f(x)$ and $p(x) \to \infty$. As $x \to -\infty$, both $f(x)$ and $p(x) \to -\infty$.
They have the same end behavior.

64. $g(x) = \dfrac{x^2 - 1}{x + 1} = \dfrac{(x - 1)(x + 1)}{(x + 1)} = x - 1$ for $x \neq -1$

   Domain: $x \neq -1$ or $(-\infty, -1) \cup (-1, \infty)$

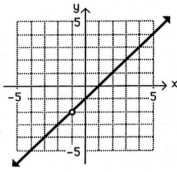

66. $s(x) = \dfrac{x - 1}{x^2 - 1} = \dfrac{x - 1}{(x - 1)(x + 1)} = \dfrac{1}{x + 1},\ x \neq \pm 1$

Domain: $x \neq \pm 1$ or $(-\infty, -1) \cup (-1, 1) \cup (1, \infty)$

$s(x) = \dfrac{1}{x + 1} = \dfrac{n(x)}{d(x)}$

$n(x) = 1 = 0$, no real roots $\Rightarrow$ no x intercepts
$s(0) = 1$: y intercept
$d(x) = x + 1 = 0$
  $x = -1$ vertical asymptote

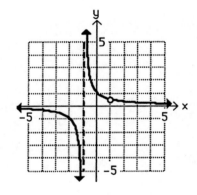

68. $S(w) = \dfrac{26 + 0.06w}{w},\ w \geq 5$

Domain: $S(w)$ is defined at all values given ($w \geq 5$).
$y = 0.06$ is the horizontal asymptote.

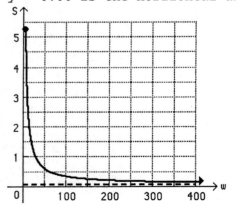

$S(w) = \dfrac{26}{w} + 0.06 \to 0.06$ as $w \to \infty$.

70. $f(x) = \dfrac{50(x + 1)}{x + 5} = \dfrac{50x + 50}{x + 5}$ $x \geq 0$

$f(0) = 10$

$y = 50$ is horizontal asymptote

$f(x) \to 50$ as $x \to \infty$

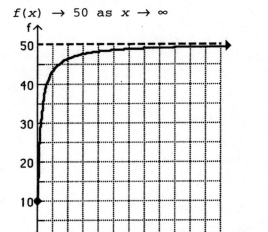

72. (A) $\overline{C}(x) = \dfrac{C(x)}{x} = \dfrac{\frac{1}{5}x^2 + 2x + 2000}{x}$

$= \dfrac{1}{5}x + 2 + \dfrac{2000}{x}$

$y = \dfrac{1}{5}x + 2$: oblique asymptote

(B) Use the minimum routine on your calculator.

The average cost per unit will be minimal at a production level of 100.

(C)

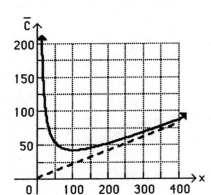

74.

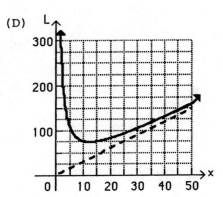

(A) area $= x \cdot \ell = 225$

$\ell = \dfrac{225}{x}$

$L = 3x + 2\ell = 3x + \dfrac{450}{x}$

$L(x) = 3x + \dfrac{450}{x} \Rightarrow L = 3x$: oblique asymptote

(B) Domain of $L(x)$: $x > 0$ or $(0, \infty)$, although one could argue about the width required for a dog.

(C) Graph $L(x)$; use the minimum routine to obtain the local minimum point: (12.247, 73.485)

$\ell = \dfrac{225}{x} = \dfrac{225}{12.247} \approx 18.372$

Dimensions of $x = 12.247$ ft by $\ell = 18.372$ ft will require the least amount of fencing, 73.485 ft.

(D)

CHAPTER 4

Exercise 4-1

2.

x	-3	-2	-1	0	1	2	3
$(g - f)(x)$	1	3	3	3	3	1	-1

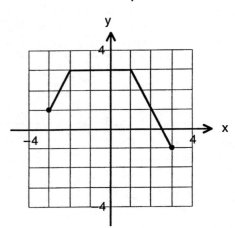

$(g - f)(-3) = g(-3) - f(-3) = 2 - 1 = 1$

$(g - f)(-2) = g(-2) - f(-2) = 3 - 0 = 3$

$(g - f)(-1) = g(-1) - f(-1) = 2 - (-1) = 2 + 1 = 3$

$(g - f)(0) = g(0) - f(0) = 1 - (-2) = 1 + 2 = 3$

$(g - f)(1) = g(1) - f(1) = 0 - (-3) = 3$

$(g - f)(2) = g(2) - f(2) = -1 - (-2) = -1 + 2 = 1$

$(g - f)(3) = g(3) - f(3) = -2 - (-1) = -2 + 1 = -1$

4. $(f \circ g)(2) = f[g(2)] = f(-1) = -1$ **6.** $(g \circ f)(3) = g[f(3)] = g(-1) = 2$

8. $f[g(0)] = f(1) = -3$ **10.** $g[f(-3)] = g(1) = 0$

12. $f(x) = 3x, \; g(x) = x - 2$

$(f + g)(x) = f(x) + g(x) = 3x + (x - 2) = 4x - 2$

$(f - g)(x) = f(x) - g(x) = 3x - (x - 2) = 2x + 2$

$(fg)(x) = f(x)g(x) = 3x(x - 2) = 3x^2 - 6x$

$\left(\dfrac{f}{g}\right)(x) = \dfrac{f(x)}{g(x)} = \dfrac{3x}{x - 2}$

Domain $f + g, \; f - g, \; fg$: $(-\infty, \infty)$

Domain $\dfrac{f}{g}$: $(-\infty, 2) \cup (2, \infty)$

14. $f(x) = 3x, \; g(x) = x^2 + 4$

$(f + g)(x) = f(x) + g(x) = 3x + (x^2 + 4) = x^2 + 3x + 4$

$(f - g)(x) = f(x) - g(x) = 3x - (x^2 + 4) = -x^2 + 3x - 4$

$(fg)(x) = f(x)g(x) = 3x(x^2 + 4) = 3x^3 + 12x$

$\left(\dfrac{f}{g}\right)(x) = \dfrac{f(x)}{g(x)} = \dfrac{3x}{x^2 + 4}$

Domain $f + g, \; f - g, \; fg, \; \dfrac{f}{g}$: $(-\infty, \infty)$

16. $f(x) = 2x - 7, \; g(x) = 9 - x^2$

$(f + g)(x) = f(x) + g(x) = (2x - 7) + (9 - x^2) = -x^2 + 2x + 2$

$(f - g)(x) = f(x) - g(x) = (2x - 7) - (9 - x^2) = x^2 + 2x - 16$

$(fg)(x) = f(x)g(x) = (2x - 7)(9 - x^2) = -2x^3 + 7x^2 + 18x - 63$

$\left(\dfrac{f}{g}\right)(x) = \dfrac{f(x)}{g(x)} = \dfrac{2x - 7}{9 - x^2}$

Domain $f + g, \; f - g, \; fg$: $(-\infty, \infty)$

Domain $\dfrac{f}{g}$: $(-\infty, -3) \cup (-3, 3) \cup (3, \infty)$

18. $f(x) = x^2$, $g(x) = x^3 + 2x + 4$
$(f \circ g)(x) = f(g(x)) = f(x^3 + 2x + 4) = (x^3 + 2x + 4)^2$
$(g \circ f)(x) = g(f(x)) = g(x^2) = (x^3)^2 + 2(x^2) + 4 = x^6 + 2x^2 + 4$
Domain $f \circ g$, $g \circ f$: $(-\infty, \infty)$

20. $f(x) = |x - 4|$, $g(x) = 3x + 2$
$(f \circ g)(x) = f(g(x)) = f(3x + 2) = |3x + 2 - 4| = |3x - 2|$
$(g \circ f)(x) = g(f(x)) = g(|x - 4|) = 3|x - 4| + 2$
Domain $f \circ g$, $g \circ f$: $(-\infty, \infty)$

22. $f(x) = x^{2/3}$, $g(x) = 8 - x^3$
$(f \circ g)(x) = f(g(x)) = f(8 - x^3) = (8 - x^3)^{2/3}$
$(g \circ f)(x) = g(f(x)) = g(x^{2/3}) = 8 - (x^{2/3})^3 = 8 - x^2$
Domain: $f \circ g$, $g \circ f$: $(-\infty, \infty)$

24. $f(x) = 3x + 2$, $g(x) = \frac{1}{3}x - \frac{2}{3}$

$(f \circ g)(x) = f(g(x)) = f\left(\frac{1}{3}x - \frac{2}{3}\right) = 3\left(\frac{1}{3}x - \frac{2}{3}\right) + 2 = x - 2 + 2 = x$

$(g \circ f)(x) = g(f(x)) = g(3x + 2) = \frac{1}{3}(3x + 2) - \frac{2}{3} = x + \frac{2}{3} - \frac{2}{3} = x$

The graphs are symmetrical with respect to the line $y = x$.

$(f \circ g)(x) = (g \circ f)(x) = x$

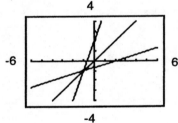

26. $f(x) = -2x + 3$, $g(x) = -\frac{1}{2}x + \frac{3}{2}$

$(f \circ g)(x) = f(g(x)) = f\left(-\frac{1}{2}x + \frac{3}{2}\right) = -2\left(-\frac{1}{2}x + \frac{3}{2}\right) + 3 = x - 3 + 3 = x$

$(g \circ f)(x) = g(f(x)) = g(-2x + 3) = -\frac{1}{2}(-2x + 3) + \frac{3}{2} = x - \frac{3}{2} + \frac{3}{2} = x$

The graphs are symmetrical with respect to the line $y = x$.

$(f \circ g)(x) = (g \circ f)(x) = x$

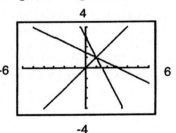

28. $f(x) = \sqrt{x + 4}$, $g(x) = \sqrt{3 - x}$
$(f + g)(x) = f(x) + g(x) = \sqrt{x + 4} + \sqrt{3 - x}$
$(f - g)(x) = f(x) - g(x) = \sqrt{x + 4} - \sqrt{3 - x}$
$(fg)(x) = f(x)g(x) = \sqrt{x + 4}\sqrt{3 - x} = \sqrt{(x + 4)(3 - x)} = \sqrt{12 - x - x^2}$
$\left(\frac{f}{g}\right)(x) = \frac{f(x)}{g(x)} = \frac{\sqrt{x + 4}}{\sqrt{3 - x}} = \sqrt{\frac{x + 4}{3 - x}}$

Domain f: $x + 4 \geq 0$ Domain g: $3 - x \geq 0$

$x \geq -4$ $x \leq 3$

$[-4, \infty)$ $(-\infty, 3]$

Domain $f + g$, $f - g$, fg: $[-4, 3]$

Domain $\dfrac{f}{g}$: $[-4, 3)$

30. $f(x) = 1 - \sqrt{x}$, $g(x) = 2 - \sqrt{x}$

$(f + g)(x) = f(x) + g(x) = (1 - \sqrt{x}) + (2 - \sqrt{x}) = 3 - 2\sqrt{x}$

$(f - g)(x) = f(x) - g(x) = (1 - \sqrt{x}) - (2 - \sqrt{x}) = 1 - \sqrt{x} - 2 + \sqrt{x} = -1$

$(fg)(x) = f(x)g(x) = (1 - \sqrt{x})(2 - \sqrt{x}) = 2 - 3\sqrt{x} + x$

$\left(\dfrac{f}{g}\right)(x) = \dfrac{f(x)}{g(x)} = \dfrac{1 - \sqrt{x}}{2 - \sqrt{x}}$

Domain $f + g$, $f - g$, fg: $[0, \infty)$

Domain $\dfrac{f}{g}$: $[0, 4) \cup (4, \infty)$

32. $f(x) = \sqrt{8 + 2x - x^2}$, $g(x) = \sqrt{x^2 - 7x + 10}$

$(f + g)(x) = f(x) + g(x) = \sqrt{8 + 2x - x^2} + \sqrt{x^2 - 7x + 10}$

$(f - g)(x) = f(x) - g(x) = \sqrt{8 + 2x - x^2} - \sqrt{x^2 - 7x + 10}$

$(fg)(x) = f(x)g(x) = \sqrt{8 + 2x - x^2}\,\sqrt{x^2 - 7x + 10}$

$= \sqrt{(8 + 2x - x^2)(x^2 - 7x + 10)}$

$= \sqrt{-x^4 + 9x^3 - 16x^2 - 36x + 80}$

$\left(\dfrac{f}{g}\right)(x) = \dfrac{f(x)}{g(x)} = \dfrac{\sqrt{8 + 2x - x^2}}{\sqrt{x^2 - 7x + 10}} = \sqrt{\dfrac{8 + 2x - x^2}{x^2 - 7x + 10}}$

Domain f: $[-2, 4]$

Domain g: $(-\infty, 2] \cup [5, \infty)$

Domain $f + g$, $f - g$, fg: $[-2, 4] \cap \{(-\infty, 2] \cup [5, \infty)\} = [-2, 2]$

Domain $\dfrac{f}{g}$: $[-2, 2)$

34. $f(x) = \sqrt{x}$, $g(x) = 2x + 5$

Domain f: $x \geq 0$ or $[0, \infty)$ Domain g: $(-\infty, \infty)$

$(f \circ g)(x) = f(g(x)) = f(2x + 5) = \sqrt{2x + 5}$

Domain $f \circ g$: $\left[-\dfrac{5}{2}, \infty\right)$

$(g \circ f)(x) = g(f(x)) = g(\sqrt{x}) = 2\sqrt{x} + 5$

Domain $g \circ f$: $[0, \infty)$

36. $f(x) = x - 3$, $g(x) = \dfrac{1}{x^2}$

Domain f: $(-\infty, \infty)$ Domain g: $(-\infty, 0) \cup (0, \infty)$

$(f \circ g)(x) = f(g(x)) = f\left(\dfrac{1}{x^2}\right) = \dfrac{1}{x^2} - 3$

Domain $f \circ g$: $(-\infty, 0) \cup (0, \infty)$

$(g \circ f)(x) = g(f(x)) = g(x - 3) = \dfrac{1}{(x - 3)^2}$

Domain $g \circ f$: $(-\infty, 3) \cup (3, \infty)$

38. $f(x) = |x - 1|,$ $\qquad\qquad\qquad g(x) = \dfrac{1}{x}$

Domain f: $(-\infty, \infty)$ $\qquad\qquad$ Domain g: $(-\infty, 0) \cup (0, \infty)$

$(f \circ g)(x) = f(g(x)) = f\left(\dfrac{1}{x}\right) = \left|\dfrac{1}{x} - 1\right|$ or $\left|\dfrac{1 - x}{x}\right|$

Domain $f \circ g$: $(-\infty, 0) \cup (0, \infty)$

$(g \circ f)(x) = g(f(x)) = g(|x - 1|) = \dfrac{1}{|x - 1|}$

Domain $g \circ f$: $(-\infty, 1) \cup (1, \infty)$

40. $(f - g)(x)$: $(-1, 7)$, $(0, 4)$, $(2, -2)$: Graph (d)

42. $(fg)(x)$: $(-1, -12)$, $(0, -4)$, $(1, 0)$, $(2, 0)$: Graph (b)

44. $\left(\dfrac{g}{f}\right)(x)$: $\left(-1, -\dfrac{3}{4}\right)$, $(0, -1)$, $(1, \varnothing)$, $(2, 0)$: Graph (f)

46. Let $f(x) = x^7$ and $g(x) = 3 - 5x$, then $h(x) = f(g(x)) = f(3 - 5x) = (3 - 5x)^7$.

48. Let $f(x) = x^{1/2}$ and $g(x) = 3x - 11$,
then $h(x) = f(g(x)) = f(3x - 11) = (3x - 11)^{1/2}$.

50. Let $g(x) = 5x + 3$ and $f(x) = x^6$, then $h(x) = g(f(x)) = g(x^6) = 5x^6 + 3$.

52. Let $g(x) = -2x + 1$ and $f(x) = x^{-1/2}$,
then $h(x) = g(f(x)) = g(x^{-1/2}) = -2x^{-1/2} + 1 = -\dfrac{2}{\sqrt{x}} + 1$.

54. $f \circ g$ and $g \circ f$ are not identical (see problems 36, 38) unless they both equal x (when they are symmetrical about the line $y = x$; see problems 24, 26).

56. Yes; if $g = 1$, then $fg = f \cdot 1 = f$ and $gf = 1 \cdot f = f$.

58. $f(x) = x - 1,$ $\qquad\qquad\qquad g(x) = x - \dfrac{6}{x - 1}$

Domain f: $(-\infty, \infty)$ $\qquad\qquad$ Domain g: $(-\infty, 1) \cup (1, \infty)$

$(f + g)(x) = f(x) + g(x) = (x - 1) + \left(x - \dfrac{6}{x - 1}\right) = 2x - 1 - \dfrac{6}{x - 1}$

$(f - g)(x) = f(x) - g(x) = (x - 1) - \left(x - \dfrac{6}{x - 1}\right) = -1 + \dfrac{6}{x - 1}$

$(fg)(x) = f(x)g(x) = (x - 1)\left(x - \dfrac{6}{x - 1}\right) = x^2 - \dfrac{6x}{x - 1} - x + \dfrac{6}{x - 1}$

$\qquad\qquad\qquad\qquad = x^2 - x + \dfrac{6 - 6x}{x - 1} = x^2 - x - 6$

$\left(\dfrac{f}{g}\right)(x) = \dfrac{f(x)}{g(x)} = \dfrac{x - 1}{x - \frac{6}{x-1}} = \dfrac{(x - 1)^2}{x^2 - x - 6} = \dfrac{(x - 1)^2}{(x - 3)(x + 2)}$

Domain $f + g$, $f - g$, fg: $(-\infty, 1) \cup (1, \infty)$

Domain $\dfrac{f}{g}$: $(-\infty, -2) \cup (-2, 1) \cup (1, 3) \cup (3, \infty)$

60. $f(x) = x + |x|$, $g(x) = x - |x|$
Domain f: $(-\infty, \infty)$ Domain g: $(-\infty, \infty)$

$(f + g)(x) = f(x) + g(x) = (x + |x|) + (x - |x|) = 2x$
$(f - g)(x) = f(x) - g(x) = (x + |x|) - (x - |x|) = 2|x|$
$(fg)(x) = f(x)g(x) = (x + |x|)(x - |x|) = 0$
$\left(\dfrac{f}{g}\right)(x) = \dfrac{f(x)}{g(x)} = \dfrac{x + |x|}{x - |x|} = 0$ (Domain $(-\infty, 0)$)

Domain $f + g$, $f - g$, fg: $(-\infty, \infty)$
Domain $\dfrac{f}{g}$: $x - |x| \neq 0$, $x \neq |x|$, $(-\infty, 0)$

62. $f(x) = \sqrt{x - 1}$, $g(x) = x^2$
Domain f: $[1, \infty)$ Domain g: $(-\infty, \infty)$
$(f \circ g)(x) = f(g(x)) = f(x^2) = \sqrt{x^2 - 1}$
$(g \circ f)(x) = g(f(x)) = g(\sqrt{x - 1}) = (\sqrt{x - 1})^2 = x - 1$
Domain $f \circ g$: $(-\infty, -1] \cup [1, \infty)$
Domain $g \circ f$: $[1, \infty)$

64. $f(x) = \dfrac{x}{x - 1}$, $g(x) = \dfrac{2x - 4}{x}$
Domain f: $(-\infty, 1) \cup (1, \infty)$ Domain g: $(-\infty, 0) \cup (0, \infty)$
$(f \circ g)(x) = f(g(x)) = f\left(\dfrac{2x - 4}{x}\right) = \dfrac{\frac{2x - 4}{x}}{\frac{2x - 4}{x} - 1} = \dfrac{2x - 4}{x - 4}$
$(g \circ f)(x) = g(f(x)) = g\left(\dfrac{x}{x - 1}\right) = \dfrac{2\left(\frac{x}{x - 1}\right) - 4}{\frac{x}{x - 1}} = \dfrac{4 - 2x}{x}$
Domain $f \circ g$: $(-\infty, 0) \cup (0, 4) \cup (4, \infty)$
Domain $g \circ f$: $(-\infty, 0) \cup (0, 1) \cup (1, \infty)$

66. $f(x) = \sqrt{x^2 - 9}$, $g(x) = \sqrt{x^2 + 25}$
Domain f: $(-\infty, -3] \cup [3, \infty)$ Domain g: $(-\infty, \infty)$

$(f \circ g)(x) = f(g(x)) = f(\sqrt{x^2 + 25}) = \sqrt{(\sqrt{x^2 + 25})^2 - 9} = \sqrt{x^2 + 25 - 9} = \sqrt{x^2 + 16}$

$(g \circ f)(x) = g(f(x)) = g(\sqrt{x^2 - 9}) = \sqrt{(\sqrt{x^2 - 9})^2 + 25} = \sqrt{x^2 - 9 + 25} = \sqrt{x^2 + 16}$
Domain $f \circ g$: $(-\infty, \infty)$
Domain $g \circ f$: $(-\infty, -3] \cup [3, \infty)$

68. $(f \circ g)(x) = \sqrt{6 - (\sqrt{x - 1})^2}$; 1st graph, domain $[1, 7]$
$= \sqrt{6 - (x - 1)}$
$= \sqrt{-x + 7}$; 2nd graph, domain $(-\infty, 7]$

The first graph is correct.

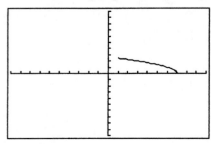   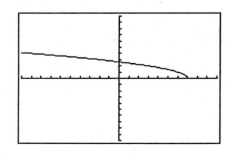

70. $(f \circ g)(x) = \sqrt{(\sqrt{4 - x^2})^2 + 5}$; 1st graph, domain $[-2, 2]$

$\qquad = \sqrt{4 - x^2 + 5}$

$\qquad = \sqrt{-x^2 + 9}$; 2nd graph, domain $[-3, 3]$

The first graph is correct.

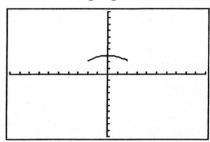 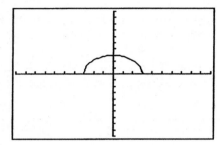

72. $(f \circ g)(x) = \sqrt{(\sqrt{x^2 - 9})^2 + 7}$; 1st graph, domain $(-\infty, 3] \cup [3, \infty)$

$\qquad = \sqrt{x^2 - 9 + 7}$

$\qquad = \sqrt{x^2 - 2}$; 2nd graph, domain $(-\infty, -\sqrt{2}] \cup [\sqrt{2}, \infty)$

The first graph is correct.

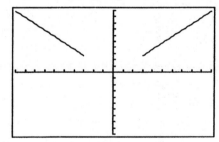 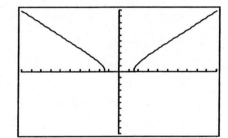

74. $x = f(p) = 5000 - 100p$

$P(x) = R(x) - C(x) = 50x - \dfrac{x^2}{100} - (20x + 40{,}000)$

$P(x) = 50x - \dfrac{x^2}{100} - 20x - 40{,}000 = 30x - \dfrac{x^2}{100} - 40{,}000$

$P(p) = 30(5000 - 100p) - \dfrac{(5000 - 100p)^2}{100} - 40{,}000$ which simplifies to

$P(p) = -100p^2 + 7000p - 140{,}000$

76. (A) $d(h) = \sqrt{h^2 + 100^2}$ using the Pythagorean theorem.

(B) $h = 5t$, $d(5t) = \sqrt{(5t)^2 + 100^2}$

$\qquad\qquad\qquad = \sqrt{25t^2 + 10{,}000}$

$\qquad\qquad\qquad = \sqrt{25(t^2 + 400)}$

$\qquad\qquad\qquad = 5\sqrt{t^2 + 400}$

78. (A) From similar triangles, $\dfrac{w}{h} = \dfrac{4}{2}$ from which gives $w(h) = 2h$.

(B) $V = 3wh$ $\qquad\qquad\qquad$ (C) $h(t) = 2 - 0.2\sqrt{t}$

$V(h) = V \cdot w = V(2h) = 3(2h)h = 6h^2$ $\qquad V(t) = V \cdot h = V(2 - 0.2\sqrt{t})$

$\qquad\qquad\qquad\qquad\qquad\qquad\qquad\qquad = 6(2 - 0.2\sqrt{t})^2$

Exercise 4-2

2. $\{(-1, 0),(0, 1),(1, -1),(2, 1)\}$ is not a one-to-one function because 2 ordered pairs, $(0, 1)$ and $(2, 1)$, have the same second term.

4. $\{(5, 4),(4, 3),(3, 2),(2, 1)\}$ is a one-to-one function because no two ordered pairs have the same second term.

6.

$-2 \longrightarrow$
$\qquad\qquad -3$
-1

$0 \longrightarrow \quad 7$

1
$2 \longrightarrow \quad 9$

Not one-to-one because two range values, -3 and 9, are paired with more than one domain value.

8.

domain		range
1	$\rightarrow$	5
2	$\rightarrow$	3
3	$\rightarrow$	1
4	$\rightarrow$	2
5	$\rightarrow$	4

One-to-one, each range value is paired with only one domain value.

10. Not one-to-one; since graph fails the horizontal line test.

12. One-to-one; passes horizontal line test.

14. Not one-to-one; fails horizontal line test.

16. One-to-one; passes horizontal line test.

18. $G(x) = -\frac{1}{3}x + 1$; linear function which passes horizontal line and is therefore one-to-one.

If $(a, f(a))$ and $(b, f(b))$ are 2 points on $G(x)$, then if

$$f(a) = f(b)$$
$$-\frac{1}{3}a + 1 = -\frac{1}{3}b + 1$$
$$-\frac{1}{3}a = -\frac{1}{3}b$$
$$a = b$$

20. $K(x) = \sqrt{4 - x}$
$$f(a) = f(b)$$
$$\sqrt{4 - a} = \sqrt{4 - b}$$
$$4 - a = 4 - b$$
$$a = b$$
K is one-to-one.

22. $N(x) = x^2 - 1$
$$f(a) = f(b)$$
$$a^2 - 1 = b^2 - 1$$
$$a^2 = b^2$$
$$a = \pm b; \ N \text{ is not one-to-one}$$

24. $f(x) = \dfrac{x^2 - |x|}{x}$

Not one-to-one, fails HLT

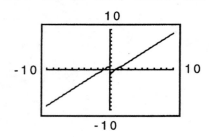

26. $f(x) = \dfrac{|x|^3 + |x|}{x}$

One-to-one, passes HLT

28. $f(x) = \dfrac{1 - x^2}{|x + 1|}$

Not one-to-one, fails HLT

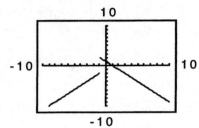

30. $f(x) = \dfrac{4x - x^3}{|x^2 - 4|}$

One-to-one, passes HLT

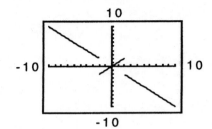

32. From graph D_f: $-2 \leq x \leq 5$; R_f: $-4 \leq y \leq 3$
from which $D_{f^{-1}}$: $-4 \leq x \leq 3$; $R_{f^{-1}}$: $-2 \leq y \leq 5$

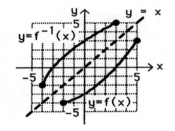

34. From graph D_f: $0 \leq x \leq 5$; R_f: $-5 \leq y \leq 5$
from which $D_{f^{-1}}$: $-5 \leq x \leq 5$; $R_{f^{-1}}$: $0 \leq y \leq 5$

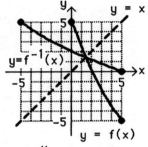

36. $f(x) = -\dfrac{1}{2}x + 2$; $g(x) = -2x + 4$

$f(g(x)) = f(-2x + 4) = -\dfrac{1}{2}(-2x + 4) + 2$

$\qquad\qquad\qquad\qquad = x - 2 + 2 = x$

$g(f(x)) = g\left(-\dfrac{1}{2}x + 2\right) = -2\left(-\dfrac{1}{2}x + 2\right) + 4$

$\qquad\qquad\qquad\qquad = x - 4 + 4 = x$

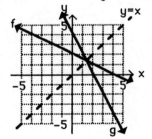

38. $f(x) = \sqrt{x + 2}$; $g(x) = x^2 - 2$ $(x \geq 0)$

$f(g(x)) = f(x^2 - 2) = \sqrt{x^2 - 2 + 2} = \sqrt{x^2} = |x| = x$

$g(f(x)) = g(\sqrt{x + 2}) = \left(\sqrt{x + 2}\right)^2 - 2 = x + 2 - 2 = x$

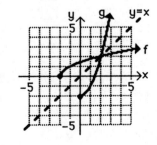

40. $f(x) = 6 - x^2 \ (x \le 0), \ g(x) = -\sqrt{6 - x}$

$f(g(x)) = f(-\sqrt{6 - x}) = 6 - (-\sqrt{6 - x})^2 = 6 - (6 - x)$

$$= 6 - 6 + x = x$$

$g(f(x)) = g(6 - x^2) = -\sqrt{6 - (6 - x^2)} = -\sqrt{6 - 6 + x^2} = -\sqrt{x^2}$

$$= -|x| = -(-x) = x$$

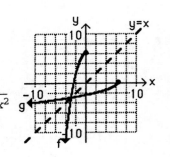

42. $f(x) = \frac{1}{2}x$; D, R: $(-\infty, \infty)$

$$\frac{1}{2}x = y$$

$$x = f^{-1}(y) = 2y$$

$$y = f^{-1}(x) = 2x; \ \text{D, R: } (-\infty, \infty)$$

44. $f(x) = -\frac{1}{3}x + \frac{5}{3}$; D, R: $(-\infty, \infty)$

$$-\frac{1}{3}x + \frac{5}{3} = y$$

$$-\frac{1}{3}x = y - \frac{5}{3}$$

$$x = f^{-1}(y) = -3y + 5$$

$$y = f^{-1}(x) = -3x + 5; \ \text{D, R: } (-\infty, \infty)$$

46. $f(x) = -2x - 7$; D, R: $(-\infty, \infty)$

$$-2x - 7 = y$$

$$-2x = y + 7$$

$$x = f^{-1}(y) = \frac{y + 7}{-2}$$

$$y = f^{-1}(x) = -\frac{1}{2}x - \frac{7}{2}; \ \text{D, R: } (-\infty, \infty)$$

48. $f(x) = \frac{3}{x + 4}$, D: $x \ne -4$, R: $y \ne 0$

$$\frac{3}{x + 4} = y$$

$$xy + 4y = 3$$

$$xy = 3 - 4y$$

$$x = f^{-1}(y) = \frac{3 - 4y}{y}$$

$$y = f^{-1}(x) = \frac{3 - 4x}{x}; \ \text{D: } x \ne 0,$$
$$\text{R: } y \ne -4$$

50. $f(x) = \frac{x - 3}{x}$; D: $x \ne 0$, R: $y \ne 1$

$$\frac{x - 3}{x} = y$$

$$xy = x - 3$$

$$xy - x = -3$$

$$x(y - 1) = -3$$

$$x = f^{-1}(y) = \frac{-3}{y - 1}$$

$$y = f^{-1}(x) = \frac{3}{1 - x}; \quad \text{D: } x \ne 1,$$
$$\text{R: } y \ne 0$$

52. $f(x) = \frac{5 - 3x}{7 - 4x}$; D: $x \ne \frac{7}{4}$, R: $y \ne \frac{3}{4}$

$$\frac{5 - 3x}{7 - 4x} = y$$

$$7y - 4xy = 5 - 3x$$

$$3x - 4xy = 5 - 7y$$

$$x(3 - 4y) = 5 - 7y$$

$$x = f^{-1}(y) = \frac{5 - 7y}{3 - 4y}$$

$$y = f^{-1}(x) = \frac{5 - 7x}{3 - 4x} \text{ or } \frac{7x - 5}{4x - 3};$$
$$\text{D: } x \ne \frac{3}{4}, \text{ R: } y \ne \frac{7}{4}$$

54. $f(x) = x^5 - 2$; D, R: $(-\infty, \infty)$

$$x^5 - 2 = y$$

$$x^5 = y + 2$$

$$x = f^{-1}(y) = \sqrt[5]{y + 2}$$

$$y = f^{-1}(x) = \sqrt[5]{x + 2}; \ \text{D, R: } (-\infty, \infty)$$

56. $f(x) = \sqrt[3]{x + 3} - 2$; D, R: $(-\infty, \infty)$

$$\sqrt[3]{x + 3} - 2 = y$$

$$\sqrt[3]{x + 3} = y + 2$$

$$x + 3 = (y + 2)^3$$

$$x = f^{-1}(y) = (y + 2)^3 - 3$$

$$y = f^{-1}(x) = (x + 2)^3 - 3;$$
$$\text{D, R: } (-\infty, \infty)$$

58. $f(x) = -\frac{1}{3}\sqrt{36 - x}$; D: $x \le 36$, R: $y \le 0$

$$-\frac{1}{3}\sqrt{36 - x} = y$$
$$\sqrt{36 - x} = -3y$$
$$36 - x = (-3y)^2$$
$$-x = 9y^2 - 36$$
$$x = f^{-1}(y) = 36 - 9y^2$$
$$y = f^{-1}(x) = 36 - 9x^2;$$
$$\text{D: } x \le 0, \ \text{R: } y \le 36$$

60. $f(x) = 4 + \sqrt{5 - x}$; D: $(-\infty, 5]$, R: $[4, \infty)$

$$4 + \sqrt{5 - x} = y$$
$$\sqrt{5 - x} = y - 4$$
$$5 - x = (y - 4)^2$$
$$-x = -5 + (y - 4)^2$$
$$x = f^{-1}(y) = 5 - (y - 4)^2$$
$$y = f^{-1}(x) = 5 - (x - 4)^2; \ \text{D: } [4, \infty), \ \text{R: } (-\infty, 5]$$

62. No, a constant function fails the horizontal line test and is not a one-to-one function; therefore, it cannot have an inverse.

64. $f(x) = 3 - (x - 5)^2$;
$$\text{D: } x \le 5, \ \text{R: } y \le 3$$
$$3 - (x - 5)^2 = y$$
$$-(x - 5)^2 = y - 3$$
$$(x - 5)^2 = 3 - y$$
$$x - 5 = \pm\sqrt{3 - y}$$
$$x = f^{-1}(y) = 5 \pm \sqrt{3 - y}$$
$$y = f^{-1}(x) = 5 - \sqrt{3 - x};$$
$$\text{D: } x \le 3, \ \text{R: } y \le 5$$

66. $f(x) = x^2 + 8x + 7$; D: $x \ge -4$, R: $y \ge -9$
$$x^2 + 8x + 7 = y$$
$$x^2 + 8x + (7 - y) = 0$$
$$x = \frac{-8 \pm \sqrt{64 - 4(7 - y)}}{2}$$
$$x = \frac{-8 \pm \sqrt{36 + 4y}}{2}$$
$$x = \frac{-8 \pm 2\sqrt{9 + y}}{2}$$
$$x = f^{-1}(y) = -4 \pm \sqrt{9 + y}$$
$$y = f^{-1}(x) = \sqrt{9 + x} - 4;$$
$$\text{D: } x \ge -9, \ \text{R: } y \ge -4$$

68. $f(x) = \sqrt{9 - x^2}$; D: $[0, 3]$, R: $[0, 3]$
$$\sqrt{9 - x^2} = y$$
$$9 - x^2 = y^2$$
$$-x^2 = y^2 - 9$$
$$x^2 = 9 - y^2$$
$$x = f^{-1}(y) = \pm\sqrt{9 - y^2}$$
$$y = f^{-1}(x) = \sqrt{9 - x^2}; \ \text{D: } [0, 3], \ \text{R: } [0, 3]$$

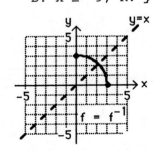

70. $f(x) = -\sqrt{9 - x^2}$; D: $[-3, 0]$, R: $[-3, 0]$

$$-\sqrt{9 - x^2} = y$$
$$\sqrt{9 - x^2} = -y$$
$$9 - x^2 = y^2$$
$$-x^2 = y^2 - 9$$
$$x^2 = 9 - y^2$$

$$x = f^{-1}(y) = \pm\sqrt{9 - y^2}$$

$$y = f^{-1}(x) = -\sqrt{9 - y^2}; \text{ D, R: } [-3, 0]$$

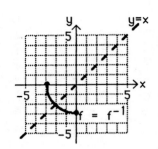

72. $f(x) = 1 - \sqrt{1 - x^2}$; D, R: $[0, 1]$

$$1 - \sqrt{1 - x^2} = y$$
$$-\sqrt{1 - x^2} = y - 1$$
$$\sqrt{1 - x^2} = 1 - y$$
$$1 - x^2 = y^2 - 2y + 1$$
$$-x^2 = y^2 - 2y$$
$$x^2 = -y^2 + 2y$$

$$x = f^{-1}(y) = \pm\sqrt{-y^2 + 2y}$$

$$y = f^{-1}(x) = \sqrt{2x - x^2}; \text{ D, R: } [0, 1]$$

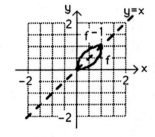

74. $f(x) = 1 + \sqrt{1 - x^2}$; D: $[-1, 0]$, R: $[1, 2]$

$$1 + \sqrt{1 - x^2} = y$$
$$\sqrt{1 - x^2} = y - 1$$
$$1 - x^2 = y^2 - 2y + 1$$
$$-x^2 = y^2 - 2y$$
$$x^2 = 2y - y^2$$

$$x = f^{-1}(y) = \pm\sqrt{2y - y^2}$$

$$y = f^{-1}(x) = -\sqrt{2x - x^2}; \text{ D: } [1, 2], \text{ R: } [-1, 0]$$

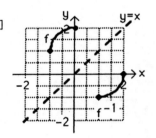

76. $f(x) = \sqrt{a^2 - x^2}$, $a > 0$, $0 \le x \le a$, $0 \le y \le a$

$$\sqrt{a^2 - x^2} = y$$
$$a^2 - x^2 = y^2$$
$$-x^2 = y^2 - a^2$$
$$x^2 = a^2 - y^2$$

$$x = f^{-1}(y) = \pm\sqrt{a^2 - y^2}$$

$$y = f^{-1}(x) = \sqrt{a^2 - x^2}; \text{ D: } [0, a], \text{ R: } [0, a]$$

78. The graph of a function that is its own inverse is symmetric with respect to the line $y = x$.

80. Let $P = (a, b)$, $Q = \left(\dfrac{a + b}{2}, \dfrac{a + b}{2}\right)$ and $R = (b, a)$, then

$$PQ = \sqrt{\left(a - \dfrac{a + b}{2}\right)^2 + \left(b - \dfrac{a + b}{2}\right)^2} = \sqrt{\left(\dfrac{a - b}{2}\right)^2 + \left(\dfrac{b - a}{2}\right)^2}$$

$$QR = \sqrt{\left(\dfrac{a + b}{2} - b\right)^2 + \left(\dfrac{a + b}{2} - a\right)^2} = \sqrt{\left(\dfrac{a - b}{2}\right)^2 + \left(\dfrac{b - a}{2}\right)^2}$$

which shows $\left(\dfrac{a + b}{2}, \dfrac{a + b}{2}\right)$ bisects line segment from (a, b) to (b, a).

82. $f(x) = (1 + x)^2$

$\qquad (1 + x)^2 = y$

$\qquad\quad 1 + x = \pm\sqrt{y}$

$\qquad x = f^{-1}(y) = \pm\sqrt{y} - 1$

$\qquad y = f^{-1}(x) = \pm\sqrt{x} - 1$

(A) $x \leq -1 \Rightarrow y \geq 0$

$\qquad f^{-1}(x) = -\sqrt{x} - 1$;

$\qquad$ D: $[0, \infty)$, R: $(-\infty, -1]$

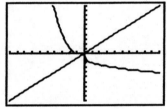
standard window

(B) $x \geq -1 \Rightarrow y \geq 0$

$\qquad f^{-1}(x) = \sqrt{x} - 1$;

$\qquad$ D: $[0, \infty)$, R: $[-1, \infty)$

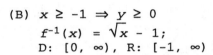
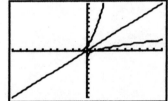
standard window

84. $f(x) = \sqrt{6x - x^2}$

$\qquad \sqrt{6x - x^2} = y$

$\qquad\quad 6x - x^2 = y^2$

$\qquad -x^2 + 6x - y^2 = 0$

$$x = \dfrac{-6 \pm \sqrt{36 - 4y^2}}{-2}$$

$$= \dfrac{6 \pm 2\sqrt{9 - y^2}}{2}$$

$$= 3 \pm \sqrt{9 - y^2}$$

$$f^{-1}(x) = 3 \pm \sqrt{9 - x^2}$$

(A) $0 \leq x \leq 3 \Rightarrow 0 \leq y \leq 3$

$\qquad f^{-1}(x) = 3 - \sqrt{9 - x^2}$;

$\qquad$ D: $[0, 3]$, R: $[0, 3]$

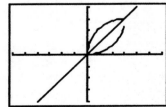

(B) $3 \leq x \leq 6 \Rightarrow 0 \leq y \leq 3$

$\qquad f^{-1}(x) = 3 + \sqrt{9 - x^2}$;

$\qquad$ D: $[0, 3]$, R: $[3, 6]$

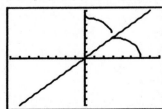

86. $q = s(p) = \dfrac{900p}{p + 20}$, $10 \leq p \leq 70$

    (A) range of s: $300 \leq q \leq 700$

       $p = 10$: $\dfrac{9000}{30} = 300$; $p = 70$: $\dfrac{63,000}{90} = 700$

         (B) $q = \dfrac{900p}{p + 20}$

             $qp + 20q = 900p$

             $qp - 900p = -20q$

             $p(q - 900) = -20q$

             $p = \dfrac{-20q}{q - 900}$

             $p = s^{-1}(q) = \dfrac{20q}{900 - q}$;

             D: $[300, 700]$, R: $[10, 70]$

    (C) No; you are not finding $s'(p)$, but $s'(q)$.

       The inverse of $q = s^{-1}(p) = \dfrac{20p}{900 - p}$.

88. $\Delta y = -5°/1000$ feet

    (A) (a, t): $(0, 63°)$, $(15, -12°)$ (thousands of feet).   (B) $t = -5a + 63$

       $m = \dfrac{\Delta y}{\Delta x} = \dfrac{-75}{15} = -5$

                           $t - 63 = -5a$

       $t - t_1 = m(a - a_1)$

                          $a = -\dfrac{1}{5}t + \dfrac{63}{5}$

       $t - 63 = -5(a - 0)$

       $t - 63 = -5a$ $a = d^{-1}(t) = -0.2t + 12.6$

          $t = -5a + 63$

Exercise 4-3

2. (A) $y = 5^x$: m   (B) $y = (0.5)^x$: f   (C) $y = 3^x$: n   (D) $y = \left(\dfrac{1}{4}\right)^x$: g

4. $3^{-\sqrt{2}} \approx 0.2114699 \approx 0.2115$ **6.** $\pi^{-\sqrt{3}} \approx 0.1376928 \approx 0.1377$

8. $\dfrac{3^\pi - 3^{-\pi}}{2} \approx 15.7562896 \approx 15.76$

10. $y = 5^x$
Increasing, y-intercept: 1,
horizontal asymptote: $y = 0$

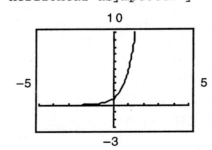

12. $y = \left(\dfrac{1}{5}\right)^x = 5^{-x}$

Decreasing, y-intercept: 1,
horizontal asymptote: $y = 0$

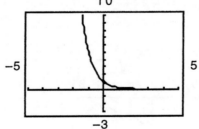

14. $f(x) = -5^x$
Decreasing, y-intercept: -1,
horizontal asymptote: $y = 0$

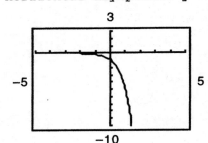

16. $f(x) = 4(5^x)$
Increasing, y-intercept: 4,
horizontal asymptote: $y = 0$

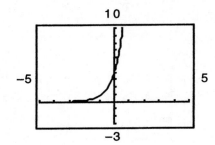

18. $y = 5^{x+2} + 4$
Increasing, y-intercept: 29,
horizontal asymptote: $y = 4$

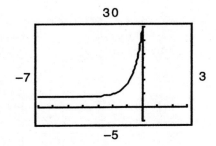

20. $(4^{3x})^{2y} = 4^{3x(2y)}$
$= 4^{6xy}$

22. $\dfrac{5^{x-3}}{5^{x-4}} = 5^{x-3-(x-4)}$
$= 5$

24. $(2^x 3^y)^z = (2^x)^z (3^y)^z$
$= 2^{xz} 3^{yz}$

26. $10^{2-3x} = 10^{5x-6}$
$2 - 3x = 5x - 6$
$8x = 8$
$x = 1$

28. $4^{5x-x^2} = 4^{-6}$
$5x - x^2 = -6$
$x^2 - 5x - 6 = 0$
$(x - 6)(x + 1) = 0$
$x = 6 \qquad x = -1$

30. $5^3 = (x + 2)^3$
$5 = x + 2$
$x = 3$

32. $9^{x-1} = 3^x$
$(3^2)^{x-1} = 3^x$
$3^{2x-2} = 3^x$
$2x - 2 = x$
$x = 2$

34. $100^{x-1} = 1000^{2x}$
$(10^2)^{x-1} = (10^3)^{2x}$
$10^{2x-2} = 10^{6x}$
$2x - 2 = 6x$
$4x = -2$
$x = -\dfrac{1}{2}$

36. $4^{x^2} = 2^{x+3}$
$(2^2)^{x^2} = 2^{x+3}$
$2^{2x^2} = 2^{x+3}$
$2x^2 = x + 3$
$2x^2 - x - 3 = 0$
$(x + 1)(2x - 3) = 0$
$x = -1 \qquad x = \dfrac{3}{2}$

38. $a^4 = b^4$, $a \neq b$. Any real number a, with $b = -a$ will satisfy this condition. For example, $2^4 = (-2)^4$. The third exponential property states that if $a > 0$, $b > 0$ (both positive), then $a^x = b^x \Rightarrow a = b$.

40. $y = 0^x$ is the graph of the horizontal line $y = 0$ only to the right of the origin, since $0^x = 0$ for all $x > 0$.

42. $y = f(x) + 1$; horizontal shift up 1. **44.** $y = f(x + 1)$; vertical shift left 1.

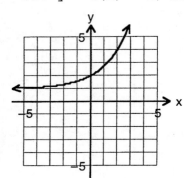

$(0, 1) \Rightarrow (0, 2)$

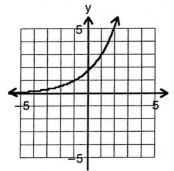

$(0, 1) \Rightarrow (-1, 1)$

46. $y = 3 - 5f(x)$; reflection about
the x-axis, vertical stretch by a
factor of 5, horizontal shift up 3.

48. $y = 2f(x + 1) - 1$; vertical shift
left 1, vertical stretch by a factor
of 2, horizontal shift down 1.

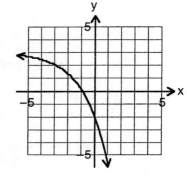

$(0, 1) \Rightarrow (0, -2)$

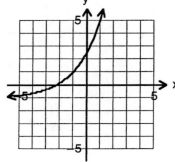

$(0, 1) \Rightarrow (-1, 1)$

50. $f(x) = a(b^x) + c$
Increasing function
Asymptote is x-axis: $c = 0$
$(-1, 0.5)$, $(0, 1)$, $(3, 8)$

52. $f(x) = a(b^x) + c$
Decreasing function
Asymptote is x-axis: $c = 0$
$(-1, 32)$, $(0, 4)$, $(1, 0.5)$

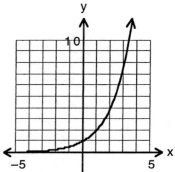

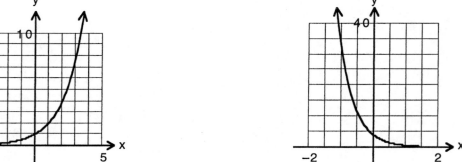

54. $f(x) = a(b^x) + c$
Increasing function
Asymptote: $y = 4$
$(-10, 0)$, $(0, 3)$, $(10, 3.75)$

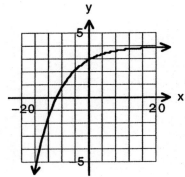

56. $f(x) = a(b^x) + c$
Decreasing function
Asymptote: $y = -5$
$(-4, 11)$, $(0, -4)$, $(2, -4.75)$

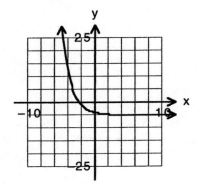

58. $(3^x - 3^{-x})(3^x + 3^{-x}) = (3^x)(3^x) + (3^{-x})(3^x) - (3^x)(3^{-x}) - (3^{-x})(3^{-x})$
$\qquad = 3^{2x} + 3^0 - 3^0 - 3^{-2x}$
$\qquad = 3^{2x} + 1 - 1 - 3^{-2x}$
$\qquad = 3^{2x} - 3^{-2x}$

60. $(3^x - 3^{-x})^2 + (3^x + 3^{-x})^2 = 3^{2x} - 2 \cdot 3^{x-x} + 3^{-2x} + 3^{2x} + 2 \cdot 3^{x-x} + 3^{-2x}$
$\qquad = 2(3^{2x}) + 2(3^{-2x})$

62. $h(x) = 3x(2^{-x}) - 1$

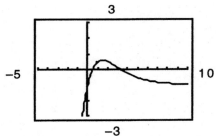

local maximum at $\approx (1.44, 0.59)$
x-intercept ≈ 0.46, 3.31
horizontal asymptote: $y = -1$
as $x \to \infty$, $y \to -1$
as $x \to -\infty$, $y \to -\infty$

64. $g(x) = \dfrac{3^x + 3^{-x}}{2}$

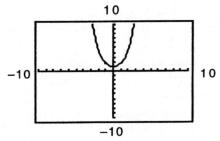

local minimum at $(0, 1)$
no x-intercept
no horizontal asymptote
as $x \to \infty$, $y \to \infty$
as $x \to -\infty$, $y \to \infty$

66. $N = N_0 2^{t/d}$, $d = 0.5$, $N_0 = 100$
$\quad = 100 \cdot 2^{t/(1/2)}$
$\quad = 100 \cdot 2^{2t}$

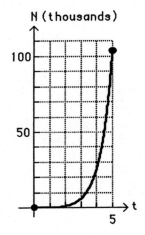

68. $P = P_0 2^{t/d} = 30,000,000 \cdot 2^{t/19}$

(A) $P(10) = 30,000,000 \cdot 2^{10/19} \approx 43,000,000$

(B) $P(30) = 30,000,000 \cdot 2^{30/19} \approx 90,000,000$

70. $A = A_0\left(\dfrac{1}{2}\right)^{t/h}$, $h = 6$, $A_0 = 12$

$\quad = 12\left(\dfrac{1}{2}\right)^{t/6}$

(A) $A(3) = 12\left(\dfrac{1}{2}\right)^{3/6} \approx 8.49$ mg   (B) $A(24) = 12\left(\dfrac{1}{2}\right)^{24/6} \approx 0.750$ mg

72. $A = P\left(1 + \dfrac{r}{m}\right)^n$, $P = \$2500$, $r = 0.07$, $m = 4$

$\quad = 2500\left(1 + \dfrac{0.07}{4}\right)^{4t}$

(A) $\dfrac{3}{4}$ yrs: $n = 3$ (B) 15 yrs: $n = 4 \times 15 = 60$

$A\left(\dfrac{3}{4}\right) = 2500\left(1 + \dfrac{0.07}{4}\right)^3 = \$2633.56$ $A(15) = 2500\left(1 + \dfrac{0.07}{4}\right)^{60} = \$7079.54$

74. $A = P\left(1 + \dfrac{r}{m}\right)^n$, $A = \$15,000$, for 5 years, $r = 0.0975$, $m =$ weekly (52)

$n = 52 \times 5 = 260$

$15,000 = P\left(1 + \dfrac{0.0975}{52}\right)^{260}$

$\quad P = \$9217$

76. A_1: $P = 4000$, $r = 0.09$, $m = 52$

A_2: $P = 6000$, $r = 0.07$, $m = 52$

$\quad A_1 > A_2$

$A_1 = 4000\left(1 + \dfrac{0.09}{52}\right)^m$

$A_2 = 6000\left(1 + \dfrac{0.07}{52}\right)^m$

Graph A_1 and A_2 to study the inequality. The graphs intersect at $x \approx 1056$.

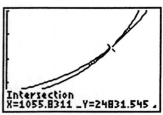

Intersection
X=1055.8311 Y=24831.545 .

Yes, after 1,056 weeks.

78. $5000\left(1 + \dfrac{r}{365}\right)^{365} \geq 5000\left(1 + \dfrac{0.13}{2}\right)^2$

$\left(1 + \dfrac{r}{365}\right) \geq \left(1 + \dfrac{0.13}{2}\right)^{2/365}$

$r \geq 0.125973313$, about 12.6%

80. $y = ab^x$

$y = 30363.17638(0.7896877851)^x$
$f(0) = 30363.17638$; purchase price \$30363.
$f(10) = 2863.527817$; value after 10 years \$2864.

Exercise 4-4

2. (A) $y = e^{-1.2x}$
Decreasing (f or g); through $(-1, 3.3) \Rightarrow g$
(B) $y = e^{0.7x}$
Increasing (m or n); through $(1, 2) \Rightarrow n$
(C) $y = e^{-0.4x}$
Decreasing (f or g); through $(-1, 1.5) \Rightarrow f$
(D) $y = e^{1.3x}$
Increasing (m or n); through $(1, 3.7) \Rightarrow m$

4. $e - e^{-1} \approx 2.350$ **6.** $e^{\sqrt{2}} \approx 4.113$ **8.** $e^{-e} \approx 0.06599$ **10.** $(e^{-x})^4 = e^{-4x}$

12. $e^{-4x}e^{6x} = e^{-4x+6x} = e^{2x}$ **14.** $\dfrac{e^{4-3x}}{e^{2-5x}} = e^{(4-3x)-(2-5x)} = e^{4-3x-2+5x} = e^{2x+2}$

16. (A) $\left(1 + \dfrac{1}{x}\right)$ is not constant and b (in b^x) is.   (B) $\left(1 + \dfrac{1}{x}\right)^x \to e$ as $x \to \infty$

18. $y = -e^{-x}$
Increasing, no x-intercepts,
y-intercept: $-e^0 = -1$,
horizontal asymptote: $y = 0$.

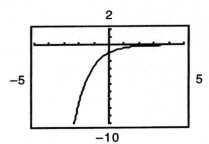

20. $y = 100e^{0.1x}$
Increasing, no x-intercepts,
y-intercept: $100e^0 = 100$,
horizontal asymptote: $y = 0$.

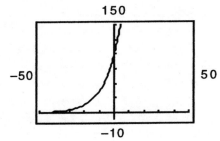

22. $g(t) = 10e^{-0.2t}$
Decreasing, no x-intercepts,
y-intercept: $10e^0 = 10$,
horizontal asymptote: $y = 0$

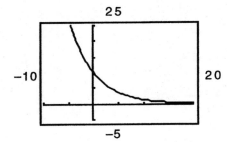

24. $G(x) = e^{2x} - 3$
Increasing, x-intercept ≈ 0.55,
y-intercept: $e^0 - 3 = -2$,
horizontal asymptote: $y = -3$

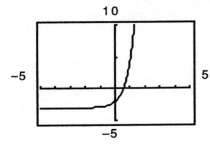

26. $h(t) = 3 + e^{-2t}$
Decreasing, no x-intercepts,
y-intercept: $3 + e^0 = 4$,
horizontal asymptote: $y = 3$

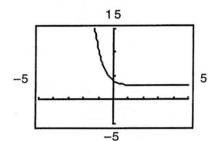

28. $f(x) = e^x$
Shift 3 units left: $g(x) = e^{x+3}$

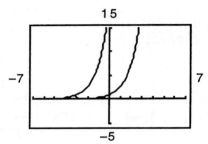

30. $f(x) = e^x$
Shift down 1 unit: $g(x) = e^x - 1$

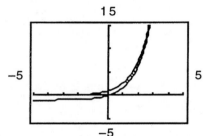

32. $f(x) = e^x$
Shift 1 unit right: $f_1(x) = e^{x-1}$
Reflect about the y-axis: $f_2(x) = e^{-(x-1)}$
Contract vertically by a factor of 0.5:
$g(x) = 0.5e^{-(x-1)}$

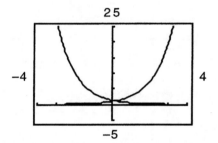

34. $\dfrac{5x^4e^{5x} - 4x^3e^{5x}}{x^8} = \dfrac{x^3e^{5x}(5x - 4)}{x^8} = \dfrac{e^{5x}(5x - 4)}{x^5}$

36. $e^x(e^{-x} + 1) - e^{-x}(e^x + 1) = e^{x-x} + e^x - e^{-x+x} - e^{-x}$
$= e^0 + e^x - e^0 - e^{-x}$
$= e^x - e^{-x}$

38. $\dfrac{e^x(e^x + e^{-x}) - (e^x - e^{-x})e^x}{e^{2x}} = \dfrac{e^{2x} + e^{x-x} - e^{2x} + e^{-x+x}}{e^{2x}}$
$= \dfrac{2e^0}{e^{2x}} = \dfrac{2}{e^{2x}}$

40. $(x - 3)e^x = 0 \Rightarrow x - 3 = 0, \; e^x = 0$, no solution, $e^x > 0$
$x = 3$

42. $3xe^{-x} + x^2e^{-x} = 0 \Rightarrow e^{-x}(3x + x^2) = 0; \; e^{-x} > 0$
$x^2 + 3x = 0$
$x(x + 3) = 0$
$x = 0, \; x = -3$

44. $g(x) = -3 + e^{1+x}$
No local extrema
y-intercept: $-3 + e \approx -0.28$
x-intercept: $0.0986 \approx 0.10$
as $x \to \infty$, $g \to \infty$;
as $x \to -\infty$, $g \to -3$
horizontal asymptote: $y = -3$

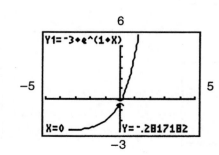

46. $n(x) = e^{-|x|}$
local maximum at $(0, 1)$
y-intercept: 1
x-intercept: none
as $x \to \infty$, $n \to 0$; as $x \to -\infty$, $n \to 0$
horizontal asymptote: $y = 0$

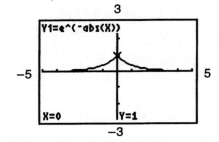

48. $r(x) = e^{x^2}$
local minimum at $(0, 1)$
y-intercept: 1
x-intercept: none
as $x \to \infty$, $r \to \infty$,
as $x \to -\infty$, $r \to \infty$
No horizontal asymptote

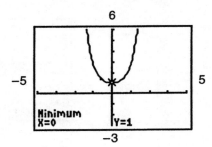

50. $G(x) = \dfrac{100}{1 + e^{-x}}$
No local extrema
y-intercept: 50
x-intercept: none
as $x \to \infty$, $G \to 100$;
as $x \to -\infty$, $G \to 0$
horizontal asymptotes: $y = 0$, $y = 100$

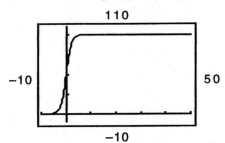

52. As $x \to \infty$, $f(x) = (1 + x)^{1/x} \to 1$
Graph $y_1 = f(x)$ and $y_2 = 1$

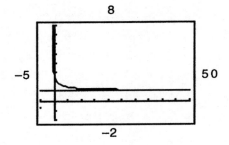

54. $f(x) = e^x$;
$P_2(x) = 1 + x + \dfrac{1}{2}x^2 + \dfrac{1}{6}x^3$

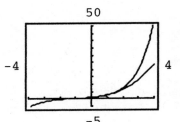

56. $f(x) = e^x$;
$P_4(x) = 1 + x + \dfrac{1}{2}x^2 + \dfrac{1}{6}x^3 + \dfrac{1}{24}x^4 + \dfrac{1}{120}x^5$

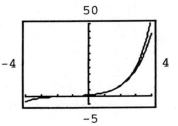

58. $g_1(x) = xe^x$, $g_2(x) = x^2e^x$, $g_3(x) = x^3e^x$
as $x \to \infty$, $g(x) \to \infty$, as $x \to -\infty$, $g(x) \to 0$. $y = 0$ is a horizontal asymptote.
$g_n(x) = x^ne^x$: as $x \to \infty$, $g_n \to \infty$; as $x \to -\infty$, $g_n \to 0$.

60. $P = P_0 e^{kt}$
$P = 100e^{0.023t}$
$P(8) = 100e^{0.023(8)}$
$P(8) = 120$ million

62. 1996, $t = 0$:
G: 84 million, -0.15%
E: 64 million, 1.9%
$P_G = 84e^{-0.0015t}$;
$P_E = 64e^{0.019t}$
Graph P_G and P_E:

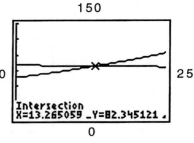

$1996 + 13 = 2009$

64. $P = 14.7e^{-0.21h}$

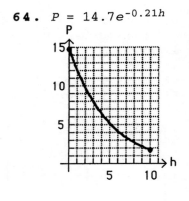

66. $I = I_0 e^{-0.23d}$: $I/I_0 = e^{-0.23d}$
(A) for $d = 10$: $I/I_0 = e^{-0.23(10)} \approx 0.10 \approx 10\%$
(B) for $d = 20$: $I/I_0 = e^{-0.23(20)} \approx 0.01 \approx 1\%$

68. $A = Pe^{rt}$, $P = \$7500$, $r = 8.35\%$
(A) $A(5.5) = 7500e^{0.0835(5.5)} = \$11,871.65$
(B) $A(12) = 7500e^{0.0835(12)} = \$20,427.93$

70. $A = P\left(1 + \dfrac{r}{n}\right)^m$

Alamo: $A = 10,000\left(1 + \dfrac{0.0825}{4}\right)^4 = \$10,850.88$

Lamar: $A = Pe^{rt} = 10,000e^{0.0805(1)} = \$10,838.29$

72. $A = Pe^{rt}$
$50,000 = Pe^{(0.10*5.5)}$
$P = \dfrac{50,000}{e^{0.55}}$
$\quad = \$28,847.49$

74. 1996, $t = 0$; $P = 28$ million, $r = 19\%$
(A) 2000, $t = 4$: $A = 28e^{(0.19 \times 4)} \approx 59.87$ million
(B) 2004, $t = 8$: $A = 28e^{(0.19 \times 8)} \approx 128.02$ million

76. $N = 2(1 - e^{-0.037t})$
(A) 2 days: $N = 2(1 - e^{(-0.037 \times 2)})$
$\qquad\qquad\quad = 0.14266$ million
$\qquad\qquad\quad \approx 143,000$

   10 days: $N = 2(1 - e^{(-0.037 \times 10)})$
$\qquad\qquad\quad = 0.61853$ million
$\qquad\qquad\quad \approx 619,000$

(B) $\dfrac{1}{2}$ viewers: $1 = 2(1 - e^{-0.037t})$
$\qquad\qquad 0.5 = 1 - e^{-0.037t}$
$\qquad\qquad 0.5 = e^{-0.037t}$

Graph $y_1 = 0.5$, $y_2 = e^{-0.037t}$
The graphs intersect at $x = 18.7337$. Approximately 19 days.

(C) Graph $y_1 = N$ in the window $[0, 100]$ by $[0, 3]$, and $y_2 = 2$.
   $N \to 2$ million viewers, the upper limit for the number of potential viewers.

78. $T = T_m + (T_0 - T_m)e^{-kt}$; $T_0 = 72°F$, $T_m = 40°F$, $k = 0.4$, $t = 5$
$T = 40 + (72 - 40)e^{-0.4(5)}$
$T = 40 + 32e^{-0.4(5)}$
$T \approx 44°F$

80. $q = 0.000008(1 - e^{-2t})$
Graph q in the window $[0, 50]$ by $[0, 0.00001]$.
As $x \to \infty$, $y \to 0.000008$.
$t \to 0.00008$ coulombs, the upper limit for the capacitor charge.

82. $N = \dfrac{200}{4 + 21e^{-0.1t}}$

(A) 3 days: $N = \dfrac{200}{4 + 21e^{-0.1(3)}}$

$\approx 10.2264 \approx 10$ computers

6 days: $N = \dfrac{200}{4 + 21e^{-0.1(6)}}$

$\approx 12.8824 \approx 13$ computers

(B) 30 computers: $30 = \dfrac{200}{4 + 21e^{-0.1t}}$

$120 + 630e^{-0.1t} = 200$
$630e^{-0.1t} = 80$
$e^{-0.1t} = \dfrac{8}{63}$

Graph $y_1 = e^{-0.1t}$, $y_2 = \dfrac{8}{63}$ in the window $[0, 40]$ by $[0, 2]$. They intersect at $x \approx 20.6369 \approx 21$ days.

(C) As $t \to \infty$, $N \to 50$ computers.
The following graph shows N and
$y = 50$ in the window $[0, 75]$
by $[0, 60]$:

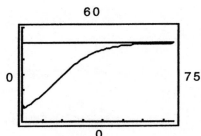

Exercise 4-5

2. $\log_5 125 = 3 \Leftrightarrow 125 = 5^3$

4. $\log_{10} 1000 = 3 \Leftrightarrow 1000 = 10^3$

6. $\log_4 2 = \dfrac{1}{2} \Leftrightarrow 2 = 4^{1/2}$

8. $\log_{1/3} 27 = -3 \Leftrightarrow 27 = \left(\dfrac{1}{3}\right)^{-3}$

10. $10,000 = 10^4 \Leftrightarrow \log_{10} 10,000 = 4$

12. $9 = 27^{2/3} \Leftrightarrow \log_{27} 9 = \dfrac{2}{3}$

14. $\dfrac{1}{8} = 2^{-3} \Leftrightarrow \log_2 \dfrac{1}{8} = -3$

16. $4 = \sqrt[3]{64} = 64^{1/3} \Leftrightarrow \log_{64} 4 = \dfrac{1}{3}$

18. $\log_{25} 1 = 0$

20. $\log_7 7 = 1$

22. $\log_{10} 10^5 = 5 \log_{10} 10$
$= 5(1)$
$= 5$

24. $\log_{10} 100 = \log_{10} 10^2$
$= 2 \log_{10} 10$
$= 2$

26. $\log_2 \sqrt{8} = \log_2 8^{1/2}$
$= \dfrac{1}{2} \log_2 8$
$= \dfrac{1}{2} \cdot 3$
$= \dfrac{3}{2}$

28. $e^{\log_e(x-1)} = x - 1$

30. $10^{-3 \log_{10} u} = 10^{\log_{10} u^{-3}}$

$= u^{-3}$

32. $\log_3 x = 3 \Leftrightarrow 3^3 = x$

$x = 27$

34. $\log_8 64 = y \Leftrightarrow 8^y = 64$

$8^y = 8^2$

$y = 2$

36. $\log_b 10^{-3} = -3$

$b^{-3} = 10^{-3}$

$b = 10$

38. $\log_b b = 1$

any $b > 0$ and $b \neq 1$

40. $\log_8 x = \frac{1}{3}$

$8^{1/3} = x$

$x = 2$

42. $\log_{49}\left(\frac{1}{7}\right) = y$

$49^y = \frac{1}{7}$

$7^{2y} = 7^{-1}$

$2y = -1$

$y = -\frac{1}{2}$

44. $\log_b 4 = \frac{2}{3}$

$b^{2/3} = 4$

$b = 4^{3/2}$

$b = 8$

46. $\log_b u^{1/2} v^{1/3} = \log_b u^{1/2} + \log_b v^{1/3} = \frac{1}{2} \log_b u + \frac{1}{3} \log_b v$

48. $\log_b \frac{u^3}{v^5} = \log_b u^3 - \log_b v^5 = 3 \log_b u - 5 \log_b v$

50. $\log_b \frac{uv}{w} = \log_b uv - \log_b w = \log_b u + \log_b v - \log_b w$

52. $\log_b \frac{1}{M^5} = \log_b 1 - \log_b M^5 = 0 - 5 \log_b M = -5 \log_b M$

54. $\log_b \sqrt{u^2 + 1} = \log_b (u^2 + 1)^{1/2} = \frac{1}{2} \log_b (u^2 + 1)$

56. $\log_b \frac{m^5 n^3}{\sqrt{p}} = \log_b m^5 n^3 - \log_b \sqrt{p}$

$= \log_b m^5 + \log_b n^3 - \log_b p^{1/2}$

$= 5 \log_b m + 3 \log_b n - \frac{1}{2} \log_b p$

58. $\log_b \sqrt[5]{\left(\frac{x}{y^4 z^9}\right)^3} = \log_b \left(\frac{x}{y^4 z^9}\right)^{3/5}$

$= \frac{3}{5} \log_b \frac{x}{y^4 z^9}$

$= \frac{3}{5}[\log_b x - \log_b (y^4 z^9)]$

$= \frac{3}{5}[\log_b x - \log_b y^4 - \log_b z^9]$

$= \frac{3}{5}[\log_b x - 4 \log_b y - 9 \log_b z]$

60. $\log_b m - \frac{1}{2} \log_b n = \log_b m - \log_b n^{1/2}$

$= \log_b \frac{m}{n^{1/2}} = \log_b \frac{m}{\sqrt{n}}$

62. $\log_b w + \log_b x - \log_b y = \log_b wx - \log_b y$

$$= \log_b \frac{wx}{y}$$

64. $\frac{1}{3} \log_b w - 3 \log_b x - 5 \log_b y = \log_b w^{1/3} - \log_b x^3 - \log_b y^5$

$$= \log_b \frac{w^{1/3}}{x^3} - \log_b y^5$$

$$= \log_b \frac{\sqrt[3]{w}}{x^3 y^5}$$

66. $7(4 \log_b m + \frac{1}{3} \log_b n) = 7(\log_b m^4 + \log_b n^{1/3})$

$$= 7(\log_b m^4 \sqrt[3]{n})$$

$$= \log_b (m^4 \sqrt[3]{n})^7$$

68. $\frac{1}{3}(4 \log_b x - 2 \log_b y) = \frac{1}{3}(\log_b x^4 - \log_b y^2)$

$$= \frac{1}{3}\left(\log_b \frac{x^4}{y^2}\right)$$

$$= \log_b \left(\frac{x^4}{y^2}\right)^{1/3} = \log_b \sqrt[3]{\frac{x^4}{y^2}}$$

70. $\log_b[(5x - 4)^3(3x + 2)^4] = \log_b(5x - 4)^3 + \log_b(3x + 2)^4$

$$= 3 \log_b(5x - 4) + 4 \log_b(3x + 2)$$

72. $\log_b \frac{(x - 3)^5}{(5 + x)^3} = \log_b(x - 3)^5 - \log_b(5 + x)^3$

$$= 5 \log_b(x - 3) - 3 \log_b(5 + x)$$

74. $\log_b \frac{\sqrt{x - 1}}{x^3} = \log_b \sqrt{x - 1} - \log_b x^3$

$$= \frac{1}{2} \log_b(x - 1) - 3 \log_b x$$

76. $\log_b(x^5 + 5x^4 - 14x^3) = \log_b[x^3(x^2 + 5x - 14)]$

$$= \log_b x^3 + \log_b(x^2 + 5x - 14)$$

$$= 3 \log_b x + \log_b[(x + 7)(x - 2)]$$

$$= 3 \log_b x + \log_b(x + 7) + \log_b(x - 2)$$

78. $\log_{10}(5 - x) = 3 \log_{10} 2$

$$= \log_{10} 2^3$$

$\log_{10}(5 - x) = 3 \log_{10} 2$

$\log_{10}(5 - x) = \log_{10} 2^3$

$$5 - x = 8$$

$$x = -3$$

80. $\log_{10}(x^2 - 2x - 2) = 2 \log_{10}(x - 2)$

$\log_{10}(x^2 - 2x - 2) = \log_{10}(x - 2)^2$

$$x^2 - 2x - 2 = (x - 2)^2$$

$$x^2 - 2x - 2 = x^2 - 4x + 4$$

$$2x = 6$$

$$x = 3$$

82. $\log_7 4x - \log_7(x + 1) = \frac{1}{2}\log_7 4$

$$\log_7 \frac{4x}{x + 1} = \log_7 4^{1/2}$$

$$\frac{4x}{x + 1} = 2$$

$$4x = 2x + 2$$

$$2x = 2$$

$$x = 1$$

84. $\log_4 x + \log_4(x + 2) = \frac{1}{2}\log_4 9$

$$\log_4(x(x + 2)) = \log_4 9^{1/2}$$

$$x(x + 2) = \sqrt{9}$$

$$x^2 + 2x = 3$$

$$x^2 + 2x - 3 = 0$$

$$(x + 3)(x - 1) = 0$$

$$x = -3 \text{ (reject)}, \; x = 1$$

86. $\frac{3}{2}\log_b 4 - \frac{2}{3}\log_b 8 + 2\log_b 2 = \log_b x$

$$\log_b 4^{3/2} - \log_b 8^{2/3} + \log_b 2^2 = \log_b x$$

$$\log_b 8 - \log_b 4 + \log_b 4 = \log_b x$$

$$\log_b 8 = \log_b x$$

$$x = 8$$

88. $\log_b 12 = \log_b 2^2(3)$

$$= 2\log_b 2 + \log_b 3$$

$$= 2(0.69) + 1.10$$

$$= 2.48$$

90. $\log_b \frac{5}{3} = \log_b 5 - \log_b 3$

$$= 1.61 - 1.10$$

$$= 0.51$$

92. $\log_b 16 = \log_b 2^4$

$$= 4\log_b 2$$

$$= 4(0.69)$$

$$= 2.76$$

94. $\log_b \sqrt{3} = \frac{1}{2}\log_b 3$

$$= \frac{1}{2}(1.10)$$

$$= 0.55$$

96. $\log_b \sqrt[3]{1.5} = \frac{1}{3}\log_b \frac{3}{2}$

$$= \frac{1}{3}[\log_b 3 - \log_b 2]$$

$$= \frac{1}{3}[1.10 - 0.69]$$

$$= 0.13\overline{6}$$

98. $f(x) = \log_2(x + 3)$
(A) Shift $y = \log_2 x$
    3 units left.

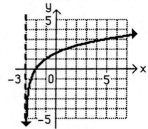

(B) $y = \log_2(x + 3)$
    $x + 3 = 2^y$
    $x = 2^y - 3$
    $f^{-1}(x) = 2^x - 3$

100. $f(x) = \log_2 x + 3$
(A) Shift $y = \log_2 x$
    3 units up.

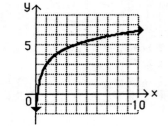

(B) $y = \log_2 x + 3$
    $y - 3 = \log_2 x$
    $x = 2^{y-3}$
    $f^{-1}(x) = 2^{x-3}$

102. (A) $f = \left\{ (x, y) \mid y = \left(\dfrac{1}{3}\right)^x = 3^{-x} \right\}$

Graph f, f^{-1} and $y = x$:

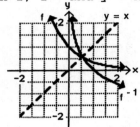

(B) Domain of f: $(-\infty, \infty)$
Range of f: $(0, \infty)$
Domain of f^{-1}: $(0, \infty)$
Range of f^{-1}: $(-\infty, \infty)$

(C) If $y = 3^{-x}$ then

$-x = \log_3 y$
$x = -\log_3 y$
$f^{-1}(x) = -\log_3 x$

or

If $y = \left(\dfrac{1}{3}\right)^x$ then

$x = \log_{1/3} y$
$f^{-1}(x) = \log_{1/3} x$

104. $g(x) = 3^{2x-3} - 2$
$y = 3^{2x-3} - 2$
$y + 2 = 3^{2x-3}$
$2x - 3 = \log_3(y + 2)$
$2x = \log_3(y + 2) + 3$
$x = \dfrac{1}{2}[\log_3(y + 2) + 3]$
$f^{-1}(x) = \dfrac{1}{2}[\log_3(x + 2) + 3]$

106. $f(x) = 2 + \log_e(5x - 3)$
$y = 2 + \log_e(5x - 3)$
$y - 2 = \log_e(5x - 3)$
$5x - 3 = e^{y-2}$
$5x = e^{y-2} + 3$
$x = \dfrac{1}{5}(e^{y-2} + 3)$
$f^{-1}(x) = \dfrac{1}{5}(e^{x-2} + 3)$

108. The graph of $y = 2^{|x|}$ has the shape of a parabola opening upward. The reflection is not a function since y is not one-to-one.

110. $\log_e x - \log_e C + kt = 0$

$\log_e\left(\dfrac{x}{C}\right) + kt = 0$

$\log_e\left(\dfrac{x}{C}\right) = -kt$

$e^{-kt} = \dfrac{x}{C}$

$x = Ce^{-kt}$

112. $\log_b m^p = \log_b (\underbrace{m \cdot m \cdot m \cdot \ldots \cdot m}_{p \text{ factors}})$

$= \underbrace{\log_b m + \log_b m + \ldots + \log_b m}_{p \text{ terms}}$

$= p \log_b m$

Exercise 4-6

2. $\log 843,250 \approx 5.9260$

4. $\log 0.035604 \approx -1.4485$

6. $\ln 2,843,100 \approx 14.8604$

8. $\ln 0.0000324 \approx -10.3374$

10. $\log x = 1.9168$
$x = 10^{1.9168}$
$x \approx 82.57$

12. $\log x = -2.0411$
$x = 10^{-2.0411}$
$x \approx 0.009097$

14. $\ln x = 5.0884$
$x = e^{5.0884}$
$x \approx 162.1$

16. $\ln x = -4.1083$
$x = e^{-4.1083}$
$x \approx 0.01644$

18. $n = \dfrac{\log 2}{\log 1.12} \approx 6.116$

20. $n = \dfrac{\ln 4}{\ln 1.2} \approx 7.604$

22. $x = \dfrac{\ln 0.1}{-0.0025} \approx 921.034$

24. $t = \dfrac{\log 200}{\log 2} \approx 7.644$

26. $x = \log(2.0991 \times 10^{17}) \approx 17.322$

28. $x = \ln(4.0304 \times 10^{-8}) \approx -17.027$

30. $\log x = -12.73164$
$x = 10^{-12.73164}$
$x \approx 1.8551 \times 10^{-13}$

32. $\ln x = 18.891143$
$x = e^{18.891143}$
$x \approx 1.6007 \times 10^{8}$

34. $f(x) = 2 \ln x + 2$
$y = 2 \ln x + 2$
$y - 2 = 2 \ln x$
$\dfrac{1}{2}(y - 2) = \ln x$
$x = e^{1/2(y-2)}$
$f^{-1}(x) = e^{0.5(x-2)}$
Graph f, f^{-1} and $y = x$ in a standard window.

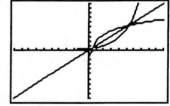

36. $f(x) = 4 \ln(x - 3)$
$y = 4 \ln(x - 3)$
$\dfrac{y}{4} = \ln(x - 3)$
$x - 3 = e^{y/4}$
$x = e^{y/4} + 3$
$f^{-1}(x) = e^{x/4} + 3$
Graph f, f^{-1} and $y = x$ in a standard window.

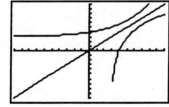

38. $f(x) = 2 - \ln(1 + |x|)$

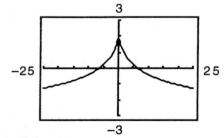

Domain: $(-\infty, \infty)$
Range: $(-\infty, 2]$
x-intercepts: ± 6.39
y-intercept: 2
no asymptotes

40. $f(x) = -1 + \ln(|1 - x^2|)$, $x \neq \pm 1$

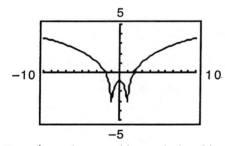

Domain: $(-\infty, -1) \cup (-1, 1) \cup (1, \infty)$
Range: $(-\infty, \infty)$
x-intercepts: ± 1.93
y-intercept: -1
vertical asymptotes: $x = -1$, $x = 1$

42. $\log \frac{1}{2} = -0.3010 < 0$, thus when $3 > 2$ is multiplied on both sides by $\log \frac{1}{2}$ (a negative number) the order of the inequality should be reversed $3 \log \frac{1}{2} < 2 \log \frac{1}{2}$ rather than $3 \log \frac{1}{2} > 2 \log \frac{1}{2}$ as shown.

44. $f(x) = \ln x$ $g(x) = \ln(\ln x)$

(A) $\ln 1000 \approx 6.9$ $\ln(\ln(1000)) \approx 1.9$
$\ln 10{,}000 \approx 9.2$ $\ln(\ln(10{,}000)) \approx 2.2$
an increase of 2.3   an increase of 0.3

(B) $\ln(\ln(x))$ has domain $(1, \infty)$ and range $(-\infty, \infty)$.

(C) Answers may vary. See graph.

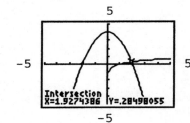

46. $f(x) = \log x$, $g(x) = 4 - x^2$; intersection at $(1.93, 0.28)$.

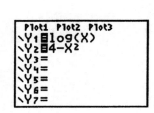
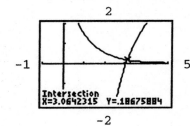

48. $f(x) = 3\ln(x - 2)$, $g(x) = 4e^{-x}$; intersection at $(3.06, 0.19)$.

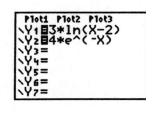
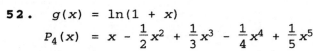

50. $g(x) = \ln(1 + x)$
$P_2(x) = x - \frac{1}{2}x^2 + \frac{1}{3}x^3$

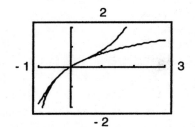

52. $g(x) = \ln(1 + x)$
$P_4(x) = x - \frac{1}{2}x^2 + \frac{1}{3}x^3 - \frac{1}{4}x^4 + \frac{1}{5}x^5$

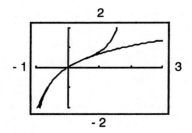

54. (A) $D = 10 \log \dfrac{I}{I_0} = 10 \log \dfrac{3.2 \times 10^{-6}}{10^{-12}} \approx 65$ decibels

(B) $D = 10 \log \dfrac{I}{I_0} = 10 \log \dfrac{8.3 \times 10^2}{10^{-12}}$

$= 10 \log(8.3 \times 10^{14}) \approx 149.19 \approx 150$ decibels

56. $D_2 - D_1 = 10 \log \dfrac{10{,}000 I_1}{I_0} - 10 \log \dfrac{I_1}{I_0}$

$= 10[\log 10{,}000 + \log I_1 - \log I_0 - \log I_1 + \log I_0]$

$= 10[\log 10{,}000]$

$= 10[4]$

$= 40$ decibels

58. $M = \dfrac{2}{3} \log \dfrac{E}{E_0} = \dfrac{2}{3} \log \dfrac{7.08 \times 10^{16}}{10^{4.4}} \approx 8.3$

60.

$M_1 = 5.6 = \dfrac{2}{3} \log \dfrac{E_1}{10^{4.4}}$ $M_2 = 8.6 = \dfrac{2}{3} \log \dfrac{E_2}{10^{4.4}}$

$8.4 = \log E_1 - \log 10^{4.4}$ $12.9 = \log E_2 - \log 10^{4.4}$

$8.4 = \log E_1 - 4.4$ $12.9 = \log E_2 - 4.4$

$12.8 = \log E_1$ $17.3 = \log E_2$

$E_1 = 10^{12.8}$ $E_2 = 10^{17.3}$

$\dfrac{E_2}{E_1} = \dfrac{10^{17.3}}{10^{12.8}} = 10^{4.5} \approx 31622.777$

$\approx 32{,}000$ times as powerful

62. $v = c \ln \dfrac{w_t}{w_b} = 5.2 \ln 6.2 \approx 9.49 \dfrac{\text{km}}{\text{sec}}$

64. (A) Milk: $pH = -\log [H^+] = -\log (2.83 \times 10^{-7}) \approx 6.5$ acidic

(B) Garden mulch: $pH = -\log [H^+] = -\log (3.78 \times 10^{-6}) \approx 5.4$ acidic

66. $pH = -\log[H^+]$

$5.7 = -\log[H^+]$

$-5.7 = \log[H^+]$

$H^+ = 10^{-5.7}$

$\approx 2 \times 10^{-6}$ moles per liter

Exercise 4-7

2. $10^x = 14.3$

$x = \log 14.3$

$x \approx 1.16$

4. $10^{5x-2} = 348$

$5x - 2 = \log 348$

$x = \dfrac{2 + \log 348}{5} \approx 0.908$

6. $e^{-x} = 0.0142$

$-x = \ln 0.0142$

$x = -\ln 0.0142$

$x \approx 4.25$

8. $e^{3x+5} = 23.8$

$3x + 5 = \ln 23.8$

$x = \dfrac{\ln 23.8 - 5}{3}$

$x \approx -0.610$

10. $3^x = 4$

$\ln 3^x = \ln 4$

$x \ln 3 = \ln 4$

$x = \dfrac{\ln 4}{\ln 3}$

$x \approx 1.26$

12. $3^{-x} = 0.074$

$\ln 3^{-x} = \ln 0.074$

$-x \ln 3 = \ln 0.074$

$x = \dfrac{-\ln 0.074}{\ln 3}$

$x \approx 2.37$

14. $\log x - \log 8 = 1$

$\log \dfrac{x}{8} = 1$

$\dfrac{x}{8} = 10^1$

$x = 80$

16. $\log(x - 9) + \log 100x = 3$

$\log[(x - 9)(100x)] = 3$

$(x - 9)(100x) = 10^3$

$100x^2 - 900x - 1000 = 0$

$x^2 - 9x - 10 = 0$

$(x - 10)(x + 1) = 0$

$x = 10, \ x = -1 \ \text{(reject)}$

18. $\log(2x + 1) = 1 + \log(x - 2)$

$\log(2x + 1) - \log(x - 2) = 1$

$\log \dfrac{2x + 1}{x - 2} = 1$

$\dfrac{2x + 1}{x - 2} = 10^1$

$2x + 1 = 10x - 20$

$-8x = -21$

$x = \dfrac{21}{8}$

20. $3 = 1.06^x$

$\ln 3 = \ln 1.06^x$

$\ln 3 = x \ln 1.06$

$x = \dfrac{\ln 3}{\ln 1.06}$

$x \approx 18.9$

Graph $y_1 = 3$, $y_2 = 1.06^x$.

They intersect at $x \approx 18.9$.

22. $e^{0.32x} = 632$

$\ln e^{0.32x} = \ln 632$

$0.32x = \ln 632$

$x = \dfrac{\ln 632}{0.32}$

$x \approx 20.2$

Graph $y_1 = e^{0.32x}$, $y_2 = 632$.

They intersect at $x \approx 20.2$.

24. $438 = 200e^{0.25x}$

$2.19 = e^{0.25x}$

$\ln 2.19 = \ln e^{0.25x}$

$\ln 2.19 = 0.25x$

$x = \dfrac{\ln 2.19}{0.25}$

$x \approx 3.14$

Graph $y_1 = 438$, $y_2 = 200e^{0.25x}$.

They intersect at $x \approx 3.14$.

26. $e^{x^2} = 125$

$\ln e^{x^2} = \ln 125$

$x^2 = \ln 125$

$x = \pm\sqrt{\ln 125}$

$x \approx \pm 2.20$

Graph $y_1 = e^{x^2}$, $y_2 = 125$.

They intersect at $x \approx \pm 2.20$.

28. $\log(6x + 5) - \log 3 = \log 2 - \log x$

$\log \dfrac{6x + 5}{3} = \log \dfrac{2}{x}$

$\dfrac{6x + 5}{3} = \dfrac{2}{x}$

$6x^2 + 5x = 6$

$6x^2 + 5x - 6 = 0$

$(3x - 2)(2x + 3) = 0$

$x = \dfrac{2}{3}, \ x = -\dfrac{3}{2} \ \text{(reject)}$

30. $\ln(x + 1) = \ln(3x + 1) - \ln x$

$\ln(x + 1) = \ln \dfrac{3x + 1}{x}$

$x + 1 = \dfrac{3x + 1}{x}$

$x^2 + x = 3x + 1$

$x^2 - 2x - 1 = 0$

$x = \dfrac{2 \pm \sqrt{8}}{2} = \dfrac{2 \pm 2\sqrt{2}}{2}$

$x = 1 \pm \sqrt{2}$

$1 - \sqrt{2}$ must be rejected

$x = 1 + \sqrt{2}$

32.
$$1 - \log(x - 2) = \log(3x + 1)$$
$$1 = \log(3x + 1) + \log(x - 2)$$
$$1 = \log[(3x + 1)(x - 2)]$$
$$(3x + 1)(x - 2) = 10^1$$
$$3x^2 - 5x - 2 = 10$$
$$3x^2 - 5x - 12 = 0$$
$$(x - 3)(3x + 4) = 0$$
$$x = 3, \quad x = -\frac{4}{3} \text{ (reject)}$$

34.
$$(\log x)^3 = \log x^4$$
$$(\log x)^3 = 4 \log x$$
$$(\log x)^3 - 4 \log x = 0$$
$$\log x[(\log x)^2 - 4] = 0$$
$$\log x = 0, \quad (\log x)^2 - 4 = 0$$
$$x = 1 \qquad (\log x)^2 = 4$$
$$\log x = \pm 2$$
$$x = 100, \frac{1}{100}$$

36.
$$\log(\log x) = 1$$
$$\log x = 10$$
$$x = 10^{10}$$

38.
$$3^{\log x} = 3x$$
$$\log 3^{\log x} = \log(3x)$$
$$\log x \log 3 = \log 3 + \log x$$
$$\log x \log 3 - \log x = \log 3$$
$$\log x(\log 3 - 1) = \log 3$$
$$\log x = \frac{\log 3}{\log 3 - 1}$$
$$x = 10^{(\log 3)/(\log 3 - 1)}$$

40. (A)
$$\ln(\ln x) + \ln x = 2$$
$$\ln[(\ln x)(x)] = 2$$
$$x \ln x = e^2$$
$$\ln x = \frac{e^2}{x}$$
$$x = e^{e^2/x}$$

It is difficult to isolate the x's.

(B) 1 solution:

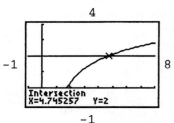

42. (A) $e^{x/4} = 5 \log x + 4 \ln x$
logs of different bases are involved.

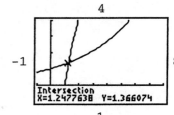

$x \approx 1.2848, \; 10.738$

44. $\log_4 23 = \dfrac{\ln 23}{\ln 4}$
≈ 2.2618

46. $\log_2 0.005439 = \dfrac{\ln 0.005439}{\ln 2}$
≈ -7.5224

48. $\log_{12} 435.62 = \dfrac{\ln 435.62}{\ln 12}$
≈ 2.4455

50. $A = P\left(1 + \dfrac{r}{n}\right)^{nt}$ for t

$$\dfrac{A}{P} = \left(1 + \dfrac{r}{n}\right)^{nt}$$

$$\ln\dfrac{A}{P} = \ln\left(1 + \dfrac{r}{n}\right)^{nt}$$

$$\ln\dfrac{A}{P} = nt\,\ln\left(1 + \dfrac{r}{n}\right)$$

$$t = \dfrac{\ln\frac{A}{P}}{n\,\ln(1 + \frac{r}{n})}$$

52. $t = \dfrac{-1}{k}(\ln A - \ln A_0)$ for A

$$-kt = \ln A - \ln A_0$$

$$-kt = \ln\dfrac{A}{A_0}$$

$$e^{-kt} = \dfrac{A}{A_0}$$

$$A = A_0 e^{-kt}$$

54. $L = 8.8 + 5.1\log D$ for D

$$\log D = \dfrac{L - 8.8}{5.1}$$

$$D = 10^{(L-8.8)/5.1}$$

56. $S = R\left[\dfrac{(1 + i)^n - 1}{i}\right]$ for n

$$\dfrac{Si}{R} + 1 = (1 + i)^n$$

$$\ln\left(\dfrac{Si}{R} + 1\right) = n\,\ln(1 + i)$$

$$n = \dfrac{\ln(\frac{Si}{R} + 1)}{\ln(1 + i)}$$

58. $y = \dfrac{e^x - e^{-x}}{2}$

$$2y = e^x - \dfrac{1}{e^x}$$

$$2ye^x = e^{2x} - 1$$

$e^{2x} - 2ye^x - 1 = 0$ which is quadratic in e^x with solutions

$\quad e^x = y \pm \sqrt{y^2 + 1}$, reject $y - \sqrt{y^2 + 1}$ since $e^x > 0$

$$e^x = y + \sqrt{y^2 + 1}$$

$$x = \ln[y + \sqrt{y^2 + 1}]$$

60. $y = \dfrac{e^x + e^{-x}}{e^x - e^{-x}} \cdot \dfrac{e^x}{e^x} = \dfrac{e^{2x} + 1}{e^{2x} - 1}$

$$y(e^{2x} - 1) = e^{2x} + 1$$

$$ye^{2x} - y = e^{2x} + 1$$

$$ye^{2x} - e^{2x} = y + 1$$

$$e^{2x}(y - 1) = y + 1$$

$$e^{2x} = \dfrac{y + 1}{y - 1}$$

$$2x = \ln\dfrac{y + 1}{y - 1}$$

$$x = \dfrac{1}{2}\ln\dfrac{y + 1}{y - 1}$$

62. $y = \log_3(4 + x) - 5$

$$y = \dfrac{\ln(4 + x)}{\ln 3} - 5$$

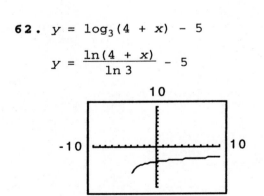

64. $y = \log_3 x + \log_2 x$

$y = \dfrac{\ln x}{\ln 3} + \dfrac{\ln x}{\ln 2}$

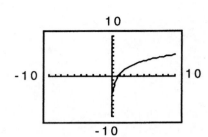

66. $3^{-x} - 3x = 0$
Graph $y = 3^{-x} - 3x$. The x-intercept (zero) is at $x = 0.25$ to 2 decimal places.

68. $x2^x - 1 = 0$
Graph $y = x2^x - 1$. The x-intercept (zero) is at $x = 0.64$ to 2 decimal places.

70. $xe^{2x} - 1 = 0$
Graph $y = xe^{2x} - 1$. The x-intercept (zero) is at $x = 0.43$ to 2 decimal places.

72. $e^{-x} - 2x = 0$
Graph $y = e^{-x} - 2x$. The x-intercept (zero) is at $x = 0.35$ to 2 decimal places.

74. $\ln x + x^2 = 0$
Graph $y = \ln x + x^2$. The x-intercept (zero) is at $x = 0.65$ to 2 decimal places.

76. $\ln x + x = 0$
Graph $y = \ln x + x$. The x-intercept (zero) is at $x = 0.57$ to 2 decimal places.

78.
$$A = P\left[1 + \frac{r}{m}\right]^n$$
$$4P = P\left[1 + \frac{0.2}{1}\right]^n$$
$$4 = [1.2]^n$$
$$\ln 4 = \ln 1.2^n$$
$$n = \frac{\ln 4}{\ln 1.2}$$
$$n \approx 7.6$$
8 yrs. to nearest year

80.
$$A = Pe^{rt}$$
$$8000 = 5000e^{0.09t}$$
$$1.6 = e^{0.09t}$$
$$\ln 1.6 = 0.09t$$
$$t = \frac{\ln 1.6}{0.09} \approx 5.22 \text{ years}$$

82. (A) $L = 8.8 + 5.1 \log D$
$L = 8.8 + 5.1 \log 6$
$L \approx 12.8$

(B) $20.6 = 8.8 + 5.1 \log D$
$11.8 = 5.1 \log D$
$\dfrac{11.8}{5.1} = \log D$
$D = 10^{11.8/5.1} \approx 205.93$
$D \approx 206$ in.

84.
$$P = P_0 e^{rt}$$
$$1.7 \times 10^{14} = 4 \times 10^9 e^{0.02t}$$
$$e^{0.02t} = 42,500$$
$$0.02t = \ln 42,500$$
$$t = \frac{\ln 42,500}{0.02}$$
$$t = 533 \text{ years to nearest year}$$

86.
$$A = A_0 e^{-0.000124t}$$
$$\frac{A_0}{2} = A_0 e^{-0.000124t}$$
$$e^{-0.000124t} = 0.5$$
$$-0.000124t = \ln 0.5$$
$$t = \frac{\ln 0.5}{-0.000124}$$
$$t = 5590 \text{ years to 3 significant digits}$$

88.
$$N = 2(1 - e^{-0.037t})$$
$$2(0.8) = 2(1 - e^{-0.037t})$$
$$1 - e^{-0.037t} = 0.8$$
$$e^{-0.037t} = 0.2$$
$$-0.037t = \ln 0.2$$
$$t = \frac{\ln 0.2}{-0.037}$$
$$t = 43 \text{ days to nearest day}$$

90.
$$I = I_0 e^{-kd}$$
$$\frac{I_0}{2} = I_0 e^{-k(14.3)}$$
$$e^{-14.3k} = 0.5$$
$$-14.3k = \ln 0.5$$
$$k = \frac{\ln 0.5}{-14.3}$$
$$k \approx 0.0485$$

Photic zone $\approx 1\%$ of I_0:
$$I = I_0 e^{-0.0485d}$$
$$0.01 I_0 = I_0 e^{-0.0485d}$$
$$\ln 0.01 = -0.0485d$$
$$d = \frac{\ln 0.01}{-0.0485}$$
$$d \approx 95.0 \text{ feet}$$

92. (A)
```
LnReg
 y=a+blnx
 a=-33059.95492
 b=9037.919003
 r²=.9524161893
 r=.9759181263

■
```

Graph $y = a + b \ln x$; find the value of y for $x = 96$ and $x = 110$.

1996: $x = 96$; yield ≈ 8192 million bushels

2010: $x = 110$; yield ≈ 9423 million bushels

(B) 1996: $y = 7,949$ million bushels is less than the projected amount. This figure will change the equation (and graph) and will lower the 2010 estimate.

CHAPTER 5

Exercise 5-1

2. $W(0) = (1, 0)$

4. $W(3\pi) = W(\pi) = (-1, 0)$

6. $W(-5\pi) = W(\pi) = (-1, 0)$

8. $W\left(\frac{\pi}{2}\right) = (0, 1)$

10. $W\left(-\frac{3\pi}{2}\right) = W\left(\frac{\pi}{2}\right) = (0, 1)$

12. $W\left(-\frac{15\pi}{2}\right) = W\left(\frac{\pi}{2}\right) = (0, 1)$

14. $W\left(\frac{\pi}{3}\right) = \left(\frac{1}{2}, \frac{\sqrt{3}}{2}\right)$

16. $W\left(-\frac{\pi}{6}\right) = \left(\frac{\sqrt{3}}{2}, -\frac{1}{2}\right)$

18. $W\left(-\frac{\pi}{4}\right) = \left(\frac{1}{\sqrt{2}}, \frac{-1}{\sqrt{2}}\right) = \left(\frac{\sqrt{2}}{2}, \frac{-\sqrt{2}}{2}\right)$

20. $W\left(\frac{11\pi}{6}\right) = \left(\frac{\sqrt{3}}{2}, -\frac{1}{2}\right)$

22. $W\left(-\frac{7\pi}{6}\right) = \left(-\frac{\sqrt{3}}{2}, \frac{1}{2}\right)$

24. $W\left(-\frac{10\pi}{3}\right) = W\left(\frac{2\pi}{3}\right) = \left(-\frac{1}{2}, \frac{\sqrt{3}}{2}\right)$

26. $W(1)$ is in quadrant I; a, +; b, +   **28.** $W(4)$ is in quadrant III; a, -; b, -

30. $W(7)$ is in quadrant I; a, +; b, +   **32.** $W(-4.5)$ is in quadrant II; a, -; b, +

34. $W(-1.8)$ is in quadrant III; a, -; b, -

36. $W(x) = (-1, 0) \Rightarrow x = \pi$, $x = \pi + 2k\pi$, k any integer

38. $W(x) = \left(\frac{1}{\sqrt{2}}, -\frac{1}{\sqrt{2}}\right) \Rightarrow x = \frac{7\pi}{4}$, $x = \frac{7\pi}{4} + 2k\pi$, k any integer

40. $W(x)$ is the coordinates of a point on a unit circle that is $|x|$ units from $(1, 0)$, in a counterclockwise direction if x is positive and in a clockwise direction if x is negative. $W(x - 6\pi)$ has the same coordinates as $W(x)$, since we return to the same point every time we go around the unit circle any integer multiple of 2π units (the circumference of the circle) in either direction.

42. If $W(x) = (a, b)$, $W(x + \pi) = (a, b)$ is False.

44. If $W(x) = (a, b)$, $W(-x) = (a, -b)$ is True.

46. If $W(x) = (a, b)$, $W(x + 2\pi) = (-a, -b)$ is False.

48. $W(x) = \left(\frac{\sqrt{3}}{2}, \frac{1}{2}\right) \Rightarrow x = -\frac{11\pi}{6}, \frac{\pi}{6}$

50. $W(x) = \left(\frac{1}{2}, -\frac{\sqrt{3}}{2}\right) \Rightarrow x = -\frac{\pi}{3}, \frac{5\pi}{3}$

52. $W(x) = \left(-\frac{1}{\sqrt{2}}, \frac{1}{\sqrt{2}}\right) \Rightarrow x = -\frac{5\pi}{4}, \frac{3\pi}{4}$

54. $W(x) = W\left(\frac{2\pi}{3}\right) \Rightarrow x = \frac{2\pi}{3} + 2k\pi$, k an integer

Exercise 5-2

2. $W(x) = (a, b)$

   (A) $b = \sin x$ (B) $\frac{1}{a} = \sec x$ (C) $\frac{b}{a} = \tan x$

   (D) $\frac{1}{b} = \csc x$ (E) $a = \cos x$ (F) $\frac{a}{b} = \cot x$

4. $\sin 0 = 0$

6. $\cos\left(\frac{\pi}{6}\right) = \frac{\sqrt{3}}{2}$

8. $\cos\left(\frac{\pi}{2}\right) = 0$

10. $\cos\left(\frac{\pi}{3}\right) = \frac{1}{2}$

12. $\cot 0$ is not defined

14. $\cot\left(\frac{\pi}{4}\right) = 1$

16. $\csc\left(\frac{\pi}{3}\right) = \frac{2}{\sqrt{3}}$

18. $\tan 0 = 0$

20. $\cot\left(\frac{\pi}{6}\right) = \sqrt{3}$

22. $\tan x > 0$ for $W(x)$ in quadrants I or III

24. sec x > 0 for $W(x)$ in quadrants I or IV

26. csc x < 0 for $W(x)$ in quadrants III or IV

28. sin 3.104 ≈ 0.03758   **30.** sec(-1.555) ≈ 63.31

32. cot 0.7854 ≈ 1.000   **34.** $\sin\left(\dfrac{3\pi}{2}\right)$ = -1   **36.** tan π = 0

38. $\cos\left(\dfrac{2\pi}{3}\right)$ = -$\dfrac{1}{2}$ **40.** $\tan\left(-\dfrac{3\pi}{2}\right)$ is not defined   **42.** $\cot\left(-\dfrac{\pi}{3}\right)$ = -$\dfrac{1}{\sqrt{3}}$

44. $\sin\left(-\dfrac{\pi}{4}\right)$ = -$\dfrac{1}{\sqrt{2}}$ **46.** $\csc\left(\dfrac{4\pi}{3}\right)$ = -$\dfrac{2}{\sqrt{3}}$ **48.** $\tan\left(\dfrac{5\pi}{4}\right)$ = 1

50. (A) sin 0.8 = 0.7   (B) cos 0.8 = 0.7   (C) cot 0.8 = 1

52. (A) csc 2.5 = 2   (B) cot 5.6 = -1   (C) tan 4.3 = 2

54. cos x > 0: QI, QIV
    tan x < 0: QII, QIV
        both: QIV

56. sin x > 0 and csc x < 0 is never true because sin x = $\dfrac{1}{\text{csc } x}$ ⇒ they have same sign.

58. sin x is defined for all x, 0 ≤ x ≤ 2π

60. cot x is not defined for x = 0, π, 2π

62. csc x is not defined for x = 0, π, 2π

64. (A) cos x varies from 1 to 0 as x varies over $\left[0, \dfrac{\pi}{2}\right]$

   (B) cos x varies from 0 to -1 as x varies over $\left[\dfrac{\pi}{2}, \pi\right]$

   (C) cos x varies from -1 to 0 as x varies over $\left[\pi, \dfrac{3\pi}{2}\right]$

   (D) cos x varies from 0 to 1 as x varies over $\left[\dfrac{3\pi}{2}, 2\pi\right]$

66. cos(tan 5.183) ≈ -0.3847   **68.** sec[cot(-3.566)] ≈ -1.669

70. cos(-x) = cos x = -$\dfrac{1}{2}$ **72.** sec(-x) = sec x = 1

74. csc(-x) = -csc x = -(-1) = 1

76. sin x = $\dfrac{\sqrt{3}}{2}$, cot x < 0 ⇒ $W(x)$ is in quadrant II, x = $\dfrac{2\pi}{3}$

   cos x = -$\dfrac{1}{2}$, tan x = -$\sqrt{3}$, csc x = $\dfrac{2}{\sqrt{3}}$, sec x = -2, cot x = -$\dfrac{1}{\sqrt{3}}$

78. $\sec x = 2$, $\sin x < 0 \Rightarrow W(x)$ is in quadrant IV, $x = \dfrac{5\pi}{3}$

$\sin x = -\dfrac{\sqrt{3}}{2}$, $\cos x = \dfrac{1}{2}$, $\tan x = -\sqrt{3}$, $\cot x = -\dfrac{1}{\sqrt{3}}$, $\csc x = -\dfrac{2}{\sqrt{3}}$

80. $\cot x = -1$, $\sin x > 0 \Rightarrow W(x)$ is in quadrant II, $x = \dfrac{3\pi}{4}$

$\sin x = \dfrac{1}{\sqrt{2}}$, $\cos x = -\dfrac{1}{\sqrt{2}}$, $\tan x = -1$, $\csc x = \sqrt{2}$, $\sec x = -\sqrt{2}$

82. $\sin x = -\dfrac{\sqrt{3}}{2}$

$x = \dfrac{4\pi}{3}$

84. $\tan x = -1$

$x = \dfrac{3\pi}{4}$

86. $\csc x = -\sqrt{2}$

$x = \dfrac{5\pi}{4}$

88.

STATEMENT	REASON
$\tan^2 x + 1 = \left(\dfrac{\sin x}{\cos x}\right)^2 + 1$	(A) quotient identity (4)
$= \dfrac{\sin^2 x}{\cos^2 x} + 1$	algebra
$= \dfrac{\sin^2 x + \cos^2 x}{\cos^2 x}$	algebra
$= \dfrac{1}{\cos^2 x}$	(B) Pythagorean identity (9)
$= \left(\dfrac{1}{\cos x}\right)^2$	algebra
$= \sec^2 x$	(C) reciprocal identity (2)

90. $A = \dfrac{1}{2}nr^2 \sin \dfrac{2\pi}{n}$

$= \dfrac{1}{2}(4)(3)^2 \sin \dfrac{2\pi}{4}$

$\approx 18 \text{ in}^2$

92. $A = \dfrac{1}{2}nr^2 \sin \dfrac{2\pi}{n}$

$= \dfrac{1}{2}(8)(10)^2 \sin \dfrac{2\pi}{8}$

$= 400 \cdot \dfrac{1}{\sqrt{2}} = \dfrac{400\sqrt{2}}{\sqrt{2} \cdot \sqrt{2}} = 200\sqrt{2}$

$\approx 282.8 \text{ cm}^2$

94. $a_1 = 1$

$a_2 = 1 + \cos 1 \approx 1.540302$

$a_3 = 1.540302 + \cos 1.540302 \approx 1.570792$

$a_4 = 1.570792 + \cos 1.570792 \approx 1.570796$

$a_5 = 1.570796 + \cos 1.570796 \approx 1.570796$

$\dfrac{\pi}{2} \approx 1.570796$

Exercise 5-3

2. $\dfrac{1}{5}$ rotation $= \dfrac{1}{5}(360°)$

$= 72°$

4. $\dfrac{3}{8}$ rotation $= \dfrac{3}{8}(360°)$

$= 135°$

6. $\frac{7}{6}$ rotations $= \frac{7}{6}(360°)$
$= 420°$

8. $\theta = \frac{s}{r} = \frac{16}{8}$
$\theta = 2$

10. $\theta = \frac{s}{r} = \frac{27}{18}$
$\theta = 1.5$

12. $\frac{1}{6}$ rotation $= \frac{1}{6}(2\pi)$
$= \frac{\pi}{3}$

14. $\frac{5}{12}$ rotation $= \frac{5}{12}(2\pi)$
$= \frac{5\pi}{6}$

16. $\frac{11}{8}$ rotations $= \frac{11}{8}(2\pi)$
$= \frac{11\pi}{4}$

18. $60°\left(\frac{\pi}{180°}\right) = \frac{\pi}{3}$

$120°\left(\frac{\pi}{180°}\right) = \frac{2\pi}{3}$

$180°\left(\frac{\pi}{180°}\right) = \pi$

$240°\left(\frac{\pi}{180°}\right) = \frac{4\pi}{3}$

$300°\left(\frac{\pi}{180°}\right) = \frac{5\pi}{3}$

$360°\left(\frac{\pi}{180°}\right) = 2\pi$

20. $-90°\left(\frac{\pi}{180°}\right) = -\frac{\pi}{2}$

$-180°\left(\frac{\pi}{180°}\right) = -\pi$

$-270°\left(\frac{\pi}{180°}\right) = -\frac{3\pi}{2}$

$-360°\left(\frac{\pi}{180°}\right) = -2\pi$

22. $\frac{\pi}{6} \cdot \frac{180°}{\pi} = 30°$

$\frac{\pi}{3} \cdot \frac{180°}{\pi} = 60°$

$\frac{\pi}{2} \cdot \frac{180°}{\pi} = 90°$

$\frac{2\pi}{3} \cdot \frac{180°}{\pi} = 120°$

$\frac{5\pi}{6} \cdot \frac{180°}{\pi} = 150°$

$\pi \cdot \frac{180°}{\pi} = 180°$

24. $-\frac{\pi}{4} \cdot \frac{180°}{\pi} = -45°$

$-\frac{\pi}{2} \cdot \frac{180°}{\pi} = -90°$

$-\frac{3\pi}{4} \cdot \frac{180°}{\pi} = -135°$

$-\pi \cdot \frac{180°}{\pi} = -180°$

26. $14°18'37" = 14° + \frac{18}{60} + \frac{37}{3600}$
$\approx 14.310°$

28. $184°31'7" = 184 + \frac{31}{60} + \frac{7}{3600}$
$\approx 184.519°$

30.

32.
```
156.808▶DMS
        156°48'28.8"
```
$\approx 156°48'29"$

34. $25° \cdot \frac{\pi}{180°} \approx 0.436$

36. $203.097° \cdot \frac{\pi}{180°} \approx 3.545$

38. $56°11'52" = \left(56 + \frac{11}{60} + \frac{52}{3600}\right)\left(\frac{\pi}{180}\right) \approx 0.981$

40. $0.08 \cdot \frac{180°}{\pi} \approx 4.58°$

42. $3.07 \cdot \frac{180°}{\pi} \approx 175.90°$

44. $-1.72 \cdot \frac{180°}{\pi} \approx -98.55°$

46. 135° is in Quadrant II

48. -60° is in Quadrant IV

50. 3 is in Quadrant II

52. 360° is a quadrantal angle

54. -6 is in Quadrant I

56. $\frac{2\pi}{3}$ is in Quadrant II

58. $-\frac{3\pi}{4}$ is in Quadrant III

60. $-\frac{3\pi}{2}$ is a quadrantal angle

62. -565° is in Quadrant II

64. $\frac{23\pi}{3}$ is in Quadrant IV

66. 1°: The terminal side of the angle has been rotated $\frac{1}{360}$th of a revolution.

68. 330° is not coterminal with 30°

70. $-\frac{11\pi}{6}$ is coterminal with 30°

72. 750° is coterminal with 30°

74. $-\frac{7\pi}{4}$ is not coterminal with $\frac{3\pi}{4}$

76. -225° is coterminal with $\frac{3\pi}{4}$

78. $-\frac{5\pi}{4}$ is coterminal with $\frac{3\pi}{4}$

80. 7°12" = 7.2°

$$\frac{500}{C} = \frac{7.2°}{360°}$$

$$C = \frac{(500)(360°)}{7.2°}$$

$$C = 25,000 \text{ miles}$$

82. Since the circumference of the earth is given by $C = 2\pi r$, if C is known, then r can be found by using $r = C/2\pi$. Once the radius is known, the surface area and volume can be found using the formulas $S = 4\pi r^2$ and $V = 4\pi r^3/3$, respectively.

84. At 1:30 the minute hand points straight down and the hour hand has made $\frac{1}{8}\left(\frac{\pi}{4}\right)$ revolution $\Rightarrow$ angle between hands $= \pi - \frac{\pi}{4} = \frac{3\pi}{4}$

86. 6π in. comes off the pulley each revolution; 4 ft = 48 inches.

$$s = r\theta$$
$$48 = 3\theta$$
$$\theta = \frac{48}{3} = 16 \text{ rad}$$

88. 24 hours = 1 revolution

9 hours $= \frac{9}{24} = \frac{3}{8}$ revolution

$\frac{3}{8}(2\pi) = \frac{3\pi}{4}$ rad ≈ 2.36 rad

90. $s = r\theta$ $\theta = \frac{s}{r}$

     $= 20(15)$ $\theta = \frac{300}{30} = 10$ radians

     $= 300$ cm   rear wheel

   front wheel

92. $s = r\theta = 381,000(0.0092)$

$s = 3505.2$
$s \approx 3500$ km

94. $s = r\theta = 500(8)\left(\frac{\pi}{180}\right)$

$s = 69.81317$
$s \approx 70$ ft

Exercise 5-4

2. $(-3, 4)$; $r = \sqrt{(-3)^2 + 4^2} = 5$; QII

$\sin\theta = \frac{4}{5}$, $\cos\theta = -\frac{3}{5}$, $\tan\theta = -\frac{4}{3}$

$\csc\theta = \frac{5}{4}$, $\sec\theta = -\frac{5}{3}$, $\cot\theta = -\frac{3}{4}$

4. $(\sqrt{3}, 1)$; $r = \sqrt{(\sqrt{3})^2 + 1^2} = 2$; QI

$\sin\theta = \frac{1}{2}$, $\cos\theta = \frac{\sqrt{3}}{2}$, $\tan\theta = \frac{1}{\sqrt{3}}$

$\csc\theta = 2$, $\sec\theta = \frac{2}{\sqrt{3}}$, $\cot\theta = \sqrt{3}$

6. $\tan 89° \approx 57.29$

8. $\csc 13 \approx 2.380$

10. $\tan 4.327 \approx 2.465$

12. $\sec(-247.39°) = (\cos(-247.39°))^{-1} \approx -2.601$

14. $\cos 235°12'47" \approx -0.5705$

16. $\cos 0° = 1$

18. $\cos 30° = \dfrac{\sqrt{3}}{2}$

20. $\csc 60° = \dfrac{2}{\sqrt{3}}$

22. $\cot 45° = 1$

24. $\cot 90° = 0$

26. $\sec 0° = 1$

28. $\alpha = 45°$

30. $\alpha = \dfrac{\pi}{4}$

32. $\alpha = \dfrac{\pi}{4}$

34. $\sin 150° = \sin 30° = \dfrac{1}{2}$

36. $\sin\left(\dfrac{\pi}{2}\right) = 1$

38. $\sec(-30°) = \sec 30° = \dfrac{2}{\sqrt{3}}$

40. $\cot\left(-\dfrac{\pi}{4}\right) = -\cot\dfrac{\pi}{4} = -1$

42. $\cos\left(\dfrac{2\pi}{3}\right) = -\cos\dfrac{\pi}{3} = -\dfrac{1}{2}$

44. $\cot 225° = \cot 45° = 1$

46. $\sec\left(\dfrac{11\pi}{6}\right) = \sec\dfrac{\pi}{6} = \dfrac{2}{\sqrt{3}}$

48. $\tan 690° = \tan 330° = -\tan 30° = -\dfrac{1}{\sqrt{3}}$

50. For $0° \le \theta < 360°$, $\sec\theta$ is not defined for 90° and 270°, because $\cos 90° = 0$ and $\cos 270° = 0$.

52. For $0° \le \theta < 360°$, $\cot\theta$ is not defined for 0° and 180°, because $\sin 0° = 0$ and $\sin 180° = 0$.

54. $\sin\theta$ is defined for all θ.

56. $\sin\theta = \dfrac{-\sqrt{3}}{2}$
$\theta = 240° = \dfrac{4\pi}{3}$ rad

58. $\tan\theta = -\sqrt{3}$
$\theta = 120° = \dfrac{2\pi}{3}$ rad

60. $\sec\theta = -\sqrt{2}$
$\theta = 135° = \dfrac{3\pi}{4}$ rad

62. $\tan\theta = -\dfrac{4}{3}$ (QII, QIV) and $\sin\theta < 0$ (QIII, QIV) $\Rightarrow$ QIV

$a = 3$, $b = -4$: $r^2 = a^2 + b^2$
$r^2 = 3^2 + (-4)^2$
$r = 5$

$\tan\theta = \dfrac{b}{a} = -\dfrac{4}{3}$ $\sin\theta = \dfrac{b}{r} = -\dfrac{4}{5}$ $\cos\theta = \dfrac{a}{r} = \dfrac{3}{5}$

$\cot\theta = \dfrac{a}{b} = -\dfrac{3}{4}$ $\csc\theta = \dfrac{r}{b} = -\dfrac{5}{4}$ $\sec\theta = \dfrac{r}{a} = \dfrac{5}{3}$

64. $\cos\theta = -\dfrac{\sqrt{5}}{3}$ (QII, QIII) and $\tan\theta > 0$ (QI, QIII) $\Rightarrow$ QIII

$a = -\sqrt{5}$, $r = 3$: $a^2 + b^2 = r^2$
$(-\sqrt{5})^2 + b^2 = 3^2$
$b^2 = 4$
$b = -2$

$\cos\theta = \dfrac{a}{r} = -\dfrac{\sqrt{5}}{3}$ $\sin\theta = \dfrac{b}{r} = -\dfrac{2}{3}$ $\tan\theta = \dfrac{b}{a} = \dfrac{-2}{-\sqrt{5}} = \dfrac{2}{\sqrt{5}}$

$\sec\theta = \dfrac{r}{a} = -\dfrac{3}{\sqrt{5}}$ $\csc\theta = \dfrac{r}{b} = -\dfrac{3}{2}$ $\cot\theta = \dfrac{a}{b} = \dfrac{-\sqrt{5}}{-2} = \dfrac{\sqrt{5}}{2}$

66. When the terminal side of an angle lies along the horizontal axis, $y = 0$ which implies $\csc \theta = \frac{r}{b}$ and $\cot \theta = \frac{a}{b}$ are not defined.

68. $\cot \theta = -\frac{1}{\sqrt{3}}$, $0° \le \theta < 360°$

Ref $\sphericalangle$ = $60°$, QII, QIV:
$\theta = 120°, 300°$

70. $\sec \theta = -\sqrt{2}$, $0 \le \theta < 2\pi$

Ref $\sphericalangle$ = $\frac{\pi}{4}$, QII, III:
$\theta = \frac{3\pi}{4}, \frac{5\pi}{4}$

72. (A) $s = r\theta \Rightarrow 8 = 2 \cdot \theta \Rightarrow \theta = 4$ radians

(B) $\cos \theta = \frac{a}{2} \Rightarrow \cos 4 = \frac{a}{2} \Rightarrow a \approx -1.307$

$\sin \theta = \frac{b}{2} \Rightarrow \sin 4 = \frac{b}{2} \Rightarrow b \approx -1.514$

$(-1.307, -1.514)$

74. $\tan \theta = \frac{2\sqrt{3}}{2} = \sqrt{3} \Rightarrow \theta = \frac{\pi}{3}$

$r = \sqrt{2^2 + (2\sqrt{3})^2}$
$= \sqrt{16}$
$= 4$
$s = r\theta$
$= 4\left(\frac{\pi}{3}\right)$
$= \frac{4\pi}{3}$

76. $I = k \cos \theta = \begin{cases} k \cos 20° \approx 0.93969k \\ k \cos 50° \approx 0.642787k \\ k \cos 90° = k(0) = 0 \end{cases}$

78. $y = \sin 6\pi t + \sqrt{16 - (\cos 6\pi t)^2}$, $t \ge 0$

$y(0.2) = \sin(6\pi(0.2)) + \sqrt{16 - (\cos(6\pi(0.2)))^2}$
$= 3.32955... \approx 3.33$

80. $A = \frac{n}{2} \sin \frac{360°}{n}$

(A) $n = 8$: $A = \frac{8}{2} \sin \frac{360°}{8} \approx 2.82843$

$n = 100$: $A = \frac{100}{2} \sin \frac{360°}{100} \approx 3.13953$

$n = 1,000$: $A = \frac{1000}{2} \sin \frac{360°}{1000} \approx 3.14157$

$n = 10,000$: $A = \frac{10,000}{2} \sin \frac{360°}{10,000} \approx 3.14159$

(B) $A \to \pi = 3.1415296...$ as $n \to \infty$

82. $m = \tan \theta$, $0° \le \theta \le 180°$

(A) $\theta = 5.34°$: $m_1 = \tan 5.34° \approx 0.09$
$\theta = 92.40°$: $m_2 = \tan 92.4° \approx -23.86$

(B) $\theta = 106°$: $m = \tan 106° = -3.49$
through $(6, -4)$:
$y - (-4) = -3.49(x - 6)$
$y + 4 = -3.49x + 20.94$
$y = -3.49x + 16.94$

Exercise 5-5

2. $\cot \theta = \frac{a}{b}$

4. $\cos \theta = \frac{a}{c}$

6. $\sec \theta = \frac{c}{a}$

8. $\frac{b}{a} = \tan \theta$

10. $\frac{b}{c} = \sin \theta$

12. $\frac{c}{b} = \csc \theta$

14. $\sin \theta = 0.0859$
$\theta = \sin^{-1} 0.0859$
$\theta \approx 4.93°$

16. $\theta = \cos^{-1} 0.5097$
$\approx 59.36°$

18. $\tan \theta = 1.993$
$\theta = \tan^{-1} 1.993$
$\theta \approx 63.35°$

20. $\beta = 33.7°$, $b = 22.4$

$\alpha = 90° - 33.7° = 56.30°$

$$\tan \beta = \frac{b}{a}$$

$$\tan 33.7° = \frac{22.4}{a}$$

$$a = \frac{22.4}{\tan 33.7°}$$

$$a = 33.587\ldots \approx 33.6$$

$$\sin \beta = \frac{b}{c}$$

$$\sin 33.7° = \frac{22.4}{c}$$

$$c = \frac{22.4}{\sin 33.7°}$$

$$c = 40.3717\ldots \approx 40.4$$

22. $\beta = 62°30'$, $c = 42.5$

$\alpha = 90° - 62°30' = 27°30'$

$$\cos \beta = \frac{a}{c}$$

$$\cos 60°30' = \frac{a}{42.5}$$

$$a = 42.5 \cos 62°30'$$

$$a = 19.6243\ldots \approx 19.6$$

$$\sin \beta = \frac{b}{c}$$

$$\sin 62°30' = \frac{b}{42.5}$$

$$b = 42.5 \sin 62°30'$$

$$b = 37.69796\ldots \approx 37.7$$

24. $\alpha = 54°$, $c = 4.3$

$\beta = 90° - 54° = 36°$

$$\cos \beta = \frac{a}{c}$$

$$\cos 36° = \frac{a}{4.3}$$

$$a = 4.3 \cos 36°$$

$$a = 3.47877\ldots \approx 3.5$$

$$\sin \beta = \frac{b}{c}$$

$$\sin 36° = \frac{b}{4.3}$$

$$b = 4.3 \sin 36°$$

$$b = 2.52748\ldots \approx 2.5$$

26. $\alpha = 35.73°$, $b = 6.482$

$\beta = 90° - 35.73° = 54.27°$

$$\tan \alpha = \frac{a}{b}$$

$$\tan 35.73° = \frac{a}{6.482}$$

$$a = 6.482 \tan 35.73°$$

$$a = 4.6629\ldots \approx 4.663$$

$$\cos \alpha = \frac{b}{c}$$

$$\cos 35.73° = \frac{6.482}{c}$$

$$c = \frac{6.482}{\cos 35.73°}$$

$$c = 7.9849\ldots \approx 7.985$$

28. $a = 22.0$, $b = 46.2$

$$\tan \alpha = \frac{b}{a}$$

$$\tan \alpha = \frac{22.0}{46.2}$$

$$\alpha = \tan^{-1}\left(\frac{22.0}{46.2}\right)$$

$$\alpha = 25.463\ldots \approx 25.5° \ (25°30')$$

$$\beta = 90° - 25.5° = 64.5° \ (64°30')$$

$$c = \sqrt{46.2^2 + 22.0^2}$$

$$c = 51.17069\ldots \approx 51.2$$

30. $b = 50.0$, $c = 165$

$$\sin \beta = \frac{b}{c}$$

$$\sin \beta = \frac{50.0}{165}$$

$$\beta = \sin^{-1}\frac{50.0}{165}$$

$$\beta - 17.6397\ldots \approx 17.6° \ (17°40')$$

$$\alpha = 90° - 17.6° = 72.4° \ (72°20')$$

$$a = \sqrt{165^2 - 50^2}$$

$$= 157.24185\ldots \approx 157$$

32. (A) $\sin \theta = \frac{AD}{1} = AD$ (B) $\tan \theta = \frac{DC}{1} = DC$ (C) $\csc \theta = \csc \angle OED = \frac{OE}{1} = OE$

34. (A) As $\theta \rightarrow 90°$, $\sin \theta \rightarrow 1$ (B) As $\theta \rightarrow 90°$, $\tan \theta \rightarrow \infty$ (increases without bound)
(C) As $\theta \rightarrow 90°$, $\csc \theta \rightarrow 1$

36. (A) As $\theta \rightarrow 0°$, $\cos \theta \rightarrow 1$ (B) As $\theta \rightarrow 0°$, $\cot \theta \rightarrow \infty$ (increases without bound)
(C) As $\theta \rightarrow 0°$, $\sec \theta \rightarrow 1$

38.

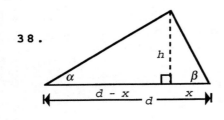

$$\cot \alpha = \frac{d - x}{h} \qquad\qquad \cot \beta = \frac{x}{h}$$
$$h \cot \alpha = d - x \qquad\qquad\quad x = h \cot \beta$$
$$x = d - h \cot \alpha$$
$$d - h \cot \alpha = h \cot \beta$$
$$h \cot \beta + h \cot \alpha = d$$
$$h(\cot \beta + \cot \alpha) = d$$
$$h = \frac{d}{\cot \beta + \cot \alpha}$$

40.

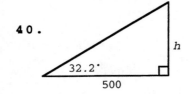

$$\tan 32.2° = \frac{h}{500}$$
$$h = 500 \tan 32.2°$$
$$h \approx 314.8668\ldots$$
$$h \approx 315 \text{ meters}$$

42.

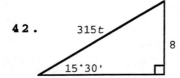

$$d = rt = 315t:$$
$$\sin 15°30' = \frac{8}{315t}$$
$$315t = \frac{8}{\sin 15°30'}$$
$$t = \frac{8}{315 \sin 15°30'}$$
$$t \approx 0.0950 \text{ hr.}$$
$$t \approx 5.7 \approx 6 \text{ min}$$

44.

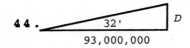

$$\tan 32' = \frac{D}{93,000,000}$$
$$D = 93,000,000 \tan 32'$$
$$D \approx 865,708.3127$$
$$D \approx 870,000 \text{ miles to 2 significant digits}$$

46. The angle formed at the center of the circle is $\frac{360°}{9} = 40°$. Bisecting this angle to form a right triangle gives 20°.

$$\sin 20° = \frac{\frac{1}{2}s}{4.06}$$
$$\frac{1}{2}s = 4.06 \sin 20°$$
$$s = 8.12 \sin 20° \approx 2.777203564 \approx 2.78 \text{ inches}$$

48. $g = \dfrac{v}{t \sin \theta}$

$g = \dfrac{9.0}{4.0 \sin 4°}$

$g \approx 32.3 \text{ ft/sec}^2$

50. $\sec \theta = \dfrac{d}{4} \qquad\qquad \tan \theta = \dfrac{x}{4}$

$d = 4 \sec \theta \qquad\qquad x = 4 \tan \theta$

(A) Cost = C = cost along shore + cost underwater

$$C = 20,000(20 - x) + 30,000d$$
$$C(\theta) = 20,000(20 - 4 \tan \theta) + 30,000(4 \sec \theta)$$
$$C(\theta) = 120,000 \sec \theta - 80,000 \tan \theta + 400,000$$

(B)

θ	$C(\theta) = 120{,}000 \sec\theta - 80{,}000\tan\theta + 400{,}000$
10°	\$507,745
20°	\$498,584
30°	\$492,376
40°	\$489,521
50°	\$491,347

 52.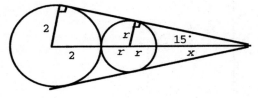

Method 1:

(1) $\sin 15° = \dfrac{r}{r+x} \Rightarrow r + x = \dfrac{r}{\sin 15°}$

(2) $\sin 15° = \dfrac{2}{2+r+r+x} = \dfrac{2}{2+r+\frac{r}{\sin 15°}}$

$r = \dfrac{\frac{2}{\sin 15°} - 2}{1 + \frac{1}{\sin 15°}} = 1.2$ inches

Method 2:

(1) $\sin 15° = \dfrac{r}{r+x}$

$r\sin 15° + x\sin 15° = r$

$x\sin 15° = r - r\sin 15°$

$x = \dfrac{r - r\sin 15°}{\sin 15°}$

(2) $\sin 15° = \dfrac{2}{2+2r+x}$

$2\sin 15° + 2r\sin 15° + x\sin 15° = 2$

$x\sin 15° = 2 - 2\sin 15° + 2r\sin 15°$

$x = \dfrac{2 - 2\sin 15° + 2r\sin 15°}{\sin 15°}$

$\dfrac{r - r\sin 15°}{\sin 15°} = \dfrac{2 - 2\sin 15° - 2r\sin 15°}{\sin 15°}$

$r - r\sin 15° = 2 - 2\sin 15° - 2r\sin 15°$

$r + r\sin 15° = 2 - 2\sin 15°$

$r(1 + \sin 15°) = 2(1 - \sin 15°)$

$r = \dfrac{2(1 - \sin 15°)}{1 + \sin 15°} \approx 1.17758 \approx 1.2$ inches

Exercise 5-6

2.

function	period
cosine	2π
tangent	π
secant	2π

4. (A) The graph of $y = \sin x$ deviates 1 unit from the x-axis.
(B) The graph of $y = \cot x$ deviates indefinitely far from the x-axis.
(C) The graph of $y = \sec x$ deviates indefinitely far from the x-axis.

6. (A) $y = \cos x$: $[-2\pi, 2\pi]$
x-intercepts: $-\dfrac{3\pi}{2}, \dfrac{-\pi}{2}, \dfrac{\pi}{2}, \dfrac{3\pi}{2}$

(B) $y = \tan x$: $[-2\pi, 2\pi]$
x-intercepts: $-2\pi, -\pi, 0, \pi, 2\pi$

(C) $y = \sec x$: $[-2\pi, 2\pi]$
x-intercepts: none

8. (A) $y = \sin x$ is defined for all x on $[-2\pi, 2\pi]$
(B) $y = \cot x$ is not defined for $x = -2\pi, -\pi, 0, \pi, 2\pi$ on $[-2\pi, 2\pi]$
(C) $y = \sec x$ is not defined for $x = -\dfrac{3\pi}{2}, -\dfrac{\pi}{2}, \dfrac{\pi}{2}, \dfrac{3\pi}{2}$ on $[-2\pi, 2\pi]$

10. vertical asymptotes: (A) $y = \sin x$: none   (B) $y = \cot x$: -2π, $-\pi$, 0, π, 2π

(C) $y = \sec x$: $-\dfrac{3\pi}{2}$, $-\dfrac{\pi}{2}$, $\dfrac{\pi}{2}$, $\dfrac{3\pi}{2}$

12. (A) $y = \sin x$

(B) $y = \cot x$

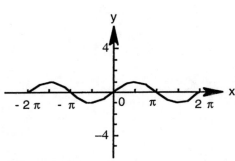

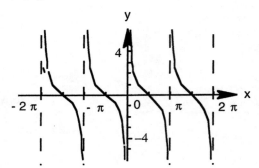

(C) $y = \sec x$

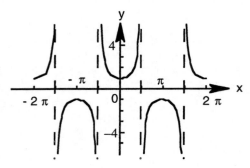

14. (A) Shifting $y = \sec x$, $\dfrac{\pi}{2}$ to the right produces $y = \csc x$.

(B) Shifting $y = \sec x$, $\dfrac{\pi}{2}$ to left and a reflection in the x-axis produces

$y = \csc x$. $\left[y = -\sec\left(x + \dfrac{\pi}{2}\right) \right]$

16. (A)

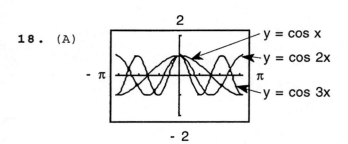

(B) The x-intercepts do not change.

(C) The graphs deviated 1, 3, and 2 units from the x-axis.

(D) The amount of deviation from the x-axis appears to be $|A|$.

18. (A)

(B) 1, 2, and 3

(C) For $y = \cos nx$, n a postive integer, n periods would appear in this viewing window.

20. (A) y = sin(x + π/2)   y = sin x   y = sin(x - π/2)

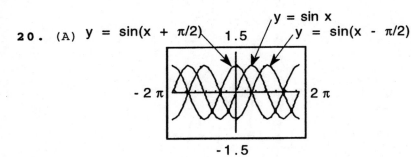

(B) The graph of $y = \sin(x + C)$ is shifted C units to the left for $C > 0$ and $|C|$ units to the right for $C < 0$.

22. In all three cases the calculator gives a division by zero error.

(A) $\csc \pi = \dfrac{1}{\sin \pi} = \dfrac{1}{0}$ (B) $\tan \dfrac{\pi}{2} = \dfrac{1}{0}$ (C) $\cot 0 = \dfrac{1}{0}$

24. $h(x) = \tan x$, $g(x) = x$

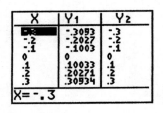
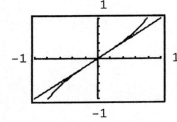

X	Y₁	Y₂
-.3	-.3093	-.3
-.2	-.2027	-.2
-.1	-.1003	-.1
0	0	0
.1	.10033	.1
.2	.20271	.2
.3	.30934	.3

X= -.3

For x close to zero the two graphs are almost identical.

Exercise 5-7

2. $y = \dfrac{1}{4} \cos x$, $-2\pi \le x \le 2\pi$

Amplitude $A = \dfrac{1}{4}$

Period $P = 2\pi$

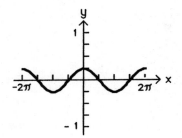

4. $y = -2 \sin x$, $-2\pi \le x \le 2\pi$

Amplitude $A = |-2| = 2$

Period $P = 2\pi$

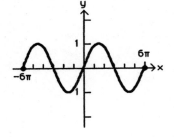

6. $y = \cos 2x$, $-\pi \le x \le \pi$

Amplitude $A = 1$

Period $P = \dfrac{2\pi}{2} = \pi$

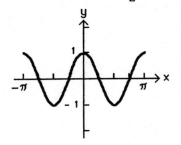

8. $y = \sin\left(\dfrac{x}{3}\right)$, $-6\pi \le x \le 6\pi$

Amplitude $A = 1$

Period $P = \dfrac{2\pi}{\frac{1}{3}} = 6\pi$

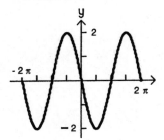

10. $y = \cos(\pi x)$, $-2 \leq x \leq 2$

Amplitude $A = 1$

Period $P = \dfrac{2\pi}{\pi} = 2$

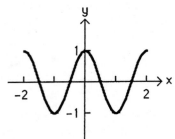

12. $y = 2 \sin 4x$, $-\pi \leq x \leq \pi$

Amplitude $A = 2$

Period $P = \dfrac{2\pi}{4} = \dfrac{\pi}{2}$

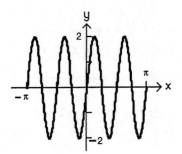

14. $y = -\dfrac{1}{3} \cos 2\pi x$, $-2 \leq x \leq 2$

Amplitude $A = \left| -\dfrac{1}{3} \right| = \dfrac{1}{3}$

Period $P = \dfrac{2\pi}{2\pi} = 1$

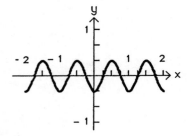

16. $y = -\dfrac{1}{4} \sin\left(\dfrac{x}{2}\right)$, $-4\pi \leq x \leq 4\pi$

Amplitude $A = \left| -\dfrac{1}{4} \right| = \dfrac{1}{4}$

Period $P = \dfrac{2\pi}{\frac{1}{2}} = 4\pi$

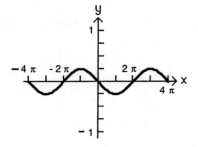

18. $y = 3 + 3 \cos\left(\dfrac{\pi x}{2}\right)$, $-4 \leq x \leq 4$

Amplitude $A = 3$

Period $P = \dfrac{2\pi}{\frac{\pi}{2}} = 4$

Shift 3 units up

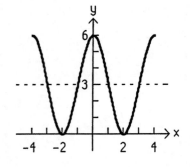

20. $y = 3 - 2 \sin\left(\dfrac{x}{2}\right)$, $-4\pi \leq x \leq 4\pi$

Amplitude $A = |-2| = 2$

Period $P = \dfrac{2\pi}{\frac{1}{2}} = 4\pi$

Shift 3 units up

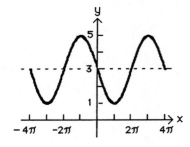

22. From the graph, $A = \frac{1}{4}$, $P = 8\pi$

$$\frac{2\pi}{B} = 8\pi \Rightarrow B = \frac{1}{4}$$

$$y = \frac{1}{4} \sin\left(\frac{x}{4}\right), \quad -4\pi \leq x \leq 8\pi$$

24. From the graph, $A = \frac{1}{2}$, reflected about the x-axis, $P = 4$

$$\frac{2\pi}{B} = 4 \Rightarrow B = \frac{\pi}{2}$$

$$y = -\frac{1}{2} \sin\left(\frac{\pi x}{2}\right), \quad -2 \leq x \leq 4$$

26. From the graph, $A = 0.1$, $P = \frac{\pi}{4}$

$$\frac{2\pi}{B} = \frac{\pi}{4} \Rightarrow B = 8$$

$$y = 0.1 \cos 8x, \quad -\frac{\pi}{8} \leq x \leq \frac{\pi}{4}$$

28. From the graph, $A = 1$, reflected about the x-axis, $P = 0.5$

$$\frac{2\pi}{B} = \frac{1}{2} \Rightarrow B = 4\pi$$

$$y = -\cos(4\pi x), \quad -0.25 \leq x \leq 0.5$$

30.

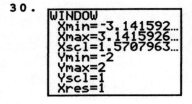
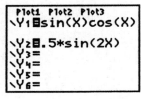
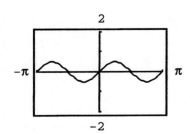

32.

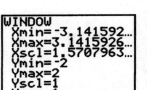
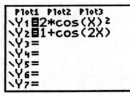
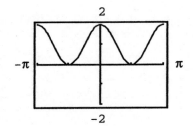

34. $y = \cos(x - \pi)$, $-\pi \leq x \leq 3\pi$

   Amplitude = 1

   Period = $\frac{2\pi}{1} = 2\pi$

   Phase Shift = $-\frac{-\pi}{1} = \pi$

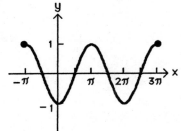

36. $y = 2 \sin\left(x + \frac{\pi}{4}\right)$, $-2\pi \leq x \leq 2\pi$

   Amplitude = 2

   Period = $\frac{2\pi}{1} = 2\pi$

   Phase Shift = $-\frac{\frac{\pi}{4}}{1} = -\frac{\pi}{4}$

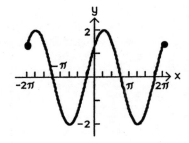

38. $y = \cos\left[2\pi\left(x - \frac{1}{2}\right)\right] = \cos(2\pi x - \pi)$, $-1 \le x \le 2$

Amplitude = 1

Period = $\frac{2\pi}{2\pi} = 1$

Phase Shift = $-\frac{-\pi}{2\pi} = \frac{1}{2}$

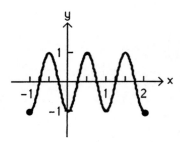

40. $y = 2\sin\left(\pi x - \frac{\pi}{4}\right)$, $-1 \le x \le 3$

Amplitude = 2

Period = $\frac{2\pi}{\pi} = 2$

Phase Shift = $-\frac{-\frac{\pi}{4}}{\pi} = \frac{1}{4}$

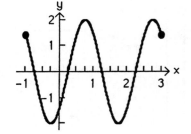

42. $y = -2\cos(4x + \pi)$, $-\pi \le x \le \pi$

Amplitude = 2

Period = $\frac{2\pi}{4} = \frac{\pi}{2}$

Phase Shift = $-\frac{\pi}{4}$

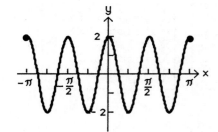

44. $y = 1 + \cos(x - \pi)$, $-\pi \le x \le 3\pi$

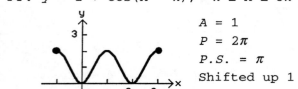

$A = 1$
$P = 2\pi$
$P.S. = \pi$
Shifted up 1

46. $y = -1 - 2\cos(4x + \pi)$, $-\pi \le x \le \pi$

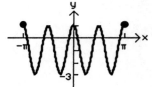

$A = 2$
$P = \frac{2\pi}{4} = \frac{\pi}{2}$
$P.S. = -\frac{\pi}{4}$

Shifted down 1

48. From the graph, Amplitude = 4 and

Period = $4 = \frac{2\pi}{B} \Rightarrow B = \frac{\pi}{2}$

Phase Shift = $-\frac{C}{B} = -1 \Rightarrow B = C = \frac{\pi}{2}$

$y = 4\sin\left(\frac{\pi}{2}x + \frac{\pi}{2}\right)$, $-1 \le x \le 3$

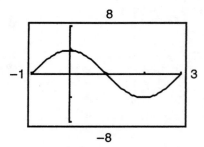

50. From graph, Amplitude = $\frac{1}{2}$ reflected across the

x-axis, and Period = $8\pi \Rightarrow \frac{2\pi}{B} = 8\pi \Rightarrow B = \frac{1}{4}$

Phase Shift = $-\frac{C}{B} = -\pi \Rightarrow \frac{C}{\frac{1}{4}} = \pi \Rightarrow C = \frac{\pi}{4}$

$y = -\frac{1}{2} \cos\left(\frac{x}{4} + \frac{\pi}{4}\right), \quad -3\pi \le x \le 5\pi$

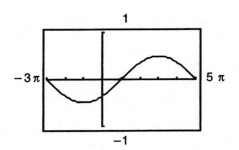

52. $y = 5.4 \sin\left[\frac{\pi}{2.5}(t - 1)\right], \quad 0 \le t \le 6$

Amplitude = 5.4

Period = $\frac{2\pi}{\frac{\pi}{2.5}} = 5$

Phase Shift = $-\frac{-\frac{\pi}{2.5}}{\frac{\pi}{2.5}} = 1$

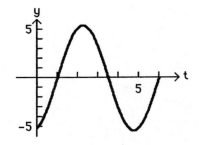

54. $y = 25 \cos[5\pi(t - 0.1)], \quad 0 \le t \le 2$

Amplitude = 25

Period = $\frac{2\pi}{5\pi} = \frac{2}{5}$

Phase Shift = $-\frac{-0.5\pi}{5\pi} = 0.1$

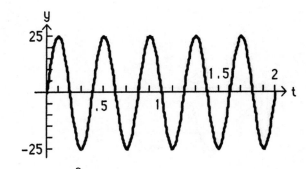

56.

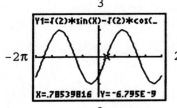

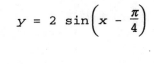

$y = 2 \sin\left(x - \frac{\pi}{4}\right)$

58.

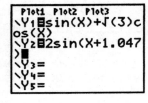

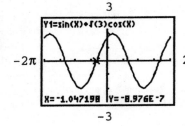

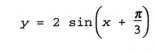

$y = 2 \sin\left(x + \frac{\pi}{3}\right)$

60.

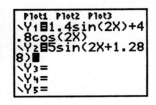

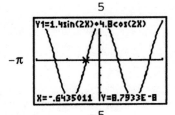

62. The amplitude is decreasing.

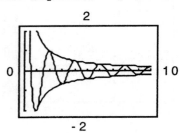

The amplitude is decreasing with time. This is often referred to as a **damped sine wave**. Examples are a car's vertical motion, which is damped by the suspension system after the car goes over a bump, and the slowing down of a pendulum that is released away from the vertical line of suspension (air resistance and friction).

64. The amplitude is increasing.

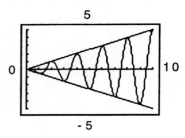

The amplitude is increasing with time. In physical and electrical systems this is referred to as **resonance**. Some examples are the swinging of a bridge during high winds and the movement of tall buildings during an earthquake. Some bridges and buildings are destroyed when the resonance reaches the elastic limits of the structure.

66.

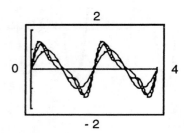

68. $I = 30 \sin 120t$

$A = 30$

$P = \dfrac{2\pi}{120} = \dfrac{\pi}{60}$

frequency $= \dfrac{60}{\pi}$ Hz

70. $E = A \cos Bt$

$A = 110$

$P = \dfrac{1}{60} = \dfrac{2\pi}{B} \Rightarrow B = 120\pi$

$E = 110 \cos(120\pi t), \ t \geq 0$

72. $V(t) = 0.45 - 0.37 \cos \dfrac{\pi t}{2}, \ 0 \leq t \leq 8$

The graph shows the volume of air in the lungs t seconds after exhaling.

74. $I = 30 \cos(120\pi t - \pi)$, $0 \le t \le \dfrac{3}{60}$

$A = 30$, $P = \dfrac{2\pi}{120\pi} = \dfrac{1}{60}$,

$PS = -\dfrac{-\pi}{120\pi} = \dfrac{1}{120}$

76. $\theta = \dfrac{\pi}{2} + 6\pi t$

$y = 3 \sin \theta = 3 \sin\left(6\pi t + \dfrac{\pi}{2}\right)$

$y = 3 \sin\left(6\pi t + \dfrac{\pi}{2}\right)$, $0 \le t \le 1$

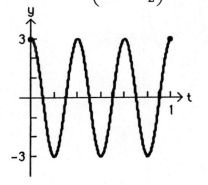

78. (A)

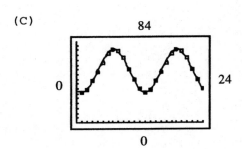

(B) $A = \dfrac{(\text{Max } y - \text{Min } y)}{2} = \dfrac{76 - 31}{2} = 22.5$

$B = \dfrac{2\pi}{12} \Rightarrow B = \dfrac{\pi}{6}$

$k = \text{Min } y + A = 31 + 22.5 = 53.5$

$C \approx -2.1$

$y = 53.5 + 22.5 \sin\left(\dfrac{\pi x}{6} - 2.1\right)$

(C)

(D)

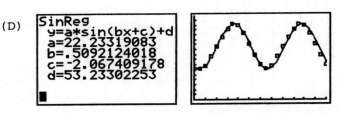

Exercise 5-8

2. $y = \tan x$, $0 \le x \le 2\pi$

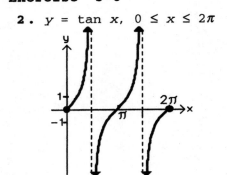

4. $y = \csc x$, $-\pi < x < \pi$

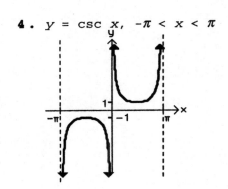

6. $y = 3 \tan 2x$, $-\pi < x < \pi$

period $= \dfrac{\pi}{B} = \dfrac{\pi}{2}$

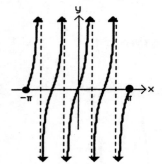

8. $y = -\dfrac{1}{2} \cot(2\pi x)$, $0 < x < 1$

period $= \dfrac{\pi}{2\pi} = \dfrac{1}{2}$

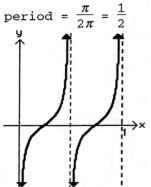

10. $y = \sec \pi x$, $-1.5 \le x \le 3.5$

period $= \dfrac{2\pi}{\pi} = 2$

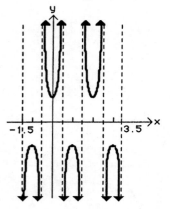

12. $y = \dfrac{1}{2} \tan\left(\dfrac{x}{2}\right)$, $-\pi < x < 3\pi$

period $= \dfrac{\pi}{\frac{1}{2}} = 2\pi$

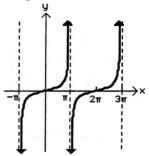

14. $y = 2 \csc\left(\dfrac{x}{2}\right)$, $0 < x < 8\pi$

period $= \dfrac{2\pi}{\frac{1}{2}} = 4\pi$

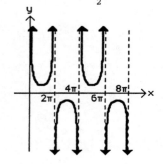

16. $y = \tan\left(x - \dfrac{\pi}{2}\right)$, $-\pi < x < \pi$

period $= \dfrac{\pi}{1} = \pi$

phase shift $= -\dfrac{-\frac{\pi}{2}}{1} = \dfrac{\pi}{2}$

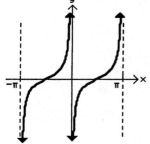

18. $y = \cot(2x - \pi)$, $-\frac{\pi}{2} \leq x \leq \frac{\pi}{2}$, has

period = $\frac{\pi}{2}$ and phase shift = $\frac{\pi}{2}$.

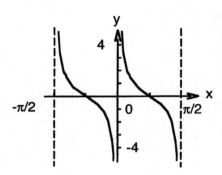

20. $y = \csc\left(\pi x - \frac{\pi}{2}\right)$, $-1 < x < 1$,

has period = $\frac{2\pi}{\pi} = 2$ and

phase shift = $\frac{\pi/2}{\pi} = \frac{1}{2}$.

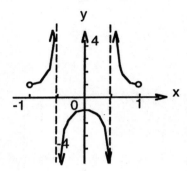

22. $y = \cot x + \tan x$, $P = \pi$

$y = 2 \csc 2x$

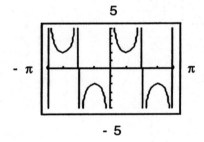

24. $y = \csc x - \cot x$, $P = 2\pi$

$y = \tan\left(\frac{x}{2}\right)$

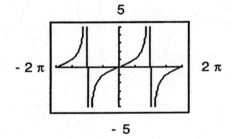

26. $y = 4 \tan(2x + \pi)$, $-\pi \leq x \leq \pi$

period = $\frac{\pi}{2}$

phase shift = $-\frac{\pi}{2}$

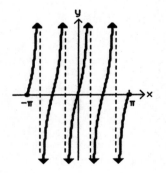

28. $y = -3 \cot(\pi x - \pi)$, $-2 < x < 2$

period = $\frac{\pi}{\pi} = 1$

phase shift = $-\frac{-\pi}{\pi} = 1$

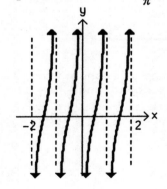

30. $y = 2 \sec\left(\pi x - \dfrac{\pi}{2}\right)$, $-1 < x < 3$

period $= \dfrac{2\pi}{\pi} = 2$

phase shift $= -\dfrac{-\frac{\pi}{2}}{\pi} = \dfrac{1}{2}$

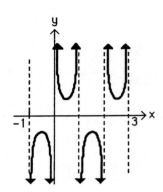

32. 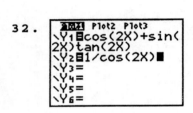 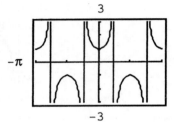 $y = \sec 2x$

34.  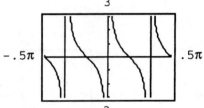 $y = \cot 3x$

36. (A) $\tan\theta = \dfrac{a}{20} \Rightarrow a = 20\tan\left(\dfrac{\pi t}{2}\right)$

(B)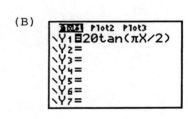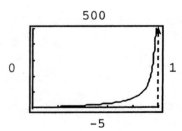

(C) Initially the distance from N is zero. The distance increases slowly at first, then begins to increase rapidly without end.

Exercise 5-9

2. $\sin^{-1} 0 = 0$ **4.** $\arccos\dfrac{\sqrt{3}}{2} = \dfrac{\pi}{6}$ **6.** $\tan^{-1} 1 = \dfrac{\pi}{4}$

8. $\cos^{-1}\left(\dfrac{1}{2}\right) = \dfrac{\pi}{3}$ **10.** $\arctan\left(\dfrac{1}{\sqrt{3}}\right) = \dfrac{\pi}{6}$ **12.** $\tan^{-1} 0 = 0$

14. $\cos^{-1} 0.4038 \approx 1.155$ **16.** $\tan^{-1} 43.09 \approx 1.548$

18. arcsin 1.131 is undefined.   **20.** $\arccos\left(-\dfrac{1}{2}\right) = \dfrac{2\pi}{3}$

22. $\tan^{-1}(-1) = -\dfrac{\pi}{4}$ **24.** $\sin^{-1}\left(-\dfrac{\sqrt{3}}{2}\right) = -\dfrac{\pi}{3}$ **26.** $\cos^{-1}\left(-\dfrac{\sqrt{3}}{2}\right) = \dfrac{5\pi}{6}$

28. $\sin[\sin^{-1}(-0.6)] = -0.6$ **30.** $\tan[\tan^{-1}(-1.5)] = -1.5$ **32.** $\tan\left(\cos^{-1}\dfrac{1}{2}\right) = \sqrt{3}$

34. $\cos\left[\sin^{-1}\left(-\dfrac{\sqrt{2}}{2}\right)\right] = \dfrac{\sqrt{2}}{2}$ **36.** $\tan^{-1}(-4.038) \approx -1.328$

38. $\sec(\sin^{-1}(-0.0399) \approx 1.001$ **40.** $\sqrt{2} + \tan^{-1}\sqrt[3]{5} \approx 2.456$ **42.** $\cos^{-1}\left(-\dfrac{1}{2}\right) = 120°$

44. $\arctan(-1) = -45°$ **46.** $\sin^{-1}(-1) = -90°$ **48.** $\tan^{-1}(12.4304) \approx 85.40°$

50. $\arccos(-0.9206) \approx 157.01°$ **52.** $\sin^{-1}(-0.7071) \approx -45.00°$

54. $\cos^{-1}[\cos(-0.5)] = 0.5$. For the identity $\cos^{-1}(\cos x) = x$ to hold, x must be in the restricted domain of the cosine function; that is, $0 \le x \le \pi$. The number -0.5 is not in the restricted domain.

56.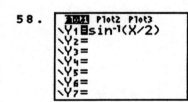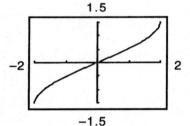

58.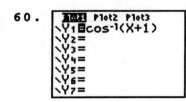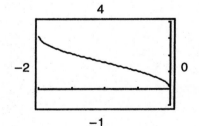

60.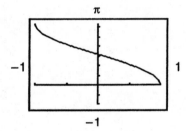

62.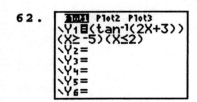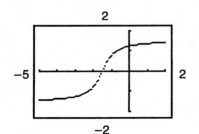

64. (A)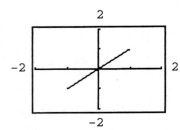

(B) The graph is the same. The domain of the inverse sine is the interval [-1, 1].

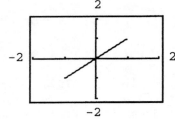

66. for $-1 < x < 0$, $\quad \dfrac{\pi}{2} < \cos^{-1} x < \pi$

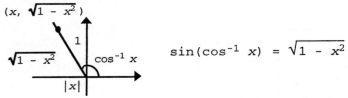

$\sin(\cos^{-1} x) = \sqrt{1 - x^2}$

for $0 < x < 1$, $\quad 0 < \cos^{-1} < \dfrac{\pi}{2}$

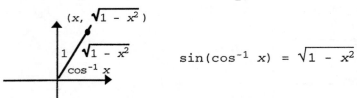

$\sin(\cos^{-1} x) = \sqrt{1 - x^2}$

$\sin(\cos^{-1} x) = \sqrt{1 - x^2}$ in both cases.

68. for $-1 < x < 1$ $\quad -\dfrac{\pi}{2} < \sin^{-1} x < 0$

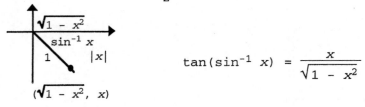

$\tan(\sin^{-1} x) = \dfrac{x}{\sqrt{1 - x^2}}$

for $0 < x < 1$, $\quad 0 < \sin^{-1} x < \dfrac{\pi}{2}$

$\tan(\sin^{-1} x) = \dfrac{x}{\sqrt{1 - x^2}}$

$\tan(\sin^{-1} x) = \dfrac{x}{\sqrt{1 - x^2}}$ in both cases.

70. Solve for x:
$$y - 3 = 5 \sin(x - 1)$$
$$\frac{y - 3}{5} = \sin(x - 1)$$
$$\sin^{-1} \frac{y - 3}{5} = x - 1$$
$$1 + \sin^{-1} \frac{y - 3}{5} = x$$

$$f^{-1}(x) = 1 + \sin^{-1} \frac{x - 3}{5} \quad \text{for} \quad -1 \leq \frac{x - 3}{5} \leq 1$$
$$-5 \leq x - 3 \leq 5$$
$$-2 \leq x \leq 8$$

72. (A)

 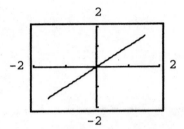

(B) The domain for $\sin x$ is $(-\infty, \infty)$ and the range is $[-1, 1]$, which is the domain for $\sin^{-1} x$. Thus, $y = \sin^{-1}(\sin x)$ has a graph over the interval $(-\infty, \infty)$, but $\sin^{-1}(\sin x) = x$ only on the restricted domain of $\sin x$, $[-\pi/2, \pi/2]$.

 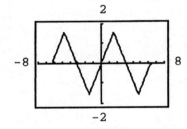

74. 17 mm: $\theta = 2 \tan^{-1} \frac{21.634}{x} = 2 \tan^{-1} \frac{21.634}{17} \approx 103.68°$

70 mm: $\theta = 2 \tan^{-1} \frac{21.634}{x} = 2 \tan^{-1} \frac{21.634}{70} \approx 34.35°$

76. (A)

 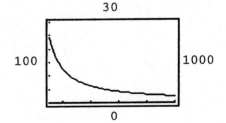

(B)

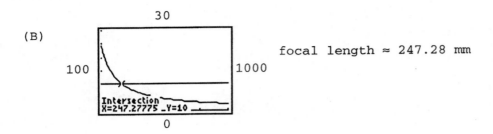

focal length ≈ 247.28 mm

78. $L = \pi D + (d - D)\theta + 2C \sin \theta$

$= \pi D + (d - D)\cos^{-1}\left(\dfrac{D - d}{2C}\right) + 2C \sin\left(\cos^{-1} \dfrac{D - d}{2C}\right)$

$= \pi(6) + (4 - 6)\cos^{-1}\left(\dfrac{6 - 4}{2(10)}\right) + 2(10)\sin\left(\cos^{-1} \dfrac{6 - 4}{2(10)}\right)$

$= 6\pi - 2 \cos^{-1}(0.1) + 20 \sin(\cos^{-1}(0.1))$

$= 35.81$ inches

80. (A)

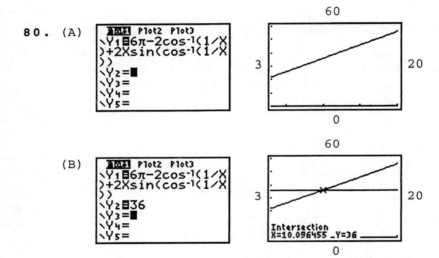

(B)

Distance between centers ≈ 10.10 in.

82. $d = 2r \tan^{-1} \dfrac{x}{r}$

$= 2(50)\tan^{-1} \dfrac{25}{50}$

$= 100 \tan^{-1} 0.5$

≈ 46.36 feet

CHAPTER 6

Exercise 6-1

2. Verify: $\cos \theta \csc \theta = \cot \theta$

$$\cos \theta \csc \theta = \cos \theta \cdot \frac{1}{\sin \theta}$$

$$= \frac{\cos \theta}{\sin \theta}$$

$$= \cot \theta$$

4. Verify: $\tan \theta \csc \theta \cos \theta = 1$

$$\tan \theta \csc \theta \cos \theta = \frac{\sin \theta}{\cos \theta} \cdot \frac{1}{\sin \theta} \cdot \cos \theta$$
$$= 1$$

6. Verify: $\cot(-x)\tan(x) = -1$

$$\cot(-x)\tan(x) = \frac{\cos(-x)}{\sin(-x)} \cdot \frac{\sin x}{\cos x}$$

$$= \frac{\cos x}{-\sin x} \cdot \frac{\sin x}{\cos x}$$

$$= -1$$

8. Verify: $\tan \alpha = \frac{\cos \alpha \sec \alpha}{\cot \alpha}$

$$\frac{\cos \alpha \sec \alpha}{\cot \alpha} = \frac{\cos \alpha \cdot \frac{1}{\cos \alpha}}{\frac{\cos \alpha}{\sin \alpha}}$$

$$= \frac{1}{\frac{\cos \alpha}{\sin \alpha}}$$

$$= \frac{\sin \alpha}{\cos \alpha}$$

$$= \tan \alpha$$

10. Verify: $\tan u + 1 = \sec u(\sin u + \cos u)$

$$\sec u(\sin u + \cos u) = \frac{1}{\cos u}(\sin u + \cos u)$$
$$= \frac{\sin u}{\cos u} + \frac{\cos u}{\cos u}$$
$$= \tan u + 1$$

12. Verify: $\frac{\cos^2 x - \sin^2 x}{\sin x \cos x} = \cot x - \tan x$

$$\frac{\cos^2 x - \sin^2 x}{\sin x \cos x} = \frac{\cos^2 x}{\sin x \cos x} - \frac{\sin^2 x}{\sin x \cos x}$$

$$= \frac{\cos x}{\sin x} - \frac{\sin x}{\cos x}$$

$$= \cot x - \tan x$$

14. Verify: $\frac{\cos^2 t}{\sin t} + \sin t = \csc t$

$$\frac{\cos^2 t}{\sin t} + \sin t = \frac{\cos^2 t + \sin^2 t}{\sin t}$$

$$= \frac{1}{\sin t}$$
$$= \csc t$$

16. Verify: $\dfrac{\sin u}{1 - \cos^2 u} = \csc u$

$$\dfrac{\sin u}{1 - \cos^2 u} = \dfrac{\sin u}{\sin^2 u}$$
$$= \dfrac{1}{\sin u}$$
$$= \csc u$$

18. Verify: $(1 - \sin t)(1 + \sin t) = \cos^2 t$

$$(1 - \sin t)(1 + \sin t) = 1 - \sin t + \sin t - \sin^2 t$$
$$= 1 - \sin^2 t$$
$$= \cos^2 t$$

20. Verify: $(\sin x + \cos x)^2 = 1 + 2 \sin x \cos x$

$$(\sin x + \cos x)^2 = \sin^2 x + 2 \sin x \cos x + \cos^2 x$$
$$= \sin^2 x + \cos^2 x + 2 \sin x \cos x$$
$$= 1 + 2 \sin x \cos x$$

22. Verify: $(\csc t - 1)(\csc t + 1) = \cot^2 t$

$$(\csc t - 1)(\csc t + 1) = \csc^2 t - \csc t + \csc t - 1$$
$$= \csc^2 t - 1$$
$$= 1 + \cot^2 t - 1$$
$$= \cot^2 t$$

24. Verify: $\sec^2 u - \tan^2 u = 1$

$$\sec^2 u - \tan^2 u = 1 + \tan^2 u - \tan^2 u$$
$$= 1$$

26. Verify: $\sin m(\csc m - \sin m) = \cos^2 m$

$$\sin m(\csc m - \sin m) = \sin m\left(\dfrac{1}{\sin m} - \sin m\right)$$
$$= 1 - \sin^2 m$$
$$= \cos^2 m$$

28. $-\pi \le x \le \pi$

    (A) $y = \sec^2 x$ (B) $y = \tan^2 x$

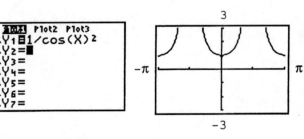
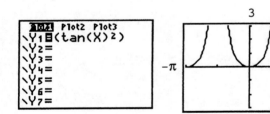

    (C) $y = \sec^2 x - \tan^2 x$

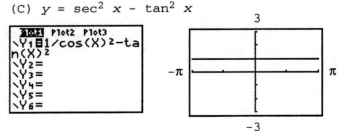

30. $-\pi \le x \le \pi$

(A) $y = \dfrac{\sin x}{\cos x \cdot \tan x}$

(B) $y = 1$

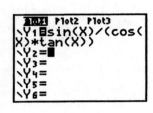
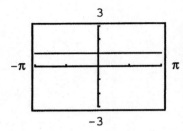
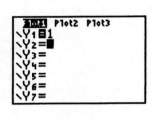
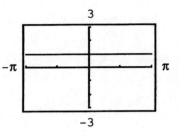

32. Verify: $\dfrac{1 - \cos^2 y}{(1 - \sin y)(1 + \sin y)} = \tan^2 y$

$$\dfrac{1 - \cos^2 y}{(1 - \sin y)(1 + \sin y)} = \dfrac{\sin^2 y}{1 - \sin^2 y}$$

$$= \dfrac{\sin^2 y}{\cos^2 y}$$

$$= \left(\dfrac{\sin y}{\cos y}\right)^2$$

$$= \tan^2 y$$

34. Verify: $\sin \theta + \cos \theta = \dfrac{\tan \theta + 1}{\sec \theta}$

$$\dfrac{\tan \theta + 1}{\sec \theta} = \dfrac{\frac{\sin \theta}{\cos \theta} + 1}{\frac{1}{\cos \theta}} \cdot \dfrac{\cos \theta}{\cos \theta}$$

$$= \sin \theta + \cos \theta$$

36. Verify: $1 - \sin y = \dfrac{\cos^2 y}{1 + \sin y}$

$$\dfrac{\cos^2 y}{1 + \sin y} = \dfrac{\cos^2 y}{1 + \sin y} \cdot \dfrac{1 - \sin y}{1 - \sin y}$$

$$= \dfrac{(1 - \sin^2 y)(1 - \sin y)}{(1 - \sin^2 y)}$$

$$= 1 - \sin y$$

38. Verify: $\sec^2 x + \csc^2 x = \sec^2 x \csc^2 x$

$$\sec^2 x + \csc^2 x = \dfrac{1}{\cos^2 x} + \dfrac{1}{\sin^2 x}$$

$$= \dfrac{\sin^2 x + \cos^2 x}{\sin^2 x \cos^2 x}$$

$$= \dfrac{1}{\cos^2 x \sin^2 x}$$

$$= \dfrac{1}{\cos^2 x} \cdot \dfrac{1}{\sin^2 x}$$

$$= \sec^2 x \csc^2 x$$

40. Verify: $\dfrac{1 + \sec\theta}{\sin\theta + \tan\theta} = \csc\theta$

$$\dfrac{1 + \sec\theta}{\sin\theta + \tan\theta} = \dfrac{1 + \dfrac{1}{\cos\theta}}{\sin\theta + \dfrac{\sin\theta}{\cos\theta}} \cdot \dfrac{\cos\theta}{\cos\theta}$$

$$= \dfrac{\cos\theta + 1}{\sin\theta\cos\theta + \sin\theta}$$

$$= \dfrac{\cos\theta + 1}{\sin\theta(\cos\theta + 1)}$$

$$= \dfrac{1}{\sin\theta}$$

$$= \csc\theta$$

42. Verify: $\ln(\cot x) = \ln(\cos x) - \ln(\sin x)$

$$\ln(\cos x) - \ln(\sin x) = \ln\left(\dfrac{\cos x}{\sin x}\right)$$

$$= \ln(\cot x)$$

44. Verify: $\ln(\csc x) = -\ln(\sin x)$

$$-\ln(\sin x) = -\ln\left(\dfrac{1}{\csc x}\right)$$

$$= -(\ln 1 - \ln(\csc x))$$

$$= -(0 - \ln(\csc x))$$

$$= \ln(\csc x)$$

46. Verify: $\dfrac{1 - \csc y}{1 + \csc y} = \dfrac{\sin y - 1}{\sin y + 1}$

$$\dfrac{1 - \csc y}{1 + \csc y} = \dfrac{1 - \dfrac{1}{\sin y}}{1 + \dfrac{1}{\sin y}} \cdot \dfrac{\sin y}{\sin y}$$

$$= \dfrac{\sin y - 1}{\sin y + 1}$$

48. Verify: $\sin^4 x + 2\sin^2 x \cos^2 x + \cos^4 x = 1$

$$\sin^4 x + 2\sin^2 x \cos^2 x + \cos^4 x = (\sin^2 x + \cos^2 x)^2$$

$$= 1^2$$

$$= 1$$

50. Verify: $\csc n - \dfrac{\sin n}{1 + \cos n} = \cot n$

$$\csc n - \dfrac{\sin n}{1 + \cos n} = \dfrac{1}{\sin n} - \dfrac{\sin n}{1 + \cos n}$$

$$= \dfrac{1 + \cos n - \sin^2 n}{\sin n(1 + \cos n)}$$

$$= \dfrac{1 - \sin^2 n + \cos n}{\sin n(1 + \cos n)}$$

$$= \dfrac{\cos^2 n + \cos n}{\sin n(1 + \cos n)}$$

$$= \dfrac{\cos n(\cos n + 1)}{\sin n(1 + \cos n)}$$

$$= \dfrac{\cos n}{\sin n}$$

$$= \cot n$$

52. Verify: $\dfrac{\sin^2 t + 4 \sin t + 3}{\cos^2 t} = \dfrac{3 + \sin t}{1 - \sin t}$

$$\frac{\sin^2 t + 4 \sin t + 3}{\cos^2 t} = \frac{(\sin t + 1)(\sin t + 3)}{1 - \sin^2 t}$$

$$= \frac{(1 + \sin t)(3 + \sin t)}{(1 + \sin t)(1 - \sin t)}$$

$$= \frac{3 + \sin t}{1 - \sin t}$$

54. Verify: $\dfrac{\cos^3 u + \sin^3 u}{\cos u + \sin u} = 1 - \sin u \cos u$

$$\frac{\cos^3 u + \sin^3 u}{\cos u + \sin u} = \frac{(\cos u + \sin u)(\cos^2 u - \cos u \sin u + \sin^2 u)}{(\cos u + \sin u)}$$

$$= \cos^2 u + \sin^2 u - \cos u \sin u$$

$$= 1 - \sin u \cos u$$

56. Verify: $(\cot u - \csc u)^2 = \dfrac{1 - \cos u}{1 + \cos u}$

$$(\cot u - \csc u)^2 = \left(\frac{\cos u}{\sin u} - \frac{1}{\sin u}\right)^2$$

$$= \left(\frac{\cos u - 1}{\sin u}\right)^2$$

$$= \frac{(\cos u - 1)^2}{\sin^2 u}$$

$$= \frac{(\cos u - 1)(\cos u - 1)}{1 - \cos^2 u}$$

$$= \frac{-(1 - \cos u)(\cos u - 1)}{(1 - \cos u)(1 + \cos u)}$$

$$= \frac{-\cos u + 1}{1 + \cos u}$$

$$= \frac{1 - \cos u}{1 + \cos u}$$

58. Verify: $\dfrac{\sec^4 x - 1}{\tan^2 x} = 2 + \tan^2 x$

$$\frac{\sec^4 x - 1}{\tan^2 x} = \frac{(\sec^2 x - 1)(\sec^2 x + 1)}{\tan^2 x}$$

$$= \frac{(1 + \tan^2 x - 1)(1 + \tan^2 x + 1)}{\tan^2 x}$$

$$= \frac{\tan^2 x(2 + \tan^2 x)}{\tan^2 x}$$

$$= 2 + \tan^2 x$$

60. Verify: $\dfrac{\sin x}{1 - \cos x} = \dfrac{1 + \cos x}{\sin x}$

$$\frac{1 + \cos x}{\sin x} = \frac{1 + \cos x}{\sin x} \cdot \frac{1 - \cos x}{1 - \cos x}$$

$$= \frac{1 - \cos^2 x}{\sin x (1 - \cos x)}$$

$$= \frac{\sin^2 x}{\sin x (1 - \cos x)}$$

$$= \frac{\sin x}{1 - \cos x}$$

62. As the graph shows, $\dfrac{\cos(-x)}{\sin x \cot(-x)} = 1$ is not an identity since the left hand side is -1 for all x for which it is defined.

 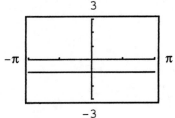

64. As the graph shows, $\dfrac{\cos x}{\sin(-x) \cot(-x)} = 1$ appears to be an identity.

$$\frac{\cos x}{\sin(-x)\cot(-x)} = \frac{\cos x}{-\sin x \cdot \frac{\cos(-x)}{\sin(-x)}}$$

$$= \frac{\cos x}{-\sin x \cdot \frac{\cos x}{-\sin x}}$$

$$= 1$$

 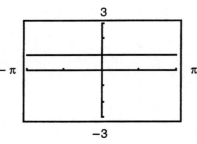

66. As the graphs show, $\dfrac{1 - \tan^2 x}{1 - \cot^2 x} = \tan^2 x$ does not appear to be an identity.

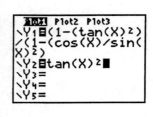 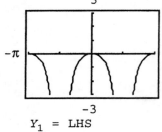 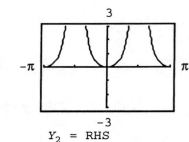 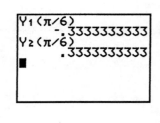

Y_1 = LHS Y_2 = RHS

The last screen shows a value of x for which both sides are defined but not equal.

68. As the graph shows, $\dfrac{\tan^2 x - 1}{1 - \cot^2 x} = \tan^2 x$ appear to be an identity.

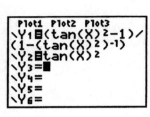 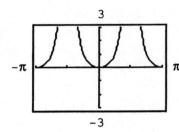

$$\frac{\tan^2 x - 1}{1 - \cot^2 x} = \frac{\dfrac{\sin^2 x}{\cos^2 x} - 1}{1 - \dfrac{\cos^2 x}{\sin^2 x}}$$

$$= \frac{\dfrac{\sin^2 x - \cos^2 x}{\cos^2 x}}{\dfrac{\sin^2 x - \cos^2 x}{\sin^2 x}}$$

$$= \frac{1}{\cos^2 x} \cdot \frac{\sin^2 x}{1}$$

$$= \tan^2 x$$

70. As the graph shows, $\dfrac{\cos x}{1 - \sin x} + \dfrac{\cos x}{1 + \sin x} = 2 \sec x$ appears to be an identity.

 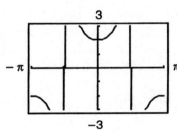

$$\frac{\cos x}{1 - \sin x} + \frac{\cos x}{1 + \sin x}$$

$$= \frac{\cos x(1 + \sin x) + \cos x(1 - \sin x)}{(1 - \sin x)(1 + \sin x)}$$

$$= \frac{\cos x + \cos x \sin x + \cos x - \cos x \sin x}{1 - \sin^2 x}$$

$$= \frac{2 \cos x}{\cos^2 x}$$

$$= \frac{2}{\cos x}$$

$$= 2 \sec x$$

72. As the graphs show, $\dfrac{\cos x}{\sin x + 1} - \dfrac{\cos x}{\sin x - 1} = 2 \csc x$ does not appear to be an identity.

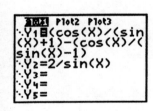 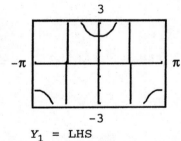 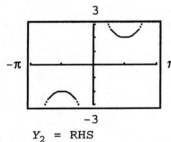

$Y_1 = $ LHS $\qquad\qquad$ $Y_2 = $ RHS

The last screen shows a value of x for which both sides are defined but not equal.

74. Verify: $\dfrac{3 \cos^2 z + 5 \sin z - 5}{\cos^2 z} = \dfrac{3 \sin z - 2}{1 + \sin z}$

$$\frac{3 \cos^2 z + 5 \sin z - 5}{\cos^2 z} = \frac{3(1 - \sin^2 z) - 5(1 - \sin z)}{1 - \sin^2 z}$$

$$= \frac{(1 - \sin z)[3(1 + \sin z) - 5]}{(1 - \sin z)(1 + \sin z)}$$

$$= \frac{3(1 + \sin z) - 5}{1 + \sin z}$$

$$= \frac{3 + 3 \sin z - 5}{1 + \sin z}$$

$$= \frac{3 \sin z - 2}{1 + \sin z}$$

76. Verify: $\dfrac{\sin x \cos y + \cos x \sin y}{\cos x \cos y - \sin x \sin y} = \dfrac{\tan x + \tan y}{1 - \tan x \tan y}$

$$\frac{\tan x + \tan y}{1 - \tan x \tan y} = \frac{\frac{\sin x}{\cos x} + \frac{\sin y}{\cos y}}{1 - \frac{\sin x}{\cos x} \cdot \frac{\sin y}{\cos y}} \cdot \frac{\cos x \cos y}{\cos x \cos y}$$

$$= \frac{\sin x \cos y + \cos x \sin y}{\cos x \cos y - \sin x \sin y}$$

78. Verify: $\dfrac{\cot \alpha + \cot \beta}{\cot \alpha \cot \beta - 1} = \dfrac{\tan \alpha + \tan \beta}{1 - \tan \alpha \tan \beta}$

$$\frac{\tan \alpha + \tan \beta}{1 - \tan \alpha \tan \beta} = \frac{\frac{1}{\cot \alpha} + \frac{1}{\cot \beta}}{1 - \frac{1}{\cot \alpha} \cdot \frac{1}{\cot \beta}} \cdot \frac{\cot \alpha \cot \beta}{\cot \alpha \cot \beta}$$

$$= \frac{\cot \beta + \cot \alpha}{\cot \alpha \cot \beta - 1}$$

$$= \frac{\cot \alpha + \cot \beta}{\cot \alpha \cot \beta - 1}$$

80.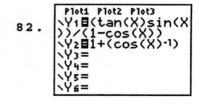

$$f(x) = \frac{1 + \sin x}{2 \cos x} - \frac{\cos x}{2 + 2 \sin x} = \frac{1 + \sin x}{2 \cos x} - \frac{\cos x}{2(1 + \sin x)}$$

$$= \frac{1}{2} \cdot \left[\frac{1 + \sin x}{\cos x} - \frac{\cos x}{1 + \sin x} \right]$$

$$= \frac{1}{2} \cdot \left[\frac{(1 + \sin x)^2 - \cos^2 x}{\cos x (1 + \sin x)} \right]$$

$$= \frac{1}{2} \cdot \left[\frac{1 + 2 \sin x + \sin^2 x - \cos^2 x}{\cos x (1 + \sin x)} \right]$$

$$= \frac{1}{2} \cdot \left[\frac{1 + 2 \sin x + \sin^2 x - (1 - \sin^2 x)}{\cos x (1 + \sin x)} \right]$$

$$= \frac{1}{2} \cdot \left[\frac{2 \sin x + 2 \sin^2 x}{\cos x (1 + \sin x)} \right]$$

$$= \frac{1}{2} \cdot \left[\frac{2 \sin x (1 + \sin x)}{\cos x (1 + \sin x)} \right]$$

$$= \tan x$$

82.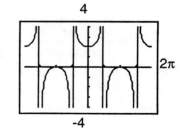

$$f(x) = \frac{\tan x \sin x}{1 - \cos x} = \frac{\frac{\sin x}{\cos x} \cdot \sin x}{1 - \cos x}$$

$$= \frac{\sin^2 x}{\cos x(1 - \cos x)}$$

$$= \frac{1 - \cos^2 x}{\cos x(1 - \cos x)}$$

$$= \frac{(1 - \cos x)(1 + \cos x)}{\cos x(1 - \cos x)}$$

$$= \frac{1 + \cos x}{\cos x}$$

$$= \frac{1}{\cos x} + 1$$

$$= 1 + \sec x$$

84.

```
Plot1 Plot2 Plot3
\Y1■(3sin(X)-2si
n(X)cos(X))/1-co
s(X))-(1+cos(X))
/sin(X)
\Y2■2sin(X)
\Y3=
\Y4=
```

$$f(x) = \frac{3 \sin x - 2 \sin x \cos x}{1 - \cos x} - \frac{1 + \cos x}{\sin x}$$

$$= \frac{\sin x(3 \sin x - 2 \sin x \cos x) - (1 + \cos x)(1 - \cos x)}{\sin x(1 - \cos x)}$$

$$= \frac{3 \sin^2 x - 2 \sin^2 x \cos x - (1 - \cos^2 x)}{\sin x(1 - \cos x)}$$

$$= \frac{3 \sin^2 x - 2 \sin^2 x \cos x - \sin^2 x}{\sin x(1 - \cos x)}$$

$$= \frac{2 \sin^2 x(1 - \cos x)}{\sin x(1 - \cos x)}$$

$$= 2 \sin x$$

86. $\sqrt{1 - \sin^2 x} = \cos x$; $\sqrt{1 - \sin^2 x} \geq 0 \Rightarrow \cos x \geq 0 \Rightarrow x$ must be in quadrants I or IV.

88. $\sqrt{1 - \sin^2 x} = -\cos x$. $\sqrt{1 - \sin^2 x} \geq 0 \Rightarrow -\cos x \geq 0$
$\cos x \leq 0 \Rightarrow x$ in quadrants II or III.

90. $\sqrt{1 - \cos^2 x} = |\sin x|$. Both sides $\geq 0 \Rightarrow x$ in all quadrants.

92. $\dfrac{\sin x}{\sqrt{1 - \sin^2 x}} = -\tan x$. $\sqrt{1 - \sin^2 x} \geq 0 \Rightarrow$ identity when $\sin x$ and $\tan x$ have opposite signs $\Rightarrow x$ in quadrants II or III.

94. $\sqrt{a^2 - u^2} = \sqrt{a^2 - a^2 \cos^2 x} = \sqrt{a^2(1 - \cos^2 x)}$
$= a\sqrt{\sin^2 x}$ and since for $0 < x < \pi$, $\sqrt{\sin^2 x} = \sin x$
$= a \sin x$

96. $\sqrt{a^2 + u^2} = \sqrt{a^2 + a^2 \cot^2 x} = \sqrt{a^2(1 + \cot^2 x)}$

$\qquad = a\sqrt{\csc^2 x}$ and since for $0 < x < \dfrac{\pi}{2}$, $\sqrt{\csc^2 x} = \csc x$

$\qquad = a \csc x$

Exercise 6-2

2. Verify: $\cos(x + 2\pi) = \cos x$

$\qquad \cos(x + 2\pi) = \cos x \cos 2\pi - \sin x \sin 2\pi$

$\qquad\qquad\qquad = \cos x(1) - \sin x(0)$

$\qquad\qquad\qquad = \cos x$

4. Verify: $\cot(x + \pi) = \cot x$

$\qquad \cot(x + \pi) = \dfrac{\cos(x + \pi)}{\sin(x + \pi)}$

$\qquad\qquad\qquad = \dfrac{\cos x \cos \pi - \sin x \sin \pi}{\sin x \cos \pi + \sin \pi \cos x}$

$\qquad\qquad\qquad = \dfrac{\cos x(-1) - \sin x(0)}{\sin x(-1) + (0)\cos x}$

$\qquad\qquad\qquad = \dfrac{-\cos x}{-\sin x}$

$\qquad\qquad\qquad = \cot x$

6. Verify: $\sin(x + 2k\pi) = \sin x$, k an integer

$\qquad \sin(x + 2k\pi) = \sin x \cos(2k\pi) + \sin(2k\pi)\cos x$

$\qquad\qquad\qquad = \sin x(1) + (0)\cos x$

$\qquad\qquad\qquad = \sin x$

8. Verify: $\tan(x + k\pi) = \tan x$, k an integer

$\qquad \tan(x + k\pi) = \dfrac{\tan x + \tan k\pi}{1 - \tan x \tan k\pi}$

$\qquad\qquad\qquad = \dfrac{\tan x + 0}{1 - \tan x(0)}$

$\qquad\qquad\qquad = \tan x$

10. Verify: $\tan\left(\dfrac{\pi}{2} - x\right) = \cot x$

$\qquad \tan\left(\dfrac{\pi}{2} - x\right) = \dfrac{\sin(\frac{\pi}{2} - x)}{\cos(\frac{\pi}{2} - x)}$

$\qquad\qquad\qquad = \dfrac{\cos x}{\sin x}$

$\qquad\qquad\qquad = \cot x$

12. Verify: $\sec\left(\dfrac{\pi}{2} - x\right) = \csc x$

$\qquad \sec\left(\dfrac{\pi}{2} - x\right) = \dfrac{1}{\cos(\frac{\pi}{2} - x)}$

$\qquad\qquad\qquad = \dfrac{1}{\sin x}$

$\qquad\qquad\qquad = \csc x$

14. $\sin(x - 45°) = \sin x \cos 45° - \sin 45° \cos x$

$$= \sin x \cdot \frac{\sqrt{2}}{2} - \frac{\sqrt{2}}{2} \cos x$$

$$= \frac{\sqrt{2}}{2} (\sin x - \cos x)$$

16. $\cos(x + 180°) = \cos x \cos 180° - \sin x \sin 180°$

$$= \cos x(-1) - \sin x(0)$$

$$= -\cos x$$

18. $\tan\left(\dfrac{\pi}{4} - x\right) = \dfrac{\tan \frac{\pi}{4} - \tan x}{1 + \tan \frac{\pi}{4} \tan x}$

$$= \frac{1 - \tan x}{1 + \tan x}$$

20. $\sin 75° = \sin(45° + 30°) = \sin 45° \cos 30° + \sin 30° \cos 45°$

$$= \frac{1}{\sqrt{2}} \cdot \frac{\sqrt{3}}{2} + \frac{1}{2} \cdot \frac{\sqrt{2}}{2}$$

$$= \frac{\sqrt{3} + 1}{2\sqrt{2}} \quad \text{or} \quad \frac{\sqrt{3} + 1}{2\sqrt{2}} \cdot \frac{\sqrt{2}}{\sqrt{2}} = \frac{\sqrt{6} + \sqrt{2}}{4}$$

22. $\cos \dfrac{\pi}{12} = \cos\left(\dfrac{\pi}{4} - \dfrac{\pi}{6}\right) = \cos \dfrac{\pi}{4} \cos \dfrac{\pi}{6} + \sin \dfrac{\pi}{4} \sin \dfrac{\pi}{6}$

$$= \frac{1}{\sqrt{2}} \cdot \frac{\sqrt{3}}{2} + \frac{1}{\sqrt{2}} \cdot \frac{1}{2}$$

$$= \frac{\sqrt{3} + 1}{2\sqrt{2}} \cdot \frac{\sqrt{2}}{\sqrt{2}}$$

$$= \frac{\sqrt{6} + \sqrt{2}}{4}$$

24. $\sin 22° \cos 38° + \cos 22° \sin 38° = \sin(22° + 38°) = \sin 60° = \dfrac{\sqrt{3}}{2}$

26. $\dfrac{\tan 110° - \tan 50°}{1 + \tan 110° \tan 50°} = \tan(110° - 50°) = \tan 60° = \sqrt{3}$

28. $\sin x = \dfrac{2}{3}$ (QII), $\cos y = -\dfrac{1}{4}$ (QIII).

Angle x: $a = -\sqrt{3^2 - 2^2} = -\sqrt{5} \Rightarrow \cos x = -\dfrac{\sqrt{5}}{3}$

Angle y: $b = -\sqrt{4^2 - (-1)^2} = -\sqrt{15} \Rightarrow \sin y = -\dfrac{\sqrt{15}}{4}$

$\sin(x - y) = \sin x \cos y - \sin y \cos x$

$$= \frac{2}{3} \cdot \left(-\frac{1}{4}\right) - \frac{-\sqrt{15}}{4} \cdot \frac{-\sqrt{5}}{3}$$

$$= \frac{-2 - 5\sqrt{3}}{12}$$

$$\tan x = -\frac{2}{\sqrt{5}}, \quad \tan y = \sqrt{15}$$

$$\tan(x + y) = \frac{\tan x + \tan y}{1 - \tan x \tan y} = \frac{-\frac{2}{\sqrt{5}} + \sqrt{15}}{1 - \frac{-2}{\sqrt{5}} \cdot \sqrt{15}} \cdot \frac{\sqrt{5}}{\sqrt{5}} = \frac{-2 + 5\sqrt{3}}{\sqrt{5} + 2\sqrt{15}}$$

30. $\cos x = -\frac{1}{3}$ (QII), $\tan y = \frac{1}{2}$ (QIII)

Angle x: $b = \sqrt{3^2 - (-1)^2} = \sqrt{8}$

$$\sin x = \frac{\sqrt{8}}{3}, \quad \tan x = -\sqrt{8}$$

Angle y: $c = \sqrt{(-2)^2 + (-1)^2} = \sqrt{5}$

$$\cos y = \frac{-2}{\sqrt{5}}, \quad \sin y = \frac{-1}{\sqrt{5}}$$

$$\sin(x - y) = \sin x \cos y - \sin y \cos x$$

$$= \frac{\sqrt{8}}{3} \cdot \frac{-2}{\sqrt{5}} - \frac{-1}{\sqrt{5}} \cdot \frac{-1}{3} = \frac{-4\sqrt{2} - 1}{3\sqrt{5}}$$

$$\tan(x + y) = \frac{\tan x + \tan y}{1 - \tan x \tan y} = \frac{-\sqrt{8} + \frac{1}{2}}{1 - (-\sqrt{8})(\frac{1}{2})} \cdot \frac{2}{2} = \frac{1 - 4\sqrt{2}}{2 + 2\sqrt{2}}$$

32. Verify: $\sin 2x = \sin(x + x)$

$$\sin(x + x) = \sin x \cos x + \cos x \sin x$$

$$= 2 \sin x \cos x$$

34. Verify: $\cot(x - y) = \frac{\cot x \cot y + 1}{\cot y - \cot x}$

$$\cot(x - y) = \frac{\cos(x - y)}{\sin(x - y)}$$

$$= \frac{\cos x \cos y + \sin x \sin y}{\sin x \cos y - \sin y \cos x} \cdot \frac{\frac{1}{\sin x \sin y}}{\frac{1}{\sin x \sin y}}$$

$$= \frac{\cot x \cot y + 1}{\cot y - \cot x}$$

36. Verify: $\cot 2x = \frac{\cot^2 x - 1}{2 \cot x}$

$$\cot 2x = \cot(x + x)$$

$$= \frac{\cos(x + x)}{\sin(x + x)}$$

$$= \frac{\cos x \cos x - \sin x \sin x}{\sin x \cos x + \sin x \cos x}$$

$$= \frac{\cos^2 x - \sin^2 x}{2 \sin x \cos x} \cdot \frac{\frac{1}{\sin^2 x}}{\frac{1}{\sin^2 x}}$$

$$= \frac{\cot^2 x - 1}{2 \cot x}$$

38. Verify: $\dfrac{\sin(u + v)}{\sin(u - v)} = \dfrac{\tan u + \tan v}{\tan u - \tan v}$

$$\frac{\sin(u + v)}{\sin(u - v)} = \frac{\sin u \cos v + \sin v \cos u}{\sin u \cos v - \sin v \cos u} \cdot \frac{\frac{1}{\cos u \cos v}}{\frac{1}{\cos u \cos v}}$$

$$= \frac{\tan u + \tan v}{\tan u - \tan v}$$

40. Verify: $\tan x - \tan y = \dfrac{\sin(x - y)}{\cos x \cos y}$

$$\frac{\sin(x - y)}{\cos x \cos y} = \frac{\sin x \cos y - \sin y \cos x}{\cos x \cos y}$$

$$= \frac{\sin x \cos y}{\cos x \cos y} - \frac{\sin y \cos x}{\cos x \cos y}$$

$$= \tan x - \tan y$$

42. Verify: $\tan(x + y) = \dfrac{\cot x + \cot y}{\cot x \cot y - 1}$

$$\tan(x + y) = \frac{\tan x + \tan y}{1 - \tan x \tan y} \cdot \frac{\frac{1}{\tan x \tan y}}{\frac{1}{\tan x \tan y}}$$

$$= \frac{\frac{1}{\tan y} + \frac{1}{\tan x}}{\frac{1}{\tan x \tan y} - 1}$$

$$= \frac{\cot y + \cot x}{\cot x \cot y - 1}$$

$$= \frac{\cot x + \cot y}{\cot x \cot y - 1}$$

44. Verify: $\dfrac{\sin(x + h) - \sin x}{h} = \sin x\left(\dfrac{\cos h - 1}{h}\right) + \cos x\left(\dfrac{\sin h}{h}\right)$

$$\frac{\sin(x + h) - \sin x}{h} = \frac{\sin x \cos h + \sin h \cos x - \sin x}{h}$$

$$= \frac{\sin x(\cos h - 1) + \sin h \cos x}{h}$$

$$= \sin x\left(\frac{\cos h - 1}{h}\right) + \cos x\left(\frac{\sin h}{h}\right)$$

46. $x = 3.042, \; y = 2.384$

$$\begin{aligned}
\sin(x - y) &= \sin(3.042 - 2.384) \\
&= \sin(0.658) \\
&\approx 0.6115
\end{aligned}$$

$$\begin{aligned}
\sin(x - y) &= \sin x \cos y - \sin y \cos x \\
&= \sin 3.042 \cos 2.384 - \sin 2.384 \cos 3.042 \\
&\approx 0.6115
\end{aligned}$$

$$\begin{aligned}
\tan(x + y) &= \tan(3.042 + 2.384) \\
&= \tan 5.426 \\
&\approx -1.155
\end{aligned}$$

$$\begin{aligned}
\tan(x + y) &= \frac{\tan x + \tan y}{1 - \tan x \tan y} \\
&= \frac{\tan 3.042 + \tan 2.384}{1 - \tan 3.042 \tan 2.384} \\
&\approx -1.155
\end{aligned}$$

48. $x = 128.3°,\ y = 25.62°$

$$\sin(x - y) = \sin(128.3° - 25.62°)$$
$$= \sin(102.68°)$$
$$\approx 0.9756$$

$$\sin x \cos y - \sin y \cos x = \sin 128.3° \cos 25.62° - \sin 25.62° \cos 128.3°$$
$$\approx 0.9756$$

$$\tan(x + y) = \tan(128.3° + 25.62°)$$
$$= \tan(153.92°)$$
$$\approx -0.4895$$

$$\frac{\tan x + \tan y}{1 - \tan x \tan y} = \frac{\tan 128.3° + \tan 25.62°}{1 - \tan 128.3° \tan 25.62°}$$
$$\approx -0.4895$$

50. Evaluate each side for a particular set of values of x and y for which each side is defined. If the left side is not equal to the right side, then the equation is not an identity. For example, for $x = 2$ and $y = 1$, both sides are defined, but are not equal.

52. $y = \sin\left(x - \dfrac{\pi}{3}\right) = \sin x \cos \dfrac{\pi}{3} - \sin \dfrac{\pi}{3} \cos x = \dfrac{1}{2} \sin x - \dfrac{\sqrt{3}}{2} \cos x$

$y_1 = \sin(x - \pi/3)$

$y_2 = \dfrac{1}{2} \sin x - \dfrac{\sqrt{3}}{2} \cos x$

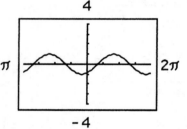

54. $y = \cos\left(x + \dfrac{5\pi}{6}\right) = \cos x \cos\left(\dfrac{5\pi}{6}\right) - \sin x \sin \dfrac{5\pi}{6} = -\dfrac{\sqrt{3}}{2} \cos x - \dfrac{1}{2} \sin x$

$y_1 = \cos(x + 5\pi/6)$

$y_2 = -\dfrac{\sqrt{3}}{2} \cos x - \dfrac{1}{2} \sin x$

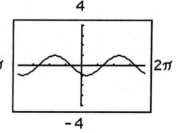

56. $y = \tan\left(x - \dfrac{\pi}{4}\right) = \dfrac{\tan x - \tan \frac{\pi}{4}}{1 + \tan x \tan \frac{\pi}{4}} = \dfrac{\tan x - 1}{1 + \tan x}$

$y_1 = \tan(x - \pi/4)$

$y_2 = \dfrac{\tan x - 1}{1 + \tan x}$

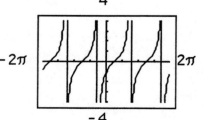

58. $\cos\left[\sin^{-1}\left(-\dfrac{3}{5}\right) + \cos^{-1}\left(\dfrac{4}{5}\right)\right]$

$\qquad = \cos\left[\sin^{-1}\left(-\dfrac{3}{5}\right)\right]\cos\left[\cos^{-1}\left(\dfrac{4}{5}\right)\right] - \sin\left[\sin^{-1}\left(-\dfrac{3}{5}\right)\right]\sin\left[\cos^{-1}\left(\dfrac{4}{5}\right)\right]$

$\qquad = \left(\dfrac{4}{5}\right)\left(\dfrac{4}{5}\right) - \left(-\dfrac{3}{5}\right)\left(\dfrac{3}{5}\right) = \dfrac{16}{25} + \dfrac{9}{25} = 1$

60. $\cos\left[\arccos\left(-\dfrac{\sqrt{3}}{2}\right) - \arcsin\left(-\dfrac{1}{2}\right)\right]$

$\qquad = \cos\left(\arccos\left(-\dfrac{\sqrt{3}}{2}\right)\right)\cos\left(\arcsin\left(-\dfrac{1}{2}\right)\right) + \sin\left(\arccos\left(-\dfrac{\sqrt{3}}{2}\right)\right)\sin\left(\arcsin\left(-\dfrac{1}{2}\right)\right)$

$\qquad = \left(-\dfrac{\sqrt{3}}{2}\right)\left(\dfrac{\sqrt{3}}{2}\right) + \left(\dfrac{1}{2}\right)\left(-\dfrac{1}{2}\right)$

$\qquad = -\dfrac{3}{4} - \dfrac{1}{4}$

$\qquad = -1$

62. Angle x: $b = x$, $c = 1$, $a = \sqrt{1 - x^2}$
Angle y: $a = y$, $c = 1$, $b = \sqrt{1 - y^2}$

$\cos(\sin^{-1} x - \cos^{-1} y) = \cos(\sin^{-1} x)\cos(\cos^{-1} y) + \sin(\sin^{-1} x)\sin(\cos^{-1} y)$

$\qquad\qquad = \sqrt{1 - x^2} \cdot y + x \cdot \sqrt{1 - y^2}$

$\qquad\qquad = y\sqrt{1 - x^2} + x\sqrt{1 - y^2}$

64. Verify: $\sin(x + y + z) = \sin x \cos y \cos z + \cos x \sin y \cos z$
$\qquad\qquad\qquad + \cos x \cos y \sin z - \sin x \sin y \sin z$

$\sin(x + y + z) = \sin((x + y) + z)$

$\qquad\qquad = \sin(x + y)\cos z + \sin z \cos(x + y)$

$\qquad\qquad = \cos z[\sin x \cos y + \sin y \cos x]$

$\qquad\qquad\quad + \sin z[\cos x \cos y - \sin x \sin y]$

$\qquad\qquad = \sin x \cos y \cos z + \cos x \sin y \cos z$

$\qquad\qquad\quad + \cos x \cos y \sin z - \sin x \sin y \sin z$

66. $y = \sin 0.8x \cos 0.3x - \cos 0.8x \sin 0.3x = \sin((0.8 - 0.3)x) = \sin(0.5x)$

$y_1 = \sin 0.8x \cos 0.3x - \cos 0.8x \sin 0.3x$

$y_2 = \sin 0.5x$

68. $y = 3x + 1$ and $y = \dfrac{1}{2}x - 1$

$\tan(\theta_2 - \theta_1) = \dfrac{m_2 - m_1}{1 + m_1 m_2}$

$\tan(\theta_2 - \theta_1) = \dfrac{3 - \frac{1}{2}}{1 + 3\left(\frac{1}{2}\right)} \cdot \dfrac{2}{2} = \dfrac{6 - 1}{2 + 3} = 1$

$\theta_2 - \theta_1 = 45°$

70. $\alpha = 43°$, $M = 0.25$ inch, $N = 0.11$ inch

$$\tan \beta = \tan \alpha - \frac{N}{M} \sec \alpha$$

$$= \tan 43° - \frac{0.11}{0.25} \sec 43°$$

$$\approx 0.33089$$

$$\beta \approx 18°$$

Exercise 6-3

2. Verify: $\sin 2x = 2 \sin x \cos x$ for $x = 45°$

$$\sin 2x = \sin(2 \cdot 45°) = \sin 90° = 1$$

$$2 \sin x \cos x = 2 \sin 45° \cos 45° = 2 \cdot \frac{\sqrt{2}}{2} \cdot \frac{\sqrt{2}}{2} = 1$$

4. Verify: $\tan 2x = \dfrac{2 \tan x}{1 - \tan^2 x}$ for $x = \dfrac{\pi}{6}$

$$\tan 2x = \tan\left(2 \cdot \frac{\pi}{6}\right) = \tan \frac{\pi}{3} = \sqrt{3}$$

$$\frac{2 \tan x}{1 - \tan^2 x} = \frac{2 \tan \frac{\pi}{6}}{1 - \tan^2 \frac{\pi}{6}} = \frac{2\left(\frac{1}{\sqrt{3}}\right)}{1 - \left(\frac{1}{\sqrt{3}}\right)^2} = \frac{\frac{2}{\sqrt{3}}}{1 - \frac{1}{3}} \cdot \frac{3\sqrt{3}}{3\sqrt{3}} = \frac{6}{3\sqrt{3} - \sqrt{3}} \cdot \frac{\sqrt{3}}{\sqrt{3}} = \frac{6\sqrt{3}}{6} = \sqrt{3}$$

6. Verify: $\cos \dfrac{x}{2} = \pm\sqrt{\dfrac{1 + \cos x}{2}}$, $x = \dfrac{\pi}{2}$

$\dfrac{x}{2} = \dfrac{\pi}{4}$, Quad I: sign of $\cos \dfrac{x}{2}$ is $+$.

$$\cos \frac{x}{2} = \cos \frac{\frac{\pi}{2}}{2} = \cos \frac{\pi}{4} = \frac{1}{\sqrt{2}} = \frac{\sqrt{2}}{2}$$

$$\sqrt{\frac{1 + \cos x}{2}} = \sqrt{\frac{1 + \cos \frac{\pi}{2}}{2}}$$

$$= \sqrt{\frac{1 + 0}{2}}$$

$$= \frac{1}{\sqrt{2}} = \frac{\sqrt{2}}{2}$$

8. $\tan 75° = \tan \dfrac{150°}{2} = \sqrt{\dfrac{1 - \cos 150°}{1 + \cos 150°}}$

$$= \sqrt{\frac{1 - \frac{-\sqrt{3}}{2}}{1 + \frac{-\sqrt{3}}{2}}}$$

$$= \sqrt{\frac{2 + \sqrt{3}}{2 - \sqrt{3}} \cdot \frac{\sqrt{2 - \sqrt{3}}}{\sqrt{2 - \sqrt{3}}}}$$

$$= \frac{1}{2 - \sqrt{3}} \cdot \frac{2 + \sqrt{3}}{2 + \sqrt{3}}$$

$$= 2 + \sqrt{3}$$

10. $\tan 15° = \tan \dfrac{30°}{2} = \sqrt{\dfrac{1 - \cos 30°}{1 + \cos 30°}}$

$\qquad = \sqrt{\dfrac{1 - \frac{\sqrt{3}}{2}}{1 + \frac{\sqrt{3}}{2}}}$

$\qquad = 2 - \sqrt{3}$ (See problem 8 for the simplification procedure.)

12.

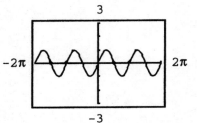

14. $y_1 = \tan 2x$

$\quad y_2 = \dfrac{2 \tan x}{1 - \tan^2 x}$

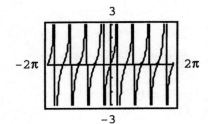

16. Verify: $\sin 2x = (\tan x)(1 + \cos 2x)$

$\qquad (\tan x)(1 + \cos 2x) = \dfrac{\sin x}{\cos x}(1 + 2\cos^2 x - 1)$

$\qquad\qquad\qquad\qquad = \dfrac{\sin x}{\cos x}(2\cos^2 x)$

$\qquad\qquad\qquad\qquad = 2\sin x \cos x$

$\qquad\qquad\qquad\qquad = \sin 2x$

18. Verify: $\cos^2 x = \dfrac{1}{2}(\cos 2x + 1)$

$\qquad \dfrac{1}{2}(\cos 2x + 1) = \dfrac{1}{2}(2\cos^2 x - 1 + 1)$

$\qquad\qquad\qquad\qquad = \dfrac{1}{2}(2\cos^2 x)$

$\qquad\qquad\qquad\qquad = \cos^2 x$

20. Verify: $1 + \sin 2t = (\sin t + \cos t)^2$

$\qquad 1 + \sin 2t = 1 + 2\sin t \cos t$

$\qquad\qquad\qquad = \sin^2 t + \cos^2 t + 2\sin t \cos t$

$\qquad\qquad\qquad = \sin^2 t + 2\sin t \cos t + \cos^2 t$

$\qquad\qquad\qquad = (\sin t + \cos t)^2$

22. Verify: $\cos^2 \dfrac{x}{2} = \dfrac{1 + \cos x}{2}$

$\qquad \cos^2 \dfrac{x}{2} = \left(\pm\sqrt{\dfrac{1 + \cos x}{2}}\right)^2$

$\qquad\qquad = \dfrac{1 + \cos x}{2}$

24. Verify: $\cot 2x = \dfrac{1 - \tan^2 x}{2 \tan x}$

$$\cot 2x = \cot(x + x)$$

$$= \frac{1}{\tan(x + x)}$$

$$= \frac{1 - \tan^2 x}{\tan x + \tan x}$$

$$= \frac{1 - \tan^2 x}{2 \tan x}$$

26. Verify: $\cot \dfrac{\theta}{2} = \dfrac{1 + \cos \theta}{\sin \theta}$

$$\cot \frac{\theta}{2} = \frac{1}{\tan \frac{\theta}{2}} = \frac{1}{\frac{\sin \theta}{1 + \cos \theta}} = \frac{1 + \cos \theta}{\sin \theta}$$

28. Verify: $\dfrac{\cos 2u}{1 - \sin 2u} = \dfrac{1 + \tan u}{1 - \tan u}$

$$\frac{\cos 2u}{1 - \sin 2u} = \frac{\cos^2 u - \sin^2 u}{1 - 2 \sin u \cos u}$$

$$= \frac{(\cos u - \sin u)(\cos u + \sin u)}{\cos^2 u - 2 \sin u \cos u + \sin^2 u}$$

$$= \frac{(\cos u - \sin u)(\cos u + \sin u)}{(\cos u - \sin u)^2}$$

$$= \frac{\cos u + \sin u}{\cos u - \sin u} \cdot \frac{\frac{1}{\cos u}}{\frac{1}{\cos u}}$$

$$= \frac{1 + \tan u}{1 - \tan u}$$

30. Verify: $\sec 2x = \dfrac{\sec^2 x}{2 - \sec^2 x}$

$$\sec 2x = \frac{1}{\cos 2x}$$

$$= \frac{1}{2 \cos^2 x - 1} \cdot \frac{\frac{1}{\cos^2 x}}{\frac{1}{\cos^2 x}}$$

$$= \frac{\frac{1}{\cos^2 x}}{2 - \frac{1}{\cos^2 x}}$$

$$= \frac{\sec^2 x}{2 - \sec^2 x}$$

32. Verify: $\cos 2\alpha = \dfrac{\cot \alpha - \tan \alpha}{\cot \alpha + \tan \alpha}$

$$\frac{\cot \alpha - \tan \alpha}{\cot \alpha + \tan \alpha} = \frac{\frac{\cos \alpha}{\sin \alpha} - \frac{\sin \alpha}{\cos \alpha}}{\frac{\cos \alpha}{\sin \alpha} + \frac{\sin \alpha}{\cos \alpha}} \cdot \frac{\sin \alpha \cos \alpha}{\sin \alpha \cos \alpha}$$

$$= \frac{\cos^2 \alpha - \sin^2 \alpha}{\cos^2 \alpha + \sin^2 \alpha}$$

$$= \frac{\cos 2\alpha}{1}$$

$$= \cos 2\alpha$$

34. $\cos x = -\dfrac{4}{5}, \ \dfrac{\pi}{2} < x < \pi$

$a = -4, \ r = 5, \ b = 3$

$\sin 2x = 2 \sin x \cos x = 2 \cdot \dfrac{3}{5} \cdot \left(-\dfrac{4}{5}\right) = -\dfrac{24}{25}$

$\cos 2x = 1 - 2 \sin^2 x = 1 - 2\left(\dfrac{3}{5}\right)^2 = 1 - \dfrac{18}{25} = \dfrac{7}{25}$

$\tan 2x = \dfrac{2 \tan x}{1 - \tan^2 x} = \dfrac{2(-\frac{3}{4})}{1 - (-\frac{3}{4})^2} = \dfrac{-\frac{6}{4}}{1 - \frac{9}{16}} \cdot \dfrac{16}{16} = \dfrac{-24}{16 - 9} = -\dfrac{24}{7}$

36. $\cot x = -\dfrac{5}{12}, \ -\dfrac{\pi}{2} < x < 0$

$a = 5, \ b = -12, \ r = 13$

$\sin 2x = 2 \sin x \cos x = 2 \cdot \dfrac{-12}{13} \cdot \dfrac{5}{13} = -\dfrac{120}{169}$

$\cos 2x = 1 - 2 \sin^2 x = 1 - 2\left(-\dfrac{12}{13}\right)^2 = 1 - \dfrac{288}{169} = \dfrac{-119}{169}$

$\tan 2x = \dfrac{2 \tan x}{1 - \tan^2 x} = \dfrac{2(-\frac{12}{5})}{1 - (-\frac{12}{5})^2} = \dfrac{-\frac{24}{5}}{1 - \frac{144}{25}} \cdot \dfrac{25}{25} = \dfrac{-120}{25 - 144} = \dfrac{120}{119}$

38. $\cos x = -\dfrac{1}{4}, \ \pi < x < \dfrac{3\pi}{2}$

$a = -1, \ r = 4, \ b = -\sqrt{15}$

$\dfrac{\pi}{2} < \dfrac{x}{2} < \dfrac{3\pi}{4}$ (QII)

$\sin \dfrac{x}{2} = \pm\sqrt{\dfrac{1 - \cos x}{2}} = \sqrt{\dfrac{1 - \frac{-1}{4}}{2}} = \sqrt{\dfrac{4 + 1}{8}} = \dfrac{\sqrt{5}}{2\sqrt{2}} \cdot \dfrac{\sqrt{2}}{\sqrt{2}} = \dfrac{\sqrt{10}}{4}$

$\cos \dfrac{x}{2} = \pm\sqrt{\dfrac{1 + \cos x}{2}} = -\sqrt{\dfrac{1 + \frac{-1}{4}}{2}} = -\sqrt{\dfrac{4 - 1}{8}} = \dfrac{-\sqrt{3}}{2\sqrt{2}} \cdot \dfrac{\sqrt{2}}{\sqrt{2}} = \dfrac{-\sqrt{6}}{4}$

$\tan \dfrac{x}{2} = \dfrac{1 - \cos x}{\sin x} = \dfrac{1 - \frac{-1}{4}}{\frac{-\sqrt{15}}{4}} = \dfrac{4 + 1}{-\sqrt{15}} \cdot \dfrac{\sqrt{15}}{\sqrt{15}} = \dfrac{-5\sqrt{15}}{15} = -\dfrac{\sqrt{15}}{3}$

40. $\tan x = \frac{3}{4}$, $-\pi < x < -\frac{\pi}{2}$

$a = -4$, $b = -3$, $r = 5$, $-\frac{\pi}{2} < \frac{x}{2} < -\frac{\pi}{4}$ (QIV)

$$\sin \frac{x}{2} = \pm\sqrt{\frac{1 - \cos x}{2}} = -\sqrt{\frac{1 - \frac{-4}{5}}{2}} = -\sqrt{\frac{5 + 4}{10}} = -\frac{3}{\sqrt{10}} \cdot \frac{\sqrt{10}}{\sqrt{10}} = \frac{-3\sqrt{10}}{10}$$

$$\cos \frac{x}{2} = \pm\sqrt{\frac{1 + \cos x}{2}} = \sqrt{\frac{1 + \frac{-4}{5}}{2}} = \sqrt{\frac{5 - 4}{10}} = \frac{1}{\sqrt{10}} \cdot \frac{\sqrt{10}}{\sqrt{10}} = \frac{\sqrt{10}}{10}$$

$$\tan \frac{x}{2} = \frac{1 - \cos x}{\sin x} = \frac{1 - \frac{-4}{5}}{-\frac{3}{5}} = \frac{5 + 4}{-3} = \frac{9}{-3} = -3$$

42. Find the exact values of $\sin \theta$ and $\cos \theta$, given $\sec 2\theta = -\frac{5}{4}$, $0° < \theta < 90°$.

(A) $0° < \theta < 90° \Rightarrow 0° < 2\theta < 180°$ and since $\sec 2\theta = \frac{-5}{4} < 0$, 2θ is in QII.

(B) $\sec 2\theta = \frac{-5}{4} \Rightarrow \cos 2\theta = \frac{-4}{5}$

$$\sin 2\theta = \sqrt{1 - \cos^2 2\theta} = \sqrt{1 - (\tfrac{-4}{5})^2} = \sqrt{1 - \frac{16}{25}} = \sqrt{\frac{9}{25}} = \frac{3}{5}$$

(C) $\sin \theta = \pm\sqrt{\dfrac{1 - \cos 2\theta}{2}}$

$\cos \theta = \pm\sqrt{\dfrac{1 + \cos 2\theta}{2}}$

(D) & (E) θ is a quadrant I angle, so

$$\sin \theta = \sqrt{\frac{1 - \cos 2\theta}{2}} = \sqrt{\frac{1 - \frac{-4}{5}}{2}} = \sqrt{\frac{5 + 4}{10}} = \frac{3}{\sqrt{10}} \cdot \frac{\sqrt{10}}{\sqrt{10}} = \frac{3\sqrt{10}}{10}$$

$$\cos \theta = \sqrt{\frac{1 + \cos 2\theta}{2}} = \sqrt{\frac{1 + \frac{-4}{5}}{2}} = \sqrt{\frac{5 - 4}{10}} = \frac{1}{\sqrt{10}} \cdot \frac{\sqrt{10}}{\sqrt{10}} = \frac{\sqrt{10}}{10}$$

44. $x = 72.358°$

(A) $\tan 2x = \tan(2 \cdot 72.358°) = \tan 144.716° \approx -0.70762$

$\tan 2x = \dfrac{2 \tan x}{1 - \tan^2 x} = \dfrac{2 \tan 72.358°}{1 - \tan^2 72.358°} \approx -0.70762$

(B) $\cos \dfrac{x}{2} = \cos \dfrac{72.358°}{2} = \cos 36.179° \approx 0.80718$

$\cos \dfrac{x}{2} = \sqrt{\dfrac{1 + \cos x}{2}} = \sqrt{\dfrac{1 + \cos 72.358°}{2}} \approx 0.80718$

46. $x = 4$

(A) $\tan 2x = \tan(2 \cdot 4) = \tan 8 \approx -6.7997$

$\tan 2x = \dfrac{2 \tan x}{1 - \tan^2 x} = \dfrac{2 \tan 4}{1 - \tan^2 4} \approx -6.7997$

(B) $\cos \dfrac{x}{2} = \cos \dfrac{4}{2} = \cos 2 \approx -0.41615$

$\cos \dfrac{x}{2} = -\sqrt{\dfrac{1 + \cos x}{2}} = -\sqrt{\dfrac{1 + \cos 4}{2}} \approx -0.41615$ (Quadrant III)

48.

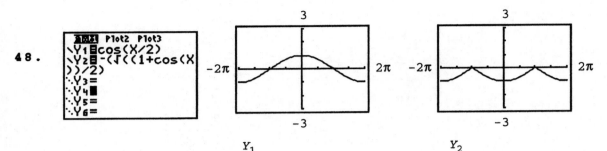

Y_1

Y_2

Y_1 and Y_2 are identities on the intervals $[-2\pi,\ -\pi]$ and $[\pi,\ 2\pi]$.

50.

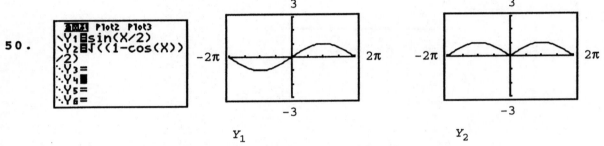

Y_1

Y_2

Y_1 and Y_2 are identities on the interval $[0,\ 2\pi]$.

52. Verify: $\sin 3x = 3 \sin x - 4 \sin^3 x$

$$\begin{aligned}
\sin 3x = \sin(2x + x) &= \sin 2x \cos x + \sin x \cos 2x \\
&= 2 \sin x \cos x \cos x + \sin x (1 - 2 \sin^2 x) \\
&= 2 \sin x \cos^2 x + \sin x - 2 \sin^3 x \\
&= 2 \sin x (1 - \sin^2 x) + \sin x - 2 \sin^3 x \\
&= 2 \sin x - 2 \sin^3 x + \sin x - 2 \sin^3 x \\
&= 3 \sin x - 4 \sin^3 x
\end{aligned}$$

54. Verify: $\sin 4x = (\cos x)(4 \sin x - 8 \sin^3 x)$

$$\begin{aligned}
\sin 4x = \sin(2x + 2x) & \\
&= \sin 2x \cos 2x + \sin 2x \cos 2x \\
&= 2 \sin 2x \cos 2x \\
&= 2(2 \sin x \cos x)(1 - 2 \sin^2 x) \\
&= \cos x (4 \sin x)(1 - 2 \sin^2 x) \\
&= (\cos x)(4 \sin x - 8 \sin^3 x)
\end{aligned}$$

56. Use $\sin 2\theta = 2 \sin \theta \cos \theta$

$$\begin{aligned}
\sin \left[2 \cos^{-1} \frac{3}{5} \right] &= 2 \sin \left(\cos^{-1} \frac{3}{5} \right) \cos \left(\cos^{-1} \frac{3}{5} \right) \\
&= 2 \cdot \frac{4}{5} \cdot \frac{3}{5} \\
&= \frac{24}{25}
\end{aligned}$$

58. Use $\tan 2\theta = \dfrac{2 \tan \theta}{1 - \tan^2 \theta}$

$$\tan\left[2 \tan^{-1}\left(-\frac{3}{4}\right)\right] = \frac{2 \tan(\tan^{-1}(-\frac{3}{4}))}{1 - \tan^2(\tan^{-1}(-\frac{3}{4}))}$$

$$= \frac{2(-\frac{3}{4})}{1 - (-\frac{3}{4})^2} \cdot \frac{16}{16}$$

$$= \frac{-24}{16 - 9}$$

$$= -\frac{24}{7}$$

60. Use $\sin \dfrac{\theta}{2} = \pm\sqrt{\dfrac{1 - \cos \theta}{2}}$, QIV

$$\sin\left[\frac{1}{2} \tan^{-1}\left(-\frac{4}{3}\right)\right] = -\sqrt{\frac{1 - \cos(\tan^{-1}(-\frac{4}{3}))}{2}}$$

$$= -\sqrt{\frac{1 - \frac{3}{5}}{2}}$$

$$= -\sqrt{\frac{5 - 3}{10}}$$

$$= -\frac{\sqrt{2}}{\sqrt{10}} \cdot \frac{\sqrt{10}}{\sqrt{10}}$$

$$= \frac{-2\sqrt{5}}{10}$$

$$= -\frac{\sqrt{5}}{5}$$

62. $f(x) = \csc x + \cot x = \dfrac{1}{\sin x} + \dfrac{\cos x}{\sin x}$

$$= \frac{1 + \cos x}{\sin x}$$

$$= \frac{1}{\frac{\sin x}{1 + \cos x}}$$

$$= \frac{1}{\tan \frac{x}{2}}$$

$$= \cot \frac{x}{2}$$

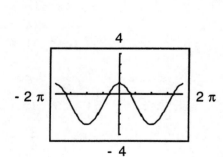

64. $f(x) = \dfrac{1 + 2 \cos 2x}{1 + 2 \cos x} = \dfrac{1 + 2(2 \cos^2 x - 1)}{1 + 2 \cos x}$

$$= \frac{1 + 4 \cos^2 x - 2}{1 + 2 \cos x}$$

$$= \frac{4 \cos^2 x - 1}{1 + 2 \cos x}$$

$$= \frac{(2 \cos x + 1)(2 \cos x - 1)}{(1 + 2 \cos x)}$$

$$= -1 + 2 \cos x$$

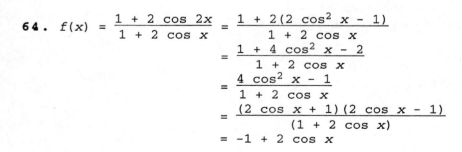

66. $f(x) = \dfrac{\cot\,x}{1 + \cos\,2x} = \dfrac{\frac{\cos\,x}{\sin\,x}}{1 + (2\cos^2\,x - 1)}$

$\qquad\qquad = \dfrac{\frac{\cos\,x}{\sin\,x}}{2\cos^2\,x}$

$\qquad\qquad = \dfrac{\cos\,x}{\sin\,x} \cdot \dfrac{1}{2\cos^2\,x}$

$\qquad\qquad = \dfrac{1}{2\sin\,x\,\cos\,x}$

$\qquad\qquad = \dfrac{1}{\sin\,2x}$

$\qquad\qquad = \csc\,2x$

68. $\tan\,2\theta = \dfrac{2\tan\,\theta}{1 - \tan^2\,\theta}, \ \tan\,\theta = \dfrac{2}{x}, \ \tan\,2\theta = \dfrac{6}{x}$

$\qquad \dfrac{6}{x} = \dfrac{2 \cdot \frac{2}{x}}{1 - \left(\frac{2}{x}\right)^2} \cdot \dfrac{x^2}{x^2}$

$\qquad \dfrac{6}{x} = \dfrac{4x}{x^2 - 4}$

$\qquad 6x^2 - 24 = 4x^2$

$\qquad\quad x^2 = 12$

$\qquad\qquad x = 2\sqrt{3} \approx 3.464$ ft.

$\qquad \tan\,\theta = \dfrac{2}{x} = \dfrac{2}{2\sqrt{3}} = \dfrac{1}{\sqrt{3}}$

$\qquad\qquad \theta = 30.000°$

70.

$AM = \sqrt{s^2 + \left(\dfrac{s}{2}\right)^2} = \sqrt{\dfrac{5s^2}{4}} = \dfrac{\sqrt{5} \cdot s}{2}$

$MN = \sqrt{\left(\dfrac{s}{2}\right)^2 + \left(\dfrac{s}{2}\right)^2} = \sqrt{\dfrac{s^2}{2}} = \dfrac{\sqrt{2} \cdot s}{2}$

$\sin\,\dfrac{\theta}{2} = \dfrac{\frac{MN}{2}}{AM} = \dfrac{\frac{\sqrt{2} \cdot s}{4}}{\frac{\sqrt{5} \cdot s}{2}} = \dfrac{\sqrt{2}}{2\sqrt{5}} = \sqrt{\dfrac{1 - \cos\,\theta}{2}}$

$\dfrac{1 - \cos\,\theta}{2} = \dfrac{2}{20} = \dfrac{1}{10}$

$1 - \cos\,\theta = \dfrac{2}{10} = \dfrac{1}{5}$

$\qquad \cos\,\theta = \dfrac{4}{5}$

Exercise 6-4

2. $\cos\,x\,\cos\,y = \dfrac{1}{2}[\cos(x + y) + \cos(x - y)]$

$\quad \cos\,7A\,\cos\,5A = \dfrac{1}{2}[\cos(7A + 5A) + \cos(7A - 5A)]$

$\qquad\qquad\qquad = \dfrac{1}{2}(\cos\,12A + \cos\,2A)$

$\qquad\qquad\qquad = \dfrac{1}{2}\cos\,12A + \dfrac{1}{2}\cos\,2A$

4. $\cos x \sin y = \dfrac{1}{2}[\sin(x + y) - \sin(x - y)]$

$$\cos 2\theta \sin 3\theta = \dfrac{1}{2}[\sin(2\theta + 3\theta) - \sin(2\theta - 3\theta)]$$

$$= \dfrac{1}{2}[\sin 5\theta - \sin(-\theta)]$$

$$= \dfrac{1}{2}[\sin 5\theta + \sin \theta]$$

$$= \dfrac{1}{2} \sin 5\theta + \dfrac{1}{2} \sin \theta$$

6. $\cos x + \cos y = 2 \cos \dfrac{x + y}{2} \cos \dfrac{x - y}{2}$

$$\cos 7\theta + \cos 5\theta = 2 \cos \dfrac{7\theta + 5\theta}{2} \cos \dfrac{7\theta - 5\theta}{2}$$

$$= 2 \cos 6\theta \cos \theta$$

8. $\sin x - \sin y = 2 \cos \dfrac{x + y}{2} \sin \dfrac{x - y}{2}$

$$\sin u - \sin 5u = 2 \cos \dfrac{u + 5u}{2} \sin \dfrac{u - 5u}{2}$$

$$= 2 \cos 3u \sin(-2u)$$

$$= -2 \cos 3u \sin 2u$$

10. $\cos x \sin y = \dfrac{1}{2}[\sin(x + y) - \sin(x - y)]$

$$\cos 75° \sin 15° = \dfrac{1}{2}[\sin(75° + 15°) - \sin(75° - 15°)]$$

$$= \dfrac{1}{2}[\sin 90° - \sin 60°]$$

$$= \dfrac{1}{2}\left(1 - \dfrac{\sqrt{3}}{2}\right)$$

$$= \dfrac{1}{2}\left(\dfrac{2 - \sqrt{3}}{2}\right)$$

$$= \dfrac{2 - \sqrt{3}}{4}$$

12. $\sin x \sin y = \dfrac{1}{2}[\cos(x - y) - \cos(x + y)]$

$$\sin 105° \sin 165° = \dfrac{1}{2}[\cos(105° - 165°) - \cos(105° + 165°)]$$

$$= \dfrac{1}{2}[\cos(-60°) - \cos 270°]$$

$$= \dfrac{1}{2}\left[\dfrac{1}{2} - 0\right]$$

$$= \dfrac{1}{4}$$

14. $\sin x + \sin y = 2 \sin \dfrac{x + y}{2} \cos \dfrac{x - y}{2}$

$\sin 195° + \sin 105° = 2 \sin \dfrac{195° + 105°}{2} \cos \dfrac{195° - 105°}{2} x$

$= 2 \sin 150° \cos 45°$

$= 2 \left(\dfrac{1}{2}\right)\left(\dfrac{\sqrt{2}}{2}\right)$

$= \dfrac{\sqrt{2}}{2}$

16. $\sin x - \sin y = 2 \cos \dfrac{x + y}{2} \sin \dfrac{x - y}{2}$

$\sin 75° - \sin 165° = 2 \cos \dfrac{75° + 165°}{2} \sin \dfrac{75° - 165°}{2}$

$= 2 \cos 120° \sin(-45°)$

$= 2 \left(-\dfrac{1}{2}\right)\left(-\dfrac{\sqrt{2}}{2}\right)$

$= \dfrac{\sqrt{2}}{2}$

18. Verify: $\sin x \sin y = \dfrac{1}{2}[\cos(x - y) - \cos(x + y)]$

$\dfrac{1}{2}[\cos(x - y) - \cos(x + y)] = \dfrac{1}{2}[\cos x \cos y + \sin x \sin y$

$- (\cos x \cos y - \sin x \sin y)]$

$= \dfrac{1}{2}[2 \sin x \sin y]$

$= \sin x \sin y$

20. Start with the product-sum identity

$\cos u \cos v = \dfrac{1}{2}[\cos(u + v) + \cos(u - v)]$

Let
$x = u + v$
$y = u - v$
Solving this system gives $u = \dfrac{x + y}{2}$, $v = \dfrac{x - y}{2}$. Substituting into the
product-sum identity,
$\cos \dfrac{x + y}{2} \cos \dfrac{x - y}{2} = \dfrac{1}{2}[\cos x + \cos y]$
or
$\cos x + \cos y = 2 \cos \dfrac{x + y}{2} \sin \dfrac{x - y}{2}$

22. Verify: $\dfrac{\cos t - \cos 3t}{\sin t + \sin 3t} = \tan t$

$\dfrac{\cos t - \cos 3t}{\sin t + \sin 3t} = \dfrac{-2 \sin \frac{t + 3t}{2} \sin \frac{t - 3t}{2}}{2 \sin \frac{t + 3t}{2} \cos \frac{t - 3t}{2}}$ Sum-product Identities

$= \dfrac{-\sin 2t \sin(-t)}{\sin 2t \cos(-t)}$ Algebra

$= \dfrac{\sin 2t \sin t}{\sin 2t \cos t}$ Identities for negatives

$= \dfrac{\sin t}{\cos t}$ Algebra

$= \tan t$ Quotient Identity

24. Verify: $\dfrac{\sin x + \sin y}{\cos x + \cos y} = \tan \dfrac{x + y}{2}$

$$\dfrac{\sin x + \sin y}{\cos x + \cos y} = \dfrac{2 \sin \frac{x + y}{2} \cos \frac{x - y}{2}}{2 \cos \frac{x + y}{2} \cos \frac{x - y}{2}}$$ Sum-product Identities

$$= \dfrac{\sin \frac{x + y}{2}}{\cos \frac{x + y}{2}}$$ Algebra

$$= \tan \dfrac{x + y}{2}$$ Quotient Identity

26. Verify: $\dfrac{\cos x - \cos y}{\sin x + \sin y} = -\tan \dfrac{x - y}{2}$

$$\dfrac{\cos x - \cos y}{\sin x + \sin y} = \dfrac{-2 \sin \frac{x + y}{2} \sin \frac{x - y}{2}}{2 \sin \frac{x + y}{2} \cos \frac{x - y}{2}}$$ Sum-product Identities

$$= \dfrac{-\sin \frac{x - y}{2}}{\cos \frac{x - y}{2}}$$ Algebra

$$= -\tan \dfrac{x - y}{2}$$ Quotient Identity

28. Verify: $\dfrac{\sin x + \sin y}{\sin x - \sin y} = \dfrac{\tan[\frac{1}{2}(x + y)]}{\tan[\frac{1}{2}(x - y)]}$

$$\dfrac{\sin x + \sin y}{\sin x - \sin y} = \dfrac{2 \sin \frac{x + y}{2} \cos \frac{x - y}{2}}{2 \cos \frac{x + y}{2} \sin \frac{x - y}{2}}$$ Sum-product Identities

$$= \dfrac{\sin \frac{x + y}{2} \cos \frac{x - y}{2}}{\cos \frac{x + y}{2} \sin \frac{x - y}{2}}$$ Algebra

$$= \tan \dfrac{x + y}{2} \cot \dfrac{x - y}{2}$$ Quotient Identities

$$= \tan \dfrac{x + y}{2} \dfrac{1}{\tan \frac{x - y}{2}}$$ Reciprocal Identity

$$= \dfrac{\tan \frac{x + y}{2}}{\tan \frac{x - y}{2}}$$ Algebra

30. $x = 50.137°$, $y = 18.044°$
(A) $\cos 50.137° \sin 18.044° \approx 0.19853$

$\dfrac{1}{2}[\sin(50.137° + 18.044°) - \sin(50.137° - 18.044°)]$

$= \dfrac{1}{2}[\sin 68.181 - \sin 32.093] \approx 0.19853$

(B) $\cos 50.137° + \cos 18.044° \approx 1.5918$

$2 \cos \dfrac{50.137° + 18.044°}{2} \cos \dfrac{50.137° - 18.044°}{2}$

$= 2 \cos 34.0905 \cos 16.0465 \approx 1.5918$

32. $x = 0.03917$, $y = 0.61052$
(A) $\cos 0.03917 \sin 0.61052 \approx 0.57285$

$\dfrac{1}{2}[\sin(0.03917 + 0.61052) - \sin(0.03917 - 0.61052)]$

$= \dfrac{1}{2}[\sin 0.64969 - \sin(-0.57135) \approx 0.57285$

(B) cos 0.039817 + cos 0.61052 ≈ 1.8186

$$2 \cos \frac{0.03917 + 0.61052}{2} \cos \frac{0.03917 - 0.61052}{2}$$

$$= 2 \cos 0.324845 \cos(-0.285675) \approx 1.8186$$

34. $y = \cos 3x + \cos x = 2 \cos\left(\frac{3x + x}{2}\right) \cos\left(\frac{3x - x}{2}\right) = 2 \cos 2x \cos x$

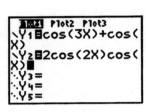 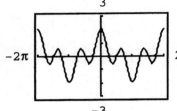

36. $y = \sin 2.1x - \sin 0.5x = 2 \cos \frac{2.1x + 0.5x}{2} \sin \frac{2.1x - 0.5x}{2}$

$$= 2 \cos 1.3x \sin 0.8x$$

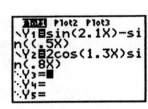 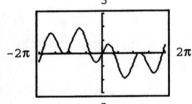

38. $y = \cos 5x \cos 3x = \frac{1}{2}[\cos(5x + 3x) + \cos(5x - 3x)] = \frac{1}{2}[\cos 8x + \cos 2x]$

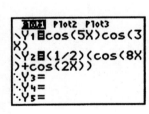 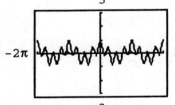

40. $y = \cos 1.9x \sin 0.5x = \frac{1}{2}[\sin(1.9x + 0.5x) - \sin(1.9x - 0.5x)]$

$$= \frac{1}{2}[\sin 2.4x - \sin 1.4x]$$

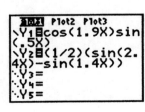 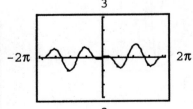

42. Verify: $\sin x \sin y \sin z = \frac{1}{4}[\sin(x + y - z) + \sin(y + z - x)$
$$+ \sin(z + x - y) - \sin(x + y + z)]$$

$\sin x \sin y \sin z = \sin x \left\{ \frac{1}{2}[\cos(y - z) - \cos(y + z)] \right\}$ Product-Sum Identity

$$= \frac{1}{2} \sin x \cos(y - z) - \frac{1}{2} \sin x \cos(y + z) \qquad \text{Algebra}$$

$$= \frac{1}{2}\left\{ \frac{1}{2}[\sin(x + y - z) + \sin(x - \{y - z\})] \right\} \qquad \begin{array}{c}\text{Product—Sum}\\\text{Identity}\end{array}$$
$$- \frac{1}{2}\left\{ \frac{1}{2}[\sin(x + y + z) + \sin(x - \{y + z\})] \right\}$$

$$= \frac{1}{4} \sin(x + y - z) + \frac{1}{4} \sin(x - y + z)$$
$$- \frac{1}{4} \sin(x + y + z) - \frac{1}{4} \sin(x - y - z) \qquad \text{Algebra}$$

$$= \frac{1}{4}[\sin(x + y - z) - \sin(x - y - z)$$
$$+ \sin(z + x - y) - \sin(x + y + z)] \qquad \text{Algebra}$$

$$= \frac{1}{4}[\sin(x + y - z) + \sin\{-(x - y - z)\}$$
$$+ \sin(z + x - y) - \sin(x + y + z)] \qquad \text{Identity for negatives}$$

$$= \frac{1}{4}[\sin(x + y - z) + \sin(y + z - x)$$
$$+ \sin(z + x - y) - \sin(x + y + z)] \qquad \text{Algebra}$$

44. (A)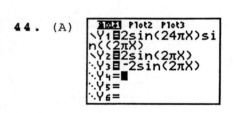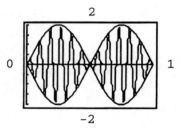

(B) $Y_1 = 2 \sin(24\pi x) \sin(2\pi x)$

$$= 2 \cdot \frac{1}{2}[\cos(24\pi x - 2\pi x) - \cos(24\pi x + 2\pi x)]$$

$$= \cos(22\pi x) - \cos(26\pi x). \text{ Graph is the same.}$$

46. (A)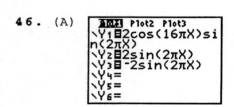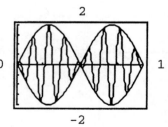

(B) $Y_1 = 2 \cos(16\pi x) \sin(2\pi x)$

$$= 2 \cdot \frac{1}{2}[\sin(16\pi x + 2\pi x) - \sin(16\pi x - 2\pi x)]$$

$$= \sin(18\pi x) - \sin(14\pi x). \text{ Graph is the same.}$$

48. (A) $0.25 \cos(256\pi t) - 0.25 \cos(288\pi t)$

$$= 0.25[\cos(256\pi t) - \cos(288\pi t)]$$

$$= 0.25\left[-2 \sin\left(\frac{256\pi t + 288\pi t}{2}\right) \sin\left(\frac{256\pi t - 288\pi t}{2}\right)\right]$$

$$= -\frac{1}{2} \sin(272\pi t) \sin(-16\pi t)$$

$$= \frac{1}{2} \sin(272\pi t) \sin(16\pi t)$$

(B) $y = 0.25 \cos(256\pi t)$

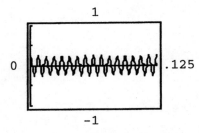

$y = -0.25 \cos(288\pi t)$

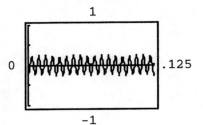

$y = 0.25 \cos(256\pi t) - 0.25 \cos(288\pi t)$

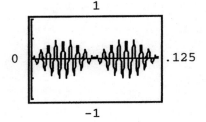

$y = 0.5 \sin(16\pi t) \sin(272\pi t)$

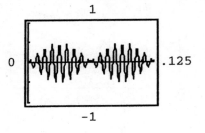

Exercise 6-5

2. $2 \cos x + 1 = 0,\ 0 \leq x < 2\pi$
$$2 \cos x = -1$$
$$\cos x = -\frac{1}{2}$$
$$x = \frac{2\pi}{3},\ \frac{4\pi}{3}$$

4. $2 \cos x + 1 = 0,$ all real x
$$2 \cos x = -1$$
$$\cos x = -\frac{1}{2}$$
$$x = \frac{2\pi}{3} + 2\pi k,\ \frac{4\pi}{3} + 2\pi k,$$
$$k \text{ any integer}$$

6. $\sqrt{3} \tan x + 1 = 0,\ 0 \leq x < \pi$
$$\sqrt{3} \tan x = -1$$
$$\tan x = \frac{-1}{\sqrt{3}}$$
$$x = \frac{5\pi}{6}$$

8. $\sqrt{3} \tan x + 1 = 0,$ all real x
$$\sqrt{3} \tan x = -1$$
$$\tan x = \frac{-1}{\sqrt{3}}$$
$$x = \frac{5\pi}{6} + k\pi,$$
$$k \text{ any integer}$$

10. $\sqrt{2} \sin \theta - 1 = 0,\ 0° \leq \theta < 360°$
$$\sqrt{2} \sin \theta = 1$$
$$\sin \theta = \frac{1}{\sqrt{2}}$$
$$\theta = 45°,\ 135°$$

12. $\sqrt{2} \sin \theta - 1 = 0,$ all θ
From problem 10,
$$\theta = 45° + k \cdot 360°,\ 135° + k \cdot 360°,$$
$$k \text{ any integer}$$

14. $5 \cos x - 2 = 0,\ 0 \leq x < 2\pi$

$$5 \cos x = 2$$
$$\cos x = \frac{2}{5}$$
$$x \approx 1.1593,\ 5.1239$$

16. $4 \tan \theta + 15 = 0,\ 0° \leq \theta < 180°$

$$4 \tan \theta = -15$$
$$\tan \theta = \frac{-15}{4}$$
$$\theta = \tan^{-1}\left(-\frac{15}{4}\right)$$
$$= -75.0686°$$
$$\theta \approx 104.9314°$$

For correct domain, $\theta = 180° - 75.0686°$

18. $5.0118 \sin x - 3.1105 = 0$, all real x

$$5.0118 \sin x = 3.1105$$
$$\sin x = \frac{3.1105}{5.0118}$$
$$x = \sin^{-1}\left(\frac{3.1105}{5.0118}\right)$$

$x \approx 0.6696$; QII: $x = \pi - 0.6696 \approx 2.4720$
$x \approx 0.6696 + 2\pi k,\ 2.4720 + 2\pi k,\ k$ any integer

20.
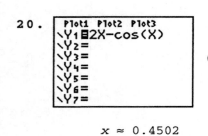
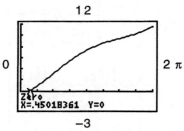

$x \approx 0.4502$

22.

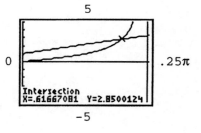

$x \approx 0.6167$

24. $\cos^2 \theta = \frac{1}{2} \cdot \sin 2\theta$, all θ

$$\cos^2 \theta = \frac{1}{2} \cdot 2 \sin \theta \cos \theta$$
$$\cos^2 \theta - \sin \theta \cos \theta = 0$$
$$\cos \theta \cdot (\cos \theta - \sin \theta) = 0$$

$\cos \theta = 0$ or $\cos \theta - \sin \theta = 0$
$\theta = 90° + k \cdot 180°$ $\cos \theta = \sin \theta$
                                       $\frac{\cos \theta}{\sin \theta} = 1$
                                         $\tan \theta = 1$
                                        $\theta = 45° + k \cdot 180°,\ k$ any integer

26. $\cos x = \cot x, \ 0 \le x < 2\pi$

$\cos x = \dfrac{\cos x}{\sin x}$

$\sin x \cos x - \cos x = 0$

$\cos x(\sin x - 1) = 0$

$\cos x = 0 \qquad\qquad \sin x - 1 = 0$

$\quad x = \dfrac{\pi}{2}, \ \dfrac{3\pi}{2} \qquad\qquad \sin x = 1$

$\qquad\qquad\qquad\qquad\qquad x = \dfrac{\pi}{2}$

28. $\tan\left(\dfrac{x}{2}\right) - 1 = 0, \ 0 \le x < 2\pi \Leftrightarrow 0 \le \dfrac{x}{2} < \pi$

$\tan \dfrac{x}{2} = 1$

$\dfrac{x}{2} = \dfrac{\pi}{4}$

$x = \dfrac{\pi}{2}$

30. $\sin^2 \theta + 2 \cos \theta = -2, \ 0° \le \theta < 360°$

$1 - \cos^2 \theta + 2 \cos \theta + 2 = 0$

$\cos^2 \theta - 2 \cos \theta - 3 = 0$

$(\cos \theta + 1)(\cos \theta - 3) = 0$

$\cos \theta + 1 = 0 \quad$ or $\quad \cos \theta - 3 = 0$

$\cos \theta = -1 \qquad\qquad \cos \theta = 3$, no solution

$\theta = 180°$

32. $\cos 2\theta + \sin^2 \theta = 0, \ 0° \le \theta < 360°$

$1 - 2 \sin^2 \theta + \sin^2 \theta = 0$

$-\sin^2 \theta = -1$

$\sin^2 \theta = 1$

$\sin \theta = \pm 1$

$\theta = 90°, \ 270°$

34. $4 \cos^2 2x - 4 \cos 2x + 1 = 0, \ 0 \le x < 2\pi \Leftrightarrow 0 \le 2x < 4\pi$

$(2 \cos 2x - 1)^2 = 0$

$\cos 2x = \dfrac{1}{2}$

$2x = \dfrac{\pi}{3}, \ \dfrac{5\pi}{3}, \ \dfrac{7\pi}{3}, \ \dfrac{11\pi}{3}$

$x = \dfrac{\pi}{6}, \ \dfrac{5\pi}{6}, \ \dfrac{7\pi}{6}, \ \dfrac{11\pi}{6}$

36. $4 \cos^2 \theta = 7 \cos \theta + 2, \ 0° \le \theta \le 180°$

$4 \cos^2 \theta - 7 \cos \theta - 2 = 0$

$(4 \cos \theta + 1)(\cos \theta - 2) = 0$

$4 \cos \theta + 1 = 0 \quad$ or $\quad \cos \theta - 2 = 0$

$4 \cos \theta = -1 \qquad\qquad \cos \theta = 2$, no solution

$\cos \theta = \dfrac{-1}{4}$

$\theta = \cos^{-1}(-0.25)$

$\theta \approx 104.5°$

38. $8 \sin^2 x + 10 \sin x = 3,\ 0 \leq x \leq \dfrac{\pi}{2}$

$$8 \sin^2 x + 10 \sin x - 3 = 0$$
$$(4 \sin x - 1)(2 \sin x + 3) = 0$$

$4 \sin x - 1 = 0$ or $2 \sin x + 3 = 0$

      $4 \sin x = 1$ $2 \sin x = -3$

        $\sin x = \dfrac{1}{4}$ $\sin x = \dfrac{-3}{2}$, no solution

           $x = \sin^{-1}(0.25)$

           $x \approx 0.2527$

40. $\cos 2x + 10 \cos x = 5,\ 0 \leq x < 2\pi$

    $2 \cos^2 x - 1 + 10 \cos x - 5 = 0$

        $2 \cos^2 x + 10 \cos x - 6 = 0$

$$\cos x = \frac{-10 \pm \sqrt{10^2 - 4(2)(-6)}}{2(2)} = \frac{-10 \pm 2\sqrt{37}}{4} = \frac{-5 \pm \sqrt{37}}{2}$$

$\cos x = \dfrac{-5 + \sqrt{37}}{2} = 0.5413812651\ldots$ or $\cos x = \dfrac{-5 - \sqrt{37}}{2} = -5.54138265\ldots$

  $x \approx 0.9987,\ 5.284\ (2\pi - 0.9987)$ no solution

42. $\cos^2 x = 3 - 5 \cos x$, all real x

$\cos^2 x + 5 \cos x - 3 = 0$ has the same solutions as problem 40,

$x \approx 0.9987 + 2\pi k,\ 5.2845 + 2\pi k,\ k$ any integer $[-0.9987 + 2\pi = 5.2845]$

44.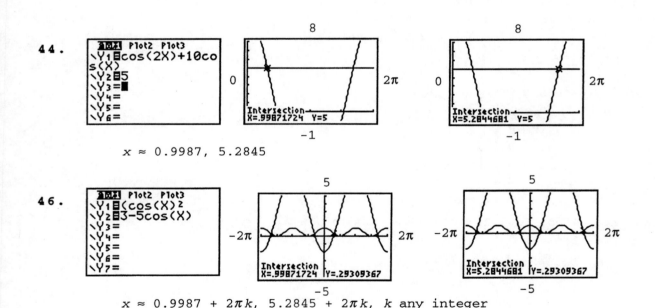

       $x \approx 0.9987,\ 5.2845$

46.

       $x \approx 0.9987 + 2\pi k,\ 5.2845 + 2\pi k,\ k$ any integer

48.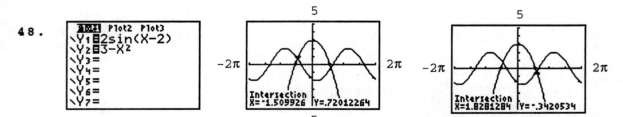

       $2 \sin(x - 2) < 3 - x^2$ on $(-1.5099,\ 1.8281)$

50.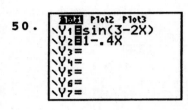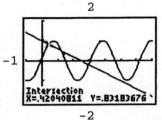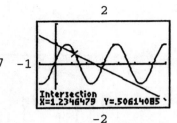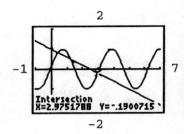

$\sin(3 - 2x) \geq 1 - 0.4x$ on $[0.4204, 1.2346]$, $[2.9752, \infty)$

52.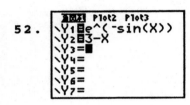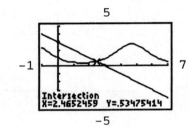

$x \approx 2.4652$

54. Evaluating $\cos^{-1}(-0.7334)$ gives a unique number, ≈ 2.3941, the value of the inverse cosine function at -0.7334, while solving $\cos x = -0.7334$ involves finding an infinite number of x values whose cosine is -0.7334 by adding $2\pi k$, k any integer, to each solution in one period of $\cos x$.

56. $\sin x + \cos x = 1$, $0 \leq x < 2\pi$

$\sin^2 x + 2 \sin x \cos x + \cos^2 x = 1$

$1 + 2 \sin x \cos x = 1$

$\sin x \cos x = 0$

$\sin x = 0$ or $\cos x = 0$

$x = 0, \pi$ $\qquad x = \dfrac{\pi}{2}, \dfrac{3\pi}{2}$

$\sin 0 + \cos 0 = 1$ $\qquad \sin \dfrac{\pi}{2} + \cos \dfrac{\pi}{2} = 1$

$\sin \pi + \cos \pi = -1$ (extraneous) $\quad \sin \dfrac{3\pi}{2} + \cos \dfrac{3\pi}{2} = -1$ (extraneous)

$x = 0, \dfrac{\pi}{2}$ are the solutions

58. $\sec x + \tan x = 1$, $0 \leq x < 2\pi$

$\sec x = 1 - \tan x$

$\sec^2 x = 1 - 2 \tan x + \tan^2 x$

$\sec^2 x = \sec^2 x - 2 \tan x$

$0 = -2 \tan x$

$\tan x = 0$

$x = 0, \pi$

$\sec 0 + \tan 0 = 1$

$\sec \pi + \tan \pi = -1$ (extraneous)

$x = 0$ is the solution

60. $2 \cos\left(\dfrac{1}{x}\right) = 950x - 4$, $0.006 < x < 0.007$

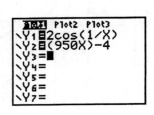 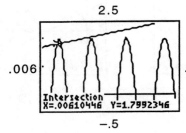 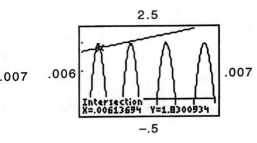

$x \approx 0.006104, \; 0.006137$

62. $g(x) = \cos\left(\dfrac{1}{x}\right)$ for $x > 0$

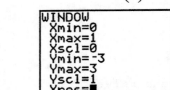  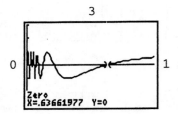

(A) 0.6366 is the largest zero. As $x \to \infty$, $1/x \to 0 \Rightarrow \cos\left(\dfrac{1}{x}\right) \to 1$ so $y = 1$ is a horizontal asymptote for the graph of g.

(B) Infinitely many zeros exist between 0 and b, for any b, however small. The exploration graphs suggest this conclusion, which is reinforced by the following reasoning: Note that for each interval $(0, b]$, however small, as x tends to zero through positive numbers, $1/x$ increases without bound, and as $1/x$ increases without bound, $\cos(1/x)$ will cross the x axis an unlimited number of times. The function g does not have a smallest zero, because, between 0 and b, no matter how small b is, there is always an unlimited number of zeros.

64. $I = 30 \sin(120\pi t)$, $I = 25$ amps

$25 = 30 \sin(120\pi t)$

$\sin(120\pi t) = \dfrac{25}{30}$

$120\pi t = \sin^{-1}\left(\dfrac{25}{30}\right)$

$t = \dfrac{1}{120\pi} \cdot \sin^{-1}\left(\dfrac{5}{6}\right)$

$t \approx 0.002613$ seconds

66. $I_L = I_E \cdot \cos^2 \theta$, $I_L = 70\% \; I_E$

$0.7 I_E = I_E \cdot \cos^2 \theta$

$0.7 = \cos^2 \theta$

$\cos \theta = \pm\sqrt{0.7}$

$\theta = \cos^{-1}(\pm\sqrt{0.7})$

$\theta \approx 33.21°, \; 146.79°, \; 213.21°, \; 326.79°$

Smallest positive θ: 33.21°

68. $r = \dfrac{3.44 \times 10^7}{1 - 0.206 \cos \theta}$

$3.78 \times 10^7 = \dfrac{3.44 \times 10^7}{1 - 0.206 \cos \theta}$

$3.78 \times 10^7 - 7{,}786{,}800 \cos \theta = 3.44 \times 10^7$

$- 7{,}786{,}800 \cos \theta = -3{,}400{,}000$

$\cos \theta \approx 0.436636359$

$\theta = \cos^{-1}(0.436636359)$

$\theta \approx 64.1°, \; 296°$

Smallest positive θ: 64.1°

70.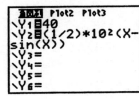

$$\theta \approx 1.779 \text{ rad}$$

72. (A) $\sin \theta = \dfrac{a}{R} = \dfrac{5.4}{R}$ $\cos \theta = \dfrac{x}{R}$

$$R = \dfrac{5.4}{\sin \theta}$$ $$x = R \cos \theta$$

$R = x + b$

$$\dfrac{5.4}{\sin \theta} = R \cos \theta + 2.4$$

$$\dfrac{5.4}{\sin \theta} = \dfrac{5.4 \cos \theta}{\sin \theta} + 2.4$$

Graphing each side of the equation and finding the intersection gives $\theta \approx 0.83644866$.

$$R = \dfrac{5.4}{\sin 0.83644866} \approx 7.274999994$$

$L = R(2\theta)$

$L \approx 7.274999994(2 \cdot 0.83644866)$

$L \approx 12.1703$ mm to 4 decimal places

(B) Increase a to 5.5 mm:

$$L = R(2\theta)$$

$$\theta = \dfrac{L}{2R}$$

$$\theta \approx \dfrac{12.17032799}{\dfrac{2(5.5)}{\sin \theta}}$$

Graphing each side of the equation and finding the intersection gives $\theta \approx 0.77096792$.

$$R \approx \dfrac{5.5}{\sin 0.770967922} \approx 7.892888691$$

$x = R \cos \theta$

$x \approx 7.892888691 \cos 0.77096792 \approx 5.661068098$

$b = R - x$

$b \approx 7.892888691 - 5.661068098$

$b \approx 2.2318$ mm to 4 decimal places

74. $r = 2 \sin \theta,\ 0° \le \theta \le 360°$

$r = 2(1 - \sin \theta)$

$2 \sin \theta = 2(1 - \sin \theta)$

$4 \sin \theta = 2$

$\sin \theta = \dfrac{1}{2},\ r = 2\left(\dfrac{1}{2}\right) = 1$

$\theta = 30°,\ 150° \Rightarrow (1, 30°),\ (1, 150°)$

76. $xy = -2$

$(u \cos \theta - v \sin \theta)(u \sin \theta + v \cos \theta) = -2$

$u^2 \sin \theta \cos \theta + uv \cos^2 \theta - uv \sin^2 \theta - v^2 \sin \theta \cos \theta = -2$

coefficient of uv term = 0:

$$\cos^2 \theta - \sin^2 \theta = 0$$
$$1 - \sin^2 \theta - \sin^2 \theta = 0$$
$$2 \sin^2 \theta = 1$$
$$\sin^2 \theta = \frac{1}{2}$$
$$\sin \theta = \pm \frac{1}{\sqrt{2}}$$
$$\theta = 45°, \ 135°, \ 225°, \ 315°$$

smallest positive $\theta = 45°$

CHAPTER 7

Note: Answers have been rounded to the number of significant digits given in Table 1; an = sign has been used rather than ≈.

Exercise 7-1

2. $\gamma = 180° - (41° + 33°)$

$\gamma = 106°$

$\dfrac{a}{\sin \alpha} = \dfrac{c}{\sin \gamma}$

$\dfrac{a}{\sin 41°} = \dfrac{21}{\sin 106°}$

$a = 14$ cm

$\dfrac{b}{\sin \beta} = \dfrac{c}{\sin \gamma}$

$\dfrac{b}{\sin 33°} = \dfrac{21}{\sin 106°}$

$b = 12$ cm

4. $\alpha = 180° - (43° + 36°)$

$\alpha = 101°$

$\dfrac{a}{\sin \alpha} = \dfrac{c}{\sin \gamma}$

$\dfrac{92}{\sin 101°} = \dfrac{c}{\sin 36°}$

$c = 55$ mm

$\dfrac{b}{\sin \beta} = \dfrac{a}{\sin \alpha}$

$\dfrac{b}{\sin 43°} = \dfrac{92}{\sin 101°}$

$b = 64$ mm

6. $\beta = 180° - (52° + 105°)$

$\beta = 23°$

$\dfrac{a}{\sin \alpha} = \dfrac{c}{\sin \gamma}$

$\dfrac{a}{\sin 52°} = \dfrac{47}{\sin 105°}$

$a = 38$ m

$\dfrac{b}{\sin \beta} = \dfrac{c}{\sin \gamma}$

$\dfrac{b}{\sin 23°} = \dfrac{47}{\sin 105°}$

$b = 19$ m

8. $\alpha = 180° - (83° + 77°)$

$\alpha = 20°$

$\dfrac{b}{\sin \beta} = \dfrac{c}{\sin \gamma}$

$\dfrac{b}{\sin 83°} = \dfrac{25}{\sin 77°}$

$b = 25$ mi

$\dfrac{a}{\sin \alpha} = \dfrac{c}{\sin \gamma}$

$\dfrac{a}{\sin 20°} = \dfrac{25}{\sin 77°}$

$a = 8.8$ mi

10. $a = 3$ ft, $b = 6$ ft, $\alpha = 30°$
SSA:
$h = b \sin \alpha = 6 \sin 30° = 3 = a \Rightarrow 1$ triangle; case (b)

12. $a = 8$ ft, $b = 6$ ft, $\alpha = 30°$
SSA:
$h = b \sin \alpha = 6 \sin 30° = 3$
$8 > 3 \Rightarrow 1$ triangle; case (d)

14. $a = 2$ ft, $b = 6$ ft, $\alpha = 30°$
SSA:
$h = b \sin \alpha = 6 \sin 30° = 3 > 2 \Rightarrow 0$ triangles; case (a)

16. $a = 5$ ft, $b = 6$ ft, $\alpha = 30°$
SSA:
$h = b \sin \alpha = 6 \sin 30° = 3$
$3 < 5 < 6 \Rightarrow 2$ triangles; case (c)

18. $\beta = 27.5°$, $\gamma = 54.5°$, $a = 9.27$ inches

$\alpha = 180° - (27.5° + 54.5°)$

$\alpha = 98°$

$\dfrac{a}{\sin \alpha} = \dfrac{b}{\sin \beta}$

$\dfrac{9.27}{\sin 98°} = \dfrac{b}{\sin 27.5°}$

$b = 4.32$ in

$\dfrac{c}{\sin \gamma} = \dfrac{a}{\sin \alpha}$

$\dfrac{c}{\sin 54.5°} = \dfrac{9.27}{\sin 98°}$

$c = 7.62$ in

20. $\alpha = 122.7°$, $\beta = 34.4°$, $b = 18.3$ km

$\gamma = 180° - (122.7° + 34.4°)$ $\qquad \dfrac{a}{\sin \alpha} = \dfrac{b}{\sin \beta}$ $\qquad\qquad \dfrac{c}{\sin \gamma} = \dfrac{b}{\sin \beta}$

$\gamma = 22.9°$ $\qquad\qquad\qquad \dfrac{a}{\sin 122.7°} = \dfrac{18.3}{\sin 34.4°}$ $\qquad \dfrac{c}{\sin 22.9°} = \dfrac{18.3}{\sin 34.4°}$

$\qquad\qquad\qquad\qquad\qquad\qquad a = 27.3$ km $\qquad\qquad c = 12.6$ km

22. $\alpha = 26.3°$, $a = 14.7$ inches, $b = 35.2$ inches

$\qquad \dfrac{a}{\sin \alpha} = \dfrac{b}{\sin \beta}$

$\qquad \dfrac{14.7}{\sin 26.3°} = \dfrac{35.2}{\sin \beta}$

$\qquad \sin \beta = 1.0609596 > 1 \Rightarrow$ No solution

24. $\beta = 27.3°$, $a = 244$ cm, $b = 135$ cm, α acute

$\qquad \dfrac{a}{\sin \alpha} = \dfrac{b}{\sin \beta}$ $\qquad\qquad\qquad \dfrac{b}{\sin \beta} = \dfrac{c}{\sin \gamma}$

$\qquad \dfrac{244}{\sin \alpha} = \dfrac{135}{\sin 27.3°}$ $\qquad\qquad \dfrac{135}{\sin 27.3°} = \dfrac{c}{\sin 96.7°}$

$\qquad\qquad \alpha = 56.0°$ $\qquad\qquad\qquad\qquad c = 292$ cm

$\quad \gamma = 180° - (56° + 27.3°) = 96.7°$

26. $\beta = 27.3°$, $a = 244$ cm, $b = 135$ cm, α obtuse

$\qquad \dfrac{a}{\sin \alpha} = \dfrac{b}{\sin \beta}$ $\qquad\qquad\qquad \dfrac{b}{\sin \beta} = \dfrac{c}{\sin \gamma}$

$\qquad \dfrac{244}{\sin \alpha} = \dfrac{135}{\sin 27.3°}$ $\qquad\qquad \dfrac{135}{\sin 27.3°} = \dfrac{c}{\sin 28.7°}$

$\qquad\qquad\quad \alpha = 124°$ $(180° - 56.0°)$ $\qquad\qquad c = 141$ cm

$\quad \gamma = 180° - (124° + 27.3°) = 28.7°$

28. $\alpha = 137.3°$, $a = 13.9$ m, $b = 19.1$ m

$\qquad \dfrac{a}{\sin \alpha} = \dfrac{b}{\sin \beta}$

$\qquad \dfrac{13.9}{\sin 137.3°} = \dfrac{19.1}{\sin \beta} \Rightarrow \beta = 68.73°$

$\quad \beta + \alpha = 206.03° > 180°$

No solution

30. $\beta = 33°50'$, $a = 673$ m, $b = 1240$ m

$\qquad \dfrac{b}{\sin \beta} = \dfrac{a}{\sin \alpha}$ $\qquad\qquad\qquad \dfrac{b}{\sin \beta} = \dfrac{c}{\sin \gamma}$

$\qquad \dfrac{1240}{\sin 33°50'} = \dfrac{673}{\sin \alpha}$ $\qquad\qquad \dfrac{1240}{\sin 33°50'} = \dfrac{c}{\sin 128°30'}$

$\qquad\qquad\quad \alpha = 17°40'$ $\qquad\qquad\qquad c = 1740$ m

$\quad \gamma = 180° - (33°50' + 17°40')$

$\quad \gamma = 128°30'$

32. $\alpha = 37.3°$, $b = 42.8$ cm

$k = 42.8 \sin 37.3° = 25.9$ is k such that $0 < a < k$ gives no solution; $a = k$ gives one solution; $k < a < b$ gives two solutions.

34. From the law of sines $\dfrac{a}{\sin \alpha} = \dfrac{c}{\sin \gamma} \Rightarrow \dfrac{a}{c} = \dfrac{\sin \alpha}{\sin \gamma}$ \hfill (1)

and $\dfrac{b}{\sin \beta} = \dfrac{c}{\sin \gamma} \Rightarrow \dfrac{b}{c} = \dfrac{\sin \beta}{\sin \gamma}$ \hfill (2)

$\dfrac{a + b}{c} = \dfrac{\sin \alpha + \sin \beta}{\sin \gamma}$ \quad adding (1) and (2)

$\qquad = \dfrac{2 \sin \frac{\alpha + \beta}{2} \cos \frac{\alpha - \beta}{2}}{2 \sin \frac{\gamma}{2} \cos \frac{\gamma}{2}}$ \quad but $\sin \dfrac{\alpha + \beta}{2} = \sin \frac{1}{2}(180 - \gamma)$

$\qquad = \dfrac{\sin \frac{\alpha + \beta}{2} \cos \frac{\alpha - \beta}{2}}{\sin \frac{\gamma}{2} \sin \frac{\alpha + \beta}{2}}$ \hfill $= \sin\left(90 - \dfrac{\gamma}{2}\right)$

$\qquad\qquad\qquad\qquad\qquad\qquad\qquad = \cos \dfrac{\gamma}{2}$

$\dfrac{a + b}{c} = \dfrac{\cos \frac{\alpha - \beta}{2}}{\sin \frac{\gamma}{2}}$ \hfill (3)

similarly, subtracting (1) and (2)

$\dfrac{a - b}{c} = \dfrac{\sin \alpha - \sin \beta}{\sin \gamma} = \dfrac{2 \cos \frac{\alpha + \beta}{2} \sin \frac{\alpha - \beta}{2}}{\sin \gamma}$

$\qquad = \dfrac{2 \cos \frac{\alpha + \beta}{2} \sin \frac{\alpha - \beta}{2}}{2 \sin \frac{\gamma}{2} \cos \frac{\gamma}{2}}$ \quad but $\cos \dfrac{\alpha + \beta}{2} = \cos \frac{1}{2}(180 - \gamma)$

$\qquad = \dfrac{\sin \frac{\gamma}{2} \sin \frac{\alpha - \beta}{2}}{\sin \frac{\gamma}{2} \cos \frac{\gamma}{2}}$ \hfill $= \cos\left(90 - \dfrac{\gamma}{2}\right)$

$\qquad\qquad\qquad\qquad\qquad\qquad\qquad = \sin \dfrac{\gamma}{2}$

$\dfrac{a - b}{c} = \dfrac{\sin \frac{\alpha - \beta}{2}}{\cos \frac{\gamma}{2}}$ \hfill (4)

dividing (4) by (3)

$\qquad\qquad \dfrac{\frac{a - b}{c}}{\frac{a + b}{c}} = \dfrac{\frac{\sin \frac{\alpha - \beta}{2}}{\cos \frac{\gamma}{2}}}{\frac{\cos \frac{\alpha - \beta}{2}}{\sin \frac{\gamma}{2}}}$

$\dfrac{a - b}{c} \cdot \dfrac{c}{a + b} = \dfrac{\sin \frac{\alpha - \beta}{2}}{\cos \frac{\gamma}{2}} \cdot \dfrac{\sin \frac{\gamma}{2}}{\cos \frac{\alpha - \beta}{2}}$

$\qquad \dfrac{a - b}{a + b} = \tan \dfrac{\alpha - \beta}{2} \tan \dfrac{\gamma}{2}$ but $\tan \dfrac{\gamma}{2} = \cot \dfrac{\alpha + \beta}{2}$

$\qquad\qquad = \tan \dfrac{\alpha - \beta}{2} \cdot \dfrac{1}{\tan \frac{\alpha + \beta}{2}}$

$\qquad \dfrac{a - b}{a + b} = \dfrac{\tan \frac{\alpha - \beta}{2}}{\tan \frac{\alpha + \beta}{2}}$

(B) from 1, $\quad a = 41 \qquad \alpha = 73°$

$\qquad\qquad\qquad b = 20 \qquad \beta = 28°$

$\dfrac{\tan \frac{73° - 28°}{2}}{\tan \frac{73° + 28°}{2}} = 0.3415$

$\qquad \dfrac{41 - 20}{41 + 20} = 0.3443$

Answers vary slightly due to rounding.

36.

$$\frac{b}{\sin 53°} = \frac{a}{\sin 28°30'} = \frac{10}{\sin 98°30'}$$

$$b = 8.08 \text{ miles from } A$$
$$a = 4.82 \text{ miles from } B$$

38.

$$\tan 43°5' = \frac{h}{x}$$

$$x = \frac{h}{\tan 43°5'}$$

$$\tan 38° = \frac{h}{2000 + x} = \frac{h}{2000 + \frac{h}{\tan 43°5'}}$$

$$2000 \tan 38° + h\left(\frac{\tan 38°}{\tan 43°5'}\right) = h$$

$$h\left(1 - \frac{\tan 38°}{\tan 43°5'}\right) = 2000 \tan 38°$$

$$h = \frac{2000 \tan 38°}{1 - \frac{\tan 38°}{\tan 43°5'}}$$

$$h \approx 9492.39$$

The distance above sea level = $5000 + h = 14{,}490$ feet to 4 significant digits.

40.

$$\frac{6.3}{\sin \alpha} = \frac{1.7}{\sin 11°} = \frac{c}{\sin \gamma}$$

$$\alpha = 45° \Rightarrow \gamma = 124° \Rightarrow c = 7.4"$$
$$\alpha = 135° \Rightarrow \gamma = 34° \Rightarrow c = 5.0"$$

42. $\sin(SEV) = \dfrac{1.085 \times 10^8}{1.495 \times 10^8}$

$$SEV = 46.5°$$

44.

$$\alpha + 42° = 90°$$
$$\alpha = 48°$$
$$\beta + 42° = 180°$$
$$\beta = 138°$$

$$11° + \beta + \gamma = 180°$$
$$11° + 138° + \gamma = 180°$$
$$\gamma = 31°$$

$$\frac{h}{\sin \gamma} = \frac{157}{\sin \alpha}$$

$$\frac{h}{\sin 31°} = \frac{157}{\sin 48°}$$

$h = 109$ ft, to the nearest foot

46.

$$\frac{180° - 63.2°}{2} = 58.4°$$

$$\frac{10.2}{\sin 63.2} = \frac{R}{\sin 58.4°}$$

$R = 9.73$ mm to 3 significant digits

$$s = R \cdot 63.2° \cdot \frac{\pi}{180°} = 10.7 \text{ mm to 3 significant digits}$$

48. Let x be the length of the side in the horizontal triangle that is also in the vertical triangle with angle γ.

In the horizontal triangle

$$\frac{x}{\sin \alpha} = \frac{d}{\sin(180° - (\alpha + \beta))}$$

$$x = d \sin \alpha \csc(\alpha + \beta)$$

In the vertical triangle

$$\tan \gamma = \frac{h}{x}$$

$$h = x \tan \alpha$$

$$= d \sin \alpha \csc(\alpha + \beta) \tan \gamma$$

$\sin(180° - (\alpha + \beta))$

$= \sin 180° \cos(\alpha + \beta) - \cos 180° \sin(\alpha + \beta)$

$= 0 \cdot \cos(\alpha + \beta) - (-1) \sin(\alpha + \beta)$

$= \sin(\alpha + \beta)$

$= \dfrac{1}{\csc(\alpha + \beta)}$

Exercise 7-2

2. A triangle can have at most one obtuse angle. Since $\alpha = 93.5°$ is obtuse both γ and β must be acute. [$\beta + \gamma = 180° - 93.5° = 86.5°$; thus both β and γ are less than 90°.]

4. $\beta = 57.3°$, $a = 6.08$ cm, $c = 5.25$ cm
$a^2 + c^2 - 2ac \cos \beta = b^2$
$6.08^2 + 5.25^2 - 2(6.08)(5.25)\cos 57.3° = b^2 \Rightarrow b = 5.48$ cm

Solve for smallest angle:
$$\frac{5.25}{\sin \gamma} = \frac{5.48}{\sin 57.3°} \qquad\qquad \frac{6.08}{\sin \alpha} = \frac{5.48}{\sin 57.3°}$$
$$\gamma = 53.7° \qquad\qquad\qquad \alpha = 69.0° \text{ or } \alpha = 180° - (57.3° + 53.7°)$$

6. $\alpha = 135°50'$, $b = 8.44$ in, $c = 20.3$ in
$b^2 + c^2 - 2bc \cos \alpha = a^2$
$8.44^2 + 20.3^2 - 2(8.44)(20.3)\cos 135°50' = a^2 \Rightarrow a = 27.0$ in

Solve for smallest angle:
$$\frac{27}{\sin 135°50'} = \frac{8.44}{\sin \beta} \qquad\qquad \frac{20.3}{\sin \gamma} = \frac{27}{\sin 135°50'}$$
$$\beta = 12°30' \qquad\qquad\qquad \gamma = 31°40' \text{ or } \gamma = 180° - (135°50 + 12°30')$$

8. If $a = 12.5$ cm, $b = 25.3$ cm, $c = 10.7$ cm, then sides a and c are not long enough to construct a triangle: $a + c < b$

10. $a = 10.5$ mi, $b = 20.7$ mi, $c = 12.2$ mi
Solve for the largest angle:
$$b^2 = a^2 + c^2 - 2ac \cos \beta$$
$$20.7^2 = 10.5^2 + 12.2^2 - 2(10.5)(12.2)\cos \beta$$
$$\cos \beta \approx -0.6612021858$$
$$\beta = 131.4°$$
$$\frac{20.7}{\sin 131.4} = \frac{12.2}{\sin \gamma} \Rightarrow \gamma = 26.2°$$
$$\alpha = 180° - (131.4° + 26.2°) = 22.4°$$

12. $a = 31.5$ m, $b = 29.4$ m, $c = 33.7$ m

Solving for the largest angle:

$$c^2 = a^2 + b^2 - 2ab \cos \gamma$$

$$33.7^2 = 31.5^2 + 29.4^2 - 2(31.5)(29.4)\cos \gamma$$

$$\cos \gamma \approx 0.389223626$$

$$\gamma = 67.1°$$

$$\frac{33.7}{\sin 67.1°} = \frac{31.5}{\sin \alpha} \Rightarrow \alpha = 59.4°$$

$$\beta = 180° - (67.1° + 59.4°) = 53.5°$$

14. $\beta + \gamma = 85.6° + 97.3° = 182.9° > 180° \Rightarrow$ no solution

16. $\beta = 27.3°$, $a = 13.7$ yds, $c = 20.1$ yd

$$b^2 = a^2 + c^2 - 2ac \cos \beta$$

$$= 13.7^2 + 20.1^2 - 2(13.7)(20.1)\cos 27.3°$$

$$b = 10.1 \text{ yd}$$

$$\frac{10.1}{\sin 27.3°} = \frac{13.7}{\sin \alpha}$$

$$\alpha = 38.5°$$

$$\gamma = 180° - (27.3° + 38.5°) = 114.2°$$

(Answers will vary due to method used.)

18. $\beta = 132.4°$, $\gamma = 17.3°$, $b = 67.6$ km

$\alpha = 180° - (\beta + \gamma) = 180° - (132.4° + 17.3°) = 30.3°$

$$\frac{a}{\sin \alpha} = \frac{b}{\sin \beta} = \frac{c}{\sin \gamma}$$

$$\frac{a}{\sin 30.3°} = \frac{67.6}{\sin 132.4°} = \frac{c}{\sin 17.3°}$$

$a = 46.2$ km; $c = 27.2$ km

20. $\gamma = 66.4°$, $b = 25.5$ m, $c = 25.5$ m

$$b = c \Rightarrow \gamma = \beta = 66.4°$$

$$\alpha = 180° - (\gamma + \beta) = 180° - (2(66.4°)) = 47.2°$$

$$\frac{25.5}{\sin 66.4°} = \frac{a}{\sin 47.2°}$$

$$a = 20.4 \text{ m}$$

22. $a = 10.5$ cm, $b = 5.23$ cm, $c = 8.66$ cm

Angle opposite longest side:

$$a^2 = b^2 + c^2 - 2bc \cos \alpha$$

$$10.5^2 = 5.23^2 + 8.66^2 - 2(5.23)(8.66)\cos \alpha$$

$$\alpha = 95.0°$$

$$\frac{10.5}{\sin 95.0°} = \frac{5.23}{\sin \beta}$$

$$\beta = 29.7°$$

$$\gamma = 180° - (\alpha + \beta) = 180° - (95° + 29.7°)$$

$$\gamma = 55.3°$$

24. $\alpha = 46.7°$, $a = 18.1$ m, $b = 22.6$ m

$$\frac{a}{\sin \alpha} = \frac{b}{\sin \beta}$$

$$\frac{18.1}{\sin 46.7} = \frac{22.6}{\sin \beta} \Rightarrow \beta = 65.3° \text{ or } \beta' = 114.7°$$

$$\beta = 65.3° \Rightarrow \gamma = 180° - (65.3° + 46.7°) = 68.0°$$

$$\beta' = 114.7° \Rightarrow \gamma' = 180° - (114.7° + 46.7°) = 18.6°$$

$$\frac{18.1}{\sin 46.7°} = \frac{c}{\sin 68.0°} = \frac{c'}{\sin 18.6°}$$

$$c = 23.1 \text{ m}$$
$$c' = 7.93 \text{ m}$$

Triangle I: $\beta = 65.3°$, $\gamma = 68.0°$, $c = 23.1$ m
Triangle II: $\beta = 114.7°$, $\gamma = 18.6°$, $c = 7.93$ m

26. $\gamma = 47.9°$, $b = 35.2$ in, $c = 25.5$ in

$$\frac{c}{\sin \gamma} = \frac{b}{\sin \beta}$$

$$\frac{25.5}{\sin 47.9°} = \frac{35.2}{\sin \beta}$$

$$\sin \beta = 1.0242176 \Rightarrow \text{No solution}$$

28. Given $c^2 = a^2 + b^2$:

$$c^2 = a^2 + b^2 - 2ab \cos \gamma \text{ law of cosines}$$
$$a^2 + b^2 = a^2 + b^2 - 2ab \cos \gamma \text{ substitution}$$
$$-2ab \cos \gamma = 0$$
$$\cos \gamma = 0$$
$$\gamma = 90°$$

30.

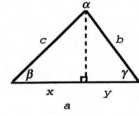

$$a = x + y : \cos \beta = \frac{x}{c} \Rightarrow x = c \cos \beta$$
$$: \cos \gamma = \frac{y}{b} \Rightarrow y = b \cos \gamma$$
$$a = c \cos \beta + b \cos \gamma$$

$$\cos \beta = \frac{a + x}{c} \qquad\qquad \cos(180 - \gamma) = \frac{x}{b}$$
$$a + x = c \cos \beta \qquad\qquad -\cos \gamma = \frac{x}{b}$$
$$a = c \cos \beta - x \qquad\qquad x = -b \cos \gamma$$
$$a = c \cos \beta - (-b \cos \gamma)$$
$$a = c \cos \beta + b \cos \gamma$$

32. $AB = \sqrt{85^2 + 73^2 - 2(85)(73) \cos 110°} \approx 130$ m

34. $13.8^2 = 8.26^2 + 8.26^2 - 2(8.26)(8.26) \cos \theta$

$$\theta \approx 113.3°$$

36. $c = \sqrt{8^2 + 3^2 - 2(8)(3) \cos(144°50')} \approx 10.6$ ft

38. After 2 hours, Plane A has traveled 800 miles, Plane B 1000 miles. The angle between them is 45°.

$$c = \sqrt{1000^2 + 800^2 - 2(1000)(800)\cos 45°} \approx 713 \text{ mi}$$

40. The angle at the center is $\frac{360°}{9} = 40°$. An isosceles triangle is formed, so the other two angles are $70° \left(\frac{180° - 40°}{2} \right)$. Let x be the chord formed in the circle. Using the law of sines to solve,

$$\frac{7.09}{\sin 70°} = \frac{x}{\sin 40°}$$
$$x \approx 4.849846$$

The perimeter, to 3 significiant digits, is $9x = 43.6$ cm.

42.
$$OA = \sqrt{3^2 + 4^2} = 5 \qquad\qquad AB^2 = OA^2 + OB^2 - 2(OA)(OB)\cos \theta$$
$$OB = \sqrt{5^2 + 1^2} = \sqrt{26} \qquad (\sqrt{5})^2 = 5^2 + (\sqrt{26})^2 - 2(5)(\sqrt{26})\cos \theta$$
$$AB = \sqrt{(4-5)^2 + (3-1)^2} = \sqrt{5} \qquad \theta \approx 0.446 \text{ radian}$$

44. The sides of the triangle have lengths of $5 + 2 = 7$, $8 + 2 = 10$, and $8 + 5 = 13$. Find angle γ first (angle opposite longest side):

$$13^2 = 10^2 + 7^2 - 2(10)(7)\cos \gamma$$
$$\gamma \approx 98.2132 \approx 98°10'$$

Angle α: $\dfrac{13}{\sin 98°10} = \dfrac{7}{\sin \alpha}$

$$\alpha \approx 32.20845 \approx 32°10'$$

Angle β: $\beta = 180° - (\alpha + \gamma) \approx 180° - (98°10' + 32°10') \approx 49°40'$

46.
$$AB = \sqrt{4.3^2 + 8.1^2} = \sqrt{84.1}$$
$$AC = \sqrt{8.1^2 + 2.8^2} = \sqrt{73.45}$$
$$BC = \sqrt{4.3^2 + 2.8^2} = \sqrt{26.33}$$

$$(AB)^2 = (AC)^2 + (CB)^2 - 2(AC)(BC)\cos(ACB)$$
$$84.1 = 73.45 + 26.33 - 2\sqrt{73.45}\,\sqrt{26.33}\,\cos(ACB)$$

Angle $ACB = 80°$

48.
$$(CS)^2 = R^2 + (ST)^2 - 2(R)(ST)\cos 122.4°$$
$$(CS)^2 = 3964^2 + 1034^2 - 2(3964)(1034)\cos 122.4°$$
$$CS \approx 4602$$

height $= CS - R \approx 4602 - 3964 \approx 638$ miles

Exercise 7-3

2. $|\mathbf{u} + \mathbf{v}| = \sqrt{|\mathbf{u}|^2 + |\mathbf{v}|^2} = \sqrt{62^2 + 34^2} = 71$ mph

$\tan \theta = \dfrac{|\mathbf{v}|}{|\mathbf{u}|} = \dfrac{34}{62} \Rightarrow \theta = 29°$

4. $|\mathbf{u} + \mathbf{v}| = \sqrt{|\mathbf{u}|^2 + |\mathbf{v}|^2} = \sqrt{48^2 + 31^2} = 57$ kg

$\tan \theta = \dfrac{|\mathbf{v}|}{|\mathbf{u}|} = \dfrac{31}{48} \Rightarrow \theta = 33°$

6. $|u + v| = \sqrt{|u|^2 + |v|^2} = \sqrt{143^2 + 57.4^2} = 154$ km/hr.

$\tan \theta = \dfrac{|v|}{|u|} = \dfrac{57.4}{143} \Rightarrow \theta = 21.9°$

8. $|u| = |u + v|\cos \theta = 250 \cos 65° = 110$ lb. to 2 significant digits
$|v| = |u + v|\sin \theta = 250 \sin 65° = 230$ lb. to 2 significant digits

10. $|u| = |u + v|\cos \theta = 28 \cos 12° = 27$ mph to 2 significant digits
$|v| = |u + v|\sin \theta = 28 \sin 12° = 5.8$ mph to 2 significant digits

12. The magnitude of a vector is a length and therefore cannot be negative.

14. $|u + v| = \sqrt{|u|^2 + |v|^2 - 2|u||v|\cos(180° - \theta)}$

$= \sqrt{120^2 + 84^2 - 2(120)(84)\cos(180° - 44°)}$

$= 190$ gm

$\dfrac{190}{\sin 136°} = \dfrac{84}{\sin \alpha}$

$\alpha = 18°$

16. $|u + v| = \sqrt{|u|^2 + |v|^2 - 2|u||v|\cos(180° - \theta)}$

$= \sqrt{8.0^2 + 2.0^2 - 2(8.0)(2.0)\cos(180° - 64°)}$

$= 9.1$ knots

$\dfrac{2.0}{\sin \alpha} = \dfrac{9.1}{\sin 116°}$

$\alpha = 11°$

18. $\dfrac{33}{\sin 137°} = \dfrac{|v|}{\sin 17°} \Rightarrow |v| = 14$ kg; $\dfrac{|u|}{\sin 26°} = \dfrac{33}{\sin 137°} \Rightarrow |u| = 21$ kg

20. $\dfrac{437}{\sin 129.5°} = \dfrac{|u|}{\sin 32.7°} = \dfrac{|v|}{\sin 17.8°} \Rightarrow |u| = 306$ mph and $|v| = 173$ mph

22. Since the zero vector has arbitrary direction, it can be parallel (or perpendicular) to any vector.

24. $|\overline{v}| = \sqrt{15^2 + 3.9^2 - 2(15)(3.9)\cos(25° + 45°)} \approx 14$ mph
$\dfrac{3.9}{\sin \theta} = \dfrac{14}{\sin(70°)} \Rightarrow \theta = 15°$
heading $= 25° + 15° = 40°$
14 mph at 40°

26. $\sqrt{255^2 - 46^2} = 251$
$\sin \theta = \dfrac{46}{255}$
$\theta = 10.4°$
251 mph at 349.6° (360° - 10.4°)

28. $R = \sqrt{3600^2 + 2900^2 - 2(3600)(2900)\cos 149°} = 6300$

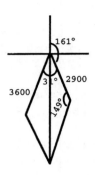

$\dfrac{6300}{\sin 149°} = \dfrac{2900}{\sin \alpha} \Rightarrow \alpha = 13.71°$

The third angle: $180° - (149° + 14°) = 17°$
direction $= 161° + 17° = 178°$
6300 kg @ 178°

30. (A) parallel force $= 2500 \sin 15° = 650$ lb
    (B) force perpendicular $= 2500 \cos 15° = 2400$ lb

32. Left: $41 \sin 31° = 21$; Right: $31 \sin 41° = 20$
    $21 > 20 \Rightarrow$ slide left

Exercise 7-4

2. $\overrightarrow{AB} = \langle 1 - (-1), -1 - 7 \rangle = \langle 2, -8 \rangle$ **4.** $\overrightarrow{AB} = \langle -2 - 0, 0 - (-1) \rangle = \langle -2, 1 \rangle$

6. $\overrightarrow{AB} = \langle -2 - 0, -1 - 0 \rangle = \langle -2, -1 \rangle$ **8.** $|\langle -3, 4 \rangle| = \sqrt{(-3)^2 + 4^2} = 5$

10. $|\langle -5, -2 \rangle| = \sqrt{(-5)^2 + (-2)^2} = \sqrt{29}$ **12.** $|\langle 0, -67 \rangle| = \sqrt{0^2 + (-67)^2} = 67$

14. Two geometric vectors are equal if and only if they have the same magnitude and direction.

16. (A) $\mathbf{u} + \mathbf{v} = \langle -1, 2 \rangle + \langle 3, -2 \rangle = \langle -1 + 3, 2 + (-2) \rangle = \langle 2, 0 \rangle$
    (B) $\mathbf{u} - \mathbf{v} = \langle -1, 2 \rangle - \langle 3, -2 \rangle = \langle -1 - 3, 2 - (-2) \rangle = \langle -4, 4 \rangle$
    (C) $2\mathbf{u} - \mathbf{v} + 3\mathbf{w} = 2\langle -1, 2 \rangle - \langle 3, -2 \rangle + 3\langle 0, -2 \rangle = \langle -2 - 3 + 0, 4 + 2 - 6 \rangle = \langle -5, 0 \rangle$

18. (A) $\mathbf{u} + \mathbf{v} = \langle -3, 2 \rangle + \langle -2, 2 \rangle = \langle -3 + (-2), 2 + 2 \rangle = \langle -5, 4 \rangle$
    (B) $\mathbf{u} - \mathbf{v} = \langle -3, 2 \rangle - \langle -2, 2 \rangle = \langle -3 - (-2), 2 - 2 \rangle = \langle -1, 0 \rangle$
    (C) $2\mathbf{u} - \mathbf{v} + 3\mathbf{w} = 2\langle -3, 2 \rangle - \langle -2, 2 \rangle + 3\langle -3, 0 \rangle = \langle -6 + 2 - 9, 4 - 2 + 0 \rangle = \langle -13, 2 \rangle$

20. $\langle 2, -5 \rangle = \langle 2, 0 \rangle + \langle 0, -5 \rangle = 2\langle 1, 0 \rangle - 5\langle 0, 1 \rangle = 2\mathbf{i} - 5\mathbf{j}$

22. $\langle 0, -27 \rangle = -27\langle 0, 1 \rangle = -27\mathbf{j}$

24. $\overrightarrow{AB} = \langle 0 - (-2), 2 - (-1) \rangle = \langle 2, 3 \rangle = \langle 2, 0 \rangle + \langle 0, 3 \rangle$
    $= 2\langle 1, 0 \rangle + 3\langle 0, 1 \rangle = 2\mathbf{i} + 3\mathbf{j}$

26. $\mathbf{u} - \mathbf{v} = 3\mathbf{i} - 2\mathbf{j} - (2\mathbf{i} + 4\mathbf{j}) = 3\mathbf{i} - 2\mathbf{j} - 2\mathbf{i} - 4\mathbf{j} = \mathbf{i} - 6\mathbf{j}$

28. $3\mathbf{u} + 2\mathbf{v} = 3(3\mathbf{i} - 2\mathbf{j}) + 2(2\mathbf{i} + 4\mathbf{j}) = 9\mathbf{i} - 6\mathbf{j} + 4\mathbf{i} + 8\mathbf{j} = 13\mathbf{i} + 2\mathbf{j}$

30. $\mathbf{u} - 3\mathbf{v} + 2\mathbf{w} = 3\mathbf{i} - 2\mathbf{j} - 3(2\mathbf{i} + 4\mathbf{j}) + 2(2\mathbf{i}) = 3\mathbf{i} - 2\mathbf{j} - 6\mathbf{i} - 12\mathbf{j} + 4\mathbf{i}$
    $= \mathbf{i} - 14\mathbf{j}$

32. $\mathbf{u} = \dfrac{\langle 4, -3 \rangle}{|\langle 4, -3 \rangle|} = \dfrac{\langle 4, -3 \rangle}{\sqrt{4^2 + 3^2}} = \dfrac{\langle 4, -3 \rangle}{5} = \left\langle \dfrac{4}{5}, -\dfrac{3}{5} \right\rangle$

34. $\mathbf{u} = \dfrac{\langle 2, -3 \rangle}{|\langle 2, -3 \rangle|} = \dfrac{\langle 2, -3 \rangle}{\sqrt{2^2 + (-3)^2}} = \dfrac{\langle 2, -3 \rangle}{\sqrt{13}} = \left\langle \dfrac{2}{\sqrt{13}}, \dfrac{-3}{\sqrt{13}} \right\rangle$

36. The two vectors are equal in magnitude and opposite in direction.

38. $\begin{aligned} \mathbf{u} + \mathbf{v} &= \langle a, b \rangle + \langle c, d \rangle \\ &= \langle a + c, b + d \rangle \\ &= \langle c + a, d + b \rangle \\ &= \langle c, d \rangle + \langle a, b \rangle = \mathbf{v} + \mathbf{u} \end{aligned}$

40. $\begin{aligned} \mathbf{u} + (-\mathbf{u}) &= \langle a, b \rangle + (-\langle a, b \rangle) \\ &= \langle a, b \rangle + \langle -a, -b \rangle \\ &= \langle a + (-a), b + (-b) \rangle \\ &= \langle 0, 0 \rangle \\ &= \mathbf{0} \end{aligned}$

42. $\begin{aligned} m(\mathbf{u} + \mathbf{v}) &= m(\langle a, b \rangle + \langle c, d \rangle) \\ &= m\langle a + c, b + d \rangle \\ &= \langle ma + mc, mb + md \rangle \\ &= \langle ma, mb \rangle + \langle mc, md \rangle \\ &= m\langle a, b \rangle + m\langle c, d \rangle \\ &= m\mathbf{u} + m\mathbf{v} \end{aligned}$

44. $\begin{aligned} 1\mathbf{u} &= 1\langle a, b \rangle \\ &= \langle 1 \cdot a, 1 \cdot b \rangle \\ &= \langle a, b \rangle \\ &= \mathbf{u} \end{aligned}$

46. Let the left tension be represented by T_L and the right tension by T_R. Then
$T_L \sin 4.2° + T_R \sin 5.3° = 112$
$T_L \cos 4.2° = T_R \cos 5.3°$

Solving the second equation for T_L:
$T_L = T_R \dfrac{\cos 5.3°}{\cos 4.2°}$

Substituting: $\dfrac{T_R(\cos 5.3°)(\sin 4.2°)}{\cos 4.2°} + T_R \sin 5.3° = 112$

Graph $y1 = \dfrac{x(\cos 5.3°)(\sin 4.2°)}{\cos 4.2°} + x \sin 5.3°$ and $y2 = 112$.

$T_R \approx 677$ lb, $T_L \approx 676$ lb.

48. Let the left tension be represented by T_L and the right tension by T_R. Then
$T_L \sin 45° + T_R \sin 20° = 500$
$T_L \cos 45° = T_R \cos 20°$

Solving the second equation for T_L: $T_L = \dfrac{T_R \cos 20°}{\cos 45°}$

Substituting: $\dfrac{T_R(\cos 20°)(\sin 45°)}{\cos 45°} + T_R \sin 20° = 500$

Graph $y1 = \dfrac{x(\cos 20°)(\sin 45°)}{\cos 45°} + x \sin 20°$ and $y2 = 500$.

$T_R \approx 390$ lb, $T_L \approx 518$ lb

50. Angle $ABC = 30°$
$BC \sin 30° = 1000 \Rightarrow BC = 2000$ kg, tension
$BC \cos 30° = AB \Rightarrow AB = 2000 \cos 30° \approx 1730$ kg, compression

52. Angle ABC: $\cos(ABC) = \dfrac{5}{6} \Rightarrow ABC \approx 33.6°$ (Answers may vary due to rounding.)

$AB \sin 33.6° = 5000$
$\quad\quad\quad AB \approx 9040$ kg, compression
$BC = AB \cos 33.6° \approx 9040 \cos 33.6° \approx 7530$ kg, tension

Exercise 7-5

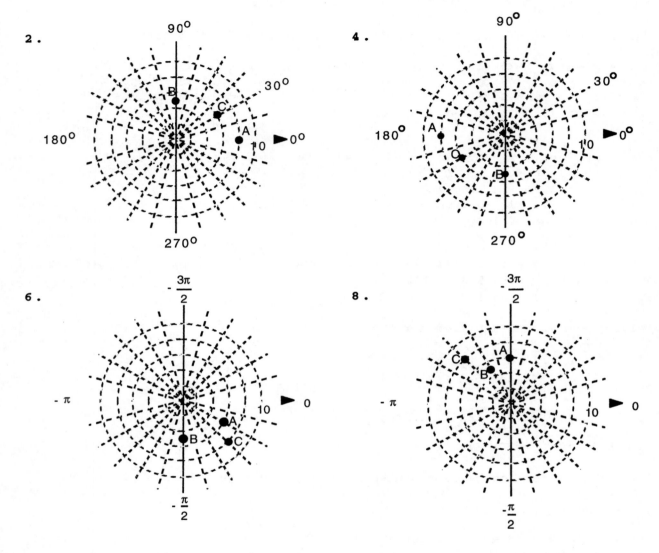

2.

4.

6.

8.

10. (-6, -210°): The polar axis is rotated 210° clockwise (negative direction) and the point is located 6 units from the pole along the negative polar axis. (-6, 150°): The polar axis is rotated 150° counterclockwise (positive direction) and the point is located 6 units from the pole along the negative polar axis. (6, 330°): The polar axis is rotated 330° counterclockwise (positive direction) and the point is located 6 units along the positive polar axis.

12.

θ	$10 \cos \theta$
0	10
$\pi/6$	$5\sqrt{3}$
$\pi/4$	$5\sqrt{2}$
$\pi/3$	5
$\pi/2$	0
$2\pi/3$	-5
$3\pi/4$	$-5\sqrt{2}$
$5\pi/6$	$-5\sqrt{3}$
π	-10

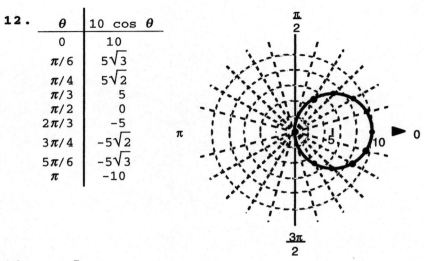

14. $r = 5$

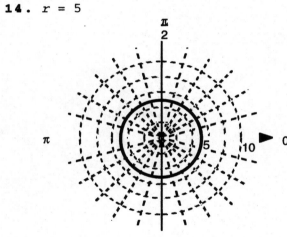

16. $\theta = \dfrac{\pi}{6}$

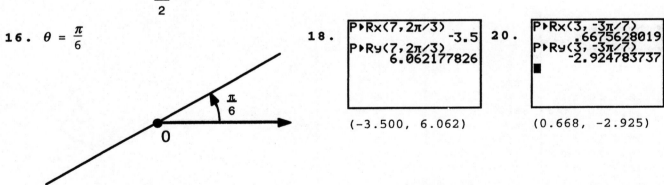

18.
```
P▸Rx(7,2π/3)
                -3.5
P▸Ry(7,2π/3)
        6.062177826
```
$(-3.500, 6.062)$

20.
```
P▸Rx(3, -3π/7)
        .6675628019
P▸Ry(3, -3π/7)
        -2.924783737
■
```
$(0.668, -2.925)$

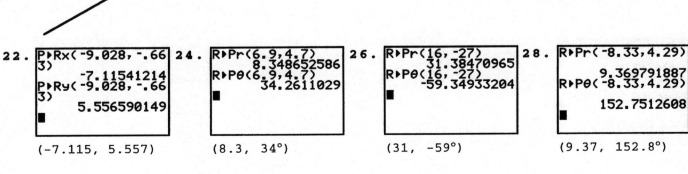

22.
```
P▸Rx(-9.028, -.66
3)
        -7.11541214
P▸Ry(-9.028, -.66
3)
        5.556590149
■
```
$(-7.115, 5.557)$

24.
```
R▸Pr(6.9,4.7)
        8.348652586
R▸Pθ(6.9,4.7)
        34.2611029
■
```
$(8.3, 34°)$

26.
```
R▸Pr(16, -27)
        31.38470965
R▸Pθ(16, -27)
        -59.34933204
■
```
$(31, -59°)$

28.
```
R▸Pr(-8.33,4.29)
        9.369791887
R▸Pθ(-8.33,4.29)
        152.7512608
■
```
$(9.37, 152.8°)$

30.

θ varies from	$\cos\theta$ varies from	$4\cos\theta$ varies from
0 to $\pi/2$	1 to 0	4 to 0
$\pi/2$ to π	0 to -1	0 to -4
π to $3\pi/2$	-1 to 0	-4 to 0
$3\pi/2$ to 2π	0 to 1	0 to 4

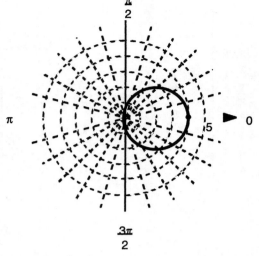

32.

θ varies from	2θ varies from	$\cos 2\theta$ varies from	$8\cos 2\theta$ varies from
0 to $\pi/4$	0 to $\pi/2$	1 to 0	8 to 0
$\pi/4$ to $\pi/2$	$\pi/2$ to π	0 to -1	0 to -8
$\pi/2$ to $3\pi/4$	π to $3\pi/2$	-1 to 0	-8 to 0
$3\pi/4$ to π	$3\pi/2$ to 2π	0 to 1	0 to 8
π to $5\pi/4$	2π to $5\pi/2$	1 to 0	8 to 0
$5\pi/4$ to $3\pi/2$	$5\pi/2$ to 3π	0 to -1	0 to -8
$3\pi/2$ to $7\pi/4$	3π to $7\pi/2$	-1 to 0	-8 to 0
$7\pi/4$ to 2π	$7\pi/2$ to 4π	0 to 1	0 to 8

34.

θ varies from	3θ varies from	$\sin 3\theta$ varies from	$6\sin 3\theta$ varies from
0 to $\pi/6$	0 to $\pi/2$	0 to 1	0 to 6
$\pi/6$ to $\pi/3$	$\pi/2$ to π	1 to 0	6 to 0
$\pi/3$ to $\pi/2$	π to $3\pi/2$	0 to -1	0 to -6
$\pi/2$ to $2\pi/3$	$3\pi/2$ to 2π	-1 to 0	-6 to 0
$2\pi/3$ to $5\pi/6$	2π to $5\pi/2$	0 to 1	0 to 6
$5\pi/6$ to π	$5\pi/2$ to 3π	1 to 0	6 to 0
π to $7\pi/6$	3π to $7\pi/2$	0 to -1	0 to -6
$7\pi/6$ to $5\pi/3$	$7\pi/2$ to 5π	-1 to 0	-6 to 0
$\vdots$	$\vdots$	$\vdots$	$\vdots$

36.

θ varies from	$\cos \theta$ varies from	$3 \cos \theta$ varies from	$3 + 3 \cos \theta$ varies from
0 to $\pi/2$	1 to 0	3 to 0	6 to 3
$\pi/2$ to π	0 to -1	0 to -3	3 to 0
π to $3\pi/2$	-1 to 0	-3 to 0	0 to 3
$3\pi/2$ to 2π	0 to 1	0 to 3	3 to 6

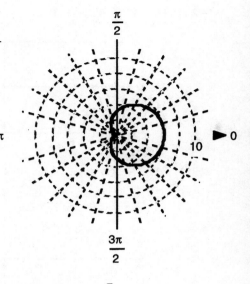

38.

θ varies from	$\cos \theta$ varies from	$4 \cos \theta$ varies from	$2 + 4 \cos \theta$ varies from
0 to $\pi/2$	1 to 0	4 to 0	6 to 2
$\pi/2$ to π	0 to -1	0 to -4	2 to -2
π to $3\pi/2$	-1 to 0	-4 to 0	-2 to 2
$3\pi/2$ to 2π	0 to 1	0 to 4	2 to 6

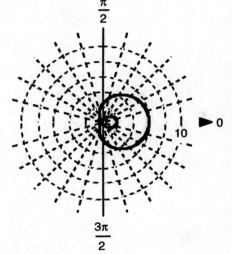

40. $r = 2 + 2 \cos \theta$ $r = 4 + 2 \cos \theta$ $r = 2 + 4 \cos \theta$

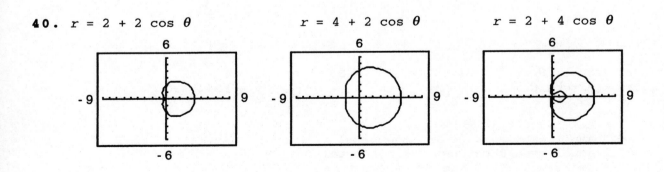

42. (A) $r = 4 \cos \theta$

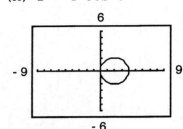

$r = 4 \cos 3\theta$

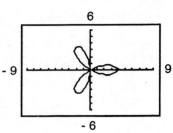

$r = 4 \cos 5\theta$

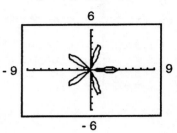

(B) 7 leaves in $r = 4 \cos 7\theta$

(C) n leaves in $r = a \cos(n\theta)$
$\quad a > 0$ and n odd

44. (A) $r = 4 \cos 2\theta$

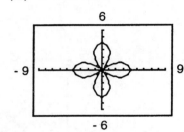

$r = 4 \cos 4\theta$

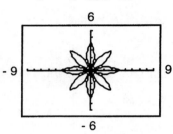

$r = 4 \cos 6\theta$

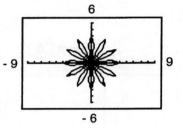

(B) 16 leaves in $r = 4 \cos 8\theta$

(C) $2n$ leaves in $r = a \cos n\theta$
$\quad a > 0$ and n even

46. $6x - x^2 = y^2$
$\qquad 6x = x^2 + y^2$
$6r \cos \theta = r^2$
$\qquad r = 6 \cos \theta$

48. $x^2 + y^2 = 9$
$\qquad r^2 = 9$
or $\;\; r = \pm 3$

50. $2xy = 1$
$2(r \cos \theta \; r \sin \theta) = 1$
$r^2(2 \sin \theta \cos \theta) = 1$
$\qquad r^2 \sin 2\theta = 1$
$$r^2 = \frac{1}{\sin 2\theta}$$
$\qquad r^2 = \csc 2\theta$

52. $r(2 \cos \theta + \sin \theta) = 4$
$2(r \cos \theta) + r \sin \theta = 4$
$\qquad\qquad 2x + y = 4$

54. $\qquad r = 8 \cos \theta$
$\qquad r^2 = 8r \cos \theta$
$x^2 + y^2 = 8x$

56. $\qquad r = 4$
$\qquad r^2 = 16$
$x^2 + y^2 = 16$

58. $\underline{n}$ $\qquad \underline{r = 1 + 2 \cos (n\theta)}$
1 $\qquad$ 1 small petal inside 1 large petal
2 $\qquad$ 2 small petals between 2 large petals
3 $\qquad$ 3 small petals inside 3 large petals
4 $\qquad$ 4 small petals between 4 large petals

$r = 1 + 2 \cos(n\theta)$ will have n large and n small petals. For n odd the small petals are within the large petals. For n even the small petals are between the large petals.

60. $r = 2 \cos \theta$ (1)
    $r = 2 \sin \theta$ (2)
    $0 \le \theta \le \pi$
    Divide (2) by (1):

$$1 = \frac{2 \sin \theta}{2 \cos \theta} = \tan \theta$$

$$\theta = \frac{\pi}{4} \Rightarrow r = \sqrt{2}$$

$$\left(\sqrt{2}, \frac{\pi}{4} \right)$$

[Note: (0, 0) is not a solution to this system even though the graphs cross at the origin.]

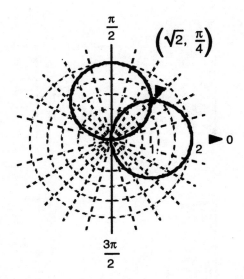

62. (1) $r = 8 \sin \theta$
    (2) $r = 8 \cos 2\theta$
      $0° \le \theta \le 360°$

$$\sin \theta = \cos 2\theta = 1 - 2 \sin^2 \theta$$
$$2 \sin^2 \theta + \sin \theta - 1 = 0$$
$$(2 \sin \theta - 1)(\sin \theta + 1) = 0$$
$$2 \sin \theta - 1 = 0 \qquad \sin \theta + 1 = 0$$
$$\sin \theta = \frac{1}{2} \qquad\qquad \sin \theta = -1$$
$$\theta = 30°, 150° \qquad \theta = 270°$$
$$r = 4, 4 \qquad\qquad r = -8$$

(4, 30°), (4, 150°), (-8, 270°)

[Note: (0, 0) is not a solution to this system even though the graphs cross at the origin.]

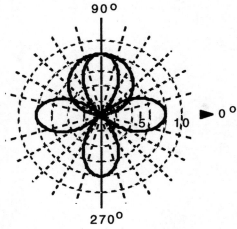

64. $P_1(2, 30°)$ and $P_2(3, 60°)$

$$d = \sqrt{(r_1)^2 + (r_2)^2 - 2r_1 r_2 \cos(\theta_2 - \theta_1)}$$
$$d = \sqrt{2^2 + 3^2 - 2(2)(3) \cos(60° - 30°)}$$
$$d = \sqrt{13 - 12 \cos 30°}$$
$$d \approx 1.615$$

66. at 45°: $9k$, at 90°: $14k$, at 120°: $13k$, at 150°: $11k$

68. (A) $e = 0.6$:

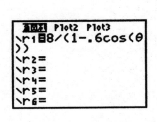

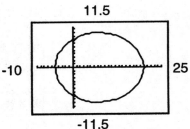

ellipse

(B) $e = 1$:

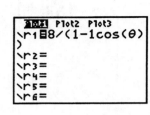

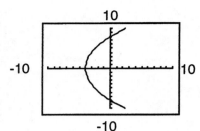

parabola

(C) $e = 2$:

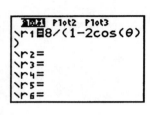

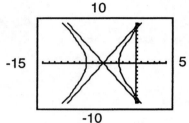

hyperbola

Exercise 7-6

2.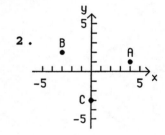

4.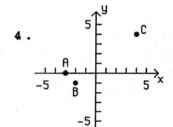

6.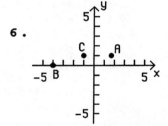

8.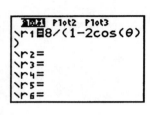

10. (A) $-1 + i\sqrt{3}$

A sketch shows that $-1 + i\sqrt{3}$ is associated with $\theta = 120°$, $r = 2$
$-1 + i\sqrt{3} = 2(\cos 120° + i \sin 120°) = 2e^{120°i}$

(B) $-3i$
A sketch shows that $\theta = -90°$, $r = 3$
$-3i = 3(\cos(-90°) + i \sin(-90°)) = 3e^{(-90°)i}$

(C) $-7 - 4i$

$\gamma = \sqrt{(-7)^2 + (-4)^2} = \sqrt{65} \approx 8.06$

$\theta = -180° + \tan^{-1}\left(\dfrac{4}{7}\right) \approx -150.26°$

```
-1+i√(3)
            2e^(120i)
-3i
            3e^(-90i)
-7-4i
8.06e^(-150.26i)
```

$-7 - 4i \approx 8.06(\cos(-150.26°) + i \sin(-150.26°)) \approx 8.06e^{(-150.26°)i}$

12. (A) $\sqrt{3} - i$

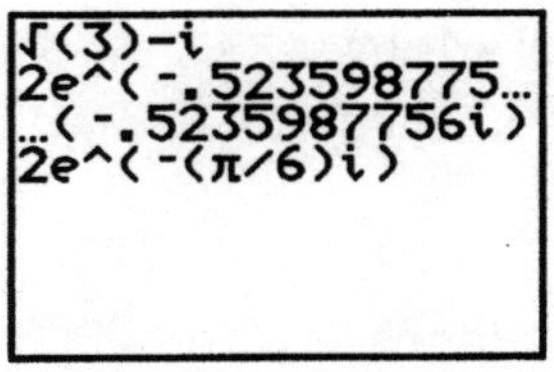

A sketch shows that $\theta = -\frac{\pi}{6}$, $r = 2$

$\sqrt{3} - i = 2\left(\cos\left(-\frac{\pi}{6}\right)\right) + i\ \sin\left(-\frac{\pi}{6}\right) = 2e^{-(\pi/6)i}$

(B) $-2 + 2i$

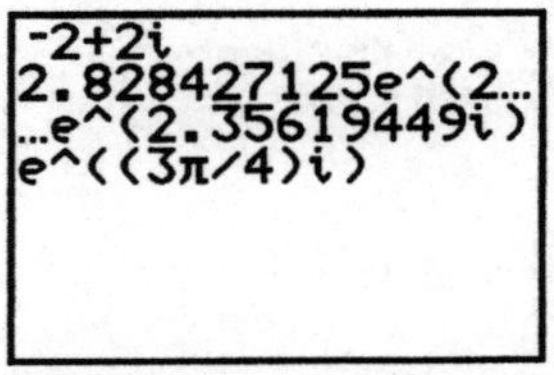

A sketch shows that $\theta = \frac{3\pi}{4}$, $r = \sqrt{8} = 2\sqrt{2}$

$-2 + 2i = 2\sqrt{2}\left(\cos\frac{3\pi}{4} + i\ \sin\frac{3\pi}{4}\right) = 2\sqrt{2}e^{(3\pi/4)i}$

(C) $6 - 5i$

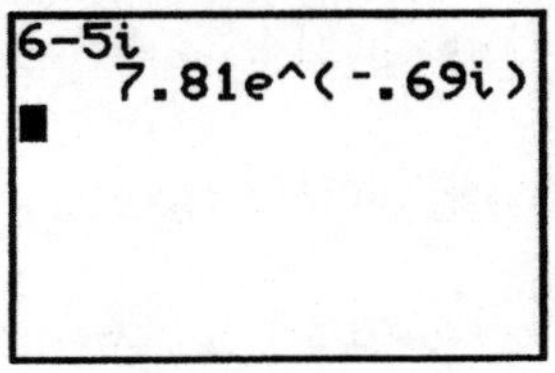

$r = \sqrt{6^2 + (-5)^2} = \sqrt{61} \approx 7.81$

$\theta = \tan^{-1}\left(-\frac{5}{6}\right) \approx -0.69$

$6 - 5i \approx 7.81(\cos(-0.69) + i\ \sin(-0.69)) \approx 7.81e^{-0.69i}$

14. (A) $2e^{30°i} = 2(\cos 30° + i\ \sin 30°)$

$\qquad = 2\left(\frac{\sqrt{3}}{2} + \frac{1}{2}i\right)$

$\qquad = \sqrt{3} + i$

(B) $\sqrt{2}e^{(-3\pi/4)i} = \sqrt{2}\left(\cos\left(-\frac{3\pi}{4}\right) + i\ \sin\left(-\frac{3\pi}{4}\right)\right)$

$\qquad = \sqrt{2}\left(-\frac{\sqrt{2}}{2} + i\left(-\frac{\sqrt{2}}{2}\right)\right)$

$\qquad = -1 - i$

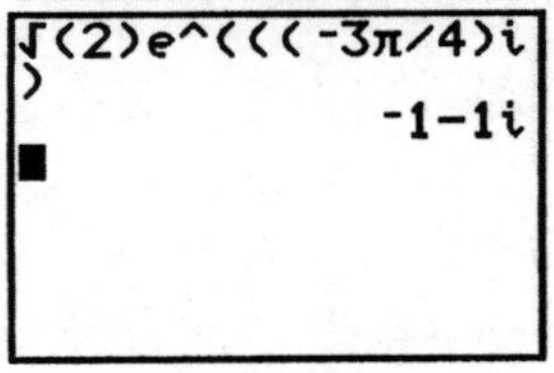

(C) $5.71e^{(-0.48)i} = 5.71(\cos(-0.48) + i\ \sin(-0.48))$

$\qquad\qquad \approx 5.06 - 2.64i$

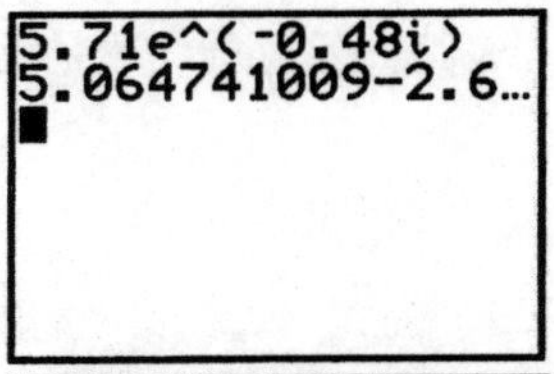

16. (A) $\sqrt{3}e^{(-\pi/2)i} = \sqrt{3}\left(\cos\left(-\frac{\pi}{2}\right) + i\ \sin\left(-\frac{\pi}{2}\right)\right)$

$\qquad = \sqrt{3}(0 - i)$

$\qquad = -i\sqrt{3}$

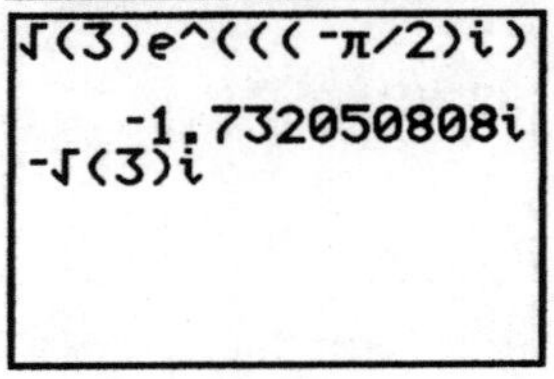

(B) $\sqrt{2}e^{135°i} = \sqrt{2}(\cos 135° + i\ \sin 135°)$

$\qquad = \sqrt{2}\left(-\frac{\sqrt{2}}{2} + i\frac{\sqrt{2}}{2}\right)$

$\qquad = -1 + i$

```
√(3)-i
2e^(-.523598775...
...(-.5235987756i)
2e^(-(π/6)i)
```

```
-2+2i
2.828427125e^(2...
...e^(2.35619449i)
e^((3π/4)i)
```

```
6-5i
      7.81e^(-.69i)
■
```

$30° = \frac{\pi}{6}$

```
2*e^((i*π/6))
      1.732050808+i
√(3)+i■
```

```
√(2)e^(((-3π/4)i
)
            -1-1i
■
```

```
5.71e^(-0.48i)
5.064741009-2.6...
■
```

```
√(3)e^(((-π/2)i)
        -1.732050808i
-√(3)i
```

$135° = \frac{3\pi}{4}$

```
√(2)e^(((3π/4)i)
            -1+1i
```

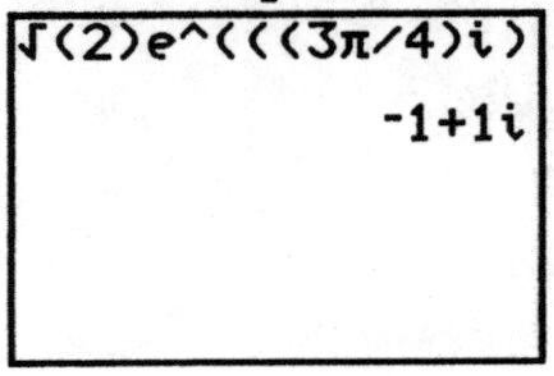

(C) $6.83e^{(-108.82°)i} = 6.83(\cos(-108.82°) + i\,\sin(-108.82°))$
$$\approx 6.83(-0.322596 + i(-0.9465367))$$
$$\approx -2.20 - 6.46i$$

$$-108.82° = -1.899267292$$

```
6.83e^(-1.899267
292i)
-2.203331489-6.…
```

18. $z_1 z_2 = r_1 e^{i\theta_1} \cdot r_2 e^{i\theta_2} = r_1 r_2 e^{i(\theta_1 + \theta_2)}$ $\qquad \dfrac{z_1}{z_2} = \dfrac{r_1 e^{i\theta_1}}{r_2 e^{i\theta_2}} = \dfrac{r_1}{r_2} e^{i(\theta_1 - \theta_2)}$

$z_1 z_2 = 6e^{132°i} \cdot 3e^{93°i} = 18e^{225°i}$ $\qquad \dfrac{z_1}{z_2} = \dfrac{6e^{132°i}}{3e^{93°i}} = 2e^{39°i}$

20. $z_1 z_2 = r_1 e^{i\theta_1} \cdot r_2 e^{i\theta_2} = r_1 r_2 e^{i(\theta_1 + \theta_2)}$ $\qquad \dfrac{z_1}{z_2} = \dfrac{r_1 e^{i\theta_1}}{r_2 e^{i\theta_2}} = \dfrac{r_1}{r_2} e^{i(\theta_1 - \theta_2)}$

$z_1 z_2 = 3e^{67°i} \cdot 2e^{97°i} = 6e^{164°i}$ $\qquad \dfrac{z_1}{z_2} = \dfrac{3e^{67°i}}{2e^{97°i}} = 1.5e^{(-30°)i}$

22. $z_1 z_2 = r_1 e^{i\theta_1} \cdot r_2 e^{i\theta_2} = r_1 r_2 e^{i(\theta_1 + \theta_2)}$

$z_1 z_2 = 7.11e^{0.79i} \cdot 2.66e^{1.07i} = 18.9126e^{1.86i} \approx 18.91e^{1.86i}$

$\dfrac{z_1}{z_2} = \dfrac{r_1 e^{i\theta_1}}{r_2 e^{i\theta_2}} = \dfrac{r_1}{r_2} e^{i(\theta_1 - \theta_2)}$

$\dfrac{z_1}{z_2} = \dfrac{7.11e^{0.79i}}{2.66e^{1.07i}} \approx 2.67e^{(-0.28)i}$

24. $(1 + i)^2 = 1 + 2i + i^2$
$$= 1 + 2i - 1$$
$$= 2i$$

$1 + i:\ r = \sqrt{2},\ \theta = 45° \Rightarrow \sqrt{2}e^{45°i}$

$(\sqrt{2}e^{45°i})^2 = \sqrt{2}e^{45°i} \cdot \sqrt{2}e^{45°i} = 2e^{90°i}$

26. $(1 + i\sqrt{3})(\sqrt{3} + i) = \sqrt{3} + i + 3i + \sqrt{3}i^2$
$$= \sqrt{3} + 4i - \sqrt{3}$$
$$= 4i$$

$(1 + i\sqrt{3}):\ r = 2,\ \theta = 60° \Rightarrow 2e^{60°i}$

$(\sqrt{3} + i):\ r = 2,\ \theta = 30° \Rightarrow 2e^{30°i}$

$(2e^{60°i})(2e^{30°i}) = 4e^{90°i}$

28. $(1 + i)^3 = 1 + 3i + 3i^2 + i^3$
$$= 1 + 3i - 3 - i$$
$$= -2 + 2i$$

$(1 + i):\ r = \sqrt{2},\ \theta = 45° \Rightarrow \sqrt{2}e^{45°i}$

$(\sqrt{2}e^{45°i})^3 = (\sqrt{2}e^{45°i})(\sqrt{2}e^{45°i})(\sqrt{2}e^{45°i})$
$$= 2\sqrt{2}e^{135°i}$$

30. $(r^{1/2}e^{(\theta/2)i})^2 = (r^{1/2})^2 e^{(2 \cdot (\theta/2)i)} = re^{i\theta}$

32. $\dfrac{z_1}{z_2} = \dfrac{r_1(\cos\theta_1 + i\sin\theta_1)}{r_2(\cos\theta_2 + i\sin\theta_2)}$

$= \dfrac{r_1}{r_2} \cdot \dfrac{\cos\theta_1 + i\sin\theta_1}{\cos\theta_2 + i\sin\theta_2} \cdot \dfrac{\cos\theta_2 - i\sin\theta_2}{\cos\theta_2 - i\sin\theta_2}$

$= \dfrac{r_1}{r_2} \cdot \dfrac{\cos\theta_1\cos\theta_2 - i\cos\theta_1\sin\theta_2 + i\cos\theta_2\sin\theta_1 - i^2\sin\theta_1\sin\theta_2}{\cos^2\theta_2 - i^2\sin^2\theta_2}$

$= \dfrac{r_1}{r_2} \cdot \dfrac{(\cos\theta_1\cos\theta_2 + \sin\theta_1\sin\theta_2) + i(\cos\theta_2\sin\theta_1 - \cos\theta_1\sin\theta_2)}{1}$

$= \dfrac{r_1}{r_2} \cdot [\cos(\theta_1 - \theta_2) + i\sin(\theta_1 - \theta_2)]$

$= \dfrac{r_1}{r_2} e^{i(\theta_1 - \theta_2)}$

34. (A) $8e^{0°i} = 8(\cos 0° + i\sin 0°)$
$= 8(1 + 0i)$
$= 8 + 0i$
$6e^{30°i} = 6(\cos 30° + i\sin 30°)$
$= 6\left(\dfrac{\sqrt{3}}{2} + \dfrac{1}{2}i\right)$
$= 3\sqrt{3} + 3i$
$(8 + 0i) + (3\sqrt{3} + 3i) = (8 + 3\sqrt{3}) + 3i$

(B) $(8 + 3\sqrt{3}) + 3i:$ $r = \sqrt{(8 + 3\sqrt{3})^2 + 3^2}$ $\tan\theta = \dfrac{3}{8 + 3\sqrt{3}}$
$= \sqrt{100 + 48\sqrt{3}}$ $\theta \approx 12.8°$
≈ 13.5

$(8 + 3\sqrt{3}) + 3i \approx 13.5e^{12.8°i}$

(C) $13.5e^{12.8°i}$ has magnitude 13.5 lb with direction 12.8°.

Exercise 7-7

2. $z^n = r^n e^{n\theta i}$
$(5e^{15°i})^3 = 5^3 e^{(3\cdot15°)i}$
$= 125e^{45°i}$

4. $z^n = r^n e^{n\theta i}$
$(\sqrt{2}e^{15°i})^8 = (\sqrt{2})^8 e^{(8\cdot15°)i}$
$= 16e^{120°i}$

6. $(\sqrt{3} + i):$ $r = 2,\ \theta = 30° \Rightarrow 2e^{30°i}$
$z^n = r^n e^{n\theta i}$
$(\sqrt{3} + i)^8 = (2e^{30°i})^8$
$= 2^8 e^{(8\cdot30°)i}$
$= 256e^{240°i}$

8. $(-1 + i):$ $r = \sqrt{2},\ \theta = 135° \Rightarrow \sqrt{2}e^{135°i}$
$z^n = r^n e^{n\theta i}$
$(\sqrt{2}e^{135°i})^4 = (\sqrt{2})^4 e^{(4\cdot135°)i}$
$= 4e^{540°i}$
$= 4(\cos 180° + i\sin 180°)$
$= 4(-1 + 0i)$
$= -4$

10. $(-\sqrt{3} + i)$: $r = 2$, $\theta = 150° \Rightarrow 2e^{150°i}$

$z^n = r^n e^{n\theta i}$

$(2e^{150°i})^5 = 2^5 e^{(5 \cdot 150°)i}$

$\qquad\qquad\quad = 32 e^{750°i}$

$\qquad\qquad\quad = 32 e^{30°i}$

$\qquad\qquad\quad = 32(\cos 30° + i \sin 30°)$

$\qquad\qquad\quad = 32\left(\dfrac{\sqrt{3}}{2} + \dfrac{1}{2} i\right)$

$\qquad\qquad\quad = 16\sqrt{3} + 16i$

12. $\left(-\dfrac{1}{2} - \dfrac{\sqrt{3}}{2}\right)$: $r = 1$, $\theta = 240° \Rightarrow 1e^{240°i}$

$z^n = r^n e^{n\theta i}$

$(1e^{240°i})^3 = 1^3 e^{(3 \cdot 240°)i}$

$\qquad\qquad\quad = 1e^{720°i}$

$\qquad\qquad\quad = 1e^{0°i}$

$\qquad\qquad\quad = \cos 0° + i \sin 0°$

$\qquad\qquad\quad = 1$

14. $z^{1/n} = r^{1/n} e^{[(\theta/n) + ((360°k)/n)]i}$

$(8e^{45°i})^{1/3} = 8^{1/3} e^{[(45°/3) + ((360°k)/3)]i}$

$\qquad\qquad\quad = 2e^{(15° + 120°k)i}$

$w_1 = 2e^{15°i}$

$w_2 = 2e^{(15° + 120°)i} = 2e^{135°i}$

$w_3 = 2e^{(15° + 240°)i} = 2e^{255°i}$

16. $z^{1/n} = r^{1/n} e^{[(\theta/n) + ((360°k)/n)]i}$

$(16e^{90°i})^{1/4} = 16^{1/4} e^{[(90°/4) + ((360°k)/4)]i}$

$\qquad\qquad\quad = 2e^{(22.5° + 90°k)i}$

$w_1 = 2e^{22.5°i}$

$w_2 = 2e^{112.5°i}$

$w_3 = 2e^{202.5°i}$

$w_4 = 2e^{292.5°i}$

18. $(-1 + i)$: $r = \sqrt{2}$, $\theta = 135° \Rightarrow \sqrt{2}e^{135°i}$

$z^{1/n} = r^{1/n} e^{[(\theta/n) + ((360°k)/n)]i}$

$(\sqrt{2}e^{135°i})^{1/3} = (2^{1/2})^{1/3} e^{[(135°/3) + ((360°k)/3)]i}$

$\qquad\qquad\qquad = 2^{1/6} e^{(45° + 120°k)i}$

$w_1 = 2^{1/6} e^{45°i}$

$w_2 = 2^{1/6} e^{165°i}$

$w_3 = 2^{1/6} e^{285°i}$

20. $z = 1 = 1e^{0°i}$

$z^{1/n} = r^{1/n} e^{[(\theta/n) + ((360°k)/n)]i}$

$(1e^{0°i})^{1/4} = 1^{1/4} e^{[0° + ((360°k)/4)]i}$

$\qquad\qquad\quad = 1e^{90°ki}$

$w_1 = 1e^{0°i} = 1 + 0i$

$w_2 = 1e^{90°i} = 0 + i$

$w_3 = 1e^{180°i} = -1 + 0i$

$w_4 = 1e^{270°i} = 0 - i$

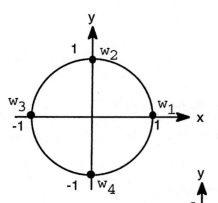

22. $z = -8 = 8e^{180°i}$

$z^{1/n} = r^{1/n} e^{[(\theta/n) + ((360°k)/n)]i}$

$(8e^{180°i})^{1/3} = 8^{1/3} e^{[(180°/3) + ((360°k)/3)]i}$

$\qquad\qquad\quad = 2e^{(60° + 120°k)i}$

$w_1 = 2e^{60°i} = 2(\cos 60° + i \sin 60°) = 1 + \sqrt{3}\,i$

$w_2 = 2e^{180°i} = 2(\cos 180° + i \sin 180°) = -2$

$w_3 = 2e^{300°i} = 2(\cos 300° + i \sin 300°) = 1 - \sqrt{3}\,i$

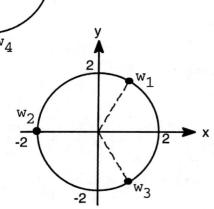

24. $z = -i = e^{-90°i}$

$z^{1/n} = r^{1/n}e^{[(\theta/n) + ((360°k)/n)]i}$

$(1e^{-90°})^{1/5} = 1^{1/5}e^{[(-90°/5) + ((360°k)/5)]i}$

$\qquad\qquad = 1e^{(-18° + 72°k)i}$

$w_1 = 1e^{(-18°)i}$

$w_2 = 1e^{54°i}$

$w_3 = 1e^{126°i}$

$w_4 = 1e^{198°i}$

$w_5 = 1e^{270°i}$

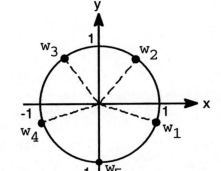

26. (A) $x^3 + 8 = 0$

$\qquad (-2)^3 + 8 = 0$

$\qquad -8 + 8 = 0,\ -2$ is a root of $x^3 + 8 = 0$

$x^3 + 8 = 0$ is degree 3 so there are two more roots.

(B)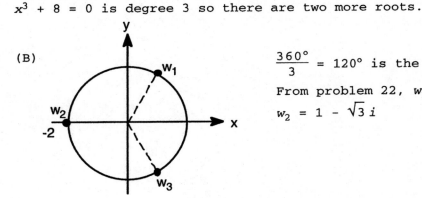

$\dfrac{360°}{3} = 120°$ is the spacing between roots

From problem 22, $w_1 = 1 + \sqrt{3}\,i$,

$\qquad w_2 = 1 - \sqrt{3}\,i$

(C) $(1 + \sqrt{3}\,i)^3 + 8 = [1 + 3(\sqrt{3}i) + 3(\sqrt{3}i)^2 + (\sqrt{3}i)^3] + 8$

$\qquad\qquad\qquad\quad = [1 + 3\sqrt{3}i - 9 - 3\sqrt{3}i] + 8$

$\qquad\qquad\qquad\quad = -8 + 8$

$\qquad\qquad\qquad\quad = 0$

(D) In the same manner, $(1 - \sqrt{3}\,i)^3 + 8 = -8 + 8 = 0$

28. $x_3 - 64 = 0$

$\qquad x_3 = 64$

$\qquad\ x = 64^{1/3} = (64e^{0°i})^{1/3}$

$\qquad z^{1/n} = r^{1/n}e^{[(\theta/n) + ((360°k)/n)]i}$

$(64e^{0°i})^{1/3} = 64^{1/3}e^{[(0°/3) + ((360°k)/3)]i}$

$\qquad\qquad\quad = 4e^{120°ki}$

$x_1 = 4e^{0°i} = 4$

$x_2 = 4e^{120°i} = 4(\cos 120° + i \sin 120°) = 4\left(-\dfrac{1}{2} + \dfrac{\sqrt{3}}{2}i\right) = -2 + 2\sqrt{3}\,i$

$x_3 = 4e^{240°i} = 4(\cos 240° + i \sin 240°) = 4\left(-\dfrac{1}{2} - \dfrac{\sqrt{3}}{2}i\right) = -2 - 2\sqrt{3}\,i$

30. $x^3 + 27 = 0$

$$x^3 = -27$$

$$x = (-27)^{1/3} = 27e^{180°i}$$

$$z^{1/n} = r^{1/n}e^{[(\theta/n) + ((360°k)/n)]i}$$

$$(27e^{180°i})^{1/3} = 27^{1/3}e^{[(180°/3) + ((360°k)/n)]i}$$
$$= 3e^{(60° + 120°k)i}$$

$$x_1 = 3e^{60°i} = 3(\cos 60° + i \sin 60°) = 3\left(\frac{1}{2} + \frac{\sqrt{3}}{2}i\right) = \frac{3}{2} + \frac{3\sqrt{3}}{2}i$$

$$x_2 = 3e^{180°i} = 3(\cos 180° + i \sin 180°) = 3(-1 + 0i) = -3$$

$$x_3 = 3e^{300°i} = 3(\cos 300° + i \sin 300°) = 3\left(\frac{1}{2} - \frac{\sqrt{3}}{2}i\right) = \frac{3}{2} - \frac{3\sqrt{3}}{2}i$$

32. For $k = 0$, $r^{1/n}e^{(\theta/n + (k \cdot 360°)/n)i} = r^{1/n}e^{(\theta/n)i}$

For $k = n$, $r^{1/n}e^{(\theta/n + (k \cdot 360°)/n)i} = r^{1/n}e^{(\theta/n + 360°)i} = r^{1/n}e^{(\theta/n)i}$

34. $x^6 + 1 = 0$

$$x^6 = -1$$

$$x = (-1)^{1/6} = 1e^{180°i}$$

$$z^{1/n} = r^{1/n}e^{[(\theta/n) + ((360°k)/n)]i}$$

$$(1e^{180°i})^{1/6} = 1^{1/6}e^{[(180°/6) + ((360°k)/6)]i}$$
$$= 1e^{(30° + 60°k)i}$$

$$x_1 = 1e^{30°i}$$
$$x_2 = 1e^{90°i}$$
$$x_3 = 1e^{150°i}$$
$$x_4 = 1e^{210°i}$$
$$x_5 = 1e^{270°i}$$
$$x_6 = 1e^{330°i}$$

36. $x^3 - i = 0$

$$x^3 = i$$

$$x = i^{1/3} = 1e^{90°i}$$

$$z^{1/n} = r^{1/n}e^{[(\theta/n) + ((360°k)/n)]i}$$

$$(1e^{90°i})^{1/3} = 1^{1/3}e^{[(90°/3) + ((360°k)/3)]i}$$
$$= 1e^{(30° + 120°k)i}$$

$$x_1 = 1e^{30°i}$$
$$x_2 = 1e^{150°i}$$
$$x_3 = 1e^{270°i}$$

38. $P(x) = x^6 - 1$; find $x = 1^{1/6} = (1e^{0°i})^{1/6}$ and write as factors.

$$z^{1/n} = r^{1/n}e^{[(\theta/n) + ((360°k)/n)]i}$$

$$(1e^{0°i})^{1/6} = 1^{1/6}e^{[(0°/6) + ((360°k)/6)]i}$$
$$= 1e^{60°ki}$$

$$x_1 = e^{0°i} = 1$$

$$x_2 = e^{60°i} = \frac{1}{2} + \frac{\sqrt{3}}{2}i$$

$$x_3 = e^{120°i} = -\frac{1}{2} + \frac{\sqrt{3}}{2}i$$

$$x_4 = e^{180°i} = -1$$

$$x_5 = e^{240°i} = -\frac{1}{2} - \frac{\sqrt{3}}{2}i$$

$$x_6 = e^{300°i} = \frac{1}{2} - \frac{\sqrt{3}}{2}i$$

$$P(x) = x^6 + 1 = (x - 1)(x + 1)\left(x - \left(\frac{1}{2} + \frac{\sqrt{3}}{2}i\right)\right)\left(x - \left(-\frac{1}{2} - \frac{\sqrt{3}}{2}i\right)\right)$$

$$\cdot \left(x - \left(-\frac{1}{2} + \frac{\sqrt{3}}{2}i\right)\right)\left(x - \left(\frac{1}{2} - \frac{\sqrt{3}}{2}i\right)\right)$$

CHAPTER 8

Exercise 8-1

2. *a*, (2, 1)

4. *c* infinitely many solutions: for any real number *s*, *x* = *s*, *y* = 2*s* - 5.

6. *x* - *y* = 2

x	*y*
0	-2
2	0

x + *y* = 4

x	*y*
0	4
4	0

(3, 1)

8. 3*x* - *y* = 2

x	*y*
0	-2
3	7

x + 2*y* = 10

x	*y*
0	5
4	3

(2, 4)

10. *m* + 2*n* = 4

m	*n*
0	2
4	0

2*m* + 4*n* = -8

m	*n*
0	-2
-4	0

parallel lines, no solution

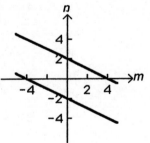

12. (1) *y* = *x* + 4
(2) *y* = 5*x* - 8

(1) → (2): 5*x* - 8 = *x* + 4
$$4x = 12$$
$$x = 3$$

(1) *y* = 3 + 4
y = 7

(3, 7)

14. (1) 2*x* - *y* = 3 ⟹ *y* = 2*x* - 3
(2) *x* + 2*y* = 14

(1) → (2): *x* + 2(2*x* - 3) = 14
$$x + 4x - 6 = 14$$
$$5x = 20$$
$$x = 4$$

(1) *y* = 2(4) - 3
y = 8 - 3
y = 5

(4, 5)

16. (1) $2x + y = 6 \Rightarrow y = -2x + 6$
(2) $x - y = -3$

(1) → (2): $x - (-2x + 6) = -3$
$x + 2x - 6 = -3$
$3x = 3$
$x = 1$

(1) $y = -2x + 6$
$y = -2(1) + 6$
$y = 4$

(1, 4)

18. (1) $9x - 3y = 24 \Rightarrow 3y = 9x - 24$
$\Rightarrow y = 3x - 8$
(2) $11x + 2y = 1$

(1) → (2): $11x + 2(3x - 8) = 1$
$11x + 6x - 16 = 1$
$17x = 17$
$x = 1$

(1) $y = 3(1) - 8$
$y = -5$

(1, -5)

20. (1) $3p + 8q = 4 \Rightarrow 8q = 4 - 3p$
$\Rightarrow q = \dfrac{4 - 3p}{8}$
(2) $15p + 10q = -10$

(1) → (2): $15p + 10 \cdot \left(\dfrac{4 - 3p}{8}\right) = -10$
$120p + 40 - 30p = -80$
$90p = -120$
$p = -\dfrac{4}{3}$

(1) $q = \dfrac{4 - 3(-\frac{4}{3})}{8}$
$q = 1$

$\left(-\dfrac{4}{3}, 1\right)$

22. (1) $y = 0.07x$
(2) $y = 80 + 0.05x$

(1) → (2): $0.07x = 80 + 0.05x$
$0.02x = 80$
$x = 4000$

(1) $y = 0.07(4000)$
$y = 280$

(4000, 280)

24. (1) $0.3s - 0.6t = 0.18$
$\Rightarrow 0.3s = 0.6t + 0.18$
$\Rightarrow s = 2t + 0.6$
(2) $0.5s - 0.2t = 0.54$

(1) → (2): $0.5(2t + 0.6) - 0.2t = 0.54$
$t + 0.3 - 0.2t = 0.54$
$0.8t = 0.24$
$t = 0.3$

(1) $s = 2(0.3) + 0.6$
$s = 1.2$

(1.2, 0.3)

26. (1) $\dfrac{7}{2}x - \dfrac{5}{6}y = 10$
$\Rightarrow \dfrac{5}{6}y = \dfrac{7}{2}x - 10$
$\Rightarrow y = \dfrac{21}{5}x - 12$
(2) $\dfrac{2}{5}x + \dfrac{4}{3}y = 6$

(1) → (2): $\dfrac{2}{5}x + \dfrac{4}{3}\left(\dfrac{21}{5}x - 12\right) = 6$
$\dfrac{2}{5}x + \dfrac{28}{5}x - 16 = 6$
$6x = 22$
$x = \dfrac{11}{3}$

(1) $y = \dfrac{21}{5} \cdot \dfrac{11}{3} - 12$
$y = \dfrac{17}{5}$

$\left(\dfrac{11}{3}, \dfrac{17}{5}\right)$

28. (1) $7x - 3y = 20$
$$-3y = -7x + 20$$
$$y = \frac{7x - 20}{3}$$

(2) $5x + 2y = 8$
$$2y = 8 - 5x$$
$$y = \frac{8 - 5x}{2}$$

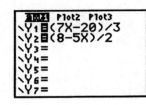
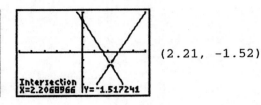

$(2.21, -1.52)$

30. (1) $5.4x + 4.2y = -12.9$
$$4.2y = -12.9 - 5.4x$$
$$y = \frac{-12.9 - 5.4x}{4.2}$$

(2) $3.7x + 6.4y = -4.5$
$$6.4y = -4.5 - 3.7x$$
$$y = \frac{-4.5 - 3.7x}{6.4}$$

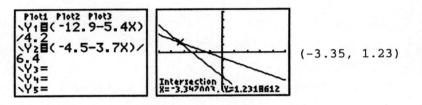

$(-3.35, 1.23)$

32. (1) $x - 2y = -3 \Rightarrow x = 2y - 3$
(2) $-2x + 4y = 6$

(1) $\rightarrow$ (2): $-2(2y - 3) + 4y = 6$
$$-4y + 6 + 4y = 6$$
$$6 = 6$$

This system has an infinite number of solutions given by the set,
$\{(x, y) \mid x - 2y = -3\}$. Any system with an identity such as $0 = 0$ has an
infinite number of solutions.

34. (1) $x = -1 + 2p - q \Rightarrow q = -x + 2p - 1$
(2) $y = 4 - p + q$

(1) $\rightarrow$ (2): $y = 4 - p - x + 2p - 1$
$$y = 3 + p - x$$
$$p = x + y - 3$$

(1) $q = -x + 2(x + y - 3) - 1$
$$q = -x + 2x + 2y - 6 - 1$$
$$q = x + 2y - 7$$

Check: (1) $-1 + 2(x + y - 3) - (x + 2y - 7)$
$$-1 + 2x + 2y - 6 - x - 2y + 7 = x$$

(2) $4 - (x + y - 3) + x + 2y - 7$
$$4 - x - y + 3 + x + 2y - 7 = y$$

36. $x = \dfrac{dh - bk}{ad - bc}$, $y = \dfrac{ak - ch}{ad - bc}$
If $ad - bc = 0$, there may be no solutions or an infinite number of solutions.

38. (1) $d = (150 - 30) \cdot t_1 \Rightarrow t_1 = \dfrac{d}{120}$

(2) $d = (150 + 30) \cdot t_2 \Rightarrow t_2 = \dfrac{d}{180}$

(3) $t_1 + t_2 = 20$
$$\frac{d}{120} + \frac{d}{180} = 20$$
$$\frac{5d}{360} = 20$$
$$d = 1440 \text{ miles}$$

40. Let v = rate of the boat and w = rate of the current.
   (1) $20 = (v + w) \cdot 2 \Rightarrow v + w = 10 \Rightarrow v = 10 - w$
   (2) $20 = (v - w) \cdot 3$

   $(1) \rightarrow (2)$: $20 = (10 - w - w) \cdot 3$
   $\qquad\qquad\quad 20 = (10 - 2w) \cdot 3$
   $\qquad\qquad\quad 20 = 30 - 6w$
   $\qquad\qquad\quad 6w = 10$
   $\qquad\qquad\quad\; w = \dfrac{5}{3}$ mph

42. Let x = grams of 12-carat alloy and y = grams of 18-carat alloy.
   (1) $\dfrac{12}{24}x + \dfrac{18}{24}y = \dfrac{14}{24} \cdot 10 \Rightarrow 12x + 18y = 140$
   (2) $x + y = 10 \Rightarrow y = 10 - x$

   $(2) \rightarrow (1)$: $12x + 18(10 - x) = 140$
   $\qquad\qquad\quad 12x + 180 - 18x = 140$
   $\qquad\qquad\qquad\qquad -6x = -40$
   $\qquad\qquad\qquad\qquad\quad x = 6\frac{2}{3}$ gram of 12-carat gold

   (2) $y = 10 - 6\frac{2}{3} = 3\frac{1}{3}$ gram of 18-carat gold

44. Let x = amount invested at 8%, y = amount invested at 12%.
   (1) $x + y = 20,000 \Rightarrow y = 20,000 - x$
   (2) $0.08x + 0.12y = 0.11(20,000)$

   $(1) \rightarrow (2)$: $0.08x + 0.12(20,000 - x) = 2200$
   $\qquad\qquad\qquad 0.08x + 2400 - 0.12x = 2200$
   $\qquad\qquad\qquad\qquad\qquad -0.04x = -200$
   $\qquad\qquad\qquad\qquad\qquad\qquad x = \$5000$ at 8%

   (1) $y = 20,000 - 5000$
   $\quad\;\; y = \$15,000$ at 12%

46. Let x = hours at Green Bay and y = hours at Sheboygan.
   (1) $800x + 500y = 62,250 \Rightarrow y = 124.5 - 1.6x$
   (2) $800x + 1000y = 76,500$

   $(1) \rightarrow (2)$: $800x + 1000(124.5 - 1.6x) = 76,500$
   $\qquad\qquad\quad 800x + 124,500 - 1600x = 76,500$
   $\qquad\qquad\qquad\qquad\qquad\quad -800x = -48,000$
   $\qquad\qquad\qquad\qquad\qquad\qquad\quad x = 60$

   (1) $y = 124.5 - 1.6(60)$
   $\quad\;\; y = 124.5 - 96$
   $\quad\;\; y = 28.5$

   60 hours at Green Bay
   28.5 hours at Sheboygan

48. (1) $8 \cdot A + 7 \cdot B = 720 \Rightarrow B = \dfrac{720 - 8A}{7}$

   (2) $4 \cdot A + 7 \cdot B = 500$

   $(1) \rightarrow (2)$: $4A + 7 \cdot \dfrac{720 - 8A}{7} = 500$
   $\qquad\qquad\quad 4A + 720 - 8A = 500$
   $\qquad\qquad\qquad\qquad -4A = -220$
   $\qquad\qquad\qquad\qquad\quad A = 55$ bags of brand A

   (1) $B = \dfrac{720 - 8(55)}{7}$
   $\quad\;\; B = 40$ bags of brand B

50. Supply: $p = 0.006q + 2$
Demand: $p = -0.014q + 13$

(A) Caps at \$4 each:
Supply: $4 = 0.006q + 2$
$0.006q = 2$
$q = 333\frac{1}{3}$ hundred $\approx$ 33,333 baseball caps

Demand: $4 = -0.014q + 13$
$0.014q = 9$
$q = 642.857$ hundred $\approx$ 64,286 baseball caps

The demand is higher than the supply.

(B) Caps at \$8 each:
Supply: $8 = 0.006q + 2$
$0.006q = 6$
$q = 1000$ hundred $= 100,000$ baseball caps

Demand: $8 = -0.014q + 13$
$0.014q = 5$
$q = 357.14286 \approx 35,714$ baseball caps

The supply is higher than the demand.

(C) Equilibrium quantity: $0.006q + 2 = -0.014q + 13$
$0.02q = 11$
$q = 550$ hundred $= 55,000$ baseball caps

Equilibrium price: $p = 0.006(550) + 2$
$p = \$5.30$

(D)

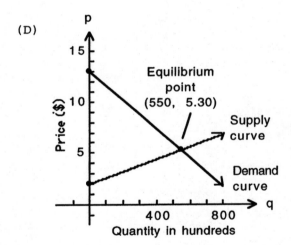

52. (A) supply: $p = aq + b$
$1.4 = a(1075) + b$
$1.2 = a(575) + b$
from which $a = 0.0004$ and $b = 0.97$. The supply equation is $p = 0.0004q + 0.97$.

(B) demand: $p = aq + b$
$1.4 = a(580) + b$
$1.2 = a(980) + b$
from which $a = -0.0005$ and $b = 1.69$. The demand equation is $p = -0.0005q + 1.69$.

(C) Solving $0.0004q + 0.97 = -0.0005q + 1.69$
$0.0009q = 0.72$
$q = 800$ bushels, equilibrium quantity

$p = 0.0004(800) + 0.97$
$p = \$1.29$ equilibrium price

54. $s = a + bt^2$

(A) Solving (1) $240 = a + b \cdot 1^2$
$\Rightarrow a = 240 - b$
(2) $192 = a + b \cdot 2^2$

(1) $\rightarrow$ (2): $192 = 240 - b + 4b$
$-48 = 3b$
$b = -16$

(1) $a = 240 - (-16) = 256$

(B) $s = 256 - 16 \cdot t^2$
$s = 256 - 16 \cdot 0^2 = 256$ ft, height of building

(C) At impact $s = 0 = 256 - 16 \cdot t^2$
$t^2 = 16$
$t = 4$ sec to reach the ground

56. (A) (1) $d = 1100(t + 6)$
(2) $d = 5000 \cdot t$

(2) $\rightarrow$ (1): $5000t = 1100(t + 6)$
$5000t = 1100t + 6600$
$3900t = 6600$
$t = 1\frac{9}{13}$ sec, underwater
$t + 6 = 7\frac{9}{13}$ sec, above water

(B) $d = 5000\,(1\frac{9}{13}) \approx 8462$ feet

Exercise 8-2

2. (1) $2m - n = 10$ (1) $2m - n = 10$ (1) $2m - 6 = 10$
(2) $m - 2n = -4$ $-2 \cdot$ (2) $\underline{-2m + 4n = 8}$ $2m = 16$
                                       $3n = 18$ $m = 8$
                                         $n = 6$

4. (1) $5x + 2y = 1$ $3 \cdot$ (1) $15x + 6y = 3$ (1) $5x + 2y = 1$
(2) $2x - 3y = -11$ $2 \cdot$ (2) $\underline{4x - 6y = -22}$ $5(-1) + 2y = 1$
                                  $19x = -19$ $2y = 6$
                                     $x = -1$ $y = 3$

6. B is 3×3. D is 2×1.   **8.** D is a column matrix.

10. One additional row would make matrix A square.

12. $A = \begin{bmatrix} 3 & -2 & 0 \\ 4 & 1 & -6 \end{bmatrix}$ **14.** $A = \begin{bmatrix} 3 & -2 & 0 \\ 4 & 1 & -6 \end{bmatrix}$
$a_{21} = 4,\ a_{13} = 0$ $a_{11} = 3,\ a_{22} = 1$

16. $\begin{bmatrix} 1 & -3 & | & 2 \\ 4 & -6 & | & -8 \end{bmatrix}$ $\frac{1}{2}R_2 \rightarrow R_2$ $\begin{bmatrix} 1 & -3 & | & 2 \\ 2 & -3 & | & -4 \end{bmatrix}$ **18.** $\begin{bmatrix} 1 & -3 & | & 2 \\ 4 & -6 & | & -8 \end{bmatrix}$ $-2R_1 \rightarrow R_1$ $\begin{bmatrix} -2 & 6 & | & -4 \\ 4 & -6 & | & -8 \end{bmatrix}$

20. $\begin{bmatrix} 1 & -3 & | & 2 \\ 4 & -6 & | & -8 \end{bmatrix}$ $-1R_2 \rightarrow R_2$ $\begin{bmatrix} 1 & -3 & | & 2 \\ -4 & 6 & | & 8 \end{bmatrix}$

22. $\begin{bmatrix} 1 & -3 & | & 2 \\ 4 & -6 & | & -8 \end{bmatrix}$ $(-\frac{1}{2}R_2) + R_1 \rightarrow R_1$ $\begin{bmatrix} -1 & 0 & | & 6 \\ 4 & -6 & | & -8 \end{bmatrix}$

24. $\begin{bmatrix} 1 & -3 & | & 2 \\ 4 & -6 & | & -8 \end{bmatrix}$ $(-3)R_1 + R_2 \rightarrow R_2$ $\begin{bmatrix} 1 & -3 & | & 2 \\ 1 & 3 & | & -14 \end{bmatrix}$

26. $\begin{bmatrix} 1 & -3 & | & 2 \\ 4 & -6 & | & -8 \end{bmatrix}$ $1R_1 + R_2 \rightarrow R_2$ $\begin{bmatrix} 1 & -3 & | & 2 \\ 5 & -9 & | & -6 \end{bmatrix}$

28. $\begin{bmatrix} -1 & 2 & | & -3 \\ 6 & -3 & | & 12 \end{bmatrix}$ $2R_1 \rightarrow R_1$ $\begin{bmatrix} -2 & 4 & | & -6 \\ 6 & -3 & | & 12 \end{bmatrix}$

30. $\begin{bmatrix} -1 & 2 & | & -3 \\ 6 & -3 & | & 12 \end{bmatrix}$ $\frac{2}{3}R_2 + R_1 \rightarrow R_1$ $\begin{bmatrix} 3 & 0 & | & 5 \\ 6 & -3 & | & 12 \end{bmatrix}$

32. $\begin{bmatrix} -1 & 2 & | & -3 \\ 6 & -3 & | & 12 \end{bmatrix}$ $4R_1 + R_2 \rightarrow R_2$ $\begin{bmatrix} -1 & 2 & | & -3 \\ 2 & 5 & | & 0 \end{bmatrix}$

34. $\begin{bmatrix} 1 & 1 & | & 5 \\ 1 & -1 & | & -3 \end{bmatrix}$ $(-1)R_1 + R_2 \rightarrow R_2$ $\begin{bmatrix} 1 & 1 & | & 5 \\ 0 & -2 & | & -8 \end{bmatrix}$

$\begin{aligned} x_1 + x_2 &= 5 \\ x_1 - x_2 &= -3 \end{aligned}$ $\qquad\qquad \begin{aligned} x_1 + x_2 &= 5 \\ -2x_2 &= -8 \end{aligned}$

$(-\tfrac{1}{2})R_2 \rightarrow R_2$ $\begin{bmatrix} 1 & 1 & | & 5 \\ 0 & 1 & | & 4 \end{bmatrix}$ $\qquad (-1)R_2 + R_1 \rightarrow R_1$ $\begin{bmatrix} 1 & 0 & | & 1 \\ 0 & 1 & | & 4 \end{bmatrix}$

$\begin{aligned} x_1 + x_2 &= 5 \\ x_2 &= 4 \end{aligned}$ $\qquad\qquad \begin{aligned} x_1 &= 1 \\ x_2 &= 4 \end{aligned}$

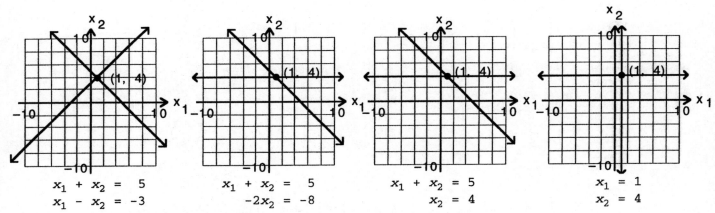

$\begin{aligned} x_1 + x_2 &= 5 \\ x_1 - x_2 &= -3 \end{aligned}$ $\qquad \begin{aligned} x_1 + x_2 &= 5 \\ -2x_2 &= -8 \end{aligned}$ $\qquad \begin{aligned} x_1 + x_2 &= 5 \\ x_2 &= 4 \end{aligned}$ $\qquad \begin{aligned} x_1 &= 1 \\ x_2 &= 4 \end{aligned}$

Each pair of lines intersects at the same point.

36. $\begin{aligned} x_1 - 3x_2 &= -5 \\ -3x_1 - x_2 &= 5 \end{aligned}$

$\begin{bmatrix} 1 & -3 & | & -5 \\ -3 & -1 & | & 5 \end{bmatrix}$ $3R_1 + R_2 \rightarrow R_2$ $\begin{bmatrix} 1 & -3 & | & -5 \\ 0 & -10 & | & -10 \end{bmatrix}$

$\begin{bmatrix} 1 & -3 & | & -5 \\ 0 & -10 & | & -10 \end{bmatrix}$ $-\tfrac{1}{10}R_2 \rightarrow R_2$ $\begin{bmatrix} 1 & -3 & | & -5 \\ 0 & 1 & | & 1 \end{bmatrix}$

$\begin{bmatrix} 1 & -3 & | & -5 \\ 0 & 1 & | & 1 \end{bmatrix}$ $3R_2 + R_1 \rightarrow R_1$ $\begin{bmatrix} 1 & 0 & | & -2 \\ 0 & 1 & | & 1 \end{bmatrix}$ $\begin{aligned} x_1 &= -2 \\ x_2 &= 1 \end{aligned}$

38. $2x_1 + x_2 = 0$
$x_1 - 2x_2 = -5$

$$\begin{bmatrix} 2 & 1 & | & 0 \\ 1 & -2 & | & -5 \end{bmatrix} \qquad R_1 \leftrightarrow R_2 \begin{bmatrix} 1 & -2 & | & -5 \\ 2 & 1 & | & 0 \end{bmatrix}$$

$$\begin{bmatrix} 1 & -2 & | & -5 \\ 2 & 1 & | & 0 \end{bmatrix} \qquad -2R_1 + R_2 \to R_2 \begin{bmatrix} 1 & -2 & | & -5 \\ 0 & 5 & | & 10 \end{bmatrix}$$

$$\begin{bmatrix} 1 & -2 & | & -5 \\ 0 & 5 & | & 10 \end{bmatrix} \qquad \tfrac{1}{5}R_2 \to R_2 \begin{bmatrix} 1 & -2 & | & -5 \\ 0 & 1 & | & 2 \end{bmatrix}$$

$$\begin{bmatrix} 1 & -2 & | & -5 \\ 0 & 1 & | & 2 \end{bmatrix} \qquad 2R_2 + R_1 \to R_1 \begin{bmatrix} 1 & 0 & | & -1 \\ 0 & 1 & | & 2 \end{bmatrix} \qquad \begin{aligned} x_1 &= -1 \\ x_2 &= 2 \end{aligned}$$

40. $2x_1 - 3x_2 = -2$
$-4x_1 + 6x_2 = 7$

$$\begin{bmatrix} 2 & -3 & | & -2 \\ -4 & 6 & | & 7 \end{bmatrix} \qquad \tfrac{1}{2}R_1 \to R_1 \begin{bmatrix} 1 & -\tfrac{3}{2} & | & -1 \\ -4 & 6 & | & 7 \end{bmatrix}$$

$$\begin{bmatrix} 1 & -\tfrac{3}{2} & | & -1 \\ -4 & 6 & | & 7 \end{bmatrix} \qquad 4R_1 + R_2 \to R_2 \begin{bmatrix} 1 & -1.5 & | & -1 \\ 0 & 0 & | & 3 \end{bmatrix} \text{ no solution}$$

42. $3x_1 - x_2 = -5$
$x_1 + 3x_2 = 5$

$$\begin{bmatrix} 3 & -1 & | & -5 \\ 1 & 3 & | & 5 \end{bmatrix} \qquad R_2 \leftrightarrow R_1 \begin{bmatrix} 1 & 3 & | & 5 \\ 3 & -1 & | & -5 \end{bmatrix}$$

$$\begin{bmatrix} 1 & 3 & | & 5 \\ 3 & -1 & | & -5 \end{bmatrix} \qquad -3R_1 + R_2 \to R_2 \begin{bmatrix} 1 & 3 & | & 5 \\ 0 & -10 & | & -20 \end{bmatrix}$$

$$\begin{bmatrix} 1 & 3 & | & 5 \\ 0 & -10 & | & -20 \end{bmatrix} \qquad -\tfrac{1}{10}R_2 \to R_2 \begin{bmatrix} 1 & 3 & | & 5 \\ 0 & 1 & | & 2 \end{bmatrix}$$

$$\begin{bmatrix} 1 & 3 & | & 5 \\ 0 & 1 & | & 2 \end{bmatrix} \qquad -3R_2 + R_1 \to R_1 \begin{bmatrix} 1 & 0 & | & -1 \\ 0 & 1 & | & 2 \end{bmatrix} \qquad \begin{aligned} x_1 &= -1 \\ x_2 &= 2 \end{aligned}$$

44. $2x_1 - 4x_2 = -2$
$-3x_1 + 6x_2 = 3$

$$\begin{bmatrix} 2 & -4 & | & -2 \\ -3 & 6 & | & 3 \end{bmatrix} \qquad \tfrac{1}{2}R_1 \to R_1 \begin{bmatrix} 1 & -2 & | & -1 \\ -3 & 6 & | & 3 \end{bmatrix}$$

$$\begin{bmatrix} 1 & -2 & | & -1 \\ -3 & 6 & | & 3 \end{bmatrix} \qquad 3R_1 + R_2 \to R_2 \begin{bmatrix} 1 & -2 & | & -1 \\ 0 & 0 & | & 0 \end{bmatrix}$$

infinitely many solutions: $x_2 = s$, $x_1 = 2s - 1$ for any real number s

46. $-6x_1 + 2x_2 = 4$
$3x_1 - x_2 = -2$

$$\begin{bmatrix} -6 & 2 & | & 4 \\ 3 & -1 & | & -2 \end{bmatrix} \qquad -\tfrac{1}{6}R_1 \to R_1 \begin{bmatrix} 1 & -\tfrac{1}{3} & | & -\tfrac{2}{3} \\ 3 & -1 & | & -2 \end{bmatrix}$$

$$\begin{bmatrix} 1 & -\tfrac{1}{3} & | & -\tfrac{2}{3} \\ 3 & -1 & | & -2 \end{bmatrix} \qquad -3R_1 + R_2 \to R_2 \begin{bmatrix} 1 & -\tfrac{1}{3} & | & -\tfrac{2}{3} \\ 0 & 0 & | & 0 \end{bmatrix}$$

infinitely many solutions: $x_2 = s$, $x_1 = \tfrac{1}{3}s - \tfrac{2}{3}$ for any real number s

48. (A) $5x - 6y = -10$ $55x - 66y = -110$
           $11x - 13y = -20$ $\underline{-55x + 65y =\ \ \ 100}$
                                        $-y = \ \ -10$
                                         $y = \ \ \ \ 10$

      $5x - 6(10) = -10$
              $5x = \ \ \ 50$
               $x = \ \ \ 10$

  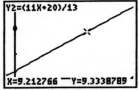 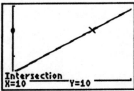

Graphs appear identical but trace shows
slight difference.

Graphical solution agrees with elimination by addition.

   (B) $5x - 6y = -10$ $-10x + 12y = \ \ \ 20$
          $10x - 13y = -20$ $\underline{10x - 13y = -20}$
                                        $-y = \ \ \ 0$
                                         $y = \ \ \ 0$

      $5x - 6(0) = -10$
               $x = \ \ -2$

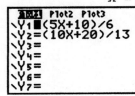 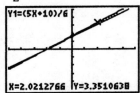 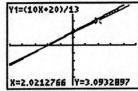 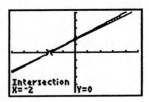

Graphs appear slightly different as
trace shows.

   Graphical solution agrees with elimination by addition.

   (C) $2[5x - 6y = -10] \to 10x - 12y = -20$. The system is dependent. The lines
coincide giving infinitely many solutions.

50. 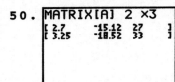 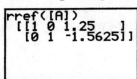 $x_1 = 1.25$
                                    $x_2 = -1.5625$

52. 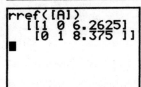 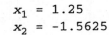 $x_1 = 6.2625$
                                    $x_2 = 8.375$

54. $N + D = 89$ (1)
        $0.05N + 0.1D = 6.05$ (2)

     $-5 \cdot (1): -5N - 5D = -445$ $(1): N + 32 = 89$
     $100 \cdot (2): \underline{\ \ 5N + 10D = \ \ \ 605}$ $N = 57$
                     $5D = \ \ \ 160$
                      $D = \ \ \ \ 32$

   $N = 57$ nickels
   $D = 32$ dimes

56. $0.146x + 0.098y = 0.11(T)$ where T = total amount invested, x = amount
             $x + y = T$ invested in fund A, and y = amount invested in
                                   fund B.

$$0.146x + 0.098y = 0.11(x + y)$$
$$0.036x = 0.012y$$
$$x = \frac{1}{3}y$$
$$\frac{1}{3}y + y = T$$
$$y = \frac{3}{4}T, \text{ invest 75\% in fund } B$$
$$x = \frac{1}{4}T, \text{ invest 25\% in fund } A$$

58. $x + y = 80$ (1)   where x = amount of 40% alcohol and
    $0.4x + 0.7y = 0.49(80)$ (2) y = amount of 70% alcohol.

$-4 \cdot (1):\ -4x - 4y = -320$ (1): $x + 24 = 80$

$10 \cdot (2):\ \underline{\ \ 4x + 7y =\ \ \ 392}$ $x = 56$

                  $3y =\ \ \ 72$

                   $y =\ \ \ 24$

Use 56 liters of 40% solution and 24 liters of 70% solution.

60.

	A	B	Total
Nitrogen	9	8	770
Phosphoric Acid	5	6	490

(1) $9A + 8B = 770$ $3 \cdot (1):\ 27A + 24B =\ \ 2310$ (1) $9(50) + 8B = 770$

(2) $5A + 6B = 490$ $-4 \cdot (2):\ \underline{-20A - 24B = -1960}$ $8B = 320$

                              $7A\ \ \ \ \ =\ \ \ 350$ $B =\ \ 40$

                              $A\ \ \ \ \ =\ \ \ \ 50$

Use 50 bags of brand A and 40 bags of brand B.

62. (A) $x + 4y = 29.95$ (1)   where x = base price and y = surcharge/lb.
       $x + 19y = 59.20$ (2)

(2) $-$ (1): $15y = 29.95$ (1): $x + 4(1.95) = 29.95$
               $y = \$1.95$ $x = 22.15$

Base price = \$22.15, surcharge = \$1.95 per additional pound.

(B) For United in problem 61:
    $x + 4y = 27.75$
    $x + 19y = 64.50$ which gives $x = \$17.95$, base price and
                              $y = \$2.45$, surcharge.

United cost = $17.95 + 2.45p$
Federated cost = $22.15 + 1.95p$ where p = weight over 1 lb.
$y_1 = 17.95 + 2.45x$ and
$y_2 = 22.15 + 1.95x$ intersect at $(8.4, 38.53)$. Packages of 8.4 lb cost \$38.53
with both carriers. Heavier packages should be shipped with Federated.

64. (A) $50(132) = 6600$ lb of Columbian
       $40(132) = 5280$ lb of Brazilian

$$\frac{6}{16} \text{ lb of Columbian} + \frac{10}{16} \text{ lb of Brazilian} = \frac{16}{16} \text{ lb of mild}$$

    6 lb of Columbian + 10 lb of Brazilian = 16 lb of mild

and multiplying both sides by $528 = \dfrac{5280}{10}$ (since Brazilian is 62.5% of mix) gives

3168 lb of Columbian + 5280 lb of Brazilian = 8448 lb of mild.
$(6600 - 3168) = 3432$ lb of Columbian left over.

(B) $\frac{12}{16}$ lb of Columbian + $\frac{4}{16}$ lb of Brazilian = $\frac{16}{16}$ lb of robust

12 lb of Columbian + 4 lb of Brazilian = 16 lb of robust

and multiplying both sides by 550 = $\frac{6600}{12}$ (since Columbian is 75% of mix) gives

6600 lb of Columbian + 2200 lb of Brazilian = 8800 lb of robust
(5280 - 2200) = 3080 lb of Brazilian left over.

Exercise 8-3

2. $\begin{bmatrix} 0 & 1 & | & 3 \\ 1 & 0 & | & -2 \end{bmatrix}$ Not reduced form; the leftmost 1 should be in row 1. Perform the row operation $R_1 \leftrightarrow R_2$.

4. $\begin{bmatrix} 1 & 0 & 0 & | & -4 \\ 0 & 1 & 0 & | & 0 \\ 0 & 0 & 1 & | & 1 \end{bmatrix}$ Reduced form

6. $\begin{bmatrix} 1 & 1 & -3 & | & 2 \\ 0 & 0 & 1 & | & 5 \\ 0 & 0 & 0 & | & 0 \end{bmatrix}$ Not reduced form; the 1 in row 2 does not have a 0 above it. Perform the row operation $3R_2 + R_1 \to R_1$.

8. $\begin{bmatrix} 1 & 0 & -1 & | & 4 \\ 0 & 2 & 1 & | & 3 \\ 0 & 0 & 0 & | & 0 \end{bmatrix}$ Not reduced form; the 2 in row 2 should be a 1. Perform the row operation $\frac{1}{2}R_2 \to R_2$.

10. $\begin{bmatrix} 1 & -3 & 0 & 0 & | & 1 \\ 0 & 0 & 1 & 1 & | & 0 \end{bmatrix}$ Reduced form

12. $\begin{bmatrix} 1 & 0 & 0 & 0 & | & -2 \\ 0 & 1 & 0 & 0 & | & 0 \\ 0 & 0 & 1 & 0 & | & 1 \\ 0 & 0 & 0 & 1 & | & 3 \end{bmatrix} \Rightarrow \begin{matrix} x_1 = -2 \\ x_2 = 0 \\ x_3 = 1 \\ x_4 = 3 \end{matrix}$

14. $\begin{bmatrix} 1 & -2 & 0 & | & -3 \\ 0 & 0 & 1 & | & 5 \\ 0 & 0 & 0 & | & 0 \end{bmatrix} \Rightarrow \begin{matrix} x_1 - 2x_2 \quad = -3 \\ x_3 = 5 \end{matrix}$: system infinite solutions

Let $x_2 = t$ any real number;
then $x_1 = 2t - 3$
$x_2 = t$
$x_3 = 5$

16. $\begin{bmatrix} 1 & 0 & | & 5 \\ 0 & 1 & | & -3 \\ 0 & 0 & | & 0 \end{bmatrix} \Rightarrow \begin{matrix} x_1 = 5 \\ x_2 = -3 \end{matrix}$

18. $\begin{bmatrix} 1 & 0 & -2 & 3 & | & 4 \\ 0 & 1 & -1 & 2 & | & -1 \end{bmatrix} \begin{matrix} x_1 - 2x_3 + 3x_4 = 4 \\ x_2 - x_3 + 2x_4 = -1 \end{matrix}$: system

$x_1 = 2s - 3t + 4$
$x_2 = s - 2t - 1$
$x_3 = s$
$x_4 = t$
s and t = any real number

20. $\begin{bmatrix} 1 & 3 & | & 1 \\ 0 & 2 & | & -4 \end{bmatrix}$ $\quad \frac{1}{2}R_2 \to R_2$ $\begin{bmatrix} 1 & 3 & | & 1 \\ 0 & 1 & | & -2 \end{bmatrix}$

$\begin{bmatrix} 1 & 3 & | & 1 \\ 0 & 1 & | & -2 \end{bmatrix}$ $\quad -3R_2 + R_1 \to R_1$ $\begin{bmatrix} 1 & 0 & | & 7 \\ 0 & 1 & | & -2 \end{bmatrix}$

22. $\begin{bmatrix} 1 & 0 & 4 & | & 0 \\ 0 & 1 & -3 & | & -1 \\ 0 & 0 & -2 & | & 2 \end{bmatrix}$ $\quad -\frac{1}{2}R_3 \to R_3$ $\begin{bmatrix} 1 & 0 & 4 & | & 0 \\ 0 & 1 & -3 & | & -1 \\ 0 & 0 & 1 & | & -1 \end{bmatrix}$

$\begin{bmatrix} 1 & 0 & 4 & | & 0 \\ 0 & 1 & -3 & | & -1 \\ 0 & 0 & 1 & | & -1 \end{bmatrix}$ $\quad \begin{matrix} 3R_3 + R_2 \to R_2 \\ \\ -4R_3 + R_1 \to R_1 \end{matrix}$ $\begin{bmatrix} 1 & 0 & 0 & | & 4 \\ 0 & 1 & 0 & | & -4 \\ 0 & 0 & 1 & | & -1 \end{bmatrix}$

24. $\begin{bmatrix} 0 & -2 & 8 & | & 1 \\ 2 & -2 & 6 & | & -4 \\ 0 & -1 & 4 & | & \frac{1}{2} \end{bmatrix}$ $\quad R_2 \leftrightarrow R_1$ $\begin{bmatrix} 2 & -2 & 6 & | & -4 \\ 0 & -2 & 8 & | & 1 \\ 0 & -1 & 4 & | & \frac{1}{2} \end{bmatrix}$

$\begin{bmatrix} 2 & -2 & 6 & | & -4 \\ 0 & -2 & 8 & | & 1 \\ 0 & -1 & 4 & | & \frac{1}{2} \end{bmatrix}$ $\quad \frac{1}{2}R_1 \to R_1$ $\begin{bmatrix} 1 & -1 & 3 & | & -2 \\ 0 & -2 & 8 & | & 1 \\ 0 & -1 & 4 & | & \frac{1}{2} \end{bmatrix}$

$\begin{bmatrix} 1 & -1 & 3 & | & -2 \\ 0 & -2 & 8 & | & 1 \\ 0 & -1 & 4 & | & \frac{1}{2} \end{bmatrix}$ $\quad -\frac{1}{2}R_2 \to R_2$ $\begin{bmatrix} 1 & -1 & 3 & | & -2 \\ 0 & 1 & -4 & | & -\frac{1}{2} \\ 0 & -1 & 4 & | & \frac{1}{2} \end{bmatrix}$

$\begin{bmatrix} 1 & -1 & 3 & | & -2 \\ 0 & 1 & -4 & | & -\frac{1}{2} \\ 0 & -1 & 4 & | & \frac{1}{2} \end{bmatrix}$ $\quad \begin{matrix} 1R_2 + R_1 \to R_1 \\ \\ 1R_2 + R_3 \to R_3 \end{matrix}$ $\begin{bmatrix} 1 & 0 & -1 & | & -\frac{5}{2} \\ 0 & 1 & -4 & | & -\frac{1}{2} \\ 0 & 0 & 0 & | & 0 \end{bmatrix}$

26. $\begin{bmatrix} 3 & 5 & -1 & | & -7 \\ 1 & 1 & 1 & | & -1 \\ 2 & 0 & 11 & | & 7 \end{bmatrix}$ $\quad R_1 \leftrightarrow R_2$ $\begin{bmatrix} 1 & 1 & 1 & | & -1 \\ 3 & 5 & -1 & | & -7 \\ 2 & 0 & 11 & | & 7 \end{bmatrix}$

$\begin{bmatrix} 1 & 1 & 1 & | & -1 \\ 3 & 5 & -1 & | & -7 \\ 2 & 0 & 11 & | & 7 \end{bmatrix}$ $\quad \begin{matrix} -3R_1 + R_2 \to R_2 \\ \\ -2R_1 + R_3 \to R_3 \end{matrix}$ $\begin{bmatrix} 1 & 1 & 1 & | & -1 \\ 0 & 2 & -4 & | & -4 \\ 0 & -2 & 9 & | & 9 \end{bmatrix}$

$\begin{bmatrix} 1 & 1 & 1 & | & -1 \\ 0 & 2 & -4 & | & -4 \\ 0 & -2 & 9 & | & 9 \end{bmatrix}$ $\quad \frac{1}{2}R_2 \to R_2$ $\begin{bmatrix} 1 & 1 & 1 & | & -1 \\ 0 & 1 & -2 & | & -2 \\ 0 & -2 & 9 & | & 9 \end{bmatrix}$

$\begin{bmatrix} 1 & 1 & 1 & | & -1 \\ 0 & 1 & -2 & | & -2 \\ 0 & -2 & 9 & | & 9 \end{bmatrix}$ $\quad \begin{matrix} -1R_2 + R_1 \to R_1 \\ \\ 2R_2 + R_3 \to R_3 \end{matrix}$ $\begin{bmatrix} 1 & 0 & 3 & | & 1 \\ 0 & 1 & -2 & | & -2 \\ 0 & 0 & 5 & | & 5 \end{bmatrix}$

$\begin{bmatrix} 1 & 0 & 3 & | & 1 \\ 0 & 1 & -2 & | & -2 \\ 0 & 0 & 5 & | & 5 \end{bmatrix}$ $\quad \frac{1}{5}R_3 \to R_3$ $\begin{bmatrix} 1 & 0 & 3 & | & 1 \\ 0 & 1 & -2 & | & -2 \\ 0 & 0 & 1 & | & 1 \end{bmatrix}$

$\begin{bmatrix} 1 & 0 & 3 & | & 1 \\ 0 & 1 & -2 & | & -2 \\ 0 & 0 & 1 & | & 1 \end{bmatrix}$ $\quad \begin{matrix} -3R_3 + R_1 \to R_1 \\ \\ 2R_3 + R_2 \to R_2 \end{matrix}$ $\begin{bmatrix} 1 & 0 & 0 & | & -2 \\ 0 & 1 & 0 & | & 0 \\ 0 & 0 & 1 & | & 1 \end{bmatrix}$ $\quad \begin{matrix} x_1 = -2 \\ x_2 = 0 \\ x_3 = 1 \end{matrix}$

28. $\begin{bmatrix} 2 & 7 & 15 & \vert & -12 \\ 4 & 7 & 13 & \vert & -10 \\ 3 & 6 & 12 & \vert & -9 \end{bmatrix} \rightarrow \begin{bmatrix} 1 & 0 & 0 & \vert & 1 \\ 0 & 1 & 0 & \vert & -2 \\ 0 & 0 & 1 & \vert & 0 \end{bmatrix}$ $\begin{array}{l} x_1 = 1 \\ x_2 = -2 \\ x_3 = 0 \end{array}$

using $\frac{1}{2}R_1 \rightarrow R_1$; $-4R_1 + R_2 \rightarrow R_2$; $-3R_1 + R_3 \rightarrow R_3$; $-\frac{1}{7}R_2 \rightarrow R_2$; $-\frac{7}{2}R_2 + R_1 \rightarrow R_1$; $\frac{9}{2}R_2 + R_3 \rightarrow R_3$;

$\frac{7}{3}R_3 \rightarrow R_3$; $-\frac{17}{7}R_3 + R_2 \rightarrow R_2$; $1R_3 + R_1 \rightarrow R_1$

30. $\begin{bmatrix} 2 & 4 & -6 & \vert & 10 \\ 3 & 3 & -3 & \vert & 6 \end{bmatrix} \rightarrow \begin{bmatrix} 1 & 0 & 1 & \vert & -1 \\ 0 & 1 & -2 & \vert & 3 \end{bmatrix}$

using $\frac{1}{2}R_1 \rightarrow R_1$; $-3R_1 + R_2 \rightarrow R_2$; $-\frac{1}{3}R_2 \rightarrow R_2$; $-2R_2 + R_1 \rightarrow R_1$

from which $x_1 + x_3 = -1$

$\qquad x_2 - 2x_3 = 3$ and letting $x_3 = t$

$x_1 = -t - 1$

$x_2 = 3 + 2t$, t any real number

32. rref $\begin{bmatrix} 2 & -1 & \vert & 0 \\ 3 & 2 & \vert & 7 \\ 1 & -1 & \vert & -2 \end{bmatrix} \rightarrow \begin{bmatrix} 1 & 0 & \vert & 0 \\ 0 & 1 & \vert & 0 \\ 0 & 0 & \vert & 1 \end{bmatrix}$, no solution

34. $\begin{bmatrix} 3 & 7 & -1 & \vert & 11 \\ 1 & 2 & -1 & \vert & 3 \\ 2 & 4 & -2 & \vert & 10 \end{bmatrix} \rightarrow \begin{bmatrix} 1 & 0 & -5 & \vert & -1 \\ 0 & 1 & 2 & \vert & 2 \\ 0 & 0 & 0 & \vert & 4 \end{bmatrix}$

using $R_1 \leftrightarrow R_2$; $-3R_1 + R_2 \rightarrow R_2$; $-2R_1 + R_3 \rightarrow R_3$; $-2R_2 + R_1 \rightarrow R_1$

from which, no solution

36. rref $\begin{bmatrix} 2 & 5 & 4 & \vert & -7 \\ -4 & -5 & 2 & \vert & 9 \\ -2 & -1 & 4 & \vert & 3 \end{bmatrix} \rightarrow \begin{bmatrix} 1 & 0 & -3 & \vert & -1 \\ 0 & 1 & 2 & \vert & -1 \\ 0 & 0 & 0 & \vert & 0 \end{bmatrix}$, infinite solutions

from which $x_1 - 3x_3 = -1$

$\qquad x_2 + 2x_3 = -1$; let $x_3 = t$

$x_1 = 3t - 1$, $x_2 = -2t - 1$, t any real number

38. $\begin{bmatrix} 2 & 8 & -6 & \vert & 4 \\ -3 & -12 & 9 & \vert & -6 \end{bmatrix} \rightarrow \begin{bmatrix} 1 & 4 & -3 & \vert & 2 \\ 0 & 0 & 0 & \vert & 0 \end{bmatrix}$, infinite solutions

using $\frac{1}{2}R_1 \rightarrow R_1$; $3R_1 + R_2 \rightarrow R_2$;

from which $x_1 + 4x_2 - 3x_3 = 2$, let $x_2 = s$ and $x_3 = t$

$x_1 = -4s + 3t + 2$, s, t any real numbers

40. rref $\begin{bmatrix} 4 & -2 & 2 & \vert & 5 \\ -6 & 3 & -3 & \vert & -2 \\ 10 & -5 & 9 & \vert & 4 \end{bmatrix} = \begin{bmatrix} 1 & -\frac{1}{2} & 0 & \vert & 0 \\ 0 & 0 & 1 & \vert & 0 \\ 0 & 0 & 0 & \vert & 1 \end{bmatrix}$, no solution

42. rref $\begin{bmatrix} -4 & 8 & 10 & \vert & -6 \\ 6 & -12 & -15 & \vert & 9 \\ -8 & 14 & 19 & \vert & -8 \end{bmatrix} = \begin{bmatrix} 1 & 0 & -\frac{3}{2} & \vert & -\frac{5}{2} \\ 0 & 1 & \frac{1}{2} & \vert & -2 \\ 0 & 0 & 0 & \vert & 0 \end{bmatrix}$, infinite solutions

$x_1 - \frac{3}{2}x_3 = -\frac{5}{2}$

$x_2 + \frac{1}{2}x_3 = -2$

let $x_3 = t$, any real number

$\qquad x_1 = \frac{3}{2}t - \frac{5}{2}$

$\qquad x_2 = -\frac{1}{2}t - 2$

$\qquad x_3 = t$

44. rref $\begin{bmatrix} 4 & -2 & 3 & | & 3 \\ 3 & -1 & -2 & | & -10 \\ 2 & 4 & -1 & | & -1 \end{bmatrix} = \begin{bmatrix} 1 & 0 & 0 & | & -1 \\ 0 & 1 & 0 & | & 1 \\ 0 & 0 & 1 & | & 3 \end{bmatrix}$ $\begin{matrix} x_1 = -1 \\ x_2 = 1 \\ x_3 = 3 \end{matrix}$

46. (A) Consistent and dependent:

$\begin{bmatrix} 1 & 0 & m & | & a \\ 0 & 1 & n & | & b \\ 0 & 0 & 0 & | & 0 \end{bmatrix}, \begin{bmatrix} 1 & m & 0 & | & a \\ 0 & 0 & 1 & | & b \\ 0 & 0 & 0 & | & 0 \end{bmatrix}$

(B) Inconsistent:

$\begin{bmatrix} 1 & 0 & m & | & 0 \\ 0 & 1 & n & | & 0 \\ 0 & 0 & 0 & | & 1 \end{bmatrix}, \begin{bmatrix} 1 & m & n & | & 0 \\ 0 & 0 & 0 & | & 1 \\ 0 & 0 & 0 & | & 0 \end{bmatrix}$

48. $\begin{matrix} x_1 + 2x_2 = 4 \\ -2x_1 + kx_2 = -8 \end{matrix}$ $\begin{bmatrix} 1 & 2 & | & 4 \\ -2 & k & | & -8 \end{bmatrix}$ $2R_1 + R_2 \rightarrow R_2$ $\begin{bmatrix} 1 & 2 & | & 4 \\ 0 & k+4 & | & 0 \end{bmatrix}$

If $k = -4$, there are an infinite number of solutions (consistent and dependent).
If $k \neq -4$, there will be exactly one solution (consistent and independent).

50. $\begin{matrix} x_1 + kx_2 = 3 \\ 2x_1 + 4x_2 = 8 \end{matrix}$ $\begin{bmatrix} 1 & k & | & 3 \\ 2 & 4 & | & 8 \end{bmatrix}$ $-2R_1 + R_2 \rightarrow R_2$ $\begin{bmatrix} 1 & k & | & 3 \\ 0 & -2k+4 & | & 2 \end{bmatrix}$

If $k = 2$, there is no solution (inconsistent).
If $k \neq 2$, there will be exactly one solution (consistent and independent).

52. rref $\begin{bmatrix} 2 & 4 & 5 & 4 & | & 8 \\ 1 & 2 & 2 & 1 & | & 3 \end{bmatrix} = \begin{bmatrix} 1 & 2 & 0 & -3 & | & -1 \\ 0 & 0 & 1 & 2 & | & 2 \end{bmatrix}$

$\quad\quad x_1 + 2x_2 - 3x_4 = -1$ let $x_2 = s$, $x_4 = t$, any real numbers.
$\quad\quad\quad\quad x_3 + 2x_4 = 2$

$x_1 = -2s + 3t - 1$
$x_2 = s$
$x_3 = -2t + 2$
$x_4 = t$

54. rref $\begin{bmatrix} 1 & 1 & 4 & 1 & | & 1.3 \\ -1 & 1 & -1 & 0 & | & 1.1 \\ 2 & 0 & 1 & 3 & | & -4.4 \\ 2 & 5 & 11 & 3 & | & 5.6 \end{bmatrix} = \begin{bmatrix} 1 & 0 & 0 & 0 & | & -1.2 \\ 0 & 1 & 0 & 0 & | & 0.6 \\ 0 & 0 & 1 & 0 & | & 0.7 \\ 0 & 0 & 0 & 1 & | & -0.9 \end{bmatrix}$ $\begin{matrix} x_1 = -1.2 \\ x_2 = 0.6 \\ x_3 = 0.7 \\ x_4 = -0.9 \end{matrix}$

56. rref $\begin{bmatrix} 1 & -3 & 1 & 1 & 2 & | & 2 \\ -1 & 5 & 2 & 2 & -2 & | & 0 \\ 2 & -6 & 2 & 2 & 4 & | & 4 \\ -1 & 3 & -1 & 0 & -1 & | & -3 \end{bmatrix} = \begin{bmatrix} 1 & 0 & 5.5 & 0 & -3.5 & | & 10.5 \\ 0 & 1 & 1.5 & 0 & -1.5 & | & 2.5 \\ 0 & 0 & 0 & 1 & 1 & | & -1 \\ 0 & 0 & 0 & 0 & 0 & | & 0 \end{bmatrix}$

$\quad x_1 + 5.5x_3 - 3.5x_5 = 10.5$
$\quad x_2 + 1.5x_3 - 1.5x_5 = 2.5$
$\quad\quad\quad\quad\quad x_4 + x_5 = -1$ let $x_3 = s$, $x_5 = t$, any real numbers

$x_1 = -5.5s + 3.5t + 10.5$
$x_2 = -1.5s + 1.5t + 2.5$
$x_3 = s$
$x_4 = -t - 1$
$x_5 = t$

58. $\begin{aligned} 3x_1 - 4x_2 &= 10 \\ 4x_1 + 2x_2 &= 6 \end{aligned}$ $\text{ref} \begin{bmatrix} 3 & -4 & | & 10 \\ 4 & 2 & | & 6 \end{bmatrix} = \begin{bmatrix} 1 & 0.5 & | & 1.5 \\ 0 & 1 & | & -1 \end{bmatrix}$

$$x_2 = -1$$
$$x_1 + 0.5(-1) = 1.5$$
$$x_1 = 2 \qquad\qquad (2, -1)$$

60. $\begin{aligned} 2x_1 - x_2 + 3x_3 &= 17 \\ -x_1 + 2x_2 - x_3 &= -12 \\ 4x_1 + x_2 - 5x_3 &= 3 \end{aligned}$ $\text{ref} \begin{bmatrix} 2 & -1 & 3 & | & 17 \\ -1 & 2 & -1 & | & -12 \\ 4 & 1 & -5 & | & 3 \end{bmatrix} = \begin{bmatrix} 1 & 0.25 & -1.25 & | & 0.75 \\ 0 & 1 & -1 & | & -5 \\ 0 & 0 & 1 & | & 2 \end{bmatrix}$

$$x_3 = 2 \qquad x_2 - x_3 = -5 \qquad x_1 + 0.25x_2 - 1.25x_3 = 0.75$$
$$x_2 - 2 = -5 \qquad x_1 + 0.25(-3) - 1.25(2) = 0.75$$
$$x_2 = -3 \qquad\qquad x_1 = 4$$

$(4, -3, 2)$

62. To use the row-echelon form, enter the original matrix into your graphing utility and find ref of the matrix. To find the solutions, start with the last row. If it contains all 0's, write equations for each row in terms of 1 or 2 variables (see problem 56). If the last row contains all but 1 zero in the next to last position, there will be no solution. Otherwise, write equations for each row. The last row will give a solution for the x_n variable. Back substitute this value into the row above until all solutions are found (see problem 60).

64. $\begin{aligned} N + D + Q &= 32 \\ 0.05N + 0.1D + 0.25Q &= 6.8 \end{aligned}$ $\Rightarrow \begin{bmatrix} 1 & 1 & 1 & | & 32 \\ 0.05 & 0.1 & 0.25 & | & 6.8 \end{bmatrix}$ which

reduces to $\begin{bmatrix} 1 & 0 & -3 & | & -72 \\ 0 & 1 & 4 & | & 104 \end{bmatrix} \Rightarrow \begin{aligned} N - 3Q &= -72 \\ D + 4Q &= 104 \end{aligned}$

If $Q = t = 24, 25, 26$ then $N = 3t - 72$ and $D = 104 - 4t$

If $Q = 26$
   $D = 104 - 4(26) = 0$
   $N = 3(26) - 72 = 6$

If $Q = 25$
   $D = 104 - 4(25) = 4$
   $N = 3(25) - 72 = 3$

If $Q = 24$
   $D = 104 - 4(24) = 8$
   $N = 3(24) - 72 = 0$

66. $500x_1 + 500x_2 + 1500x_3 = 12,000$
$0.1(500)x_1 + 0.2(500)x_2 + 0.5(1500)x_3 = 12,000(0.3)$

$\text{rref} \begin{bmatrix} 500 & 500 & 1500 & | & 12,000 \\ 50 & 100 & 750 & | & 3,600 \end{bmatrix} \rightarrow \begin{bmatrix} 1 & 0 & -9 & | & -24 \\ 0 & 1 & 12 & | & 48 \end{bmatrix}$

Let $x_3 = t$; then $x_1 = 9t - 24 \Rightarrow t \geq 3$
$x_2 = -12t + 48 \Rightarrow t \leq 4$

If $t = 3$: $x_1 = 9(3) - 24 = 3$
   $x_2 = 48 - 12(3) = 12$ (10%: 3 cc, 20%: 12 cc, 50%: 3cc)

If $t = 4$: $x_1 = 9(4) - 24 = 12$
   $x_2 = 48 - 12(4) = 0$ (10%: 12 cc, 20%: 0 cc, 50%: 4cc)

68. $y = a + bx + cx^2$

$(1, 3) \Rightarrow 3 = a + b + c$
$(2, 2) \Rightarrow 2 = a + 2b + 4c \Rightarrow$ rref $\begin{bmatrix} 1 & 1 & 1 & | & 3 \\ 1 & 2 & 4 & | & 2 \\ 1 & 3 & 9 & | & 5 \end{bmatrix} \rightarrow \begin{bmatrix} 1 & 0 & 0 & | & 8 \\ 0 & 1 & 0 & | & -7 \\ 0 & 0 & 1 & | & 2 \end{bmatrix}$
$(3, 5) \Rightarrow 5 = a + 3b + 9c$

$a = 8, \; b = -7, \; c = 2$
$y = 8 - 7x + 2x^2$

70.
$$x^2 + y^2 + ax + by + c = 0$$
$(-4, 1): \; (-4)^2 + (1)^2 - 4a + b + c = 0 \Rightarrow -4a + b + c = -17$
$(-1, 2): \; (-1)^2 + (2)^2 - a + 2b + c = 0 \Rightarrow -a + 2b + c = -5$
$(3, -6): \; (3)^2 + (-6)^2 + 3a - 6b + c = 0 \Rightarrow 3a - 6b + c = -45$

rref $\begin{bmatrix} -4 & 1 & 1 & | & -17 \\ -1 & 2 & 1 & | & -5 \\ 3 & -6 & 1 & | & -45 \end{bmatrix} \rightarrow \begin{bmatrix} 1 & 0 & 0 & | & 2 \\ 0 & 1 & 0 & | & 6 \\ 0 & 0 & 1 & | & -15 \end{bmatrix}$ $\begin{array}{l} a = 2 \\ b = 6 \\ c = -15 \end{array}$

$x^2 + y^2 + 2x + 6y - 15 = 0$

72. (A) $\begin{array}{l} 0.5x_1 + x_2 + 1.5x_3 = 350 \\ 0.6x_1 + 0.9x_2 + 1.2x_3 = 330 \\ 0.2x_1 + 0.3x_2 + 0.5x_3 = 115 \end{array} \Rightarrow \begin{bmatrix} 0.5 & 1 & 1.5 & | & 350 \\ 0.6 & 0.9 & 1.2 & | & 330 \\ 0.2 & 0.3 & 0.5 & | & 115 \end{bmatrix}$ which

reduces to $\begin{bmatrix} 1 & 0 & 0 & | & 150 \\ 0 & 1 & 0 & | & 200 \\ 0 & 0 & 1 & | & 50 \end{bmatrix}$ $\begin{array}{l} \text{150 one-person boats} \\ \text{200 two-person boats} \\ \text{50 four-person boats} \end{array}$

(B) $\begin{bmatrix} 0.5 & 1 & 1.5 & | & 350 \\ 0.6 & 0.9 & 1.2 & | & 330 \end{bmatrix} \rightarrow \begin{bmatrix} 1 & 0 & -1 & | & 100 \\ 0 & 1 & 2 & | & 300 \end{bmatrix}$
$\begin{array}{ll} x_1 = 100 + t & \text{one-person} \\ x_2 = 300 - 2t & \text{two-person} \\ x_3 = t & \text{four-person} \quad 0 \le t \le 150, \; t \text{ an integer} \end{array}$

(C) $\begin{bmatrix} 0.5 & 1 & | & 350 \\ 0.6 & 0.9 & | & 330 \\ 0.2 & 0.3 & | & 115 \end{bmatrix} \rightarrow \begin{bmatrix} 1 & 0 & | & 100 \\ 0 & 1 & | & 300 \\ 0 & 0 & | & 50 \end{bmatrix} \Rightarrow$ no solution
No production schedule will use all work hours in all departments.

74. (A) rref $\begin{bmatrix} 30 & 10 & 20 & | & 400 \\ 10 & 10 & 20 & | & 160 \\ 10 & 30 & 20 & | & 240 \end{bmatrix} \rightarrow \begin{bmatrix} 1 & 0 & 0 & | & 12 \\ 0 & 1 & 0 & | & 4 \\ 0 & 0 & 1 & | & 0 \end{bmatrix}$ $\begin{array}{l} \text{12 oz. food } A \\ \text{4 oz. food } B \\ \text{0 oz. food } C \end{array}$

(B) $\begin{bmatrix} 30 & 10 & | & 400 \\ 10 & 10 & | & 160 \\ 10 & 30 & | & 240 \end{bmatrix} \rightarrow \begin{bmatrix} 1 & 0 & | & 12 \\ 0 & 1 & | & 4 \\ 0 & 0 & | & 0 \end{bmatrix}$ $\begin{array}{l} \text{12 oz. food } A \\ \text{4 oz. food } B \end{array}$

(C) $\begin{bmatrix} 30 & 10 & 20 & | & 400 \\ 10 & 10 & 20 & | & 160 \end{bmatrix} \rightarrow \begin{bmatrix} 1 & 0 & 0 & | & 12 \\ 0 & 1 & 2 & | & 4 \end{bmatrix}$ $\begin{array}{l} \text{12 oz. food } A \\ 4 - 2t \text{ oz. of food } B \\ t \text{ oz. of food } C \text{ where } 0 \le t \le 2 \end{array}$

76. $\begin{aligned} a + b + c + d &= 5 \\ 5a + 10b + 15c + 20d &= 80 \end{aligned}$ $\Rightarrow$ $\begin{bmatrix} 1 & 1 & 1 & 1 & | & 5 \\ 5 & 10 & 15 & 20 & | & 80 \end{bmatrix} \rightarrow \begin{bmatrix} 1 & 0 & -1 & -2 & | & -6 \\ 0 & 1 & 2 & 3 & | & 11 \end{bmatrix}$

$$a - c - 2d = -6$$
$$b + 2c + 3d = 11$$

Let $c = s$, $d = t$; then
$a = s + 2t - 6$
$b = -2s - 3t + 11$
$c = s$
$d = t$

Using trial and error, start with $s = 0$, $t = 0$ and continue until all possible combinations are found.

$a = -6$,	$b = 11$,	$c = 0$,	$d = 0$	Not possible
$a = -4$,	$b = 7$,	$c = 0$,	$d = 1$	Not possible
$a = -2$,	$b = 5$,	$c = 0$,	$d = 2$	Not possible
$a = 0$,	**$b = 2$,**	**$c = 0$,**	**$d = 3$**	**Possible**
$a = 2$,	$b = -1$,	$c = 0$,	$d = 4$	Not possible
$a = -5$,	$b = 9$,	$c = 1$,	$d = 0$	Not possible
$a = -3$,	$b = 6$,	$c = 1$,	$d = 1$	Not possible
$a = -1$,	$b = 3$,	$c = 1$,	$d = 2$	Not possible
$a = 1$,	**$b = 0$,**	**$c = 1$,**	**$d = 3$**	**Possible**
$a = 3$,	$b = -3$,	$c = 1$,	$d = 4$	Not possible
$a = -4$,	$b = 7$,	$c = 2$,	$d = 0$	Not possible
$a = -2$,	$b = 6$,	$c = 2$,	$d = 1$	Not possible
$a = 0$,	**$b = 1$,**	**$c = 2$,**	**$d = 2$**	**Possible**
$a = 2$,	$b = -3$,	$c = 2$,	$d = 3$	Not possible
$a = 3$,	$b = 5$,	$c = 3$,	$d = 0$	Not possible
$a = -1$,	$b = 2$,	$c = 3$,	$d = 1$	Not possible
$a = 1$,	$b = -1$,	$c = 3$,	$d = 2$	Not possible
$a = -2$,	$b = 3$,	$c = 4$,	$d = 0$	Not possible
$a = 0$,	**$b = 0$,**	**$c = 4$,**	**$d = 1$**	**Possible**

78. rref $\begin{bmatrix} 30 & 20 & | & 650 \\ 10 & 20 & | & 350 \end{bmatrix} \rightarrow \begin{bmatrix} 1 & 0 & | & 15 \\ 0 & 1 & | & 10 \end{bmatrix}$ 15 hours company A
10 hours company B

Exercise 8-4

2. $\begin{bmatrix} 2 & -1 \\ 3 & 0 \end{bmatrix} + \begin{bmatrix} -3 & 1 \\ 2 & -3 \end{bmatrix} = \begin{bmatrix} -1 & 0 \\ 5 & -3 \end{bmatrix}$ **4.** $\begin{bmatrix} 4 & -1 & 0 \\ 2 & 1 & 3 \end{bmatrix} + \begin{bmatrix} -2 & 1 & 3 \\ 5 & 6 & -8 \end{bmatrix} = \begin{bmatrix} 2 & 0 & 3 \\ 7 & 7 & -5 \end{bmatrix}$

6. $\begin{bmatrix} 4 & -1 & 0 \\ 2 & 1 & 3 \end{bmatrix} + \begin{bmatrix} 2 & 1 \\ -6 & 3 \\ 0 & -5 \end{bmatrix}$ is not defined.

8. $\begin{bmatrix} 4 & -5 \\ 1 & 0 \\ 1 & -3 \end{bmatrix} - \begin{bmatrix} -1 & 2 \\ 6 & -2 \\ 1 & -7 \end{bmatrix} = \begin{bmatrix} 5 & -7 \\ -5 & 2 \\ 0 & 4 \end{bmatrix}$ **10.** $5\begin{bmatrix} 1 & -2 & 0 & 4 \\ -3 & 2 & -1 & 6 \end{bmatrix} = \begin{bmatrix} 5 & -10 & 0 & 20 \\ -15 & 10 & -5 & 30 \end{bmatrix}$

12. $\underset{1\times 2}{[1 \quad 5]} \underset{2\times 1}{\begin{bmatrix} 6 \\ 2 \end{bmatrix}} = [1 \cdot 6 + 5 \cdot 2] = \underset{1\times 1}{[16]}$

14. $\underset{2\times 2}{\begin{bmatrix} -1 & 1 \\ 2 & -3 \end{bmatrix}} \underset{2\times 1}{\begin{bmatrix} 4 \\ -2 \end{bmatrix}} = \begin{bmatrix} -1(4) + 1(-2) \\ 2(4) - 3(-2) \end{bmatrix} = \underset{2\times 1}{\begin{bmatrix} -6 \\ 14 \end{bmatrix}}$

16. $\begin{bmatrix} -3 & 2 \\ 4 & -1 \end{bmatrix}\begin{bmatrix} -2 & 5 \\ -1 & 3 \end{bmatrix} = \begin{bmatrix} 4 & -9 \\ -7 & 17 \end{bmatrix}$

18. $\begin{bmatrix} -2 & 5 \\ -1 & 3 \end{bmatrix}\begin{bmatrix} -3 & 2 \\ 4 & -1 \end{bmatrix} = \begin{bmatrix} 26 & -9 \\ 15 & -5 \end{bmatrix}$

20. $\underset{1\times2}{[2 \quad -1]} \underset{2\times1}{\begin{bmatrix} 3 \\ -4 \end{bmatrix}} = [2(3) - 1(-4)] = \underset{1\times1}{[10]}$

22. $\underset{2\times1}{\begin{bmatrix} 3 \\ -4 \end{bmatrix}} \underset{1\times2}{[2 \quad -1]} = \underset{2\times2}{\begin{bmatrix} 6 & -3 \\ -8 & 4 \end{bmatrix}}$

24. $\underset{1\times3}{[1 \quad -2 \quad 2]} \underset{3\times1}{\begin{bmatrix} 2 \\ -1 \\ 1 \end{bmatrix}} = [1(2) - 2(-1) + 2(1)] = \underset{1\times1}{[6]}$

26. $\underset{3\times1}{\begin{bmatrix} 2 \\ -1 \\ 1 \end{bmatrix}} \underset{1\times3}{[1 \quad -2 \quad 2]} = \underset{3\times3}{\begin{bmatrix} 2 & -4 & 4 \\ -1 & 2 & -2 \\ 1 & -2 & 2 \end{bmatrix}}$

28. $AC = \begin{bmatrix} 2 & -1 & 3 \\ 0 & 4 & -2 \end{bmatrix} \cdot \begin{bmatrix} -1 & 0 & 2 \\ 4 & -3 & 1 \\ -2 & 3 & 5 \end{bmatrix} = \begin{bmatrix} -12 & 12 & 18 \\ 20 & -18 & -6 \end{bmatrix}$

30. $AB = \begin{bmatrix} 2 & -1 & 3 \\ 0 & 4 & -2 \end{bmatrix} \cdot \begin{bmatrix} -3 & 1 \\ 2 & 5 \end{bmatrix}$ is not defined.

32. $B^2 = B \cdot B = \begin{bmatrix} -3 & 1 \\ 2 & 5 \end{bmatrix} \cdot \begin{bmatrix} -3 & 1 \\ 2 & 5 \end{bmatrix} = \begin{bmatrix} 11 & 2 \\ 4 & 27 \end{bmatrix}$

34. $B + AD = \begin{bmatrix} -3 & 1 \\ 2 & 5 \end{bmatrix} + \begin{bmatrix} 2 & -1 & 3 \\ 0 & 4 & -2 \end{bmatrix} \cdot \begin{bmatrix} 3 & -2 \\ 0 & -1 \\ 1 & 2 \end{bmatrix} = \begin{bmatrix} 6 & 4 \\ 0 & -3 \end{bmatrix}$

36. $0.1DB = 0.1\begin{bmatrix} 3 & -2 \\ 0 & -1 \\ 1 & 2 \end{bmatrix} \cdot \begin{bmatrix} -3 & 1 \\ 2 & 5 \end{bmatrix} = \begin{bmatrix} -1.3 & -0.7 \\ -0.2 & -0.5 \\ 0.1 & 1.1 \end{bmatrix}$

38. $3BA + 4AC = 3\begin{bmatrix} -3 & 1 \\ 2 & 5 \end{bmatrix} \cdot \begin{bmatrix} 2 & -1 & 3 \\ 0 & 4 & -2 \end{bmatrix} + 4\begin{bmatrix} 2 & -1 & 3 \\ 0 & 4 & -2 \end{bmatrix}\begin{bmatrix} -1 & 0 & 2 \\ 4 & -3 & 1 \\ -2 & 3 & 5 \end{bmatrix} = \begin{bmatrix} -66 & 69 & 39 \\ 92 & -18 & -36 \end{bmatrix}$

40. $-2BA + 6CD = -2\begin{bmatrix} -3 & 1 \\ 2 & 5 \end{bmatrix} \cdot \begin{bmatrix} 2 & -1 & 3 \\ 0 & 4 & -2 \end{bmatrix} + 6\begin{bmatrix} -1 & 0 & 2 \\ 4 & -3 & 1 \\ -2 & 3 & 5 \end{bmatrix}\begin{bmatrix} 3 & -2 \\ 0 & -1 \\ 1 & 2 \end{bmatrix}$ is not defined.

42. $ACD = \begin{bmatrix} 2 & -1 & 3 \\ 0 & 4 & -2 \end{bmatrix} \cdot \begin{bmatrix} -1 & 0 & 2 \\ 4 & -3 & 1 \\ -2 & 3 & 5 \end{bmatrix} \cdot \begin{bmatrix} 3 & -2 \\ 0 & -1 \\ 1 & 2 \end{bmatrix} = \begin{bmatrix} -18 & 48 \\ 54 & -34 \end{bmatrix}$

44. $BAD = \begin{bmatrix} -3 & 1 \\ 2 & 5 \end{bmatrix}\begin{bmatrix} 2 & -1 & 3 \\ 0 & 4 & -2 \end{bmatrix}\begin{bmatrix} 3 & -2 \\ 0 & -1 \\ 1 & 2 \end{bmatrix} = \begin{bmatrix} -29 & -17 \\ 8 & -34 \end{bmatrix}$

46. $A = [0.4 \quad 0.6]$, $B = \begin{bmatrix} 0.9 & 0.1 \\ 0.3 & 0.7 \end{bmatrix}$

$B = \begin{bmatrix} 0.9 & 0.1 \\ 0.3 & 0.7 \end{bmatrix}$ $\qquad AB = [0.54, \ 0.46]$

$B^2 = \begin{bmatrix} 0.84 & 0.16 \\ 0.48 & 0.52 \end{bmatrix}$ $\qquad AB^2 = [0.624, \ 0.376]$

$B^3 = \begin{bmatrix} 0.804 & 0.196 \\ 0.588 & 0.412 \end{bmatrix}$ $\qquad AB^3 = [0.6744, \ 0.3256]$

$B^4 = \begin{bmatrix} 0.7824 & 0.2176 \\ 0.6528 & 0.3472 \end{bmatrix}$ $\qquad AB^4 = [0.70464, \ 0.29536]$

$B^5 = \begin{bmatrix} 0.76944 & 0.23056 \\ 0.69168 & 0.30832 \end{bmatrix}$ $\qquad AB^5 = [0.722784, \ 0.277216]$

$\qquad\qquad\qquad\vdots \qquad\qquad\qquad\qquad\qquad\qquad \vdots$

$B^{10} \approx \begin{bmatrix} 0.7515 & 0.2485 \\ 0.7455 & 0.2545 \end{bmatrix}$ $\qquad AB^{10} \approx [0.7479, \ 0.2521]$

$B^n \to \begin{bmatrix} 0.75 & 0.25 \\ 0.75 & 0.25 \end{bmatrix}$ $\qquad AB^n \to [0.75, \ 0.25]$

48. $4 + w = 2 \Rightarrow w = -2$
$-2 + x = -3 \Rightarrow x = -1$
$-3 + y = 0 \Rightarrow y = 3$
$0 + z = 5 \Rightarrow z = 5$

50. $2x - 3y = 1$
$-4x + 5y = 1$ which has solution $x = -4$, $y = -3$

52. $\begin{bmatrix} x & -1 \\ 1 & 0 \end{bmatrix} \begin{bmatrix} 2 & 1 \\ 4 & 1 \end{bmatrix} = \begin{bmatrix} y & y \\ 2 & 1 \end{bmatrix} \Rightarrow \begin{array}{l} 2x - 4 = y \\ x - 1 = y \end{array}$ which has solution $x = 3$, $y = 2$.

54. $\begin{bmatrix} 1 & -2 \\ 2 & -3 \end{bmatrix} \begin{bmatrix} a & b \\ c & d \end{bmatrix} = \begin{bmatrix} 1 & 0 \\ 3 & 2 \end{bmatrix}$

$\begin{array}{l} a - 2c = 1 \\ 2a - 3c = 3 \end{array}$ which has solution $a = 3$, $c = 1$ and

$\begin{array}{l} b - 2d = 0 \\ 2b - 3d = 2 \end{array}$ which has solution $b = 4$, $d = 2$

56. (A) True, the sum of the two upper triangular vertices is an upper triangular matrix.

$$\begin{bmatrix} a & b \\ 0 & d \end{bmatrix} + \begin{bmatrix} x & y \\ 0 & z \end{bmatrix} = \begin{bmatrix} a + x & b + y \\ 0 & d + z \end{bmatrix}$$

(B) True, matrix addition is commutative whether the matrices are upper triangular or not.

(C) True, the product of two upper triangular matrices is an upper triangular matrix.

$$\begin{bmatrix} a & b \\ 0 & d \end{bmatrix} \cdot \begin{bmatrix} x & y \\ 0 & z \end{bmatrix} = \begin{bmatrix} ax & ay + bz \\ 0 & dz \end{bmatrix}$$

(D) False, matrix multiplication is not, in general, commutative even if the matrices are upper triangular.

$$\begin{bmatrix} x & y \\ 0 & z \end{bmatrix} \cdot \begin{bmatrix} a & b \\ 0 & d \end{bmatrix} = \begin{bmatrix} ax & bx + yd \\ 0 & dz \end{bmatrix}$$

58. $\frac{1}{2}(1.2A + B) = \frac{1}{2}\left(1.2\begin{bmatrix} 30 & 25 \\ 60 & 80 \end{bmatrix} + \begin{bmatrix} 36 & 27 \\ 54 & 74 \end{bmatrix}\right) = \begin{bmatrix} \$36 & \$28.5 \\ \$63 & \$85 \end{bmatrix}\begin{matrix} \text{Materials} \\ \text{Labor} \end{matrix}$

Guitar   Banjo

60. $1.15N - 1.20M =$

	Basic Car	Air	Markup AM/FM radio	Cruise control
Model A	$3,505	$82	$44	$29
Model B	$2,250	$99	$100	$53
Model C	$1,365	$120	$127	$55

62. (A) retail value of inventory at store 2 =
2(840) + 3(1800) + 5(2400) + 0(3300) + 6(4900) = $48,480

(B) wholesale value of inventory at store 3 =
10(700) + 4(1400) + 3(1800) + 4(2700) + 3(3500) = $39,300

(C) MN gives the total wholesale and retail values of each store.

(D) $MN = \begin{bmatrix} \$33,400 & \$42,160 \\ \$35,600 & \$48,480 \\ \$39,300 & \$50,700 \end{bmatrix}\begin{matrix} S1 \\ S2 \\ S3 \end{matrix}$

$\begin{matrix} W & R \end{matrix}$

Total wholesale and retail values of each store.

(E) $[1\ \ 1\ \ 1]M = [16\ \ 9\ \ 11\ \ 11\ \ 10]$

(F) $M\begin{bmatrix} 1 \\ 1 \\ 1 \\ 1 \\ 1 \end{bmatrix} = \begin{bmatrix} 17 \\ 16 \\ 24 \end{bmatrix}$

64. $A = \begin{bmatrix} 0 & 0 & 0 & 1 & 1 \\ 1 & 0 & 0 & 1 & 0 \\ 0 & 1 & 0 & 0 & 0 \\ 1 & 0 & 0 & 0 & 1 \\ 0 & 1 & 1 & 0 & 0 \end{bmatrix}; A + A^2 + A^3 = \begin{bmatrix} 2 & 3 & 2 & 3 & 3 \\ 3 & 2 & 2 & 3 & 4 \\ 2 & 1 & 0 & 2 & 2 \\ 3 & 3 & 2 & 2 & 3 \\ 3 & 2 & 1 & 3 & 2 \end{bmatrix}$

It is possible to travel from any origin to any destination with at most 2 intermediate connections.

66. (A) $[4\ \ \ 2]\cdot\begin{bmatrix} 15 \\ 5 \end{bmatrix} = 70$ gm of protein in mix X

(B) $[3\ \ \ 1]\cdot\begin{bmatrix} 5 \\ 15 \end{bmatrix} = 30$ gm of fat in mix Z

(C) MN gives the total amounts in grams of protein, carbohydrates, and fat in 20 oz. of each mix.

(D) $\begin{bmatrix} 4 & 2 \\ 20 & 16 \\ 3 & 1 \end{bmatrix}\begin{bmatrix} 15 & 10 & 5 \\ 5 & 10 & 15 \end{bmatrix} = \begin{bmatrix} 70g & 60g & 50g \\ 380g & 360g & 340g \\ 50g & 40g & 30g \end{bmatrix}\begin{matrix} \text{protein} \\ \text{carbohydrates} \\ \text{fat} \end{matrix}$

$\begin{matrix} X & Y & Z \end{matrix}$

in 20 oz of each mix

68. (A) $A = \begin{bmatrix} 0 & 0 & 0 & 1 & 0 \\ 1 & 0 & 1 & 1 & 0 \\ 1 & 0 & 0 & 0 & 0 \\ 0 & 0 & 1 & 0 & 1 \\ 1 & 1 & 1 & 0 & 0 \end{bmatrix}$ (B) $B = A + A^2 = \begin{bmatrix} 0 & 0 & 1 & 1 & 1 \\ 2 & 0 & 2 & 2 & 1 \\ 1 & 0 & 0 & 1 & 0 \\ 2 & 1 & 2 & 0 & 1 \\ 3 & 1 & 2 & 2 & 0 \end{bmatrix}$

(C) $BC = \begin{bmatrix} 3 \\ 7 \\ 2 \\ 6 \\ 8 \end{bmatrix}$ where $C = \begin{bmatrix} 1 \\ 1 \\ 1 \\ 1 \\ 1 \end{bmatrix}$

(D) Erlene (8), Bridget (7), Diane (6), Anne (3), Carol (2)

Exercise 8-5

2. $\begin{bmatrix} 1 & 0 \\ 0 & 1 \end{bmatrix}\begin{bmatrix} 4 & -3 \\ 0 & 2 \end{bmatrix} = \begin{bmatrix} 4 & -3 \\ 0 & 2 \end{bmatrix}$ **4.** $\begin{bmatrix} 4 & -3 \\ 0 & 2 \end{bmatrix}\begin{bmatrix} 1 & 0 \\ 0 & 1 \end{bmatrix} = \begin{bmatrix} 4 & -3 \\ 0 & 2 \end{bmatrix}$

6. $\begin{bmatrix} 1 & 0 & 0 \\ 0 & 1 & 0 \\ 0 & 0 & 1 \end{bmatrix}\begin{bmatrix} -3 & 0 & 2 \\ 1 & 1 & 5 \\ 2 & -1 & 7 \end{bmatrix} = \begin{bmatrix} -3 & 0 & 2 \\ 1 & 1 & 5 \\ 2 & -1 & 7 \end{bmatrix}$

8. $\begin{bmatrix} -3 & 0 & 2 \\ 1 & 1 & 5 \\ 2 & -1 & 7 \end{bmatrix}\begin{bmatrix} 1 & 0 & 0 \\ 0 & 1 & 0 \\ 0 & 0 & 1 \end{bmatrix} = \begin{bmatrix} -3 & 0 & 2 \\ 1 & 1 & 5 \\ 2 & -1 & 7 \end{bmatrix}$

10. $\begin{bmatrix} -2 & -1 \\ -4 & 2 \end{bmatrix} \cdot \begin{bmatrix} 1 & -1 \\ 2 & -2 \end{bmatrix} = \begin{bmatrix} -4 & 4 \\ 0 & 0 \end{bmatrix}$

$\begin{bmatrix} 1 & -1 \\ 2 & -2 \end{bmatrix} \cdot \begin{bmatrix} -2 & -1 \\ -4 & 2 \end{bmatrix} = \begin{bmatrix} 2 & -3 \\ 4 & -6 \end{bmatrix}$

No, they are not inverses of each other.

12. $\begin{bmatrix} 5 & -7 \\ -2 & 3 \end{bmatrix} \cdot \begin{bmatrix} 3 & 7 \\ 2 & 5 \end{bmatrix} = \begin{bmatrix} 1 & 0 \\ 0 & 1 \end{bmatrix}$

$\begin{bmatrix} 3 & 7 \\ 2 & 5 \end{bmatrix} \cdot \begin{bmatrix} 5 & -7 \\ -2 & 3 \end{bmatrix} = \begin{bmatrix} 1 & 0 \\ 0 & 1 \end{bmatrix}$

Yes, they are inverses of each other.

14. $\begin{bmatrix} 7 & 4 \\ -5 & -3 \end{bmatrix} \cdot \begin{bmatrix} 3 & 4 \\ -5 & -7 \end{bmatrix} = \begin{bmatrix} 1 & 0 \\ 0 & 1 \end{bmatrix}$

$\begin{bmatrix} 3 & 4 \\ -5 & -7 \end{bmatrix} \cdot \begin{bmatrix} 7 & 4 \\ -5 & -3 \end{bmatrix} = \begin{bmatrix} 1 & 0 \\ 0 & 1 \end{bmatrix}$

Yes, they are inverses of each other.

16. $\begin{bmatrix} 1 & 0 & 1 \\ -3 & 1 & -2 \\ 0 & 0 & 1 \end{bmatrix} \cdot \begin{bmatrix} 1 & 0 & -1 \\ 3 & 1 & -1 \\ 0 & 0 & 1 \end{bmatrix} = \begin{bmatrix} 1 & 0 & 0 \\ 0 & 1 & 0 \\ 0 & 0 & 1 \end{bmatrix}$

$\begin{bmatrix} 1 & 0 & -1 \\ 3 & 1 & -1 \\ 0 & 0 & 1 \end{bmatrix} \cdot \begin{bmatrix} 1 & 0 & 1 \\ -3 & 1 & -2 \\ 0 & 0 & 1 \end{bmatrix} = \begin{bmatrix} 1 & 0 & 0 \\ 0 & 1 & 0 \\ 0 & 0 & 1 \end{bmatrix}$

Yes, they are inverses of each other.

18. $\begin{bmatrix} 1 & 0 & -1 \\ 3 & 1 & -1 \\ 0 & 0 & 0 \end{bmatrix} \cdot \begin{bmatrix} 1 & 0 & -1 \\ -3 & 1 & -2 \\ 0 & 0 & 1 \end{bmatrix} = \begin{bmatrix} 1 & 0 & -2 \\ 0 & 1 & -6 \\ 0 & 0 & 0 \end{bmatrix}$

$\begin{bmatrix} 1 & 0 & -1 \\ -3 & 1 & -2 \\ 0 & 0 & 1 \end{bmatrix} \cdot \begin{bmatrix} 1 & 0 & -1 \\ 3 & 1 & -1 \\ 0 & 0 & 0 \end{bmatrix} = \begin{bmatrix} 1 & 0 & -1 \\ 0 & 1 & 2 \\ 0 & 0 & 0 \end{bmatrix}$

No, they are not inverses of each other.

20. $M = \begin{bmatrix} -1 & 5 \\ 0 & -1 \end{bmatrix};\ M^{-1} = \begin{bmatrix} -1 & -5 \\ 0 & -1 \end{bmatrix}$

$MM^{-1} = \begin{bmatrix} -1 & 5 \\ 0 & -1 \end{bmatrix}\begin{bmatrix} -1 & -5 \\ 0 & -1 \end{bmatrix} = \begin{bmatrix} 1 & 0 \\ 0 & 1 \end{bmatrix}$

22. $\begin{bmatrix} 2 & 1 \\ 5 & 3 \end{bmatrix}^{-1} = \begin{bmatrix} 3 & -1 \\ -5 & 2 \end{bmatrix};\ \begin{bmatrix} 2 & 1 \\ 5 & 3 \end{bmatrix}\begin{bmatrix} 3 & -1 \\ -5 & 2 \end{bmatrix} = \begin{bmatrix} 1 & 0 \\ 0 & 1 \end{bmatrix}$

24. $\begin{bmatrix} 2 & 1 \\ 1 & 1 \end{bmatrix}^{-1} = \begin{bmatrix} 1 & -1 \\ -1 & 2 \end{bmatrix};\ \begin{bmatrix} 2 & 1 \\ 1 & 1 \end{bmatrix}\begin{bmatrix} 1 & -1 \\ -1 & 2 \end{bmatrix} = \begin{bmatrix} 1 & 0 \\ 0 & 1 \end{bmatrix}$

26. $\begin{bmatrix} 1 & 3 & 0 \\ 1 & 2 & 3 \\ 0 & -1 & 2 \end{bmatrix}^{-1} = \begin{bmatrix} 7 & -6 & 9 \\ -2 & 2 & -3 \\ -1 & 1 & -1 \end{bmatrix}$

$\begin{bmatrix} 1 & 3 & 0 \\ 1 & 2 & 3 \\ 0 & -1 & 2 \end{bmatrix}\begin{bmatrix} 7 & -6 & 9 \\ -2 & 2 & -3 \\ -1 & 1 & -1 \end{bmatrix} = \begin{bmatrix} 1 & 0 & 0 \\ 0 & 1 & 0 \\ 0 & 0 & 1 \end{bmatrix}$

28. $\begin{bmatrix} 1 & 0 & -1 \\ 2 & -1 & 0 \\ 1 & 1 & -4 \end{bmatrix}^{-1} = \begin{bmatrix} 4 & -1 & -1 \\ 8 & -3 & -2 \\ 3 & -1 & -1 \end{bmatrix};\ \begin{bmatrix} 1 & 0 & -1 \\ 2 & -1 & 0 \\ 1 & 1 & 1 \end{bmatrix}\begin{bmatrix} 4 & -1 & -1 \\ 8 & -3 & -2 \\ 3 & -1 & -1 \end{bmatrix} = \begin{bmatrix} 1 & 0 & 0 \\ 0 & 1 & 0 \\ 0 & 0 & 1 \end{bmatrix}$

30. $\left[\begin{array}{cc|cc} 2 & -4 & 1 & 0 \\ -3 & 6 & 0 & 1 \end{array}\right] \rightarrow \left[\begin{array}{cc|cc} 1 & -2 & 0 & -\frac{1}{3} \\ 0 & 0 & 1 & \frac{2}{3} \end{array}\right] \Rightarrow$ inverse does not exist

32. $\left[\begin{array}{cc|cc} -5 & 4 & 1 & 0 \\ 4 & -3 & 0 & 1 \end{array}\right] \rightarrow \left[\begin{array}{cc|cc} 1 & 0 & 3 & 4 \\ 0 & 1 & 4 & 5 \end{array}\right]$

34. $\left[\begin{array}{ccc|ccc} 4 & 2 & -1 & 1 & 0 & 0 \\ 1 & 1 & -1 & 0 & 1 & 0 \\ -3 & -1 & 1 & 0 & 0 & 1 \end{array}\right] \rightarrow \left[\begin{array}{ccc|ccc} 1 & 0 & 0 & 0 & -\frac{1}{2} & -\frac{1}{2} \\ 0 & 1 & 0 & 1 & \frac{1}{2} & \frac{3}{2} \\ 0 & 0 & 1 & 1 & -1 & 1 \end{array}\right]$

36. $\left[\begin{array}{ccc|ccc} 1 & -1 & 0 & 1 & 0 & 0 \\ 2 & -1 & 1 & 0 & 1 & 0 \\ 0 & 1 & 1 & 0 & 0 & 1 \end{array}\right] \rightarrow \left[\begin{array}{ccc|ccc} 1 & 0 & 1 & 0 & .5 & .5 \\ 0 & 1 & 1 & 0 & 0 & 1 \\ 0 & 0 & 0 & 1 & -.5 & .5 \end{array}\right] \Rightarrow$ inverse does not exist

38. $\left[\begin{array}{ccc|ccc} 1 & -5 & -10 & 1 & 0 & 0 \\ 0 & 1 & 6 & 0 & 1 & 0 \\ 1 & -4 & -3 & 0 & 0 & 1 \end{array}\right] \rightarrow \left[\begin{array}{ccc|ccc} 1 & 0 & 0 & 21 & 25 & -20 \\ 0 & 1 & 0 & 6 & 7 & -6 \\ 0 & 0 & 1 & -1 & -1 & 1 \end{array}\right]$

40. M^{-1} exists if and only if a and d, the elements of the main diagonal, are both nonzero.

42. In problem 41, in both parts, $A^{-1} = A$ and $A^2 = I$. One could conclude that if A is a square matrix where $A = A^{-1}$ then $A^2 = I$.
$A^2 = A \cdot A = A \cdot A^{-1} = I$; A^{-1} is the multiplicative inverse of A.

44. In problem 43, in both parts, $(A^{-1})^{-1} = A$. One could conclude that if A is a square matrix where A^{-1} exists, then $(A^{-1})^{-1} = A$.
$$A \cdot A^{-1} = I$$
$$A \cdot A^{-1} = (A^{-1})(A^{-1})^{-1}$$
$$A = (A^{-1})^{-1}$$

46.

Statement	Reason
$(AB)(B^{-1}A^{-1}) = A(BB^{-1})A^{-1}$	Multiplication is associative
$= A(I)A^{-1}$	Definition of $BB^{-1} = I$
$= (AI)A^{-1}$	Multiplication is associative
$= AA^{-1}$	$AI = A$
$= I$	Definition of $AA^{-1} = I$
$= (AB)(AB)^{-1}$	Definition of I

48. F O X   I N   S O C K S
6 15 24 27 9 14 27 19 15 3 11 19

$$\begin{bmatrix} 3 & 5 \\ 1 & 2 \end{bmatrix}\begin{bmatrix} 6 & 24 & 9 & 27 & 15 & 11 \\ 15 & 27 & 14 & 19 & 3 & 19 \end{bmatrix} \Rightarrow$$ 93 36 207 78 97 37 176 65 60 21 128 49

50. $$\begin{bmatrix} 3 & 5 \\ 1 & 2 \end{bmatrix}^{-1}\begin{bmatrix} 99 & 154 & 115 & 121 & 20 & 149 & 86 & 196 & 99 \\ 38 & 58 & 43 & 43 & 7 & 56 & 29 & 73 & 38 \end{bmatrix} \Rightarrow$$
8 15 18 20 15 14 27 8 5 1 18 19 27 1 27 23 8 15
H O R T O N   H E A R S   A   W H O

52. J O H N   F I T Z G E R A L D   K E N N E D Y
10 15 8 14 27 6 9 20 26 7 5 18 1 12 4 27 11 5 14 14 5 4 25

$$\begin{bmatrix} 1 & 0 & 1 & 0 & 1 \\ 0 & 1 & 1 & 0 & 3 \\ 2 & 1 & 1 & 1 & 1 \\ 0 & 0 & 1 & 0 & 2 \\ 1 & 1 & 1 & 2 & 1 \end{bmatrix}\begin{bmatrix} 10 & 6 & 5 & 27 & 5 \\ 15 & 9 & 18 & 11 & 4 \\ 8 & 20 & 1 & 5 & 25 \\ 14 & 26 & 12 & 14 & 27 \\ 27 & 7 & 4 & 14 & 27 \end{bmatrix} \Rightarrow$$
45 104 84 62 88 33 50 74 34 94 10 31 45 9 52 46 58 98 33 85
57 110 93 79 115

54. $$\begin{bmatrix} 1 & 0 & 1 & 0 & 1 \\ 0 & 1 & 1 & 0 & 3 \\ 2 & 1 & 1 & 1 & 1 \\ 0 & 0 & 1 & 0 & 2 \\ 1 & 1 & 1 & 2 & 1 \end{bmatrix}^{-1}\begin{bmatrix} 22 & 54 & 46 & 51 & 68 \\ 15 & 58 & 80 & 68 & 135 \\ 57 & 89 & 87 & 116 & 136 \\ 5 & 45 & 53 & 39 & 81 \\ 47 & 84 & 96 & 113 & 149 \end{bmatrix} \Rightarrow$$
18 9 3 8 1 18 4   27 13 9 12 8 15 21 19 27 14 9 24 15 14 27 27 27 27
R I C H A R D   M I L H O U S   N I X O N

Exercise 8-6

2. $$\begin{bmatrix} -3 & 1 \\ -1 & 2 \end{bmatrix}\begin{bmatrix} x_1 \\ x_2 \end{bmatrix} = \begin{bmatrix} -2 \\ 5 \end{bmatrix} \Rightarrow \begin{array}{l} -3x_1 + x_2 = -2 \\ -x_1 + 2x_2 = 5 \end{array}$$

4. $$\begin{bmatrix} 1 & -2 & 0 \\ -3 & 1 & -1 \\ 2 & 0 & 4 \end{bmatrix}\begin{bmatrix} x_1 \\ x_2 \\ x_3 \end{bmatrix} = \begin{bmatrix} 3 \\ -2 \\ 5 \end{bmatrix} \Rightarrow \begin{array}{l} x_1 - 2x_2 + 0x_3 = 3 \\ -3x_1 + x_2 - x_3 = -2 \\ 2x_1 + 0x_2 + 4x_3 = 5 \end{array}$$

6. $\begin{aligned} x_1 - 2x_2 &= 7 \\ -3x_1 + x_2 &= -3 \end{aligned} \Rightarrow \begin{bmatrix} 1 & -2 \\ -3 & 1 \end{bmatrix} \begin{bmatrix} x_1 \\ x_2 \end{bmatrix} = \begin{bmatrix} 7 \\ -3 \end{bmatrix}$

8. $\begin{aligned} 2x_1 \qquad + 3x_3 &= 5 \\ x_1 - 2x_2 + x_3 &= -4 \\ -x_1 + 3x_2 \qquad &= 2 \end{aligned} \Rightarrow \begin{bmatrix} 2 & 0 & 3 \\ 1 & -2 & 1 \\ -1 & 3 & 0 \end{bmatrix} \begin{bmatrix} x_1 \\ x_2 \\ x_3 \end{bmatrix} = \begin{bmatrix} 5 \\ -4 \\ 2 \end{bmatrix}$

10. $\begin{bmatrix} x_1 \\ x_2 \end{bmatrix} = \begin{bmatrix} -2 & 1 \\ -1 & 2 \end{bmatrix} \begin{bmatrix} 3 \\ -2 \end{bmatrix} = \begin{bmatrix} -8 \\ -7 \end{bmatrix} \Rightarrow x_1 = -8, \ x_2 = -7$

12. $\begin{bmatrix} x_1 \\ x_2 \end{bmatrix} = \begin{bmatrix} 3 & -1 \\ 0 & 2 \end{bmatrix} \begin{bmatrix} -2 \\ 1 \end{bmatrix} = \begin{bmatrix} -7 \\ 2 \end{bmatrix} \Rightarrow x_1 = -7, \ x_2 = 2$

14. $\begin{bmatrix} 1 & 3 \\ 1 & 4 \end{bmatrix} \begin{bmatrix} x_1 \\ x_2 \end{bmatrix} = \begin{bmatrix} 9 \\ 6 \end{bmatrix}$

$\begin{bmatrix} x_1 \\ x_2 \end{bmatrix} = \begin{bmatrix} 1 & 3 \\ 1 & 4 \end{bmatrix}^{-1} \begin{bmatrix} 9 \\ 6 \end{bmatrix} = \begin{bmatrix} 18 \\ -3 \end{bmatrix} \qquad x_1 = 18, \ x_2 = -3$

16. $\begin{bmatrix} 1 & 1 \\ 3 & -2 \end{bmatrix} \begin{bmatrix} x_1 \\ x_2 \end{bmatrix} = \begin{bmatrix} 10 \\ 20 \end{bmatrix}$

$\begin{bmatrix} x_1 \\ x_2 \end{bmatrix} = \begin{bmatrix} 1 & 1 \\ 3 & -2 \end{bmatrix}^{-1} \begin{bmatrix} 10 \\ 20 \end{bmatrix} = \begin{bmatrix} 8 \\ 2 \end{bmatrix} \qquad x_1 = 8, \ x_2 = 2$

18. (A) $\begin{aligned} 2x_1 + x_2 &= 2 \\ 5x_1 + 3x_2 &= 13 \end{aligned}$

$\begin{bmatrix} 2 & 1 \\ 5 & 3 \end{bmatrix} \begin{bmatrix} x_1 \\ x_2 \end{bmatrix} = \begin{bmatrix} 2 \\ 13 \end{bmatrix}$

$\begin{bmatrix} x_1 \\ x_2 \end{bmatrix} = \begin{bmatrix} 2 & 1 \\ 5 & 3 \end{bmatrix}^{-1} \begin{bmatrix} 2 \\ 13 \end{bmatrix}$

$\begin{bmatrix} x_1 \\ x_2 \end{bmatrix} = \begin{bmatrix} 3 & -1 \\ -5 & 2 \end{bmatrix} \begin{bmatrix} 2 \\ 13 \end{bmatrix}$

$\begin{bmatrix} x_1 \\ x_2 \end{bmatrix} = \begin{bmatrix} -7 \\ 16 \end{bmatrix}$

(B) $\begin{aligned} 2x_1 + x_2 &= -2 \\ 5x_1 + 3x_2 &= 4 \end{aligned}$

$\begin{bmatrix} x_1 \\ x_2 \end{bmatrix} = \begin{bmatrix} 3 & -1 \\ -5 & 2 \end{bmatrix} \begin{bmatrix} -2 \\ 4 \end{bmatrix} = \begin{bmatrix} -10 \\ 18 \end{bmatrix}$

(C) $\begin{aligned} 2x_1 + x_2 &= 1 \\ 5x_1 + 3x_2 &= -3 \end{aligned}$

$\begin{bmatrix} x_1 \\ x_2 \end{bmatrix} = \begin{bmatrix} 3 & -1 \\ -5 & 2 \end{bmatrix} \begin{bmatrix} 1 \\ -3 \end{bmatrix} = \begin{bmatrix} 6 \\ -11 \end{bmatrix}$

20. (A) $\begin{aligned} 2x_1 + x_2 &= -1 \\ x_1 + x_2 &= -2 \end{aligned}$

$\begin{bmatrix} 2 & 1 \\ 1 & 1 \end{bmatrix} \begin{bmatrix} x_1 \\ x_2 \end{bmatrix} = \begin{bmatrix} -1 \\ -2 \end{bmatrix}$

$\begin{bmatrix} x_1 \\ x_2 \end{bmatrix} = \begin{bmatrix} 2 & 1 \\ 1 & 1 \end{bmatrix}^{-1} \begin{bmatrix} -1 \\ -2 \end{bmatrix}$

$\begin{bmatrix} x_1 \\ x_2 \end{bmatrix} = \begin{bmatrix} 1 & -1 \\ -1 & 2 \end{bmatrix} \begin{bmatrix} -1 \\ -2 \end{bmatrix}$

$\begin{bmatrix} x_1 \\ x_2 \end{bmatrix} = \begin{bmatrix} 1 \\ -3 \end{bmatrix}$

(B) $\begin{aligned} 2x_1 + x_2 &= 2 \\ x_1 + x_2 &= 3 \end{aligned}$

$\begin{bmatrix} x_1 \\ x_2 \end{bmatrix} = \begin{bmatrix} 1 & -1 \\ -1 & 2 \end{bmatrix} \begin{bmatrix} 2 \\ 3 \end{bmatrix} = \begin{bmatrix} -1 \\ 4 \end{bmatrix}$

(C) $\begin{aligned} 2x_1 + x_2 &= 2 \\ x_1 + x_2 &= 0 \end{aligned}$

$\begin{bmatrix} x_1 \\ x_2 \end{bmatrix} = \begin{bmatrix} 1 & -1 \\ -1 & 2 \end{bmatrix} \begin{bmatrix} 2 \\ 0 \end{bmatrix} = \begin{bmatrix} 2 \\ -2 \end{bmatrix}$

22. (A) $x_1 + 3x_2 \qquad = 0$
$x_1 + 2x_2 + 3x_3 = 2$
$\qquad -x_2 + 2x_3 = 1$

$$\begin{bmatrix} 1 & 3 & 0 \\ 1 & 2 & 3 \\ 0 & -1 & 2 \end{bmatrix} \begin{bmatrix} x_1 \\ x_2 \\ x_3 \end{bmatrix} = \begin{bmatrix} 0 \\ 2 \\ 1 \end{bmatrix}$$

$$\begin{bmatrix} x_1 \\ x_2 \\ x_3 \end{bmatrix} = \begin{bmatrix} 1 & 3 & 0 \\ 1 & 2 & 3 \\ 0 & -1 & 2 \end{bmatrix}^{-1} \begin{bmatrix} 0 \\ 2 \\ 1 \end{bmatrix}$$

$$\begin{bmatrix} x_1 \\ x_2 \\ x_3 \end{bmatrix} = \begin{bmatrix} 7 & -6 & 9 \\ -2 & 2 & -3 \\ -1 & 1 & -1 \end{bmatrix} \begin{bmatrix} 0 \\ 2 \\ 1 \end{bmatrix}$$

$$\begin{bmatrix} x_1 \\ x_2 \\ x_3 \end{bmatrix} = \begin{bmatrix} -3 \\ 1 \\ 1 \end{bmatrix}$$

(B) $x_1 + 3x_2 \qquad = -2$
$x_1 + 2x_2 + 3x_3 = 0$
$\qquad -x_2 + 2x_3 = 1$

$$\begin{bmatrix} x_1 \\ x_2 \\ x_3 \end{bmatrix} = \begin{bmatrix} 7 & -6 & 9 \\ -2 & 2 & -3 \\ -1 & 1 & -1 \end{bmatrix} \begin{bmatrix} -2 \\ 0 \\ 1 \end{bmatrix} = \begin{bmatrix} -5 \\ 1 \\ 1 \end{bmatrix}$$

(C) $x_1 + 3x_2 \qquad = 3$
$x_1 + 2x_2 + 3x_3 = 1$
$\qquad -x_2 + 2x_3 = 0$

$$\begin{bmatrix} x_1 \\ x_2 \\ x_3 \end{bmatrix} = \begin{bmatrix} 7 & -6 & 9 \\ -2 & 2 & -3 \\ -1 & 1 & -1 \end{bmatrix} \begin{bmatrix} 3 \\ 1 \\ 0 \end{bmatrix} = \begin{bmatrix} 15 \\ -4 \\ -2 \end{bmatrix}$$

24. (A) $x_1 \qquad - x_3 = 4$
$2x_1 - x_2 \qquad = 8$
$x_1 + x_2 - 4x_3 = 0$

$$\begin{bmatrix} 1 & 0 & -1 \\ 2 & -1 & 0 \\ 1 & 1 & -4 \end{bmatrix} \begin{bmatrix} x_1 \\ x_2 \\ x_3 \end{bmatrix} = \begin{bmatrix} 4 \\ 8 \\ 0 \end{bmatrix}$$

$$\begin{bmatrix} x_1 \\ x_2 \\ x_3 \end{bmatrix} = \begin{bmatrix} 1 & 0 & -1 \\ 2 & -1 & 0 \\ 1 & 1 & -4 \end{bmatrix}^{-1} \begin{bmatrix} 4 \\ 8 \\ 0 \end{bmatrix}$$

$$\begin{bmatrix} x_1 \\ x_2 \\ x_3 \end{bmatrix} = \begin{bmatrix} 4 & -1 & -1 \\ 8 & -3 & -2 \\ 3 & -1 & -1 \end{bmatrix} \begin{bmatrix} 4 \\ 8 \\ 0 \end{bmatrix}$$

$$\begin{bmatrix} x_1 \\ x_2 \\ x_3 \end{bmatrix} = \begin{bmatrix} 8 \\ 8 \\ 4 \end{bmatrix}$$

(B) $x_1 \qquad - x_3 = 4$
$2x_1 - x_2 \qquad = 0$
$x_1 + x_2 - 4x_3 = -4$

$$\begin{bmatrix} x_1 \\ x_2 \\ x_3 \end{bmatrix} = \begin{bmatrix} 4 & -1 & -1 \\ 8 & -3 & -2 \\ 3 & -1 & -1 \end{bmatrix} \begin{bmatrix} 4 \\ 0 \\ -4 \end{bmatrix} = \begin{bmatrix} 20 \\ 40 \\ 16 \end{bmatrix}$$

(C) $x_1 \qquad - x_3 = 0$
$2x_1 - x_2 \qquad = 8$
$x_1 + x_2 - 4x_3 = -8$

$$\begin{bmatrix} x_1 \\ x_2 \\ x_3 \end{bmatrix} = \begin{bmatrix} 4 & -1 & -1 \\ 8 & -3 & -2 \\ 3 & -1 & -1 \end{bmatrix} \begin{bmatrix} 0 \\ 8 \\ -8 \end{bmatrix} = \begin{bmatrix} 0 \\ -8 \\ 0 \end{bmatrix}$$

26. $-2x_1 + 4x_2 = 5$
$6x_1 - 12x_2 = 15$

$\begin{bmatrix} -2 & 4 \\ 6 & -12 \end{bmatrix}$ has no inverse.

rref $\begin{bmatrix} -2 & 4 & | & 5 \\ 6 & -12 & | & 15 \end{bmatrix} = \begin{bmatrix} 1 & -2 & | & 0 \\ 0 & 0 & | & 1 \end{bmatrix}$ No solution.

28. $x_1 - 3x_2 - 2x_3 = -1$
$-2x_1 + 7x_2 + 3x_3 = 3$

$\begin{bmatrix} 1 & -3 & -2 \\ -2 & 7 & 3 \end{bmatrix}$ has no inverse.

rref $\begin{bmatrix} 1 & -3 & -2 & | & -1 \\ -2 & 7 & 3 & | & 3 \end{bmatrix} = \begin{bmatrix} 1 & 0 & -5 & | & 2 \\ 0 & 1 & -1 & | & 1 \end{bmatrix}$

Let $x_3 = t$: $x_1 = 5t + 2$, $x_2 = t + 1$, t any real number.

30.
$$x_1 - 2x_2 + 3x_3 = 1$$
$$2x_1 - 3x_2 - 2x_3 = 3$$
$$x_1 - x_2 - 5x_3 = 4$$

$$\begin{bmatrix} 1 & -2 & 3 \\ 2 & -3 & -2 \\ 1 & -1 & -5 \end{bmatrix} \text{ has no inverse}$$

$$\text{rref} \begin{bmatrix} 1 & -2 & 3 & | & 1 \\ 2 & -3 & -2 & | & 3 \\ 1 & -1 & -5 & | & 4 \end{bmatrix} = \begin{bmatrix} 1 & 0 & -13 & | & 0 \\ 0 & 1 & -8 & | & 0 \\ 0 & 0 & 0 & | & 1 \end{bmatrix} \text{ No solution.}$$

32.
$$AX + BX = C$$
$$(A + B)X = C$$
$$X = (A + B)^{-1}C$$
$$[X \neq C(A + B)^{-1}]$$

34.
$$AX - X = C$$
$$(A - I)X = C$$
$$X = (A - I)^{-1}C$$

36.
$$AX + C = BX + D$$
$$AX - BX = D - C$$
$$(A - B)X = D - C$$
$$X = (A - B)^{-1}(D - C)$$

38. (A)
$$x_1 - 3.001x_2 = 1$$
$$x_1 - 3x_2 = 1$$

$$\begin{bmatrix} x_1 \\ x_2 \end{bmatrix} = \begin{bmatrix} 1 & -3.001 \\ 1 & -3 \end{bmatrix}^{-1} \begin{bmatrix} 1 \\ 1 \end{bmatrix} = \begin{bmatrix} 1 \\ 0 \end{bmatrix}$$

(B)
$$x_1 - 3.001x_2 = 1$$
$$x_1 - 3x_2 = 0$$

$$\begin{bmatrix} x_1 \\ x_2 \end{bmatrix} = \begin{bmatrix} 1 & -3.001 \\ 1 & -3 \end{bmatrix}^{-1} \begin{bmatrix} 1 \\ 0 \end{bmatrix} = \begin{bmatrix} -3000 \\ -1000 \end{bmatrix}$$

(C)
$$x_1 - 3.001x_2 = 0$$
$$x_1 - 3x_2 = 1$$

$$\begin{bmatrix} x_1 \\ x_2 \end{bmatrix} = \begin{bmatrix} 1 & -3.001 \\ 1 & -3 \end{bmatrix}^{-1} \begin{bmatrix} 0 \\ 1 \end{bmatrix} = \begin{bmatrix} 3001 \\ 1000 \end{bmatrix}$$

40.
$$\begin{bmatrix} 30 & 40 \\ 20 & 30 \end{bmatrix} \begin{bmatrix} A \\ B \end{bmatrix} = \begin{bmatrix} 1800 \\ 1200 \end{bmatrix}$$

(A) Allocation 1:
$$\begin{bmatrix} A \\ B \end{bmatrix} = \begin{bmatrix} 30 & 40 \\ 20 & 30 \end{bmatrix}^{-1} \cdot \begin{bmatrix} 1800 \\ 1200 \end{bmatrix} = \begin{bmatrix} 0.3 & -0.4 \\ -0.2 & 0.3 \end{bmatrix} \begin{bmatrix} 1800 \\ 1200 \end{bmatrix} = \begin{bmatrix} 60 \\ 0 \end{bmatrix}$$

Allocation 2:
$$\begin{bmatrix} A \\ B \end{bmatrix} = \begin{bmatrix} 0.3 & -0.4 \\ -0.2 & 0.3 \end{bmatrix} \begin{bmatrix} 1750 \\ 1250 \end{bmatrix} = \begin{bmatrix} 25 \\ 25 \end{bmatrix}$$

Allocation 3:
$$\begin{bmatrix} A \\ B \end{bmatrix} = \begin{bmatrix} 0.3 & -0.4 \\ -0.2 & 0.3 \end{bmatrix} \begin{bmatrix} 1720 \\ 1280 \end{bmatrix} = \begin{bmatrix} 4 \\ 40 \end{bmatrix}$$

(B)
$$\begin{bmatrix} A \\ B \end{bmatrix} = \begin{bmatrix} 0.3 & -0.4 \\ -0.2 & 0.3 \end{bmatrix} \begin{bmatrix} 1600 \\ 1400 \end{bmatrix} = \begin{bmatrix} -80 \\ 100 \end{bmatrix} \text{ Not possible}$$

$$\begin{bmatrix} A \\ B \end{bmatrix} = \begin{bmatrix} 0.3 & -0.4 \\ -0.2 & 0.3 \end{bmatrix} \begin{bmatrix} 2000 \\ 1000 \end{bmatrix} = \begin{bmatrix} 200 \\ -100 \end{bmatrix} \text{ Not possible}$$

42. (A)
$$\begin{bmatrix} 1 & -1 & 1 \\ 1 & 2 & 0 \\ 0 & 2 & 2 \end{bmatrix} \begin{bmatrix} I_1 \\ I_2 \\ I_3 \end{bmatrix} = \begin{bmatrix} 0 \\ 10 \\ 10 \end{bmatrix}$$

$$\begin{bmatrix} I_1 \\ I_2 \\ I_3 \end{bmatrix} = \begin{bmatrix} 1 & -1 & 1 \\ 1 & 2 & 0 \\ 0 & 2 & 2 \end{bmatrix}^{-1} \begin{bmatrix} 0 \\ 10 \\ 10 \end{bmatrix} = \begin{bmatrix} \frac{1}{2} & \frac{1}{2} & -\frac{1}{4} \\ -\frac{1}{4} & \frac{1}{4} & \frac{1}{8} \\ \frac{1}{4} & -\frac{1}{4} & \frac{3}{8} \end{bmatrix} \begin{bmatrix} 0 \\ 10 \\ 10 \end{bmatrix} = \begin{bmatrix} \frac{5}{2} \\ \frac{15}{4} \\ \frac{5}{4} \end{bmatrix}$$

(B) $\begin{bmatrix} I_1 \\ I_2 \\ I_3 \end{bmatrix} = \begin{bmatrix} \frac{1}{2} & \frac{1}{2} & -\frac{1}{4} \\ -\frac{1}{4} & \frac{1}{4} & \frac{1}{8} \\ \frac{1}{4} & -\frac{1}{4} & \frac{3}{8} \end{bmatrix} \begin{bmatrix} 0 \\ 10 \\ 15 \end{bmatrix} = \begin{bmatrix} \frac{5}{4} \\ \frac{35}{8} \\ \frac{25}{8} \end{bmatrix}$

(C) $\begin{bmatrix} I_1 \\ I_2 \\ I_3 \end{bmatrix} = \begin{bmatrix} \frac{1}{2} & \frac{1}{2} & -\frac{1}{4} \\ -\frac{1}{4} & \frac{1}{4} & \frac{1}{8} \\ \frac{1}{4} & -\frac{1}{4} & \frac{3}{8} \end{bmatrix} \begin{bmatrix} 0 \\ 15 \\ 10 \end{bmatrix} = \begin{bmatrix} 5 \\ 5 \\ 0 \end{bmatrix}$

44. $(-1, k_1): a(-1)^2 + b(-1) + c = k_1$
$(0, k_2): a(0)^2 + b(0) + c = k_2$
$(1, k_3): a(1)^2 + b(1) + c = k_3$

(A) $\begin{bmatrix} 1 & -1 & 1 \\ 0 & 0 & 1 \\ 1 & 1 & 1 \end{bmatrix} \begin{bmatrix} a \\ b \\ c \end{bmatrix} = \begin{bmatrix} k_1 \\ k_2 \\ k_3 \end{bmatrix} = \begin{bmatrix} -2 \\ 1 \\ 6 \end{bmatrix}$

$\begin{bmatrix} a \\ b \\ c \end{bmatrix} = \begin{bmatrix} 1 & -1 & 1 \\ 0 & 0 & 1 \\ 1 & 1 & 1 \end{bmatrix}^{-1} \begin{bmatrix} -2 \\ 1 \\ 6 \end{bmatrix} = \begin{bmatrix} \frac{1}{2} & -1 & \frac{1}{2} \\ -\frac{1}{2} & 0 & \frac{1}{2} \\ 0 & 1 & 0 \end{bmatrix} \begin{bmatrix} -2 \\ 1 \\ 6 \end{bmatrix} = \begin{bmatrix} 1 \\ 4 \\ 1 \end{bmatrix}$

(B) $\begin{bmatrix} a \\ b \\ c \end{bmatrix} = \begin{bmatrix} \frac{1}{2} & -1 & \frac{1}{2} \\ -\frac{1}{2} & 0 & \frac{1}{2} \\ 0 & 1 & 0 \end{bmatrix} \begin{bmatrix} 4 \\ 3 \\ -2 \end{bmatrix} = \begin{bmatrix} -2 \\ -3 \\ 3 \end{bmatrix}$

(C) $\begin{bmatrix} a \\ b \\ c \end{bmatrix} = \begin{bmatrix} \frac{1}{2} & -1 & \frac{1}{2} \\ -\frac{1}{2} & 0 & \frac{1}{2} \\ 0 & 1 & 0 \end{bmatrix} \begin{bmatrix} 8 \\ -5 \\ 4 \end{bmatrix} = \begin{bmatrix} 11 \\ -2 \\ -5 \end{bmatrix}$

Exercise 8-7

2. $3x + 4y < 12$

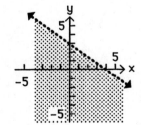

4. $3y - 2x \geq 24$

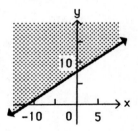

6. $y \geq \frac{1}{3}x - 2$

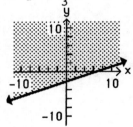

8. $x > -5$

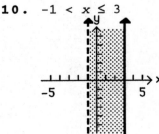

10. $-1 < x \leq 3$

12. $\begin{array}{l} x + 2y \geq 8 \\ 3x - 2y \leq 0 \end{array} \Rightarrow$ II

14. $\begin{array}{l} x + 2y \leq 8 \\ 3x - 2y \leq 0 \end{array} \Rightarrow$ III

16. $x \leq 4$
$y \geq 2$

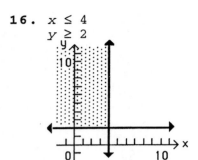

18. $3x + 4y \leq 12$
$y \geq -3$

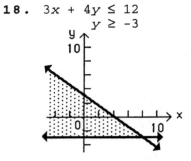

20. $2x + 5y \leq 20$
$x - 5y \leq -5$

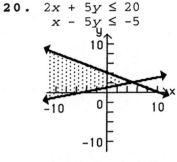

22. (A) $\begin{array}{l} x - 2y \leq 1 \\ x + 3y \geq 12 \end{array} \Rightarrow \begin{array}{l} y \geq 0.5x - 0.5 \\ y \geq -\frac{1}{3}x + 4 \end{array}$ (B) $\begin{array}{l} x - 2y \geq 1 \\ x + 3y \geq 12 \end{array} \Rightarrow \begin{array}{l} y \leq 0.5x - 0.5 \\ y \leq -\frac{1}{3}x + 4 \end{array}$

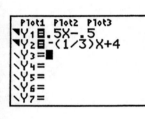
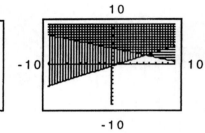
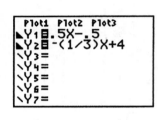
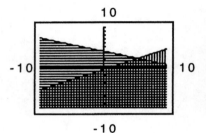

24. (A) $\begin{array}{l} 3x + y \geq -2 \\ x - 2y \geq -6 \end{array} \Rightarrow \begin{array}{l} y \geq -3x - 2 \\ y \leq \frac{1}{2}x + 3 \end{array}$ (B) $\begin{array}{l} 3x + y \leq -2 \\ x - 2y \geq -6 \end{array} \Rightarrow \begin{array}{l} y \leq -3x - 2 \\ y \geq \frac{1}{2}x + 3 \end{array}$

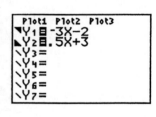
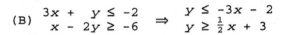
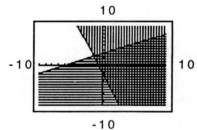
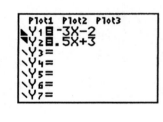
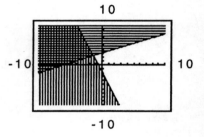

26. $x + 3y \leq 18$
$2x + y \leq 16 \Rightarrow$ III
$x \geq 0$
$y \geq 0$

Corner Points:
(0, 6), (0, 0), (8, 0), (6, 4)

28. $x + 3y \geq 18$
$2x + y \leq 16 \Rightarrow$ II
$x \geq 0$
$y \geq 0$

Corner Points:
(6, 4), (0, 6), (0, 16)

30. $4x + 3y \leq 12$
$x \geq 0$
$y \geq 0$

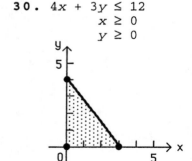

Corner Points:
(0, 0), (0, 4), (3, 0); bounded

32. $5x + 6y \geq 30$
$x \geq 0$
$y \geq 0$

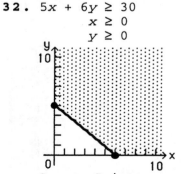

Corner Points:
(0, 5), (6, 0); unbounded

34. $x + 2y \le 10$
$3x + y \le 15$
$x \ge 0$
$y \ge 0$

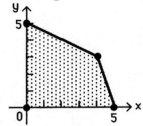

Corner Points:
   (0, 0), (0, 5), (4, 3), (5, 0);
bounded

36. $x + 2y \ge 8$
$2x + y \ge 10$
$x \ge 0$
$y \ge 0$

Corner Points:
   (8, 0), (4, 2), (0, 10); unbounded

38. $3x + y \le 21$
$x + y \le 9$
$x + 3y \le 21$
$x \ge 0$
$y \ge 0$

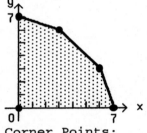

Corner Points:
   (0, 0), (0, 7), (3, 6), (6, 3),
   (7, 0); bounded

40. $3x + y \ge 30$
$x + y \ge 16$
$x + 3y \ge 24$
$x \ge 0$
$y \ge 0$

Corner Points:
   (0, 30), (7, 9), (12, 4), (24, 0);
unbounded

42. $4x + y \le 32$
$x + 3y \le 30$
$5x + 4y \ge 51$

Corner Points:
   (3, 9), (6, 8), (7, 4); bounded

44. $3x + 4y \le 48$
$x + 2y \ge 24$
$y \le 9$

The feasible region is empty.

46. $3x - y \ge 1$
$-x + 5y \ge 9$
$x + y \le 9$
$y \le 5$

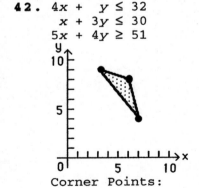

Corner Points:
   (1, 2), (2, 5), (4, 5), (6, 3); bounded

48.

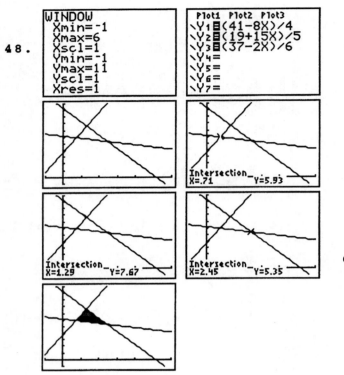

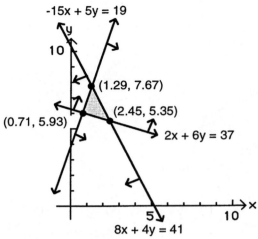

-15x + 5y = 19

(1.29, 7.67)

(2.45, 5.35)

(0.71, 5.93)

2x + 6y = 37

8x + 4y = 41

Corner Points:
(0.71, 5.93), (1.29, 7.67),
(2.45, 5.35); bounded

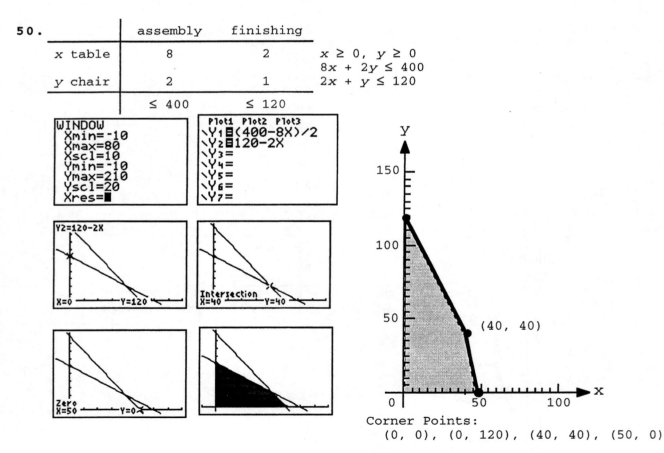

50.

	assembly	finishing
x table	8	2
y chair	2	1
	≤ 400	≤ 120

$x \geq 0, \; y \geq 0$
$8x + 2y \leq 400$
$2x + y \leq 120$

(40, 40)

Corner Points:
(0, 0), (0, 120), (40, 40), (50, 0)

52.

	assembly	finishing	profit = $P = 50x + 15y$
x table	8	2	50
y chair	2	1	15
	≤ 400	≤ 120	

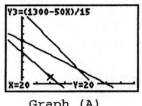

Graph (A)

(A) Graphing $50x + 15y = 1300$ above gives Graph (A) for $x = 20$, and $y = 20$. Any other production mix on this line will also result in a profit of $1300. The slope of the profit line is $-\frac{50}{15}$ and the y intercept is $\frac{P}{15}$, $y = -\frac{50}{15}x + \frac{P}{15}$, which means all profit lines have the same slope. All production schedules in the feasible region that are on the graph of $50x + 15y = 1300$ will result in a profit of $1300.

(B) The profit line that has the largest y intercept and still passes through the region of feasible solutions will produce the maximum profit.

(C) If a profit of $1950 is desired then Graph (C) shows how the profit line passes through the region of feasible solutions. A production mix of 30 chairs and 30 tables is shown but any other production mix on this line will also produce a profit of $1950. The idea is to increase the y intercept, thus increasing the profit, of the line while keeping the slope the same and making sure the line passes through at least one point in the region of feasible solutions.

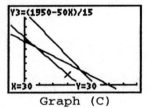

Graph (C)

54.

	food			
	M	N		
calcium	30	10	≥ 360	$30x + 10y \geq 360$
iron	10	10	≥ 160	$10x + 10y \geq 160$
vit. A	10	30	≥ 240	$10x + 30y \geq 240$
				$x \geq 0,\ y \geq 0$

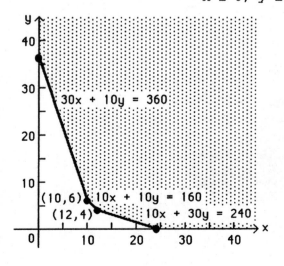

56.

	animal		
	mouse	rat	
box A	10	20	≤ 800
box B	20	10	≤ 640

$10x + 20y \leq 800$
$20x + 10y \leq 640$
$x \geq 0,\ y \geq 0$

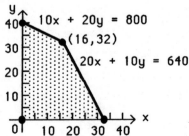

Exercise 8-8

2.

Corner points (x, y)	Objective function $z = 4x + y$
(0, 0)	0
(0, 12)	12
(7, 9)	37
(10, 0)	40

z_{max} = 40 at (10, 0)

4.

Corner points (x, y)	Objective function $z = 9x + 3y$
(0, 0)	0
(0, 12)	36
(7, 9)	90
(10, 0)	90

z_{max} = 90 at (7, 9) and (10, 0);
multiple optimal solutions

6.

Corner points (x, y)	Objective function $z = 7x + 9y$
(0, 8)	72
(0, 12)	108
(12, 0)	84
(4, 3)	55

z_{min} = 55 at (4, 3)

8.

Corner points (x, y)	Objective function $z = 5x + 4y$
(0, 8)	32
(0, 12)	48
(12, 0)	60
(4, 3)	32

z_{min} = 32 at (0, 8) and (4, 3);
multiple optimal solutions

10. $2x + y \leq 12 \quad \Rightarrow \quad y \leq -2x + 12$

$x + 3y \leq 21 \quad \Rightarrow \quad y \leq -\frac{1}{3}x + 7$

$x, y \geq 0$

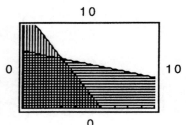

Corner points (x, y)	Objective function $z = 4x + 5y$
(0, 0)	0
(0, 7)	35
(3, 6)	42
(6, 0)	24

z_{max} = 42 at (3, 6)

12. $4x + 3y \geq 24 \quad \Rightarrow \quad y \geq -\frac{4}{3}x + 8$

$4x + y \leq 16 \quad \Rightarrow \quad y \leq -4x + 16$

$x, y \geq 0$

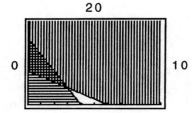

Corner points (x, y)	Objective function $z = 2x + y$
(0, 8)	8
(0, 16)	16
(3, 4)	10

z_{min} = 8 at (0, 8)

14. $3x + y \leq 24 \quad \Rightarrow \quad y \leq -3x + 24$

$x + y \leq 10 \quad \Rightarrow \quad y \leq -x + 10$

$x + 3y \leq 24 \quad \Rightarrow \quad y \leq -\frac{1}{3}x + 8$

$x, y \geq 0$

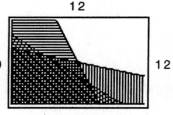

Corner points (x, y)	Objective function $z = 5x + 3y$
(0, 0)	0
(0, 8)	24
(3, 7)	36
(7, 3)	44
(8, 0)	40

z_{max} = 44 at (7, 3)

16. $2x + 3y \geq 30 \quad \Rightarrow \quad y \geq -\frac{2}{3}x + 10$

$3x + 2y \geq 30 \quad \Rightarrow \quad y \geq -\frac{3}{2}x + 15$

$x + y \leq 15 \quad \Rightarrow \quad y \leq -x + 15$

$x, \ y \geq 0$

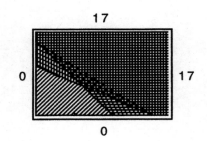

Corner points $(x, \ y)$	Objective function $z = x + 2y$
(0, 15)	30
(6, 6)	18
(15, 0)	15

$z_{min} = 15$ at $(15, 0)$

18. $x + 2y \geq 100 \quad \Rightarrow \quad y \geq -\frac{1}{2}x + 50$

$2x - y \leq 0 \quad \Rightarrow \quad y \geq 2x$

$2x + y \leq 200 \quad \Rightarrow \quad y \leq -2x + 200$

$x, \ y \geq 0$

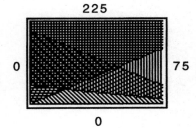

Corner points $(x, \ y)$	Objective function $z = 15x + 30y$
(0, 50)	1500
(0, 200)	6000
(50, 100)	3750
(20, 40)	1500

$z_{max} = 6000$ at $(0, 200)$

$z_{min} = 1500$ at $(0, 50)$ and $(20, 40)$; multiple optimal solutions

20. $2x + 3y \geq 120 \quad \Rightarrow \quad y \geq -\frac{2}{3}x + 40$

$3x + 2y \leq 360 \quad \Rightarrow \quad y \leq -\frac{3}{2}x + 180$

$x \leq 80$

$y \leq 120$

$x, \ y \geq 0$

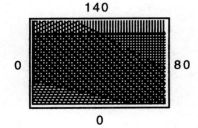

Corner points $(x, \ y)$	Objective function $z = 25x + 30y$
(0, 40)	1200
(0, 120)	3600
(40, 120)	4600
(80, 60)	3800
(80, 0)	2000
(60, 0)	1500

$z_{min} = 1200$ at $(0, 40)$

$z_{max} = 4600$ at $(40, 120)$

22. $245x_1 + 452x_2 \le 4{,}181 \quad \Rightarrow \quad x_2 \le \dfrac{-245x_1 + 4{,}181}{452}$

$290x_1 + 379x_2 \le 3{,}888 \quad \Rightarrow \quad x_2 \le \dfrac{-290x_1 + 3{,}888}{379}$

$390x_1 + 299x_2 \le 4{,}407 \quad \Rightarrow \quad x_2 \le \dfrac{-390x_1 + 4{,}407}{299}$

$x_1,\ x_2 \ge 0$

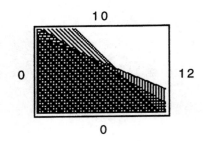

Corner points (x, y)	Objective function $P = 300x_1 + 460x_2$
(0, 0)	0
(0, 9.25)	4255
(4.52, 6.8)	4484
(8.31, 3.9)	4287
(11.3, 0)	3390

$P_{\max} = 4484$ at $(4.52,\ 6.8)$

24. $\begin{aligned} x + y &\ge 4 \\ x + 2y &\ge 6 \\ 2x + 3y &\le 12 \\ x,\ y &\ge 0 \end{aligned}$

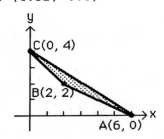

Corner points (x, y)	Objective function $z = ax + by$
$A = (6, 0)$	$6a$
$B = (2, 2)$	$2a + 2b$
$C = (0, 4)$	$4b$

(A) $z_{\min}$ at only A:

$6a < 2a + 2b \qquad\qquad 6a < 4b$

$4a < 2b \qquad \textbf{and} \qquad a < \dfrac{2}{3}b \quad \Rightarrow \quad a < \dfrac{b}{2}$

$2a < b \ \Rightarrow \ a < \dfrac{b}{2}$

(B) $z_{\min}$ at only B:

$2a + 2b < 6a \qquad\qquad 2a + 2b < 4b$

$2b < 4a \qquad\qquad\qquad 2a < 2b$

$b < 2a \qquad \textbf{and} \qquad a < b \quad \Rightarrow \quad \dfrac{1}{2}b < a < b$

$\dfrac{1}{2}b < a$

(C) $z_{\min}$ at only C:

$4b < 6a \qquad\qquad 4b < 2a + 2b$

$b < 1.5a \qquad\qquad 2b < 2a$

or $a > \dfrac{2}{3}b \quad \textbf{and} \qquad b < a$ or $a > b \ \Rightarrow \ a > b$

(D) $z_{\min}$ at both A and B:

$6a = 2a + 2b \qquad\qquad 6a < 4b$

$4a = 2b \qquad \textbf{and} \qquad 6a < 8a \ \surd \ \Rightarrow \ b = 2a$

$a = \dfrac{1}{2}b$ or $b = 2a$

(E) $z_{\min}$ at both B and C:

$2a + 2b = 4b \qquad\qquad 2a + 2b < 6a$

$2a = 2b \qquad\qquad\qquad 2a + 2a < 6a$

$a = b \ \textbf{and} \qquad\qquad 4a < 6a \ \surd \ \Rightarrow \ a = b$

26. Let x = # of mice, y = # of rats.

$10x + 20y \leq 800 \Rightarrow y \leq -\frac{1}{2}x + 40$

$20x + 10y \leq 640 \Rightarrow y \leq -2x + 64$

$x, \ y \geq 0$

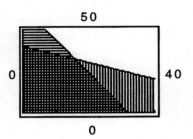

Corner points (x, y)	Objective function $z = x + y$
(0, 0)	0
(0, 40)	40
(16, 32)	48
(32, 0)	32

$z_{max} = 48$ at $(16, 32)$

48 maximum mice and rats can be used, with 16 mice and 32 rats.

28.

	students	chaperones	cost
x: bus	40	3	1200
y: van	8	1	100
	≥ 400	≤ 36	

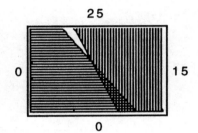

$40x + 8y \geq 400 \Rightarrow y \geq -5x + 50$

$3x + y \leq 36 \Rightarrow y \leq -3x + 36$

$x, \ y \geq 0$

Corner points (x, y)	Objective function $z = 1200x + 100y$
(10, 0)	12,000
(7, 15)	9,900
(12, 0)	14,400

$z_{min} = 9,900$ at $(7, 15)$

Rent 7 buses and 15 vans at a minimum cost of $9,900.

30.

	capital	labor	profit
x: desktop	400	40	320
y: portable	250	30	220
	$\leq 20,000$	≤ 2160	

$400x + 250y \leq 20,000 \Rightarrow y \leq -1.6x + 80$

$40x + 30y \leq 2,160 \Rightarrow y \leq \frac{4}{3}x + 72$

$x, \ y \geq 0$

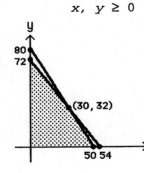

Corner points (x, y)	Objective function $z = 320x + 220y$
(0, 0)	0
(0, 72)	15,840
(30, 32)	16,640
(50, 0)	16,000

$z_{max} = 16,640$ at $(30, 32)$

(A) A company can produce a maximum of 72 computers, all portable (72 is the largest value for (x, y), a corner point, and it is a y-value).

(B) By producing 72 portable computers, the profit will be $15,840. They could have a maximum profit of $16,640 by producing 30 desktop and 32 portable computers.

32. Let x = # of sociologists, y = # of research assistants.

$$10x + 30y \geq 280$$
$$30x + 10y \geq 360$$
$$x + y \leq 40$$
$$x, \ y \geq 0$$

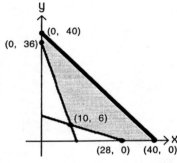

Corner points $(x, \ y)$	Objective function $C = 500x + 300y$
(0, 36)	10,800
(10, 6)	6,800
(28, 0)	14,000
(40, 0)	12,000
(0, 40)	20,000

(A) z_{min} = 6800 at (10, 6). Hire 10 sociologists and 6 research assistants for a minimum cost of $6,800.

(B) Add $y \geq x$ to the graph and delete $30x + 10y \geq 360$

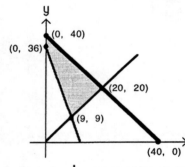

Corner points $(x, \ y)$	Objective function $C = 500x + 300y$
(0, 36)	10,800
(9, 9)	7,200
(0, 40)	12,000
(20, 20)	16,000

z_{min} = 7200 at (9, 9). Hire 9 sociologists and 9 research assistants for a minimum cost of $7,200.

34.

	calcium	iron	cholesterol	vitamin A
M	16	5	6	8
N	4	25	4	4
	≥ 320	≥ 575	≤ 300	

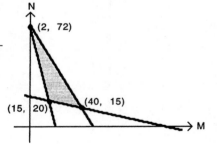

$$16M + \ 4N \geq 320$$
$$5M + 25N \geq 575$$
$$6M + \ 4N \leq 300$$
$$M, \ N \geq 0$$

Corner points $(x, \ y)$	Objective function $z = 8M + 4N$
(15, 20)	200
(2, 72)	304
(40, 15)	380

The amount of vitamin A will range from a minimum of 200 units when 15 ounces of food M and 20 ounces of food N are used to a maximum of 380 units when 40 ounces of food M and 15 ounces of food N are used.

CHAPTER 9

Exercise 9-1

2. $a_n = n + 3$
$a_1 = 1 + 3 = 4$
$a_2 = 2 + 3 = 5$
$a_3 = 3 + 3 = 6$
$a_4 = 4 + 3 = 7$

4. $a_n = \left(1 + \dfrac{1}{n}\right)^n$

$a_1 = \left(1 + \dfrac{1}{1}\right)^1 = 2$

$a_2 = \left(1 + \dfrac{1}{2}\right)^2 = \left(\dfrac{3}{2}\right)^2 = \dfrac{9}{4}$

$a_3 = \left(1 + \dfrac{1}{3}\right)^3 = \left(\dfrac{4}{3}\right)^3 = \dfrac{64}{27}$

$a_4 = \left(1 + \dfrac{1}{4}\right)^4 = \left(\dfrac{5}{4}\right)^4 = \dfrac{625}{256}$

6. $a_n = \dfrac{(-1)^{n+1}}{n^2}$

$a_1 = \dfrac{(-1)^{1+1}}{1^2} = \dfrac{(-1)^2}{1} = 1$

$a_2 = \dfrac{(-1)^{2+1}}{2^2} = \dfrac{(-1)^3}{4} = -\dfrac{1}{4}$

$a_3 = \dfrac{(-1)^{3+1}}{3^2} = \dfrac{(-1)^4}{9} = \dfrac{1}{9}$

$a_4 = \dfrac{(-1)^{4+1}}{4^2} = \dfrac{(-1)^5}{16} = -\dfrac{1}{16}$

8. $a_n = n + 3$
$a_{10} = 10 + 3$
$a_{10} = 13$

10. $a_n = \left(1 + \dfrac{1}{n}\right)^n$

$a_{200} = \left(1 + \dfrac{1}{200}\right)^{200}$

$a_{200} = \left(\dfrac{201}{200}\right)^{200}$

12. $\displaystyle\sum_{k=1}^{4} k^2 = 1^2 + 2^2 + 3^2 + 4^2$
$\qquad\qquad = 1 + 4 + 9 + 16$

14. $\displaystyle\sum_{k=1}^{5} \left(\dfrac{1}{3}\right)^k = \left(\dfrac{1}{3}\right)^1 + \left(\dfrac{1}{3}\right)^2 + \left(\dfrac{1}{3}\right)^3 + \left(\dfrac{1}{3}\right)^4 + \left(\dfrac{1}{3}\right)^5$
$\qquad\qquad = \dfrac{1}{3} + \dfrac{1}{9} + \dfrac{1}{27} + \dfrac{1}{81} + \dfrac{1}{243}$

16. $\displaystyle\sum_{k=1}^{6} (-1)^{k+1}k = (-1)^{1+1}(1) + (-1)^{2+1}(2) + (-1)^{3+1}(3) + (-1)^{4+1}(4)$
$\qquad\qquad\qquad\qquad\qquad + (-1)^{5+1}(5) + (-1)^{6+1}(6)$
$\qquad\qquad = 1 - 2 + 3 - 4 + 5 - 6$

18. $a_n = (-1)^{n+1}\left(\dfrac{1}{2^n}\right)$

$a_1 = (-1)^{1+1}\left(\dfrac{1}{2^1}\right) = \dfrac{1}{2}$

$a_2 = (-1)^{2+1}\left(\dfrac{1}{2^2}\right) = -\dfrac{1}{4}$

$a_3 = (-1)^{3+1}\left(\dfrac{1}{2^3}\right) = \dfrac{1}{8}$

$a_4 = (-1)^{4+1}\left(\dfrac{1}{2^4}\right) = -\dfrac{1}{16}$

$a_5 = (-1)^{5+1}\left(\dfrac{1}{2^5}\right) = \dfrac{1}{32}$

20. $a_n = n[1 - (-1)^n]$
$a_1 = 1[1 - (-1)^1] = 2$
$a_2 = 2[1 - (-1)^2] = 0$
$a_3 = 3[1 - (-1)^3] = 6$
$a_4 = 4[1 - (-1)^4] = 0$
$a_5 = 5[1 - (-1)^5] = 10$

22. $a_n = \left(-\dfrac{3}{2}\right)^{n-1}$

$a_1 = \left(-\dfrac{3}{2}\right)^{1-1} = 1$

$a_2 = \left(-\dfrac{3}{2}\right)^{2-1} = -\dfrac{3}{2}$

$a_3 = \left(-\dfrac{3}{2}\right)^{3-1} = \dfrac{9}{4}$

$a_4 = \left(-\dfrac{3}{2}\right)^{4-1} = -\dfrac{27}{8}$

$a_5 = \left(-\dfrac{3}{2}\right)^{5-1} = \dfrac{81}{16}$

24. $a_n = a_{n-1} + a_{n-2}, \ n \geq 3; \ a_1 = a_2 = 1$

$a_1 = 1$

$a_2 = 1$

$a_3 = a_2 + a_1 = 1 + 1 = 2$

$a_4 = a_3 + a_2 = 2 + 1 = 3$

$a_5 = a_4 + a_3 = 3 + 2 = 5$

26. $a_n = 2a_{n-1}, \ n \geq 2; \ a_1 = 2$

$a_1 = 2$

$a_2 = 2a_1 = 2(2) = 4$

$a_3 = 2a_2 = 2(4) = 8$

$a_4 = 2a_3 = 2(8) = 16$

$a_5 = 2a_4 = 2(16) = 32$

28. $-2, \ -1, \ 0, \ 1, \ \dots,$

$a_n = n - 3$

30. $-2, \ -4, \ -6, \ -8, \ \dots,$

$a_n = -2n$

32. $\dfrac{1}{2}, \ \dfrac{3}{4}, \ \dfrac{5}{6}, \ \dfrac{7}{8}, \ \dots,$

$a_n = \dfrac{2n - 1}{2n}$

34. $1, \ -2, \ 3, \ -4, \ \dots,$

$a_n = (-1)^{n+1} n$

36. $1, \ -3, \ 5, \ -7, \ \dots,$

$a_n = (-1)^{n+1}(2n - 1)$

38. $x, \ -x^3, \ x^5, \ -x^7, \ \dots,$

$a_n = (-1)^{n+1} x^{2n-1}$

40.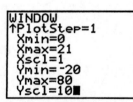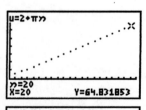

42.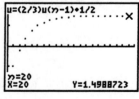

44. $\displaystyle\sum_{k=1}^{5} (-1)^{k+1}(2k - 1)^2 = (-1)^{1+1}(2(1) - 1)^2 + (-1)^{2+1}(2(2) - 1)^2 + (-1)^{3+1}(2(3) - 1)^2$

$+ (-1)^{4+1}(2(4) - 1)^2 + (-1)^{5+1}(2(5) - 1)^2$

$= 1^2 - 3^2 + 5^2 - 7^2 + 9^2$

or

$= 1 - 9 + 25 - 49 + 81$

46. $\displaystyle\sum_{k=1}^{5} x^{k-1} = x^{1-1} + x^{2-1} + x^{3-1} + x^{4-1} + x^{5-1}$

$= 1 + x + x^2 + x^3 + x^4$

48. $\displaystyle\sum_{k=0}^{4} \frac{(-1)^k x^{2k+1}}{2k+1} = \frac{(-1)^0 x^{2(0)+1}}{2(0)+1} + \frac{(-1)^1 x^{2(1)+1}}{2(1)+1} + \frac{(-1)^2 x^{2(2)+1}}{2(2)+1} + \frac{(-1)^3 x^{2(3)+1}}{2(3)+1} + \frac{(-1)^4 x^{2(4)+1}}{2(4)+1}$

$\qquad\qquad = x - \dfrac{x^3}{3} + \dfrac{x^5}{5} - \dfrac{x^7}{7} + \dfrac{x^9}{9}$

50. $2 + 3 + 4 + 5 + 6 = \displaystyle\sum_{k=1}^{5} (k+1)$ **52.** $1 - \dfrac{1}{2} + \dfrac{1}{3} - \dfrac{1}{4} = \displaystyle\sum_{k=1}^{4} \dfrac{(-1)^{k+1}}{k}$

54. $2 + \dfrac{3}{2} + \dfrac{4}{3} + \ldots + \dfrac{n+1}{n} = \displaystyle\sum_{k=1}^{n} \dfrac{k+1}{k}$ **56.** $\dfrac{1}{2} - \dfrac{1}{4} + \dfrac{1}{8} - \ldots + \dfrac{(-1)^{n+1}}{2^n} = \displaystyle\sum_{k=1}^{n} \dfrac{(-1)^{k+1}}{2^k}$

58. (A) $a_n = \dfrac{(a_{n-1})^2 + 5}{2a_{n-1}}, \ n \geq 2; \ a_1 = 2$

$\qquad a_1 = 2$

$\qquad a_2 = \dfrac{2^2 + 5}{2(2)} = \dfrac{9}{4} = 2.25$

$\qquad a_3 = \dfrac{2.25^2 + 5}{2(2.25)} = 2.236\overline{1}$

$\qquad a_4 = \dfrac{2.236\overline{1}^2 + 5}{2(2.236\overline{1})} = 2.236067978$

(B) $\sqrt{5} = 2.2360679775$ which, to nine decimal places,

$\qquad = a_4$ from (A)

(C) for

$\qquad a_1 = 3$

$\qquad a_2 = \dfrac{3^2 + 5}{2(3)} = 2.\overline{3}$

$\qquad a_3 = \dfrac{2.\overline{3}^2 + 5}{2(2.\overline{3})} = 2.238095238$

$\qquad a_4 = \dfrac{2.238095238^2 + 5}{2(2.238095238)} = 2.236068896$

$\qquad a_5 = \dfrac{2.236068896^2 + 5}{2(2.236068896)} = 2.2360679775$

$\qquad \sqrt{5} = 2.2360679775 = a_5$, to ten decimal places

60. $\{u_n\}: u_1 = 1, \quad u_n = u_{n-1} + v_{n-1}$
$\{v_n\}: v_1 = 0, \quad v_n = u_{n-1}, \ n \geq 2$

$u_1 = 1$	$v_1 = 0$
$u_2 = 1$	$v_2 = 1$
$u_3 = 2$	$v_3 = 1$
$u_4 = 3$	$v_4 = 2$
$u_5 = 5$	$v_5 = 3$
$u_6 = 8$	$v_6 = 5$
$u_7 = 13$	$v_7 = 8$
$u_8 = 21$	$v_8 = 13$
$u_9 = 34$	$v_9 = 21$
$u_{10} = 55$	$v_{10} = 34$

$\{u_n\}$ is the Fibonacci sequence
$\{v_n\}$ is the Fibonacci sequence preceded by 0.

62. $e^x = \displaystyle\sum_{k=0}^{\infty} \dfrac{x^k}{k!} \approx 1 + \dfrac{x}{1!} + \dfrac{x^2}{2!} + \ldots + \dfrac{x^n}{n!}$

$e^{-0.5} \approx 1 + \dfrac{-0.5}{1} + \dfrac{(-0.5)^2}{2!} + \dfrac{(-0.5)^3}{3!} + \dfrac{(-0.5)^4}{4!} \approx 0.6067708333$

$e^{-0.5} \approx 0.6065306597$, calculator

64. $\displaystyle\sum_{k=1}^{n} (a_k + b_k) = (a_1 + b_1) + (a_2 + b_2) + (a_3 + b_3) + \ldots + (a_n + b_n)$

$\qquad\qquad\qquad = (a_1 + a_2 + a_3 + \ldots + a_n) + (b_1 + b_2 + b_3 + \ldots + b_n)$

$\qquad\qquad\qquad = \displaystyle\sum_{k=1}^{n} a_k + \sum_{k=1}^{n} b_k$

Exercise 9-2

2. $n < 10$: 10 is the first positive integer which fails

4.

n	$n^3 + 11n$	$6n^2 + 6$
1	12	12
2	30	30
3	60	60
4	108	102 $\Rightarrow$ 4 is first positive integer which fails

6.

n	$4 + 8 + 12 + \cdots + 4n$	$2n(n + 1)$
1	4	$2(1)(1 + 1) = 4$
2	$4 + 8 = 12$	$2(2)(2 + 1) = 12$
3	$4 + 8 + 12 = 24$	$2(3)(3 + 1) = 24$

8.

n	$(a^5)^n$	a^{5n}
1	$(a^5)^1 = a^{5 \cdot 1} = a^5$	$a^{5 \cdot 1} = a^5$
2	$(a^5)^2 = a^{5 \cdot 2} = a^{10}$	$a^{5 \cdot 2} = a^{10}$
3	$(a^5)^3 = a^{5 \cdot 3} = a^{15}$	$a^{5 \cdot 3} = a^{15}$

10. P_1: $4^1 - 1 = 3$ which is divisible by 3
P_2: $4^2 - 1 = 15$ which is divisible by 3
P_3: $4^3 - 1 = 63$ which is divisible by 3

12. P_n: $4 + 8 + 12 + \cdots + 4n = 2n(n + 1)$
 P_k: $4 + 8 + 12 + \cdots + 4k = 2k(k + 1)$
 P_{k+1}: $4 + 8 + 12 + \cdots + 4k + 4(k + 1) = 2(k + 1)((k + 1) + 1) = 2(k + 1)(k + 2)$

14. P_n: $(a^5)^n = a^{5n}$
 P_k: $(a^5)^k = a^{5k}$
 P_{k+1}: $(a^5)^{k+1} = a^{5(k+1)}$

16. P_n: $4^n - 1 = 3r$, for some integer r
 P_k: $4^k - 1 = 3r$, for some integer r
 P_{k+1}: $4^{(k+1)} - 1 = 3s$, for some integer s

18. P_n: $4 + 8 + 12 + \cdots + 4n = 2n(n + 1)$
Show P_1 is true.
 P_1: $4(1) = 2(1)(1 + 1)$
 $4 = 4$ Thus P_1 is true.

Show if P_k is true, then P_{k+1} is true.
 P_k: $4 + 8 + 12 + \cdots + 4k = 2k(k + 1)$
 P_{k+1}: $4 + 8 + 12 + \cdots + 4(k + 1) = 2(k + 1)(k + 2)$

Start with P_k: $4 + 8 + 12 + \ldots + 4k = 2k(k + 1)$
 P_{k+1}: $4 + 8 + 12 + \ldots + 4k + 4(k + 1) = 2k(k + 1) + 4(k + 1)$
$$= (2k + 4)(k + 1)$$
$$= 2(k + 2)(k + 1)$$
$$= 2(k + 1)(k + 2) \Rightarrow P_{k+1} \text{ is true}$$

20. P_n: $(a^5)^n = a^{5n}$
Show P_1 is true.
 P_1: $(a^5)^1 = a^{5 \cdot 1}$
 $a^5 = a^5$ Thus P_1 is true.

Show if P_k is true, then P_{k+1} is true.
 P_k: $(a^5)k = a^{5k}$
 P_{k+1}: $(a^5)^{k+1} = a^{5(k+1)}$

Start with P_k: $(a^5)^k = a^{5k}$

$$(a^5)^k \cdot a^5 = a^{5k} \cdot a^5$$
$$(a^{5k}) \cdot a^5 = a^{5k+5}$$
$$a^{5k+5} = a^{5(k+1)}$$
$$(a^5)^{k+1} = a^{5(k+1)} \Rightarrow P_{k+1} \text{ is true}$$

22. P_n: $4^n - 1 = 3r$ for some integer r

Show P_1 is true.
$$P_1:\ 4^1 - 1 = 4 - 1 = 3 = 3 \cdot 1 \quad \text{Thus } P_1 \text{ is true.}$$

Show if P_k is true, then P_{k+1} is true.
$$P_k:\ 4^k - 1 = 3s \text{ for some integer } s$$
$$P_{k+1}:\ 4^{k+1} - 1 = 3t \text{ for some integer } t$$

Start with P_k:
$$4^k - 1 = 3s \text{ for some integer } s$$
$$4(4^k - 1) = 4(3s)$$
$$4^{k+1} - 4 = 4(3s)$$
$$4^{k+1} - 1 = 4(3s) + 3$$
$$4^{k+1} - 1 = 3(4s + 1); \text{ let } t = 4s + 1$$
$$4^{k+1} - 1 = 3t \text{ for some integer } t \Rightarrow P_{k+1} \text{ is true.}$$

24.

n	n as the sum of 3 or fewer squares of positive integers	
8	$2^2 + 2^2 = 4 + 4 = 8$	
9	$3^2 = 9$	$1^2 = 1$
10	$1^2 + 3^2 = 1 + 9 = 10$	$2^2 = 4$
11	$1^2 + 1^2 + 3^2 = 1 + 1 + 9 = 11$	$3^2 = 9$
12	$2^2 + 2^2 + 2^2 = 4 + 4 + 4 = 12$	$4^2 = 16$
13	$2^2 + 3^2 = 4 + 9 = 13$	$5^2 = 25$
14	$1^2 + 2^2 + 3^2 = 1 + 4 + 9 = 14$	
15	fails	

26. Let $a = 1$, $b = 7$, $c = 5$, $d = 5$, then
$a^2 + b^2 = c^2 + d^2$ becomes
$1^2 + 7^2 = 5^2 + 5^2$
$1 + 49 = 25 + 25$
$\quad\ 50 = 50$ which is true but
$a = c$ or $a = d$ becomes
$1 = 5$ or $1 = 5$ which is false.

28. P_n: $\dfrac{1}{2} + \dfrac{1}{4} + \dfrac{1}{8} + \cdots + \dfrac{1}{2^n} = 1 - \left(\dfrac{1}{2}\right)^n$

Show P_1 is true.

$$P_1:\ \frac{1}{2^1} = 1 - \left(\frac{1}{2}\right)^1$$

$$\frac{1}{2} = \frac{1}{2} \quad \text{Thus } P_1 \text{ is true.}$$

Show if P_k is true, then P_{k+1} is true.

$$P_k:\ \frac{1}{2} + \frac{1}{4} + \frac{1}{8} + \cdots + \frac{1}{2^k} = 1 - \left(\frac{1}{2}\right)^k$$

$$P_{k+1}:\ \frac{1}{2} + \frac{1}{4} + \frac{1}{8} + \cdots + \frac{1}{2^k} + \frac{1}{2^{k+1}} = 1 - \left(\frac{1}{2}\right)^{k+1}$$

Start with P_k:

$$\frac{1}{2} + \frac{1}{4} + \frac{1}{8} + \cdots + \frac{1}{2^k} = 1 - \left(\frac{1}{2}\right)^k$$

$$\frac{1}{2} + \frac{1}{4} + \frac{1}{8} + \cdots + \frac{1}{2^k} + \frac{1}{2^{k+1}} = 1 - \left(\frac{1}{2}\right)^k + \frac{1}{2^{k+1}}$$

$$= 1 - \left(\frac{1}{2}\right)^k + \left(\frac{1}{2}\right)^{k+1}$$

$$= 1 - \left(\frac{1}{2}\right)^k + \left(\frac{1}{2}\right)^k\left(\frac{1}{2}\right)$$

$$= 1 - \left(\frac{1}{2}\right)^k\left(1 - \frac{1}{2}\right)$$

$$= 1 - \left(\frac{1}{2}\right)^k\left(\frac{1}{2}\right)$$

$$= 1 - \left(\frac{1}{2}\right)^{k+1} \Rightarrow P_{k+1} \text{ is true}$$

30. P_n: $1 + 8 + 16 + \cdots + 8(n - 1) = (2n - 1)^2$; $n > 1$

Show P_2 is true.

$$1 + 8(2 - 1) = (2(2) - 1)^2$$
$$9 = 9 \quad \text{Thus } P_2 \text{ is true.}$$

Show if P_k is true, then P_{k+1} is true.

$$P_k: 1 + 8 + 16 + \cdots + 8(k - 1) = (2k - 1)^2; \; k > 2$$
$$P_{k+1}: 1 + 8 + 16 + \cdots + 8(k - 1) + 8((k + 1) - 1) = (2(k + 1) - 1)^2; \; k > 2$$

Start with P_k:

$$1 + 8 + 16 + \cdots + 8(k - 1) = (2k - 1)^2; \; k > 2$$

$$1 + 8 + 16 + \cdots + 8(k - 1) + 8((k + 1) - 1) = (2k - 1)^2 + 8((k + 1) - 1)$$

$$= 4k^2 - 4k + 1 + 8k$$

$$= 4k^2 + 4k + 1$$

$$= (2k + 1)^2$$

$$= (2(k + 1) - 1)^2 \Rightarrow P_{k+1} \text{ is true}$$

32. P_n: $1 \cdot 2 + 2 \cdot 3 + 3 \cdot 4 + \cdots + n(n + 1) = \dfrac{n(n + 1)(n + 2)}{3}$

Show P_1 is true.

$$1 \cdot 2 = \frac{1(2)(3)}{3}$$
$$2 = 2 \quad \text{Thus } P_1 \text{ is true.}$$

Show if P_k is true, then P_{k+1} is true.

$$P_k: 1 \cdot 2 + 2 \cdot 3 + 3 \cdot 4 + \cdots + k(k + 1) = \frac{k(k + 1)(k + 2)}{3}$$

$$P_{k+1}: 1 \cdot 2 + 2 \cdot 3 + 3 \cdot 4 + \cdots + (k + 1)(k + 1 + 1) = \frac{(k + 1)(k + 1 + 1)(k + 1 + 2)}{3}$$

Start with P_k:

$$1 \cdot 2 + 2 \cdot 3 + 3 \cdot 4 + \ldots + k(k+1) = \frac{k(k+1)(k+2)}{3}$$

$$1 \cdot 2 + 2 \cdot 3 + 3 \cdot 4 + \cdots + k(k+1) + (k+1)(k+2)$$

$$= \frac{k(k+1)(k+2)}{3} + (k+1)(k+2)$$

$$= \frac{k(k+1)(k+2)}{3} + \frac{3(k+1)(k+2)}{3}$$

$$= \frac{(k+1)(k+2)(k+3)}{3}$$

$$= \frac{(k+1)(k+1+1)(k+1+2)}{3}$$

Thus P_{k+1} is true.

34. P_n: $\dfrac{a^5}{a^n} = \dfrac{1}{a^{n-5}}$; $n > 5$

Show true for $n = 6$.

$$\frac{a^5}{a^6} = \frac{1}{a^{6-5}}$$

$$\frac{1}{a} = \frac{1}{a} \quad \text{Thus } P_6 \text{ is true.}$$

Show if P_k is true, then P_{k+1} is true; $n > 6$.

$$P_k: \frac{a^5}{a^k} = \frac{1}{a^{k-5}}$$

$$P_{k+1}: \frac{a^5}{a^{k+1}} = \frac{1}{a^{(k+1)-5}}$$

Start with P_k: $\dfrac{a^5}{a^k} = \dfrac{1}{a^{k-5}}$

$$\frac{a^5}{a^k} \cdot \frac{1}{a} = \frac{1}{a^{k-5}} \cdot \frac{1}{a}$$

$$\frac{a^5}{a^{k+1}} = \frac{1}{a^{k-4}}$$

$$\frac{a^5}{a^{k+1}} = \frac{1}{a^{(k+1)-5}} \Rightarrow P_{k+1} \text{ is true.}$$

36. P_n: $(a^n)^m = a^{mn}$; $m, n \in N$

Show true for P_1: $(a^1)^m = a^{m \cdot 1}$

$$a^m = a^m \quad \text{Thus } P_1 \text{ is true.}$$

Show if P_k is true, then P_{k+1} is true.

$$P_k: (a^k)^m = a^{mk}$$

$$P_{k+1}: (a^{k+1})^m = a^{m(k+1)}$$

Start with P_k: $(a^k)^m = a^{mk}$

$$(a^k)^m \cdot a^m = a^{mk} \cdot a^m$$

$$a^{km} \cdot a^m = a^{mk+m}$$

$$a^{km+m} = a^{m(k+1)}$$

$$a^{(k+1)m} = a^{m(k+1)}$$

$$(a^{k+1})^m = a^{m(k+1)} \Rightarrow P_{k+1} \text{ is true.}$$

38. P_n: $x^n - y^n$ is divisible by $x - y$; $x \ne y$

Show true for P_1: $\dfrac{x^1 - y^1}{x - y} = 1$ Thus P_1 is true.

Show if P_k is true, then P_{k+1} is true.

$$P_k: x^k - y^k = (x - y)[Q_1(x, y)]$$
$$P_{k+1}: x^{k+1} - y^{k+1} = (x - y)[Q_2(x, y)]$$

Start with P_k:
$$
\begin{aligned}
x^k - y^k &= (x - y)[Q_1(x, y)] \\
&= (x - y)[x^k + yQ_2(x, y)] \\
&= x^k(x - y) + y(x - y)[Q_2(x, y)] \\
&= x^k(x - y) + y(x^k - y^k) \\
&= x^{k+1} - x^k y + x^k y - y^{k+1} \\
&= x^{k+1} - y^{k+1} \quad \text{Thus } P_{k+1} \text{ is true.}
\end{aligned}
$$

40. P_n: $x^{2n} - 1$ is divisible by $x + 1$, $x \ne -1$

Show true for P_1: $x^2 - 1 = (x - 1)(x + 1) = (x + 1)[Q(x)]$

Thus P_1 is true.

Show if P_k is true, then P_{k+1} is true.

$$P_k: x^{2k} - 1 = (x + 1)[Q_1(x)]$$
$$P_{k+1}: x^{2(k+1)} - 1 = (x + 1)[Q_2(x)]$$

Consider
$$
\begin{aligned}
x^{2(k+1)} - 1 &= x^{2(k+1)} - x^2 + x^2 - 1 \\
&= x^{2k+2} - x^2 + x^2 - 1 \\
&= x^2(x^{2k} - 1) + (x - 1)(x + 1), \text{ using } P_k \\
&= x^2[(x + 1)[Q_1(x)]] + (x + 1)(x - 1) \\
&= (x + 1)[x^2 Q_1(x) + x - 1] \\
&= (x + 1)Q_2(x) \quad \Rightarrow P_{k+1} \text{ is true.}
\end{aligned}
$$

42. P_n: $\dfrac{1}{1\cdot2\cdot3} + \dfrac{1}{2\cdot3\cdot4} + \dfrac{1}{3\cdot4\cdot5} + \cdots + \dfrac{1}{n(n + 1)(n + 2)} = \dfrac{n(n + 3)}{4(n + 1)(n + 2)}$

Show P_1 is true.

$$\frac{1(1 + 3)}{4(1 + 1)(1 + 2)} = \frac{1(4)}{4(2)(3)} = \frac{1}{1\cdot2\cdot3} \Rightarrow P_n \text{ is true for } n = 1$$

Show if P_k is true, then P_{k+1} is true.

$$P_k: \frac{1}{1\cdot2\cdot3} + \frac{1}{2\cdot3\cdot4} + \frac{1}{3\cdot4\cdot5} + \cdots + \frac{1}{k(k + 1)(k + 2)} = \frac{k(k + 3)}{4(k + 1)(k + 2)}$$

$$P_{k+1}: \frac{1}{1\cdot2\cdot3} + \frac{1}{2\cdot3\cdot4} + \cdots + \frac{1}{k(k + 1)(k + 2)} + \frac{1}{(k + 1)(k + 2)(k + 3)}$$

$$= \frac{(k + 1)(k + 4)}{4(k + 2)(k + 3)}$$

$$\frac{1}{1\cdot2\cdot3} + \frac{1}{2\cdot3\cdot4} + \frac{1}{3\cdot4\cdot5} + \cdots + \frac{1}{k(k + 1)(k + 2)} + \frac{1}{(k + 1)(k + 2)(k + 3)}$$

$$= \frac{k(k + 3)}{4(k + 1)(k + 2)} + \frac{1}{(k + 1)(k + 2)(k + 3)}$$

$$= \frac{1}{(k + 1)(k + 2)} \cdot \left[\frac{k(k + 3)}{4} + \frac{1}{k + 3}\right]$$

$$= \frac{1}{(k+1)(k+2)} \cdot \left[\frac{k(k+3)^2 + 4}{4(k+3)}\right]$$

$$= \frac{1}{(k+1)(k+2)} \cdot \left[\frac{k(k^2 + 6k + 9) + 4}{4(k+3)}\right]$$

$$= \frac{1}{(k+1)(k+2)} \cdot \left[\frac{k^3 + 6k^2 + 9k + 4}{4(k+3)}\right]$$

$$= \frac{1}{(k+1)(k+2)} \cdot \frac{(k+1)^2(k+4)}{4(k+3)}$$

$$= \frac{(k+1)(k+4)}{4(k+2)(k+3)} \Rightarrow P_{k+1} \text{ is true}$$

44. $P_n: \dfrac{1}{1\cdot2} + \dfrac{1}{2\cdot3} + \dfrac{1}{3\cdot4} + \cdots + \dfrac{1}{n(n+1)} = \dfrac{n}{n+1}$

Show P_1 is true.

$$\frac{1}{1+1} = \frac{1}{2} = \frac{1}{1\cdot2} \Rightarrow P_n \text{ is true for } n = 1$$

Show if P_k is true, then P_{k+1} is true.

$$P_k: \frac{1}{1\cdot2} + \frac{1}{2\cdot3} + \frac{1}{3\cdot4} + \cdots + \frac{1}{k(k+1)} = \frac{k}{k+1}$$

$$P_{k+1}: \frac{1}{1\cdot2} + \frac{1}{2\cdot3} + \cdots + \frac{1}{(k+1)(k+2)} = \frac{k+1}{k+2}$$

$$\frac{1}{1\cdot2} + \frac{1}{2\cdot3} + \frac{1}{3\cdot4} + \cdots + \frac{1}{k(k+1)} + \frac{1}{(k+1)(k+2)} = \frac{k}{k+1} + \frac{1}{(k+1)(k+2)}$$

$$= \frac{1}{(k+1)} \cdot \left[k + \frac{1}{k+2}\right]$$

$$= \frac{1}{(k+1)} \cdot \left[\frac{k(k+2) + 1}{k+2}\right]$$

$$= \frac{1}{(k+1)} \cdot \frac{k^2 + 2k + 1}{k+2}$$

$$= \frac{1}{k+1} \cdot \frac{(k+1)^2}{k+2}$$

$$= \frac{k+1}{k+2} \Rightarrow P_{k+1} \text{ is true}$$

46. The number of diagonals in a polygon with n sides.

$P_n: 2 + 3 + 4 + \cdots + (n-2) = \dfrac{n(n-3)}{2}, \ n > 3$

Show P_4 is true.

$$\frac{4(4-3)}{2} = 2 \Rightarrow \text{true for } n = 4$$

Show if P_k is true, then P_{k+1} is true.

$P_k: 2 + 3 + 4 + \cdots + (k-2) = \dfrac{k(k-3)}{2}, \ k > 3$

$$P_{k+1}: 2 + 3 + 4 + \ldots + (k - 2) + (k - 1) = \frac{(k + 1)(k - 2)}{2}, \quad k > 3$$

$$2 + 3 + 4 + \cdots + (k - 2) + (k - 1) = \frac{k(k - 3)}{2} + k - 1$$

$$= \frac{k(k - 3) + 2(k - 1)}{2}$$

$$= \frac{k^2 - 3k + 2k - 2}{2}$$

$$= \frac{k^2 - k - 2}{2}$$

$$= \frac{(k + 1)(k - 2)}{2} \Rightarrow P_{k+1} \text{ is true}$$

48. Prove: $0 < a < 1 \Rightarrow 0 < a^n < 1: P_n \quad (n \in N)$
Show P_1 is true.
$\qquad 0 < a < 1 \Rightarrow 0 < a^1 < 1$, P_n is true for $n = 1$
Show if P_k is true, then P_{k+1} is true.
$\qquad P_k: 0 < a^k < 1$
$\qquad P_{k+1}: 0 < a^{k+1} < a < 1$
Start with P_k: $0 < a^k < 1$
$\qquad 0 < a^k \cdot a < 1 \cdot a$
$\qquad 0 < a^{k+1} < a < 1 \Rightarrow P_{k+1}$ is true

50. $P_n: 2^n > n^2$, $n \geq 5$
Show P_5 is true.
$\qquad 2^5 > 5^2$
$\qquad 32 > 25 \Rightarrow P_5$ is true
Show if P_k is true, then P_{k+1} is true, $k \geq 5$.
$\qquad P_k: 2^k > k^2$, $k \geq 5$
$\qquad P_{k+1}: 2^{k+1} > (k + 1)^2$, $k \geq 5$
Start with P_k:

$2^k > k^2$	* $k \geq 5$
$2 \cdot 2^k > 2k^2$	$k^2 \geq 25$ and $2k \geq 10$
$2^{k+1} > k^2 + k^2$	$k^2 - 2k \geq 15$
$2^{k+1} > k^2 + 2k + 1$ *	$k^2 \geq 2k + 15 > 2k + 1$
$2^{k+1} > (k + 1)^2 \Rightarrow P_{k+1}$ is true.	

52. $n^2 + 21n + 1$, $n \in N$, is prime. Prove or disprove: $n = 18$ gives $18^2 + 21(18) + 1$ $= 703 = 19(37)$, a counterexample.

54. $a_1 = 2$, $a_n = a_{n-1} + 2$; $b_n = 2n$
Show P_1 is true:
$\qquad a_1 = 2 = 2 \cdot 1 = b_1: \{a_n\} = \{b_n\}$ is true for $n = 1$
Assume $a_k = b_k$ and show $a_{k+1} = b_{k+1}$.
$\qquad a_{k+1} = a_k + 2 = b_k + 2 = 2k + 2 = 2(k + 1) = b_{k+1} \Rightarrow \{a_n\} = \{b_n\}$ for all n

56. $a_1 = 2$, $a_n = 3a_{n-1}$; $b_n = 2 \cdot 3^{n-1}$
Show P_1 is true:
$\qquad a_1 = 2 = 2 \cdot 1 = 2 \cdot 3^0 = 2 \cdot 3^{1-1} = b_1 \Rightarrow \{a_n\} = \{b_n\}$ is true for $n = 1$.
Assume $a_k = b_k$ and show $a_{k+1} = b_{k+1}$.
$\qquad a_{k+1} = 3a_k = 3b_k = 3 \cdot (2 \cdot 3^{k-1}) = 2 \cdot 3^k = b_{k+1} \Rightarrow \{a_n\} = \{b_n\}$ for all n.

Exercise 9-3

2. (A) 5, 20, 100, …

Since $\begin{array}{l} 20 - 5 = 15 \\ 100 - 20 = 80 \end{array}$ and $\dfrac{\frac{20}{5} = 4}{\frac{100}{20} = 5}$ the sequence 5, 20, 100, … is neither arithmetic nor geometric.

(B) -5, -5, -5, …

Since -5 - (-5) = 0 and $\dfrac{-5}{-5}$ = 1 the sequence -5, -5, -5, … is arithmetic with $d = 0$, and geometric with $r = 1$. The next two terms are -5, -5 in both cases.

(C) 7, 6.5, 6, …

Since 6.5 - 7 = -0.5 and 6 - 6.5 = -0.5, the sequence is arithmetic with $d = -0.5$. The next two terms are 5.5, 5. Since $\dfrac{6.5}{7}$ = 0.92857… and $\dfrac{6}{6.5}$ = 0.92307… the sequence is not geometric.

(D) 512, 256, 128, …

Since 256 - 512 = -256 and 128 - 256 = -128, the sequence is not arithmetic.

Since $\dfrac{256}{512} = \dfrac{1}{2}$ and $\dfrac{128}{256} = \dfrac{1}{2}$, the sequence is geometric with $r = \dfrac{1}{2}$. The next two terms are 64, 32.

4. $a_1 = -18, \ d = 3$

$a_2 = -18 + 3 = -15$

$a_3 = -15 + 3 = -12$

$a_4 = -12 + 3 = -9$

6. $a_1 = 3, \ d = 4$

$a_n = a_1 + d(n - 1)$

$a_{22} = 3 + 4(21) = 87$

$S_n = \dfrac{n}{2}[2a_1 + (n - 1)d]$

$S_{21} = \dfrac{21}{2}(2(3) + 20(4)) = 903$

8. $a_1 = 5, \ a_2 = 11 \Rightarrow d = 6$

$S_n = \dfrac{n}{2}[2a_1 + (n - 1)d]$

$S_{11} = \dfrac{11}{2}(2(5) + 10(6)) = 385$

10. $a_1 = -3, \ d = -4$

$a_n = a_1 + (n - 1)d$

$a_{10} = -3 + (10 - 1)(-4) = -39$

12. $a_1 = 12, \ r = \dfrac{2}{3}$

$a_n = a_{n-1}r$

$a_2 = 12\left(\dfrac{2}{3}\right) = 8$

$a_3 = 8\left(\dfrac{2}{3}\right) = \dfrac{16}{3}$

$a_4 = \dfrac{16}{3} \cdot \dfrac{2}{3} = \dfrac{32}{9}$

14. $a_1 = 64, \ r = \dfrac{1}{2}$

$a_n = a_1 r^{n-1}$

$a_{13} = 64\left(\dfrac{1}{2}\right)^{12} = \dfrac{1}{64}$

16. $a_1 = 1, \ a_7 = 729, \ r = -3$

$S_n = \dfrac{a_1 - a_1 r^n}{1 - r}$

$S_7 = \dfrac{1 - (1)(-3)^7}{1 - (-3)} = 547$

18. $a_1 = 7, \ a_8 = 28$

$a_n = a_1 + (n - 1)d$

$a_8 = a_1 + 7d$

$28 = 7 + 7d$

$21 = 7d$

$3 = d$

$a_{25} = 7 + 24(3)$

$a_{25} = 79$

20. $a_1 = 24$, $a_{24} = -28$

$a_n = a_1 + (n - 1)d$

$a_{24} = -28 = 24 + (24 - 1)d$

$$d = -\frac{52}{23}$$

$S_n = \frac{n}{2}[2a_1 + (n - 1)d]$

$$S_{24} = \frac{24}{2}\left[2(24) + (24 - 1)\left(-\frac{52}{23}\right)\right]$$

$S_{24} = -48$

22. $a_1 = \frac{1}{6}$, $a_2 = \frac{1}{4}$

$a_1 + d = a_2$

$\frac{1}{6} + d = \frac{1}{4}$

$$d = \frac{1}{12}$$

$a_n = a_1 + (n - 1)d$

$a_{19} = \frac{1}{6} + 18 \cdot \frac{1}{12} = \frac{5}{3}$

$S_n = \frac{n}{2}(a_1 + a_n)$

$S_{19} = \frac{19}{2}\left(\frac{1}{6} + \frac{5}{3}\right) = \frac{19}{2} \cdot \frac{11}{6} = \frac{209}{12}$

24. $a_9 = -12$, $a_{13} = 3$

$a_n = a_1 + (n - 1)d$

$a_9 = a_1 + 8d \Rightarrow (1): -12 = a_1 + 8d$

$a_{13} = a_1 + 12d \Rightarrow (2): 3 = a_1 + 12d$

$(1) - (2): -15 = -4d \Rightarrow d = \frac{15}{4} = 3.75$

$(1): -12 = a_1 + 8\left(\frac{15}{4}\right) \Rightarrow a_1 = -42$

26. $a_1 = 10$, $a_{10} = 30$

$a_n = a_1 r^{n-1}$

$a_{10} = 10r^9$

$30 = 10r^9$

$3 = r^9$

$r = 3^{1/9} \approx 1.13$

28. $a_1 = 3$, $r = 2$

$S_n = \frac{a_1 - a_1 r^n}{1 - r}$

$S_{10} = \frac{3 - 3(2)^{10}}{1 - 2} = 3069$

30. $a_1 = 12$, $a_4 = -\frac{4}{9}$

$a_n = a_1 r^{n-1}$ $\qquad a_n = a_{n-1}r$

$-\frac{4}{9} = 12r^3$ $\qquad a_2 = 12\left(-\frac{1}{3}\right) = -4$

$-\frac{1}{27} = r^3$ $\qquad a_3 = -4\left(-\frac{1}{3}\right) = \frac{4}{3}$

$r = -\frac{1}{3}$

32. $S_{40} = \displaystyle\sum_{k=1}^{40}(2k - 3) \Rightarrow$ arithmetic seq: $a_1 = -1$, $d = 2$

$S_n = \frac{n}{2}[2a_1 + (n - 1)d]$

$S_{40} = \frac{40}{2}[2(-1) + 39(2)] = 1520$

34. $S_7 = \displaystyle\sum_{k=1}^{7} 3k \Rightarrow$ geometric seq: $a_1 = 3$, $r = 3$

$S_n = \frac{a_1 - a_1 r^n}{1 - r}$

$S_7 = \frac{3 - 3(3)^7}{1 - 3} = 3279$

36. $f(x) = 2x - 5$: arithmetic seq: $a_1 = -3$, $d = 2$

$S_n = \frac{n}{2}[2a_1 + (n - 1)d]$

$f(1) + f(2) + f(3) + \cdots + f(20) = S_{20} = \frac{20}{2}[2(-3) + 19(2)] = 320$

38. $f(x) = 2^x$; geometric seq: $a_1 = 2$, $r = 2$

$$S_n = \frac{a_1 - a_1 r^n}{1 - r}$$

$$f(1) + f(2) + \cdots + f(10) = S_{10} = \frac{2 - 2 \cdot 2^{10}}{1 - 2} = 2046$$

40. $S = 101 + 103 + 105 + \cdots + 499 \Rightarrow$ arithmetic seq: $a_1 = 101$, $d = 2$

$a_n = a_1 + (n - 1)d$
$499 = 101 + (n - 1)2$
$398 = 2n - 2$
$400 = 2n \Rightarrow n = 200$

$$S_n = \frac{n}{2}[a_1 + a_n]$$

$$S_{200} = \frac{200}{2}[101 + 499] = 60{,}000$$

42. $2 + 4 + 6 + \cdots + 2n = n + n^2$; arithmetic seq: $a_1 = 2$, $d = 2$

$$S_n = \frac{n}{2}[2a_1 + (n - 1)d]$$

$$= \frac{n}{2}[2(2) + (n - 1)2]$$

$$= \frac{n}{2}[2n + 2]$$

$$= n^2 + n = n + n^2$$

44. $6 + x + 8$; geometric series: $a_1 = 6$, $a_3 = 8$

$a_n = a_1 r^{n-1}$
$a_3 = a_1 r^2$
$8 = 6r^2$ $a_2 = a_1 r$

$$r^2 = \frac{4}{3} \qquad\qquad = 6 \cdot \frac{2\sqrt{3}}{3}$$

$$r = \frac{2}{\sqrt{3}} = \frac{2\sqrt{3}}{3} \qquad = 4\sqrt{3}$$

46. $a_1 = -3$, $a_n = a_{n-1} + 3$, $n > 1$
$d = a_n - a_{n-1} = 3$

$$S_n = \frac{n}{2}[2a_1 + (n - 1)d]$$

$$S_n = \frac{n}{2}[2(-3) + (n - 1)3]$$

$$S_n = \frac{n}{2}[-6 + 3(n - 1)] \quad \text{or} \quad S_n = \frac{3n^2 - 9n}{2}$$

48.

```
WINDOW
 nMin=1
 nMax=15
 PlotStart=1
 PlotStep=1
 Xmin=-1
 Xmax=15
↓Xscl=5
```

```
WINDOW
↑PlotStep=1
 Xmin=-1
 Xmax=15
 Xscl=5
 Ymin=-1
 Ymax=800
 Yscl=100
```

```
Plot1 Plot2 Plot3
 nMin=1
·.u(n)⊟96+47n
 u(nMin)⊟
·.v(n)⊟8*1.5^n
 v(nMin)⊟
·.w(n)=
 w(nMin)=
```

u=96+47n
n=11
X=11   Y=613

v=8*1.5^n
n=11
X=11   Y=691.98047

n	$u(n)$	$v(n)$
8	472	205.03
9	519	307.55
10	566	461.32
11	613	691.98
12	660	1038
13	707	1557
14	754	2335.4

$n=14$

$n = 11$

50.

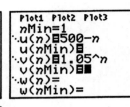
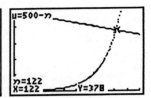

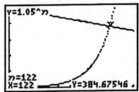

n	$u(n)$	$v(n)$
120	380	348.91
121	379	366.36
122	378	384.68
123	377	403.91
124	376	424.1
125	375	445.31
126	374	467.58
$n=120$		

$n = 122$

52. $16 + 4 + 1 + \cdots$

$a_1 = 16 \qquad S_\infty = \dfrac{a_1}{1 - r}$

$r = \dfrac{1}{4} \qquad\qquad = \dfrac{16}{1 - \frac{1}{4}} = \dfrac{64}{3}$

54. $4 + 6 + 9 + \cdots$

$a_1 = 4$

$r = \dfrac{3}{2} > 1 \Rightarrow$ no sum

56. $21 - 3 + \dfrac{3}{7} - \cdots$

$a_1 = 21 \qquad S_\infty = \dfrac{a_1}{1 - r}$

$r = -\dfrac{1}{7} \qquad\qquad = \dfrac{21}{1 - (-\frac{1}{7})} = \dfrac{147}{8}$

58. $0.\overline{5} = 0.5 + 0.05 + 0.005 + \cdots$

$a_1 = 0.5 \qquad S_\infty = \dfrac{a_1}{1 - r}$

$r = 0.1 \qquad\qquad = \dfrac{0.5}{1 - 0.1} = \dfrac{5}{9}$

60. $0.\overline{27} = 0.27 + 0.0027 + 0.000027 + \cdots$

$a_1 = 0.27 \qquad S_\infty = \dfrac{a_1}{1 - r}$

$r = 0.01 \qquad\qquad = \dfrac{0.27}{1 - 0.01} = \dfrac{3}{11}$

62. $5.\overline{63} = 5 + 0.63 + 0.0063 + \cdots$

$a_1 = 0.63 \qquad\qquad 5 + S_\infty = 5 + \dfrac{a_1}{1 - r}$

$r = 0.01 \qquad\qquad\qquad = 5 + \dfrac{0.63}{1 - 0.01} = 5 + \dfrac{7}{11} = \dfrac{62}{11}$

64. $S_n = a_1 + (a_1 + d) + (a_1 + 2d) + \cdots + (a_1 + (n - 1)d)$

$S_n = \dfrac{n}{2}[2a_1 + (n - 1)d]$

Show S_1 is true.

$S_1 = \dfrac{1}{2}[2a_1 + (1 - 1)d] = a_1 \Rightarrow$ true for $n = 1$

Assume $S_k = \dfrac{k}{2}[2a_1 + (k - 1)d]$ is true.

$S_{k+1} = S_k + a_{k+1} = S_k + a_1 + kd$

$= \dfrac{k}{2}[2a_1 + (k - 1)d] + a_1 + kd$

$= ka_1 + \dfrac{k}{2}(k - 1)d + a_1 + kd$

$= ka_1 + a_1 + \left(\dfrac{k}{2}(k - 1) + k\right)d$

$= (k + 1)a_1 + \left(\dfrac{k(k - 1) + 2k}{2}\right)d$

$= (k + 1)a_1 + \left(\dfrac{k^2 - k + 2k}{2}\right)d$

$= (k + 1)a_1 + \left(\dfrac{k^2 + k}{2}\right)d$

$= (k + 1)a_1 + \dfrac{k(k + 1)}{2}d$

$= \dfrac{k + 1}{2}[2a_1 + kd] \Rightarrow$ true for $k + 1 \Rightarrow$ true for all n.

66. $a_1 = -2$, $a_n = -3a_{n-1}$, $n > 1 \Rightarrow a_1 = -2$, $r = -3$

$S_n = \displaystyle\sum_{k=1}^{n} a_k = \dfrac{a_1 - a_1 r^n}{1 - r} = \dfrac{-2 - (-2)(-3)^n}{1 - (-3)} = \dfrac{(-3)^n - 1}{2}$

68.

$a_n = 2 + (n - 1)5$	$b_n = 2 + (n - 1)3$
$a_1 = 2$	$b_1 = 2$
$a_2 = 7$	$b_2 = 5$
$\vdots$	$\vdots$
$a_{121} = 602$	$b_{121} = 362$

Observe that $b_{121} = 362 = a_{73}$. Note also that $b_{116} = 347 = a_{70}$ which implies that every reduction of n by five from 121 in b_n is equal to the corresponding a_n reduced by 3. Thus every time b_n is reduced by 5 an a_n is produced. b_n can be reduced 24 times $\left(\dfrac{121}{5} = 24.2\right)$ in this manner. Hence, there are $25 = 24 + 1$, ($a_1 = b_1 = 2$ is common) numbers in common.

70. S_n: $a_1 + a_1 r + a_1 r^2 + \cdots + a_1 r^{n-1} = \dfrac{a_1 - a_1 r^n}{1 - r}$

Show true for S_1.

$S_1 = a_1 = a_1 \cdot \dfrac{1 - r}{1 - r} = \dfrac{a_1 - a_1 r^1}{1 - r} \Rightarrow$ true for $n = 1$

Assume $S_k = a_1 + a_1 r + a_1 r^2 + \cdots + a_1 r^{k-1} = \dfrac{a_1 - a_1 r^k}{1 - r}$ is true.

$S_{k+1} = a_1 + a_1 r + a_1 r^2 + \cdots + a_1 r^{k-1} + a_1 r^k$

$$= \frac{a_1 - a_1 r^k}{1 - r} + a_1 r^k$$

$$= \frac{a_1 - a_1 r^k}{1 - r} + \frac{a_1 r^k \cdot (1 - r)}{1 - r}$$

$$= \frac{a_1 - a_1 r^k + a_1 r^k - a_1 r^{k+1}}{1 - r}$$

$$= \frac{a_1 - a_1 r^{k+1}}{1 - r} \Rightarrow S_{k+1} \text{ is true}$$

72. $a_1 + a_4 = 2 \Rightarrow a_1 = 2 - a_4$

$(a_1)^2 + (a_4)^2 = 20 \Rightarrow (2 - (a_4)^2) + (a_4)^2 = 20$

$\qquad (a_4)^2 - 2a_4 - 8 = 0$

$\qquad (a_4 - 4)(a_4 + 2) = 0$

I. $a_4 = 4$

$a_1 = 2 - a_4 = -2$

$a_4 = a_1 + 3d$

$4 = -2 + 3d$

$d = 2$

$S_8 = \frac{8}{2}[2(-2) + 7(2)]$

$\quad = 40$

II. $a_4 = -2$

$a_1 = 2 - a_4 = 4$

$a_4 = a_1 + 3d$

$-2 = 4 + 3d$

$d = -2$

$S_8 = \frac{8}{2}[2(4) + 7(-2)]$

$\quad = -24$

74. <u>Firm A</u>

$a_1 = 25,000$

$d = 1200$

$a_{10} = 25,000 + 9(1200)$

$a_{10} = \$35,800$

<u>Firm B</u>

$a_1 = 28,000$

$d = 800$

$a_{10} = 28,000 + 9(800)$

$a_{10} = \$35,200$

76. $S_\infty = \dfrac{a_1}{1 - r}$

$600(0.7) + 600(0.7)^2 + \cdots = \dfrac{600(0.7)}{1 - 0.7} = \$1400$

78. <u>time</u>   <u>population</u>

1     $A_0 + rA_0 = A_0(1 + r)$

2     $A_0(1 + r) + A_0(1 + r)r = A_0(1 + r)(1 + r) = A_0(1 + r)^2$

$\vdots$

t $A_0(1 + r)^t$

If $r = 2\%$:

$A_0(1 + r)^t = 2A_0$

$(1 + 0.02)^t = 2$

$t = \dfrac{\ln 2}{\ln 1.02} \approx 35 \text{ years}$

80. (A) arithmetic sequence   (B) $T_n = 80 + (n)(-5)$

82. $10 + 10(0.9) + 10(0.9)^2 + \cdots$

$S_\infty = \dfrac{a_1}{1 - r}$

$\quad = \dfrac{10}{1 - 0.9} = 100 \text{ in}$

84. $\dfrac{600}{30}$ = 20 generations

direct ancestors = 2^{20} = 1,048,576

86.

$\underline{n}$	$\underline{s}$	
1	16 = 16·1	1, 3, 5, ⋯, a_n, ⋯
2	48 = 16·3	$a_n = 1 + (n - 1)2$
3	80 = 16·5	

⋮

20   (A) $d = 16 \cdot a_{20} = 16(1 + 19(2)) = 624$ feet

⋮

t (B) $d = 16 \cdot a_t = 16(1 + (t - 1)2) = 16(2t + 1 - 2) = 32t - 16$

88.

cells after t days = 2^{2t} = 1,000,000,000

$\qquad\qquad\qquad \ln 2^{2t} = \ln 1{,}000{,}000{,}000$

$\qquad\qquad\quad 2t \ln 2 = \ln 1{,}000{,}000{,}000$

$\qquad\qquad\qquad\quad t = \dfrac{\ln 1{,}000{,}000{,}000}{2 \ln 2}$

$\qquad\qquad\qquad\quad t \approx 14.95$ days

The mouse dies on the 15th day (discrete model; round up).

90. (A) $a_1 = 400$, $a_{12} = 800$ $\qquad$ (B) Find a_4: $a_4 = a_1 r^3$

$\qquad\quad a_n = a_1 r^{n-1}$ $\qquad\qquad\qquad\qquad\qquad = 400(1.065)^3$

$\qquad 800 = 400 r^{11}$ $\qquad\qquad\qquad\qquad\qquad \approx 483$ cps

$\qquad\quad 2 = r^{11}$

$\qquad\quad r \approx 1.065$

92. If $a_1 = 0.001$, $r = 2$, find a_{33}:

$\qquad a_n = a_1 r^{n-1}$

$\qquad a_{33} = 0.001(2)^{32}$ in $\times \dfrac{1 \text{ ft}}{12 \text{ in}} \times \dfrac{1 \text{ mi}}{5280 \text{ ft}}$

$\qquad\qquad \approx 68$ miles

If $a_1 = 0.002$, $r = 2$, find a_{32}:

$\qquad a_n = a_1 r^{n-1}$

$\qquad a_{32} = 0.002(2)^{31}$ in $\times \dfrac{1 \text{ ft}}{12 \text{ in}} \times \dfrac{1 \text{ mi}}{5280 \text{ ft}}$

$\qquad\qquad \approx 68$ miles

94. $a_1 = \dfrac{220}{440}$, $a_2 = \dfrac{110}{440}$, $a_3 = \dfrac{55}{440}$, ⋯ $\quad r = \dfrac{1}{2}$

$\quad S_\infty = \dfrac{a_1}{1 - r}$

$\qquad = \dfrac{\frac{220}{440}}{1 - \frac{1}{2}} = \dfrac{\frac{1}{2}}{1 - \frac{1}{2}} \cdot \dfrac{2}{2} = \dfrac{1}{1} = 1$ min

96. shutter speeds: 1, $\dfrac{1}{2}$, $\dfrac{1}{4}$, $\dfrac{1}{8}$, ⋯ $\qquad r = \dfrac{1}{2}$

$\qquad\quad$ f-stops: 1.4, 2, 2.8, 4, ⋯ $\quad r = 1.42857\ldots \approx 1.4$

Exercise 9-4

2. $10! = 10 \cdot 9 \cdot 8 \cdot \ldots \cdot 1 = 3,628,800$ **4.** $12! = 12 \cdot 11 \cdot 10 \cdot \ldots \cdot 1 = 479,001,600$

6. $\dfrac{14!}{12!} = \dfrac{14 \cdot 13 \cdot 12!}{12!}$ **8.** $\dfrac{6!}{4!2!} = \dfrac{6 \cdot 5 \cdot 4!}{2 \cdot 4!}$ **10.** $\dfrac{8!}{3!(8-3)!} = \dfrac{8!}{3!5!}$

$\qquad = 182$ $\qquad\qquad\qquad\qquad = 15$ $\qquad\qquad\qquad\qquad\quad = \dfrac{8 \cdot 7 \cdot 6 \cdot 5!}{6 \cdot 5!}$

$\qquad\qquad\qquad\qquad\qquad\qquad\qquad\qquad\qquad\qquad\qquad\qquad\qquad = 56$

12. $\dfrac{8!}{0!(8-0)!} = \dfrac{8!}{1 \cdot 8!}$ **14.** $P_{4,2} = \dfrac{4!}{(4-2)!} = \dfrac{4!}{2!} = \dfrac{4 \cdot 3 \cdot 2!}{2!} = 12$

$\qquad\qquad\quad = 1$

16. $P_{52,2} = \dfrac{52!}{(52-2)!} = \dfrac{52!}{50!} = \dfrac{52 \cdot 51 \cdot 50!}{50!} = 2652$

18. $C_{4,2} = \dfrac{4!}{2!2!} = \dfrac{24}{4} = 6$ **20.** $C_{52,2} = \dfrac{52!}{2!50!} = \dfrac{2652}{2} = 1326$

22. (A) Renting 4 videos would be a combination since they are chosen in any order.
(B) Buying 4 videos for 4 different people would be a permutation since if you mix up how they are given out, the results differ.

24. $3 \cdot 5 \cdot 2 = 30$

26. $P_{50,5} = \dfrac{50!}{(50-5)!} = \dfrac{50 \cdot 49 \cdot 48 \cdot 47 \cdot 46 \cdot 45!}{45!} = 254,251,200$

28. (A) $P_{9,3} = \dfrac{9!}{6!} = 504$ (B) $C_{9,3} = \dfrac{9!}{3!6!} = 84$ **30.** $C_{7,2} = = \dfrac{7!}{2!5!} = 21$

32. $P_{7,5} = \dfrac{7!}{2!} = 2520$ with no digit repeated
$7 \cdot 7 \cdot 7 \cdot 7 \cdot 7 = 7^5 = 16,807$ with repeated digits

34. $P_{10,3} = \dfrac{10!}{7!} = 720$ with no digit repeated
$10 \cdot 10 \cdot 10 = 10^3 = 1000$ with repeated digits

36. $C_{12,5} = \dfrac{12!}{5!7!} = 792$ with all face cards

$C_{8,5} = \dfrac{8!}{5!3!} = 56$ with only jacks and queens

38. $10 \cdot 10 \cdot 10 \cdot 10 \cdot 10 = 10^5 = 100,000$ possible 5 digit zip codes
$P_{10,5} = \dfrac{10!}{5!} = 30,240$ contain no repeated digits

40. $C_{13,2} \cdot C_{13,3} = \dfrac{13!}{2!11!} \cdot \dfrac{13!}{3!10!} = 22,308$

42. $P_{12,2} \cdot P_{15,2} \cdot P_{18,2} = \dfrac{12!}{10!} \cdot \dfrac{15!}{13!} \cdot \dfrac{18!}{16!} = 8,482,320$

44. (A) As the tables show, they are equal.

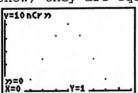

n	$u(n)$	$v(n)$
0	1	1
1	10	10
2	45	45
3	120	120
4	210	210
5	252	252
6	210	210

$n=0$

n	$u(n)$	$v(n)$
4	210	210
5	252	252
6	210	210
7	120	120
8	45	45
9	10	10
10	1	1

$n=10$

$$\frac{P_{10,n}}{n!} = \frac{10!}{(10-n)!\,n!} = C_{10,n}$$

(B) As the graphs show, they are equal.

u=(10 nPr n)/n!   v=10 nCr n

n=0   n=0
X=0   Y=1   X=0   Y=1

46. $6 \cdot 5 = 30$

48. (A) $C_{5,2} = \dfrac{5!}{2!3!} = 10$ (B) $C_{5,3} = \dfrac{5!}{3!2!} = 10$ **50.** $2 \cdot 5!5! = 28,800$

52. (A) $C_{9,4} = \dfrac{9!}{4!5!} = 126$ (B) $C_{7,2} = \dfrac{7!}{2!5!} = 21$ (C) $2C_{7,3} = \dfrac{2 \cdot 7!}{3!4!} = 70$

54. There are $C_{26,10} = 5,311,735$ hands whose cards are all red and $C_{48,6} = 12,271,512$ hands containing all four aces, so the hand with four aces is more likely.

Exercise 9-5

2. $P(E) = 0 \Rightarrow E$ is an impossible event, it cannot happen.

4. $P(\text{not Blue}) = P(R) + P(G) + P(Y)$
$= 0.26 + 0.14 + 0.30$
$= 0.7$

6. $P(\text{not } R \text{ or not } Y) = P(G) + P(B) = 0.14 + 0.30 = 0.44$

8. $P(E) = \dfrac{f(E)}{n} = \dfrac{560}{4000} = 0.14$ **10.** $P(E) = \dfrac{f(E)}{n} = \dfrac{2400}{3000} = 0.8$

12. $\dfrac{1}{P_{10,5}} = \dfrac{1}{30,240} \approx 0.000033$ **14.** $\dfrac{C_{13,5}}{C_{52,5}} = \dfrac{1287}{2,598,960} \approx 0.000495$

16. $\dfrac{C_{40,5}}{C_{52,5}} = \dfrac{658,008}{2,598,960} \approx 0.25$ **18.** $\dfrac{4^4}{6^4} = \dfrac{256}{1296} \approx 0.198$

20. $\dfrac{1}{P_{6,6}} = \dfrac{1}{6!} = \dfrac{1}{720} \approx 0.00139$ **22.** $E = $ sum of 10
$n(E): \{(6, 4), (5, 5), (4, 6)\}$
$P(E) = \dfrac{n(E)}{n(S)} = \dfrac{3}{36} = \dfrac{1}{12}$

24. $E = $ sum of 8
$n(E): \{(6, 2), (5, 3), (4, 4), (3, 5), (2, 6)\}$
$P(E) = \dfrac{n(E)}{n(S)} = \dfrac{5}{36}$

26. $E = $ sum greater than 8
$n(E): \{(6, 3), (5, 4), (4, 5), (3, 6), (6, 4), (5, 5), (4, 6), (6, 5), (5, 6), (6, 6)\}$
$P(E) = \dfrac{n(E)}{n(S)} = \dfrac{10}{36} = \dfrac{5}{18}$

28. $E = $ sum is not 2, 4, 6
$n(E) = 27$
$P(E) = \dfrac{n(E)}{n(S)} = \dfrac{27}{36} = \dfrac{3}{4}$

30. $E = $ sum is not 13
No dice have a sum of 13 so $n(E) = 36$.
$P(E) = \dfrac{n(E)}{n(S)} = \dfrac{36}{36} = 1$

32. E = sum is divisible by 4
$n(E)$: {(3, 1), (2, 2), (1, 3), (6, 2), (5, 3), (4, 4), (3, 5), (2, 6), (6, 6)}
$$P(E) = \frac{n(E)}{n(S)} = \frac{9}{36} = \frac{1}{4}$$

34. E = sum is 2, 3, 12
$n(E)$: {(1, 1), (2, 1), (1, 2), (6, 6)}
$$P(E) = \frac{n(E)}{n(S)} = \frac{4}{36} = \frac{1}{9}$$

36. E = sum divisible by 2 and 3
$n(E)$: {(5, 1), (4, 2), (3, 3), (2, 4), (1, 5), (6, 6)}
$$P(E) = \frac{n(E)}{n(S)} = \frac{6}{36} = \frac{1}{6}$$

38. $S = \{C_1, C_2, C_3\}$ where C_i represents candidate i
$$P(C_1) = P(C_2) = \frac{2}{5}$$
$$P(C_3) = \frac{1}{5}$$

40. (A) $P(E) = \dfrac{f(E)}{n}$

$P(3\text{ heads}) = \dfrac{58}{500} = 0.116$

$P(2\text{ heads}) = \dfrac{198}{500} = 0.396$

$P(1\text{ head}) = \dfrac{190}{500} = 0.38$

$P(0\text{ heads}) = \dfrac{54}{500} = 0.108$

(B) S = {(H, H, H), (H, H, T), (H, T, T), (H, T, H), (T, H, H), (T, H, T), (T, T, H), (T, T, T)}

$P(3\text{ heads}) = \dfrac{1}{8} = 0.125$

$P(2\text{ heads}) = \dfrac{3}{8} = 0.375$

$P(1\text{ head}) = \dfrac{3}{8} = 0.375$

$P(0\text{ heads}) = \dfrac{1}{8} = 0.125$

(C) Expected frequencies: $n \cdot P(E)$

$E(3\text{ heads}) = 500\left(\dfrac{1}{8}\right) = 62.5$

$E(2\text{ heads}) = 500\left(\dfrac{3}{8}\right) = 187.5$

$E(1\text{ head}) = 500\left(\dfrac{3}{8}\right) = 187.5$

$E(0\text{ heads}) = 500\left(\dfrac{1}{8}\right) = 62.5$

(D) Let 0 represent tails and 1 represent heads, then a random sequence of 0's and 1's can be used to represent repeated tosses of one coin. Answers may vary. See the discussion following example 7.

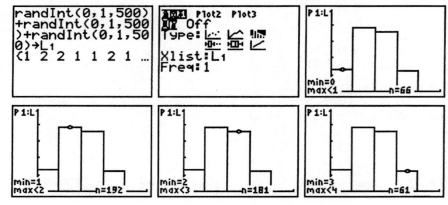

42. (A) $P(E) = \frac{1}{36} \approx 0.028$; in 12 rolls, $P(E) = \frac{12}{432}$. In order to get 9 double sixes

in 12 rolls, the probability would need to be $\frac{3}{4}$, so it is not very likely.

(B) $\frac{14}{40} = 0.35$ is far greater than 0.028. It would appear that the dice were

loaded. The empirical probability for $P(12) = \frac{14}{40} = 0.35$.

$\left(\text{The expected frequency for non-loaded dice would be } 40\left(\frac{1}{36}\right) = \frac{10}{9}.\right)$

Sample space for 44 - 48:
$\{(H, H, H), (H, T, H), (T, T, H), (T, H, H)\}$

44. $P(E) = \frac{n(E)}{n(S)} = \frac{2}{4} = \frac{1}{2}$, E = 2 heads

46. $P(E) = \frac{n(E)}{n(S)} = \frac{0}{4} = 0$, E = 0 heads(there is always 1 H)

48. $P(E) = \frac{n(E)}{n(S)} = \frac{1}{4}$, E = more than 1(= 2) tails

Sample space for 50 - 56:
$\{(1, 1), (1, 1), (1, 2), (1, 2), (1, 3), (1, 3), (2, 1), (2, 1), (2, 2), (2, 2),$
$(2, 3), (2, 3), (3, 1), (3, 1), (3, 2), (3, 2), (3, 3), (3, 3)\}$

50. $P(E) = \frac{n(E)}{n(S)} = \frac{4}{18} = \frac{2}{9}$, E = sum of 3   **52.** $P(E) = \frac{n(E)}{n(S)} = \frac{4}{18} = \frac{2}{9}$, E = sum of 5

54. $P(E) = \frac{n(E)}{n(S)} = \frac{0}{18} = 0$, E = sum of 7   **56.** $P(E) = \frac{n(E)}{n(S)} = \frac{10}{18} = \frac{5}{9}$, E = even sum

58. $\frac{C_{36,5}}{C_{52,5}} = \frac{376,992}{2,598,960} \approx 0.145$ **60.** $\frac{(13)(48)}{C_{52,5}} = \frac{624}{2,598,960} \approx 0.00024$

62. $\frac{4}{C_{52,5}} = \frac{4}{2,598,960} \approx 0.0000015$ **64.** $\frac{C_{4,2} \cdot C_{4,3}}{C_{52,5}} = \frac{(6)(4)}{2,598,960} \approx 0.000009$

66. (A) $\frac{10}{1000} = 0.01$

(B) $\frac{15 + 1 + 80 + 12}{1000} = \frac{108}{1000} = 0.108$

(C) $\frac{0 + 40 + 51 + 11 + 0 + 0 + 70 + 80 + 15 + 1 + 130 + 80 + 28}{1000} = \frac{506}{1000} = 0.506$

(D) $\frac{1000 - (1 + 12 + 21 + 20)}{1000} = \frac{946}{1000} = 0.946$

Exercise 9-6

2. $\binom{6}{4}$. Using program Pascal for 7 lines, the 5th element is 15.
To check: 6 nCr 4 = 15

4. $\binom{7}{5}$. Using program Pascal for 8 lines, the 6th element is 21.
To check: 7 nCr 5 = 21

6. $C_{5,3} = \begin{pmatrix} 5 \\ 3 \end{pmatrix}$. Using program Pascal for 6 lines, the 4th element is 10.

8. $C_{4,3} = \begin{pmatrix} 4 \\ 3 \end{pmatrix}$. Using program Pascal for 5 lines, the 4th element is 4.

10. $\begin{pmatrix} 10 \\ 6 \end{pmatrix}$ = 10 nCr 6 = 210

12. $\begin{pmatrix} 13 \\ 8 \end{pmatrix}$ = 13 nCr 8 = 1287

14. $\begin{pmatrix} 20 \\ 16 \end{pmatrix}$ = 20 nCr 16 = 4845

16. $\begin{pmatrix} 50 \\ 45 \end{pmatrix}$ = 50 nCr 45 = 2,118,760

18. $(x + 2)^3 = x^3 + \dfrac{3!}{2!1!}x^2 \cdot 2 + \dfrac{3!}{1!2!}x \cdot 2^2 + 2^3$

$\qquad = x^3 + 6x^2 + 12x + 8$

20. $(3u + 2v)^3 = (3u)^3 + \dfrac{3!}{2!1!}(3u)^2(2v) + \dfrac{3!}{1!2!}(3u)(2v)^2 + (2v)^3$

$\qquad = 27u^3 + 54u^2v + 36uv^2 + 8v^3$

22. $(x - y)^4 = x^4 + \dfrac{4!}{3!1!}x^3(-y) + \dfrac{4!}{2!2!}x^2(-y)^2 + \dfrac{4!}{1!3!}x(-y)^3 + (-y)^4$

$\qquad = x^4 - 4x^3y + 6x^2y^2 - 4xy^3 + y^4$

24. $(3p - q)^4 = (3p)^4 + \dfrac{4!}{3!1!}(3p)^3(-q) + \dfrac{4!}{2!2!}(3p)^2(-q)^2 + \dfrac{4!}{1!3!}(3p)(-q)^3 + (-q)^4$

$\qquad = 81p^4 - 108p^3q + 54p^2q^2 - 12pq^3 + q^4$

26. $(2x - 1)^5 = (2x)^5 + \dfrac{5!}{4!1!}(2x)^4(-1) + \dfrac{5!}{3!2!}(2x)^3(-1)^2 + \dfrac{5!}{2!3!}(2x)^2(-1)^3$

$\qquad\qquad + \dfrac{5!}{1!4!}(2x)(-1)^4 + (-1)^5$

$\qquad = 32x^5 - 80x^4 + 80x^3 - 40x^2 + 10x - 1$

28. $(2x - y)^6 = (2x)^6 + \dfrac{6!}{5!1!}(2x)^5(-y) + \dfrac{6!}{4!2!}(2x)^4(-y)^2 + \dfrac{6!}{3!3!}(2x)^3(-y)^3$

$\qquad\qquad + \dfrac{6!}{2!4!}(2x)^2(-y)^4 + \dfrac{6!}{1!5!}(2x)^1(-y)^5 + (-y)^6$

$\qquad = 64x^6 - 192x^5y + 240x^4y^2 - 160x^3y^3 + 60x^2y^4 - 12xy^5 + y^6$

30. $(x + 1)^8$; x^5

In the expansion $(x + 1)^8 = \displaystyle\sum_{k=0}^{8} \begin{pmatrix} 8 \\ k \end{pmatrix} x^{8-k} \cdot 1^k$, the exponent of x is 5 when $k = 3$.

Thus, the term containing x^5 is

$\qquad \begin{pmatrix} 8 \\ 3 \end{pmatrix} x^5 \cdot 1^3 = 56x^5$

32. $(3x + 1)^{12}$; x^7

In the expansion $(3x + 1)^{12} = \sum\limits_{k=0}^{12} \binom{12}{k}(3x)^{12-k} \cdot 1^k$, the exponent of x is 7 when $k = 5$. Thus, the term containing x^7 is

$$\binom{12}{5}(3x)^7 \cdot 1^5 = 792 \cdot 2187x^7 = 1,732,104x^7$$

34. $(3x - 2)^{17}$; x^5

In the expansion $(3x - 2)^{17} = \sum\limits_{k=0}^{17} \binom{17}{k}(3x)^{17-k} \cdot (-2)^k$, the exponent of x is 5 when $k = 12$. Thus, the term containing x^5 is

$$\binom{17}{12}(3x)^5(-2)^{12} = (6188)(243)(4096)x^5 = 6,159,089,664x^5$$

36. $(x^2 - 1)^9$; x^7

Since all terms contain $(x^2)^n = x^{2n}$, the expansion cannot have a term with x^7.

38. $(x^2 + 1)^{10}$; x^{14}

In the expansion $(x^2 + 1)^{10} = \sum\limits_{k=0}^{10} \binom{10}{k}(x^2)^{10-k}(1)^k$, the exponent of x is 14 when $(x^2)^7$, so $k = 3$. Thus, the term containing x^{14} is

$$\binom{10}{3}(x^2)^7(1)^3 = 120x^{14}$$

40. $(a + b)^{12}$: fifth term $= \binom{12}{4}a^8b^4 = 495a^8b^4$

42. $(x + 2y)^{20}$: third term $= \binom{20}{2}x^{18}(2y)^2$
$$= 760x^{18}y^2$$

44. $(x - 3)^{10}$: fourth term $= \binom{10}{3}(x^7)(-3)^3$
$$= -3240x^7$$

46. $(2p - 3q)^7$: fourth term $= \binom{7}{3}(2p)^4(-3q)^3$
$$= -15,120p^4q^3$$

48. $f(x) = x^4$
$$\frac{f(x + h) - f(x)}{h} = \frac{(x + h)^4 - x^4}{h}$$
$$= \frac{(x^4 + \binom{4}{1}x^3h + \binom{4}{2}x^2h^2 + \binom{4}{3}xh^3 + h^4) - x^4}{h}$$
$$= \frac{(x^4 + 4x^3h + 6x^2h^2 + 4xh^3 + h^4) - x^4}{h}$$
$$= \frac{4x^3h + 6x^2h^2 + 4xh^3 + h^4}{h}$$
$$= 4x^3 + 6x^2h + 4xh^2 + h^3$$

As $h \to 0$, $4x^3 + 6x^2h + 4xh^2 + h^3 \to 4x^3$

50. $f(x) = x^6$

$$\frac{f(x+h) - f(x)}{h} = \frac{(x+h)^6 - x^6}{h}$$

$$= \frac{\left(x^6 + \binom{6}{1}x^5h + \binom{6}{2}x^4h^2 + \binom{6}{3}x^3h^3 + \binom{6}{4}x^2h^4 + \binom{6}{5}xh^5 + h^6\right) - x^6}{h}$$

$$= \frac{(x^6 + 6x^5h + 15x^4h^2 + 20x^3h^3 + 15x^2h^4 + 6xh^5 + h^6) - x^6}{h}$$

$$= \frac{6x^5h + 15x^4h^2 + 20x^3h^3 + 15x^2h^4 + 6xh^5 + h^6}{h}$$

$$= 6x^5 + 15x^4h + 20x^3h^2 + 15x^2h^3 + 6xh^4 + h^5$$

As $h \to 0$, $6x^5 + 15x^4h + 20x^3h^2 + 15x^2h^3 + 6xh^4 + h^5 \to 6x^5$

52.

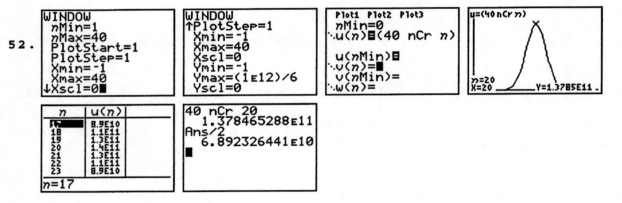

As both the graph and table show, $\binom{40}{20} = 1.378465288 \times 10^{11}$ is the largest term and one half of this largest term is $6.892326441 \times 10^{10}$. An examination of the table shows $\binom{40}{17}$ through $\binom{40}{23}$, a total of 7 terms, have values larger than one half the largest term.

54. (A)

k	$\binom{10}{k} \cdot (0.3)^{10-k} \cdot (0.7)^k$
0	5.9049×10^{-6}
1	1.37781×10^{-4}
2	0.0014467005
3	0.009001692
4	0.036756909
5	0.1029193452
6	0.200120949
7	0.266827932 ← largest
8	0.2334744405
9	0.121060821
10	0.0282475249
	1.000000000

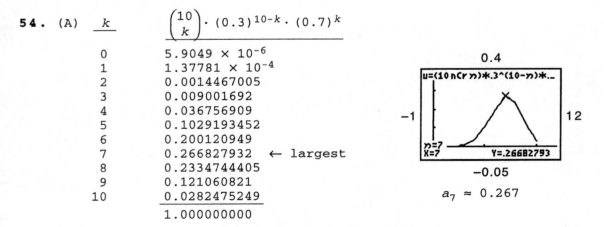

$a_7 \approx 0.267$

(B) According to the binomial formula, the sum of $a_0 + a_1 + a_2 + \ldots + a_{10} = 1$.

56. $(0.99)^6 = (1 - 0.01)^6$

$$= 1^6 + \frac{6!}{5!1!}(1)^5(-0.01) + \frac{6!}{4!2!}(1)^4(-0.01)^2 + \frac{6!}{3!3!}(1)^3(-0.01)^3$$

$$+ \frac{6!}{2!4!}(1)^2(-0.01)^4 + \frac{6!}{1!5!}(1)(-0.01)^5 + (-0.01)^6$$

$$= 1 - 0.06 + 0.0015 - 0.00002 + 0.00000015 - 0.0000000006$$
$$+ 0.000000000001$$

$$\approx 0.9414801494$$

$$= 0.9415 \text{ to four decimal places}$$

58. $\binom{n}{0} = \frac{n!}{0!(n-0)!} = \frac{n!}{n!} = 1$

$\binom{n}{n} = \frac{n!}{n!(n-n)!} = \frac{n!}{n!0!} = 1$

60. $\binom{k}{0} = \frac{k!}{0!(k-0)!} = \frac{k!}{k!} = 1$

$\binom{k+1}{0} = \frac{(k+1)!}{0!(k+1-0)!} = \frac{(k+1)!}{(k+1)!} = 1$

62. $\dfrac{n-r+1}{r}\dbinom{n}{r-1} = \dfrac{n-r+1}{r} \cdot \dfrac{n!}{(r-1)!(n-(r-1))!}$

$$= \frac{n-r+1}{r(r-1)!} \cdot \frac{n!}{(n-r+1)!}$$

$$= \frac{n-r+1}{r!} \cdot \frac{n!}{(n-r+1)(n-r)!}$$

$$= \frac{n!}{r!(n-r)!}$$

$$= \binom{n}{r}$$

CHAPTER 10

Exercise 10-1

2. $y^2 = 8x = 4(2)x$
opens right
Vertex $(0, 0)$; $a = 2$

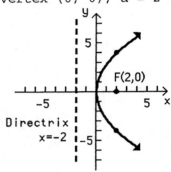

4. $x^2 = 4y = 4(1)y$
opens up
Vertex $(0, 0)$; $a = 1$

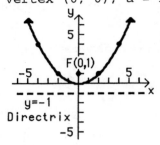

6. $y^2 = -4x = 4(-1)x$
opens left
Vertex $(0, 0)$; $a = -1$

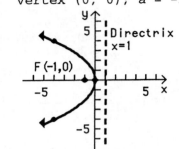

8. $x^2 = -8y = 4(-2)y$
opens down
Vertex $(0, 0)$; $a = -2$

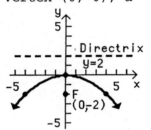

10. $x^2 = -24y = 4(-6)y$
opens down
Vertex $(0, 0)$; $a = -6$

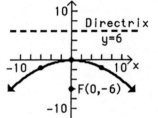

12. $y^2 = 6x = 4(1.5)x$
opens right
Vertex $(0, 0)$; $a = 1.5$

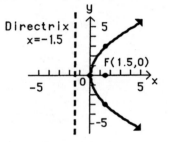

14. $x^2 = 58y$
$4a = 58$
$a = 14.5$; opens up
$F(0, 14.5)$

16. $y^2 = -93x$
$4a = -93$
$a = -23.25$; opens left
$F(-23.25, 0)$

18. $x^2 = -205y$
$4a = -205$
$a = -51.25$; opens down
$F(0, -51.25)$

20. Directrix: $y = 4$
$a = -4$; $x^2 = 4ay$
$x^2 = -16y$

22. Focus $(0, 5)$
$a = 5$; $x^2 = 4ay$
$4a = 20$
$x^2 = 20y$

24. Directrix: $x = -9$
$a = 9$; $y^2 = 4ax$
$4a = 36$
$y^2 = 36x$

26. Focus $(-4, 0)$
$a = -4$; $y^2 = 4ax$
$4a = -16 \Rightarrow y^2 = -16x$

28. x axis; through $(4, 8)$
$y^2 = 4ax$
$8^2 = 4a(4)$
$a = 4 \Rightarrow y^2 = 16x$

30. y axis;
through $(-5, 10)$
$x^2 = 4ay$
$(-5)^2 = 4a(10)$
$4a = 2.5 \Rightarrow x^2 = 2.5y$

32. $y^2 = 4ax$
$(-12)^2 = 4a(-6)$
$4p = -24 \Rightarrow y^2 = -24x$

34. (A) $y^2 = 3x \Rightarrow x = \dfrac{y^2}{3}$
$x^2 = 3y$
$\left(\dfrac{y^2}{3}\right)^2 = 3y$
$y^4 = 27y$
$y^4 - 27y = 0$
$y(y^3 - 27) = 0$
$y = 0 \qquad y = 3$
$x = 0 \qquad x = 3$

(B)

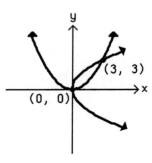

36. (A) $x^2 = 7y \Rightarrow y = \dfrac{x^2}{7}$

$y^2 = 2x$

$\left(\dfrac{x^2}{7}\right)^2 = 2x$

$x^4 = 98x$

$x(x^3 - 98) = 0$

$x = 0, \quad x = \sqrt[3]{98} \approx 4.610$

$y = 0, \quad y \approx 3.037$

(B)

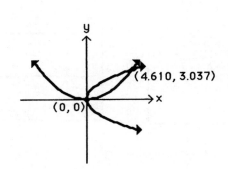

38. $x^2 = 4ay \qquad x^4 = 16a^2y^2$

$y^2 = 4bx \qquad x^4 = 16a^2 \cdot 4bx$

$x^4 - 16a^2 \cdot 4bx = 0$

$x(x^3 - 64a^2b) = 0$

$x = 0 \qquad\qquad x^3 = 64a^2b$

$x = 4\sqrt[3]{a^2b}$

$x = 0 \Rightarrow y = 0 \qquad x^2 = 16(a^{2/3})^2 (b^{1/3})^2$

$x^2 = 16a^{4/3}b^{2/3}$

$\dfrac{x^2}{4a} = y = \dfrac{16a^{4/3}b^{2/3}}{4a}$

$y = 4a^{1/3}b^{2/3} = 4\sqrt[3]{ab^2}$

Intersections at:

$(0, 0), \ (4\sqrt[3]{a^2b}, \ 4\sqrt[3]{ab^2})$

40. The x-coordinates of A and B are a. The y-coordinates may be found from
$y^2 = 4a(a) = 4a^2 \Rightarrow y = \pm 2a$, thus $A(a, -2a)$, $B(a, 2a)$.

42. $(x_2 - x_1)^2 + (y_2 - y_1)^2 = d^2$
Directrix $y = 2$; focus $(-3, 6)$
$(x - (-3))^2 + (y - 6)^2 = (y - 2)^2$
$x^2 + 6x + 9 + y^2 - 12y + 36 = y^2 - 4y + 4$
$x^2 + 6x - 8y + 41 = 0$

44. $(x_2 - x_1)^2 + (y_2 - y_1)^2 = d^2$
Directrix $x = -3$; focus $(1, 4)$
$(x - 1)^2 + (y - 4)^2 = (x - (-3))^2$
$x^2 - 2x + 1 + y^2 - 8y + 16 = x^2 + 6x + 9$
$y^2 - 8y - 8x + 8 = 0$

46.

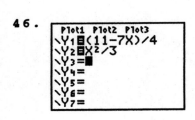

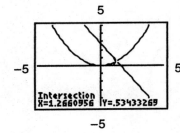

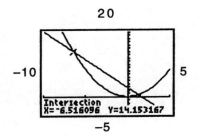

Intersection: $(1.27, 0.53)$, $(-6.52, 14.15)$

48.

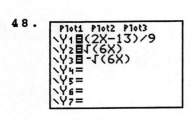

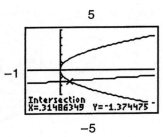

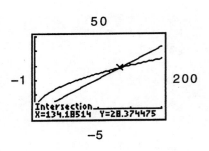

Intersection: (0.31, -1.37), (134.19, 28.37)

50. (A) $x^2 = 4ay$
$3^2 = 4a(0.15)$
$4a = 60$
$x^2 = 60y$

(B) $4a = 60$
$a = 15$ inches

52. (A) $y^2 = 4ax$
$y^2 = 4(1.5)x$
$y^2 = 6x, \ 0 \le x \le 6$

(B) $(x, 6) \Rightarrow 6^2 = 6x \Rightarrow x = 6$
$(6, 6)$
depth = 6 inches

Exercise 10-2

2. $\dfrac{x^2}{9} + \dfrac{y^2}{4} = 1$ $a^2 = b^2 + c^2$
$9 = 4 + c^2$
$c = \pm\sqrt{5}$

$F(\sqrt{5}, 0); \ F'(-\sqrt{5}, 0)$
major axis length = 6
minor axis length = 4

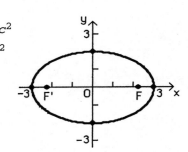

To check this graph:
$4x^2 + 9y^2 = 36$
$9y^2 = 36 - 4x^2$
$y^2 = 4 - \dfrac{4}{9}x^2$

$y = \pm\sqrt{4 - \dfrac{4}{9}x^2}$

4. $\dfrac{x^2}{4} + \dfrac{y^2}{9} = 1$ $c^2 + 4 = 9$
$c = \pm\sqrt{5}$

$F(0, \sqrt{5}); \ F'(0, -\sqrt{5})$
major axis length = 6
minor axis length = 4

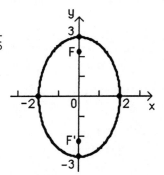

To check this graph:
$9x^2 + 4y^2 = 36$
$4y^2 = 36 - 9x^2$
$y^2 = 9 - \dfrac{9}{4}x^2$

$y = \pm\sqrt{9 - \dfrac{9}{4}x^2}$

6. $4x^2 + y^2 = 4$ $c^2 + 1 = 4$
$\dfrac{x^2}{1} + \dfrac{y^2}{4} = 1$ $c = \pm\sqrt{3}$

$F(0, \sqrt{3}); \ F'(0, -\sqrt{3})$
major axis length = 4
minor axis length = 2

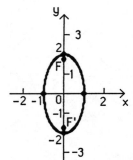

To check this graph:
$y^2 = 4 - 4x^2$
$y = \pm\sqrt{4 - 4x^2}$

8. $16x^2 + 9y^2 = 144$
$\dfrac{16x^2}{144} + \dfrac{9y^2}{144} = 1$
$\dfrac{x^2}{9} + \dfrac{y^2}{16} = 1$ graph (d)

10. $x^2 + 4y^2 = 16$
$\dfrac{x^2}{16} + \dfrac{4y^2}{16} = 1$
$\dfrac{x^2}{16} + \dfrac{y^2}{4} = 1$ graph (c)

12. $16x^2 + 25y^2 = 400$ $c^2 + 16 = 25$
$\dfrac{x^2}{25} + \dfrac{y^2}{16} = 1$ $c = \pm 3$
$F(3, 0); F'(-3, 0)$
major axis length = 10
minor axis length = 8

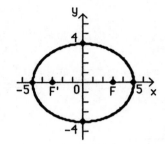

To check this graph:
$25y^2 = 400 - 16x^2$
$y^2 = 16 - \dfrac{16}{25}x^2$
$y = \pm\sqrt{16 - \dfrac{16}{25}x^2}$

14. $4x^2 + 3y^2 = 24$ $c^2 + 6 = 8$
$\dfrac{x^2}{6} + \dfrac{y^2}{8} = 1$ $c = \pm\sqrt{2}$
$F(0, \sqrt{2}); F'(0, -\sqrt{2})$
major axis length = $2\sqrt{8} \approx 5.66$
minor axis length = $2\sqrt{6} \approx 4.90$

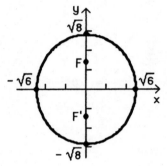

To check this graph:
$3y^2 = 24 - 4x^2$
$y^2 = 8 - \dfrac{4}{3}x^2$
$y = \pm\sqrt{8 - \dfrac{4}{3}x^2}$

16. $3x^2 + 2y^2 = 24$ $c^2 + 8 = 12$
$\dfrac{x^2}{8} + \dfrac{y^2}{12} = 1$ $c = \pm 2$
$F(0, 2); F'(0, -2)$
major axis length = $2\sqrt{12} \approx 6.93$
minor axis length = $2\sqrt{8} \approx 5.66$

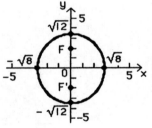

To check this graph:
$2y^2 = 24 - 3x^2$
$y^2 = 12 - 1.5x^2$
$y = \pm\sqrt{12 - 1.5x^2}$

18. $a = 6 \Rightarrow a^2 = M = 36$
$b = 3 \Rightarrow b^2 = N = 9$
$\dfrac{x^2}{36} + \dfrac{y^2}{9} = 1$

20. $a = 5 \Rightarrow a^2 = N = 25$
$b = 4 \Rightarrow b^2 = M = 16$
$\dfrac{x^2}{16} + \dfrac{y^2}{25} = 1$

22. major axis length = $14 \Rightarrow \dfrac{x^2}{7^2}$
minor axis length = $10 \Rightarrow \dfrac{y^2}{5^2}$ $\dfrac{x^2}{49} + \dfrac{y^2}{25} = 1$

24. major axis length = $24 \Rightarrow \dfrac{y^2}{12^2}$
minor axis length = $18 \Rightarrow \dfrac{x^2}{9^2}$ $\dfrac{x^2}{81} + \dfrac{y^2}{144} = 1$

26. major axis length = 24 $\Rightarrow \dfrac{x^2}{12^2}$

distance from center to foci = 10

$$a^2 - b^2 = c^2$$
$$144 - b^2 = 100$$
$$-b^2 = -44$$

$$\frac{x^2}{144} + \frac{y^2}{44} = 1$$

28. major axis length = 14 $\Rightarrow \dfrac{x^2}{7^2}$

distance from center to foci = $\sqrt{200}$

$$a^2 - b^2 = c^2$$
$$a^2 - 49 = 200$$
$$a^2 = 249$$

$$\frac{x^2}{49} + \frac{y^2}{249} = 1$$

30. An ellipse having (0, ±1) as the ends of the minor axis is almost circular when the foci are close to the origin and becomes more elongated as the distance of the foci from the origin increases.

32. $5x + 8y = 20 \rightarrow y = \dfrac{20 - 5x}{8}$

$$25x^2 + 16y^2 = 400$$

$$25x^2 + 16\left(\frac{20 - 5x}{8}\right)^2 = 400$$

$$25x^2 + 16\left(\frac{400 - 200x + 25x^2}{64}\right) = 400$$

$$100x^2 + 400 - 200x + 25x^2 = 1600$$

$$125x^2 - 200x - 1200 = 0$$

Using the quadratic formula:

$x = 4 \qquad x = -2.4$
$y = 0 \qquad y = 4$

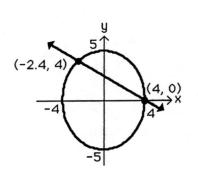

34. $3x^2 - 20y = 0 \rightarrow y = \dfrac{3x^2}{20}$

$$16x^2 + 25y^2 = 400$$

$$16x^2 + 25\left(\frac{3x^2}{20}\right)^2 = 400$$

$$256x^2 + 9x^4 = 6400$$

$$9x^4 + 256x^2 - 6400 = 0$$

$$x^2 = 16, \quad x^2 = -\frac{400}{9} \text{ (discard)}$$

Solving for x:

$x = 4, \qquad x = -4$
$y = 2.4 \qquad y = 2.4$

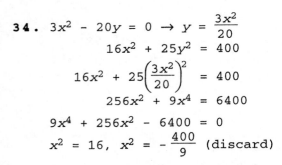

36. $x - 2y = 0 \rightarrow x = 2y$

$$3x^2 + 4y^2 = 57$$

$$3(2y)^2 + 4y^2 = 57$$
$$12y^2 + 4y^2 = 57$$
$$16y^2 = 57$$

$$y = \pm\frac{\sqrt{57}}{4}$$

$y = \dfrac{\sqrt{57}}{4}, \quad x = \dfrac{\sqrt{57}}{2}$

$y = -\dfrac{\sqrt{57}}{4}, \quad x = -\dfrac{\sqrt{57}}{2}$

(3.775, 1.887)
(-3.775, -1.887)

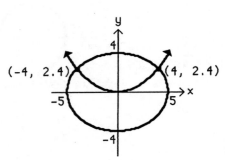

38. $x^2 - 12y = 0 \rightarrow x^2 = 12y$ $y \approx 1.124,\ x \approx 3.673$
    $3x^2 + 2y^2 = 43$ $x \approx -3.673$
    $3(12y) + 2y^2 = 43$
    $2y^2 + 36y - 43 = 0$

$y = \dfrac{-36 \pm \sqrt{1640}}{4}$ $(3.673,\ 1.124)$
                                              $(-3.673,\ 1.124)$

$y \approx 1.124,\ -19.124$ (discard)

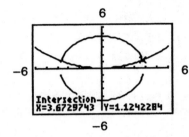   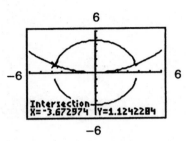

40. $\sqrt{(x - 0)^2 + (y - 9)^2} = \dfrac{3}{4}\sqrt{(x - x)^2 + (y - 16)^2}$

$x^2 + y^2 - 18y + 81 = \dfrac{9}{16}(y^2 - 32y + 256)$

$16x^2 + 16y^2 - 288y + 1296 = 9y^2 - 288y + 2304$

$16x^2 + 7y^2 = 1008$

$\dfrac{x^2}{63} + \dfrac{y^2}{144} = 1$: ellipse

42. $8x^2 + 35y^2 = 3600$ $x^2 = -25y$
    $35y^2 = 3600 - 8x^2$ $x \approx \pm 13.86$

$y^2 = \dfrac{3600 - 8x^2}{35}$

$y = \pm\sqrt{\dfrac{3600 - 8x^2}{35}} \approx -7.68,\ 7.68$ (discard)

   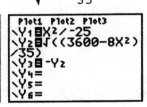   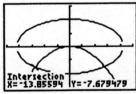   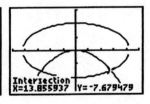

$(-13.86,\ -7.68)$
$(13.86,\ -7.68)$

44. $2x^2 + 7y^2 = 95$ $13x^2 + 6y^2 = 63$ There are no points
    $7y^2 = 95 - 2x^2$ $6y^2 = 63 - 13x^2$ of intersection.

$y^2 = \dfrac{95 - 2x^2}{7}$ $y^2 = \dfrac{63 - 13x^2}{6}$

$y = \pm\sqrt{\dfrac{95 - 2x^2}{7}}$ $y = \pm\sqrt{\dfrac{63 - 13x^2}{6}}$

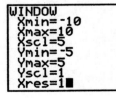   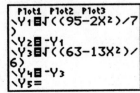   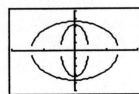

46. Let the center of the table be (0, 0) on the coordinate system. For

$\dfrac{x^2}{a^2} + \dfrac{y^2}{b^2} = 1$, $a = 4$, $b = 2$.

$c^2 + 2^2 = 4^2$

$c = \sqrt{12}$, distance from center to focus

$4 - \sqrt{12} \approx 0.54$ ft, distance from edge to focus

length of string = length of major axis = 8 ft

48. (A) $\dfrac{x^2}{a^2} + \dfrac{y^2}{b^2} = 1$

$\dfrac{x^2}{6^2} + \dfrac{y^2}{b^2} = 1$

$\dfrac{5.5^2}{6^2} + \dfrac{1^2}{b^2} = 1$

$30.25b^2 + 36 = 36b^2$

$5.75b^2 = -36$

$b^2 \approx 6.26$

$\dfrac{x^2}{36} + \dfrac{y^2}{6.26} = 1$

(B) $\dfrac{5^2}{36} + \dfrac{y^2}{6.26} = 1$

$156.5 + 36y^2 = 225.36$

$36y^2 = 68.86$

$y^2 \approx 1.91278$

$y \approx 1.38$

width = 1.38 + 1 = 2.38 feet to 2 decimal places

Exercise 10-3

2. $y^2 - x^2 = 1 \Rightarrow \dfrac{y^2}{1} - \dfrac{x^2}{1} = 1$

opens up/down; $a = 1$, $b = 1$: Graph (a)

4. $x^2 - y^2 = 4 \Rightarrow \dfrac{x^2}{4} - \dfrac{y^2}{4} = 1$

opens left/right; $a = 2$, $b = 2$; Graph (b)

6. $\dfrac{x^2}{9} - \dfrac{y^2}{25} = 1$; opens left/right

$b^2 = 25 \Rightarrow b = 5 \Rightarrow$ conjugate axis length $2b = 10$

$a^2 = 9 \Rightarrow a = 3 \Rightarrow$ transverse axis length $2a = 6$

$c^2 = a^2 + b^2 = 9 + 25 \Rightarrow c = \sqrt{34}$

foci: $F'(-\sqrt{34}, 0)$, $F(\sqrt{34}, 0)$

To check: $25x^2 - 9y^2 = 225$

$y^2 = \dfrac{25x^2 - 225}{9}$

$y = \pm\sqrt{\dfrac{25x^2 - 225}{9}}$

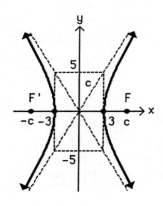

8. $\dfrac{y^2}{25} - \dfrac{x^2}{9} = 1$; opens up/down

$a^2 = 25 \Rightarrow a = 5 \Rightarrow$ transverse axis length $2a = 10$

$b^2 = 9 \Rightarrow b = 3 \Rightarrow$ conjugate axis length $2b = 6$

$c^2 = a^2 + b^2 = 25 + 9 = 34 \Rightarrow c = \sqrt{34}$

foci: $F'(0, -\sqrt{34})$, $F(0, \sqrt{34})$

To check: $9y^2 - 25x^2 = 225$

$y^2 = \dfrac{25x^2 + 225}{9}$

$y = \pm\sqrt{\dfrac{25x^2 + 225}{9}}$

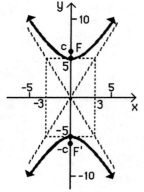

10. $x^2 - 9y^2 = 9$

$\dfrac{x^2}{9} - \dfrac{y^2}{1} = 1$; opens left/right

$a^2 = 9 \Rightarrow a = 3 \Rightarrow$ transverse axis length $2a = 6$
$b^2 = 1 \Rightarrow b = 1 \Rightarrow$ conjugate axis length $2b = 2$
$c^2 = a^2 + b^2 = 9 + 1 = 10 \Rightarrow c = \sqrt{10}$

foci: $F'(-\sqrt{10},\ 0),\ F(\sqrt{10},\ 0)$

To check: $-9y^2 = 9 - x^2$

$\qquad\qquad y^2 = \dfrac{x^2 - 9}{9}$

$\qquad\qquad y = \pm\sqrt{\dfrac{x^2 - 9}{9}}$

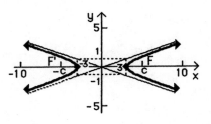

12. $4y^2 - 25x^2 = 100$

$\dfrac{y^2}{25} - \dfrac{x^2}{4} = 1$; opens up/down

$a^2 = 25 \Rightarrow a = 5 \Rightarrow$ transverse axis length $2a = 10$
$b^2 = 4 \Rightarrow b = 2 \Rightarrow$ conjugate axis length $2b = 4$
$c^2 = a^2 + b^2 = 25 + 4 = 29 \Rightarrow c = \sqrt{29}$
foci: $F'(0,\ -\sqrt{29}),\ F(0,\ \sqrt{29})$

To check: $4y^2 = 25x^2 + 100$

$\qquad\qquad y = \pm\sqrt{\dfrac{25x^2 + 100}{4}}$

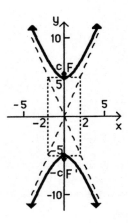

14. $3x^2 - 4y^2 = 24$

$\dfrac{x^2}{8} - \dfrac{y^2}{6} = 1$; opens right/left

$a^2 = 8 \Rightarrow a = \sqrt{8} \Rightarrow$ transverse axis length $2a = 2\sqrt{8} \approx 5.66$
$b^2 = 6 \Rightarrow b = \sqrt{6} \Rightarrow$ conjugate axis length $2b = 2\sqrt{6} \approx 4.90$

$c^2 = a^2 + b^2 = 8 + 6 \Rightarrow c = \sqrt{14}$
foci: $F'(-\sqrt{14},\ 0),\ F(\sqrt{14},\ 0)$
To check: $-4y^2 = -3x^2 + 24$

$\qquad\qquad y^2 = \dfrac{3x^2 - 24}{4}$

$\qquad\qquad y = \pm\sqrt{\dfrac{3x^2 - 24}{4}}$

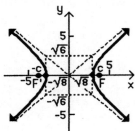

16. $3y^2 - 2x^2 = 24$

$\dfrac{y^2}{8} - \dfrac{x^2}{12} = 1$; opens up/down

$a^2 = 8 \Rightarrow a = \sqrt{8} \Rightarrow$ transverse axis length $2a = 2\sqrt{8} \approx 5.66$
$b^2 = 12 \Rightarrow b = \sqrt{12} \Rightarrow$ conjugate axis length $2b = 2\sqrt{12} \approx 6.93$
$c^2 = a^2 + b^2 = 8 + 12 = 20 \Rightarrow c = \sqrt{20}$
foci: $F'(0,\ -\sqrt{20}),\ F(0,\ \sqrt{20})$

To check: $3y^2 = 2x^2 + 24$

$\qquad\qquad y = \pm\sqrt{\dfrac{2x^2 + 24}{3}}$

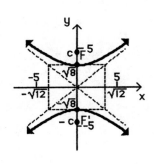

18. From the graph, $a = 3 \Rightarrow a^2 = 9$ and y is the major axis.

$$\frac{y^2}{N} - \frac{x^2}{M} = 1$$

$$\frac{y^2}{9} - \frac{x^2}{b^2} = 1$$

$(4, 5)$: $\frac{25}{9} - \frac{16}{b^2} = 1$

$25b^2 - 144 = 9b^2$

$16b^2 = 144$

$b^2 = 9$ $\qquad \frac{y^2}{9} - \frac{x^2}{9} = 1$

20. From the graph, $a = 4 \Rightarrow a^2 = 16$ and x is the major axis.

$$\frac{x^2}{M} - \frac{y^2}{N} = 1$$

$$\frac{x^2}{16} - \frac{y^2}{b^2} = 1$$

$(5, 3)$: $\frac{25}{16} - \frac{9}{b^2} = 1$

$25b^2 - 144 = 16b^2$

$9b^2 = 144$

$b^2 = 16$ $\qquad \frac{x^2}{16} - \frac{y^2}{16} = 1$

22. Transverse axis on x axis
Transverse axis length $2a = 8 \Rightarrow a = 4$
Conjugate axis length $2b = 6 \Rightarrow b = 3$

$$\frac{x^2}{4^2} - \frac{y^2}{3^2} = 1$$

$$\frac{x^2}{16} - \frac{y^2}{9} = 1$$

24. Transverse axis on y axis
Transverse axis length $2a = 16 \Rightarrow a = 8$
Conjugate axis length $2b = 22 \Rightarrow b = 11$

$$\frac{y^2}{8^2} - \frac{x^2}{11^2} = 1$$

$$\frac{y^2}{64} - \frac{x^2}{121} = 1$$

26. Transverse axis on x axis
Transverse axis length $2a = 16 \Rightarrow a = 8$
Distance of foci from center $= 10 \Rightarrow c = 10$

$c^2 = a^2 + b^2$ $\qquad \frac{x^2}{8^2} - \frac{y^2}{6^2} = 1$

$100 = 64 + b^2$ $\qquad \frac{x^2}{64} - \frac{y^2}{36} = 1$

$b^2 = 36$

28. Conjugate axis on x axis
Conjugate axis length $2b = 10 \Rightarrow b = 5$
Distance of foci from center $= \sqrt{70} \Rightarrow c = \sqrt{70}$

$c^2 = a^2 + b^2$ $\qquad \frac{y^2}{45} - \frac{x^2}{5^2} = 1$

$(\sqrt{70})^2 = a^2 + 5^2$ $\qquad \frac{y^2}{45} - \frac{x^2}{25} = 1$

$a^2 = 45$

30. Infinitely many; $\frac{x^2}{a^2} - \frac{y^2}{4a^2} = 1$, $\frac{y^2}{a^2} - \frac{4x^2}{a^2} = 1$ $(a > 0)$ are two examples.

32. $y^2 - x^2 = 3$
$\underline{y^2 + x^2 = 5}$
$2y^2 \quad\quad = 8$
$\quad\quad y^2 = 4,$
$y = 2, \quad\quad y = -2$
$x = \pm 1 \quad\quad x = \pm 1$
$(1, 2) \quad\quad (1, -2)$
$(-1, 2) \quad\quad (-1, -2)$

$x^2 = 5 - y^2$
$x^2 = 5 - (\pm 2)^2$
$\quad x = \pm 1$

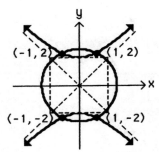

34. $2x^2 + y^2 = 17$
$\underline{x^2 - y^2 = -5}$
$3x^2 \quad\quad = 12$
$\quad\quad x^2 = 4$
$x = 2, \quad\quad x = -2$
$y = \pm 3 \quad\quad y = \pm 3$
$(2, 3) \quad\quad (-2, 3)$
$(2, -3) \quad\quad (-2, -3)$

$y^2 = 17 - 2x^2$
$y^2 = 17 - 2(\pm 2)^2$
$y^2 = 9$
$\quad y = \pm 3$

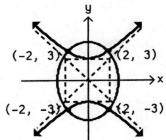

36. $y^2 - x^2 = 4$
$\quad y - x = 6 \Rightarrow x = y - 6$

$y^2 - (y - 6)^2 = 4$
$y^2 - y^2 + 12y - 36 = 4$
$\quad\quad 12y = 40$
$\quad\quad y = 3\frac{1}{3}$
$\quad\quad x = 3\frac{1}{3} - 6 = -2\frac{2}{3}$

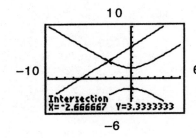

$(-2.667, 3.333)$

38. $y^2 - x^2 = 1$
$\underline{2y^2 + x^2 = 16}$
$3y^2 \quad\quad = 17$
$\quad\quad y = \pm\sqrt{\dfrac{17}{3}}$
$\quad\quad y \approx \pm 2.380$

$x^2 = y^2 - 1$
$x^2 = \dfrac{17}{3} - 1$
$x \approx \pm 2.160$

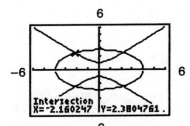

$(2.160, 2.380), \quad (2.160, -2.380),$
$(-2.160, 2.380), \quad (-2.160, -2.380)$

40. $\sqrt{(x - 0)^2 + (y - 4)^2} = \dfrac{4}{3}\sqrt{(x - x)^2 + \left(y - \dfrac{9}{4}\right)^2}$

$x^2 + y^2 - 8y + 16 = \dfrac{16}{9}\left(y^2 - \dfrac{9}{2}y + \dfrac{81}{16}\right)$

$9x^2 + 9y^2 - 72y + 144 = 16y^2 - 72y + 81$

$7y^2 - 9x^2 = 63$

$\dfrac{y^2}{9} - \dfrac{x^2}{7} = 1$: hyperbola

42. $y^2 - 3x^2 = 8$ $\qquad$ $x^2 = -\dfrac{y}{3}$

$\qquad\qquad y^2 = 3x^2 + 8$ $\qquad$ $y = -3x^2$ $\qquad$ (-1.06, -3.37), (1.06, -3.37)

$\qquad\qquad y = \pm\sqrt{3x^2 + 8}$

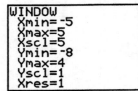
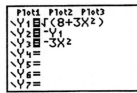
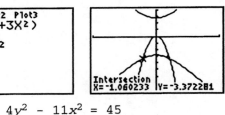
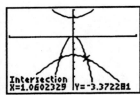

44. $8x^2 - 7y^2 = 58$ $\qquad\qquad$ $4y^2 - 11x^2 = 45$

$\qquad\qquad y^2 = \dfrac{8x^2 - 58}{7}$ $\qquad\qquad y^2 = \dfrac{11x^2 + 45}{4}$

$\qquad\qquad y = \pm\sqrt{\dfrac{8x^2 - 58}{7}}$ $\qquad\qquad y = \pm\sqrt{\dfrac{11x^2 + 45}{4}}$ $\qquad$ There are no points of intersection.

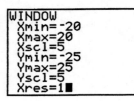
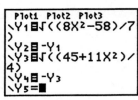
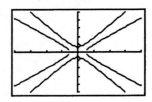

46. $\dfrac{x^2}{100^2} - \dfrac{y^2}{150^2} = 1$ $\qquad\qquad\qquad$ $\dfrac{x^2}{100^2} - \dfrac{y^2}{150^2} = 1$

$\quad\;\; \dfrac{x^2}{100^2} - \dfrac{150^2}{150^2} = 1$ $\qquad\qquad\qquad$ $\dfrac{x^2}{100^2} - \dfrac{(-350)^2}{150^2} = 1$

$\qquad\qquad x^2 = 2(100)^2$ $\qquad\qquad\qquad$ $\dfrac{x^2}{10000} - \dfrac{49}{9} = 1$

$\qquad\qquad x \approx 141$ ft, top radius $\qquad$ $9x^2 - 490000 = 90000$

$\qquad\qquad\qquad\qquad\qquad\qquad\qquad\qquad$ $9x^2 = 580000$

$\qquad\qquad\qquad\qquad\qquad\qquad\qquad\qquad$ $x^2 = 64444.\overline{4}$

$\qquad\qquad\qquad\qquad\qquad\qquad\qquad\qquad$ $x \approx 254$ ft, base radius

$a^2 = 100^2$

$a = 100$ ft, radius of smallest circular cross section

Exercise 10-4

2. (A) $(x - 3)^2 = 8(y + 2)$ $\qquad$ (B) $x'^2 = 8y'$ $\qquad$ (C) parabola

$\qquad\quad x' = x - 3$

$\qquad\quad y' = y + 2$

4. (A) $(x + 2)^2 + (y + 6)^2 = 36$ $\quad$ (B) $x'^2 + y'^2 = 36$ $\qquad$ (C) circle

$\qquad\qquad\quad x' = x + 2$

$\qquad\qquad\quad y' = y + 6$

6. (A) $\dfrac{(y - 9)^2}{10} - \dfrac{(x + 5)^2}{6} = 1$ $\quad$ (B) $\dfrac{y'^2}{10} - \dfrac{x'^2}{6} = 1$ $\qquad$ (C) hyperbola

$\qquad\qquad\quad x' = x + 5$

$\qquad\qquad\quad y' = y - 9$

8. (A) $\dfrac{(x + 7)^2}{25} - \dfrac{(y - 8)^2}{50} = 1$ $\quad$ (B) $\dfrac{x'^2}{25} - \dfrac{y'^2}{50} = 1$ $\qquad$ (C) hyperbola

$\qquad\qquad\quad x' = x + 7$

$\qquad\qquad\quad y' = y - 8$

10. (A) $(y + 2)^2 - 12(x - 3) = 0$ $\qquad\qquad\qquad\qquad\qquad$ (B) parabola

$\qquad\quad (y + 2)^2 = 12(x - 3)$

12. (A) $12(y - 5)^2 - 8(x - 3)^2 = 24$

$$\frac{(y - 5)^2}{2} - \frac{(x - 3)^2}{3} = 1$$

(B) hyperbola

14. (A) $4(x - 7)^2 + 7(y - 3)^2 = 28$

$$\frac{(x - 7)^2}{7} + \frac{(y - 3)^2}{4} = 1$$

(B) ellipse

16. $16x^2 + 9y^2 + 64x + 54y + 1 = 0$

$16x^2 + 64x + 9y^2 + 54y + 1 = 0$

$16(x^2 + 4x + 4) + 9(y^2 + 6y + 9) = -1 + 64 + 81$

$16(x + 2)^2 + 9(y + 3) = 144$

$$\frac{(x + 2)^2}{9} + \frac{(y + 3)^2}{16} = 1: \text{ ellipse}$$

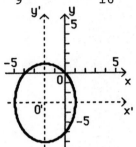

18. $y^2 + 12x + 4y - 32 = 0$

$y^2 + 4y + 4 = -12x + 32 + 4$

$(y + 2)^2 = -12(x - 3):$

parabola

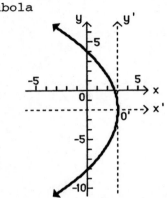

20. $x^2 + y^2 - 8x - 6y = 0$

$x^2 - 8x + 16 + y^2 - 6y + 9 = 16 + 9$

$(x - 4)^2 + (y - 3)^2 = 25: \text{ circle}$

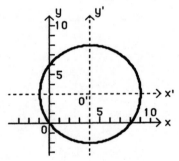

22. $16x^2 - 25y^2 - 160x = 0$

$16(x^2 - 10x + 25) - 25y^2 = 400$

$$\frac{(x - 5)^2}{25} - \frac{y^2}{16} = 1: \text{ hyperbola}$$

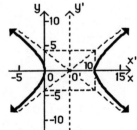

24. $Cy^2 + Ey + Dx = -F$

$$C\left(y^2 + \frac{E}{C}y + \frac{E^2}{4C^2}\right) = -Dx - F + \frac{E^2}{4C}$$

$$\left(y + \frac{E}{2C}\right)^2 = \frac{-D}{C}x - \frac{F}{C} + \frac{E^2}{4C^2}$$

$$\left(y + \frac{E}{2C}\right)^2 = \frac{-D}{C}\left(x + \frac{F}{D} - \frac{E^2}{4CD}\right)$$

$y - k = y + \dfrac{E}{2C}$ $x - h = x + \dfrac{F}{D} - \dfrac{E^2}{4CD}$

$k = \dfrac{-E}{2C}$ $h = \dfrac{E^2}{4CD} - \dfrac{F}{D} \cdot \dfrac{4C}{4C}$

$h = \dfrac{E^2 - 4CF}{4CD}$

26. Parabola: Vertex at $(4, -1)$, $y = -1$ axis, through $(2, 3)$:

$$y^2 = 4px$$
$$(y + 1)^2 = 4p(x - 4)$$
$$(3 + 1)^2 = 4p(2 - 4) \Rightarrow 4p = -8$$
$$(y + 1)^2 = -8(x - 4)$$
$$y^2 + 2y + 1 = -8x + 32$$
$$y^2 + 8x + 2y - 31 = 0$$

28. Ellipse: $x = -4$ major axis, $y = 1$ minor axis, $2a = 4$, $2b = 2$:

$$\frac{(x + 4)^2}{1^2} + \frac{(y - 1)^2}{2^2} = 1$$
$$4(x^2 + 8x + 16) + y^2 - 2y + 1 = 4$$
$$4x^2 + 32x + 64 + y^2 - 2y + 1 = 4$$
$$4x^2 + y^2 + 32x - 2y + 61 = 0$$

30. Ellipse: Vertices at $(-3, 1)$ and $(7, 1) \Rightarrow$ Center at $(2, 1)$, $2a = 10$;
Foci at $(-1, 1)$ and $(5, 1) \Rightarrow 2c = 6$
$a = 5$, $c = 3$: $b^2 = c^2 - a^2 = 25 - 9 = 16$

$$\frac{(x - 2)^2}{5^2} + \frac{(y - 1)^2}{4^2} = 1$$
$$\frac{x^2 - 4x + 4}{25} + \frac{y^2 - 2y + 1}{16} = 1$$
$$16x^2 - 64x + 64 + 25y^2 - 50y + 25 = 400$$
$$16x^2 + 25y^2 - 64x - 50y - 311 = 0$$

32. Hyperbola: Transverse axis on $y = -5$, $2a = 6$;
Conjugate axis on $x = 2$, $2b = 6$;
Center at $(2, -5)$

$$\frac{(x - 2)^2}{3^2} - \frac{(y + 5)^2}{3^2} = 1$$
$$x^2 - 4x + 4 - y^2 - 10y - 25 = 9$$
$$x^2 - y^2 - 4x - 10y - 30 = 0$$

34. Ellipse: Vertices at $(-5, -2)$, $(-1, -2) \Rightarrow$ center $= (-3, -2)$; $2a = 4$
Points at $(-3, -3)$, $(-3, -1) \Rightarrow 2b = 2$

$$\frac{(x + 3)^2}{2^2} + \frac{(y + 2)^2}{1^2} = 1$$
$$x^2 + 6x + 9 + 4(y^2 + 4y + 4) = 4$$
$$x^2 + 6x + 9 + 4y^2 + 16y + 16 - 4 = 0$$
$$x^2 + 4y^2 + 6x + 16y + 21 = 0$$

36. Hyperbola: Vertices at $(2, -2)$ and $(2, 0) \Rightarrow$ center $= (2, -1)$ and $2a = 2$
Through $(3, 1)$ and $(3, -3)$; opens up/down

$$\frac{(y + 1)^2}{1^2} - \frac{(x - 2)^2}{b^2} = 1$$
$$(3, 1): \frac{(1 + 1)^2}{1} - \frac{(3 - 2)^2}{b^2} = 1$$
$$4 - \frac{1}{b^2} = 1$$
$$4b^2 - 1 = b^2$$
$$3b^2 = 1$$
$$b^2 = \frac{1}{3}$$

$$\frac{(y + 1)^2}{1} - \frac{(x - 2)^2}{1/3} = 1$$

$$\frac{1}{3}(y + 1)^2 - (x - 2)^2 = \frac{1}{3}$$

$$y^2 + 2y + 1 - 3(x^2 - 4x + 4) = 1$$

$$y^2 + 2y + 1 - 3x^2 + 12x - 12 = 1$$

$$-3x^2 + y^2 + 12x + 2y - 12 = 0$$

$$3x^2 - y^2 - 12x - 2y + 12 = 0$$

38. $\dfrac{(x + 2)^2}{9} + \dfrac{(y + 3)^2}{16} = 1 \Rightarrow \dfrac{x'^2}{9} + \dfrac{y'^2}{16} = 1$

$c = \pm\sqrt{16 - 9} = \pm\sqrt{7}$

$x' = x + 2,\ y' = y + 3$ foci: $(0,\ \sqrt{7})'$, $(0,\ -\sqrt{7})'$

$\qquad\qquad\qquad\qquad\qquad : (-2,\ \sqrt{7} - 3),\ (-2,\ -\sqrt{7} - 3)$

40. $(y + 2)^2 = -12(x - 3)$

$\qquad y'^2 = -12x' \Rightarrow 4p = -12 \Rightarrow p = -3$

$y' = y + 2,\ x' = x - 3$

$\qquad\qquad\qquad$ focus: $(-3,\ 0)'$

$\qquad\qquad\qquad\quad : (0,\ -2)$

42. $\dfrac{(x - 5)^2}{25} - \dfrac{y^2}{16} = 1$

$x' = x - 5,\ y' = y$ foci: $(\sqrt{41},\ 0)'$, $(-\sqrt{41},\ 0)'$

$c^2 = 25 + 16 = 41$ $\qquad : (\sqrt{41} + 5,\ 0),\ (-\sqrt{41} + 5,\ 0)$

$\quad c = \pm\sqrt{41}$

44. (1) $8x^2 + 3y^2 - 14x + 17y - 39 = 0$

(2) $5x - 11y = 23$

Write (1) as $3y^2 + 17y + (8x^2 - 14x - 39) = 0$ and solve for y:

$$y = \frac{-17 \pm \sqrt{17^2 - 4 \cdot 3(8x^2 - 14x - 39)}}{2 \cdot 3} = \frac{-17}{6} \pm \frac{\sqrt{-96x^2 + 168x + 757}}{6}.$$

Solving (2) for y gives $y = \dfrac{5x - 23}{11}$.

Graph these three equations to obtain $(-2.06,\ -3.03)$ and $(3.45,\ -0.52)$.

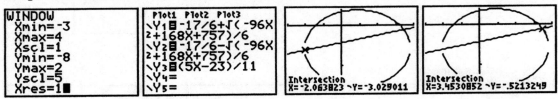

46. (1) $4x^2 - y^2 - 24x - 2y + 35 = 0$

$\qquad y^2 + 2y + (-4x^2 + 24x - 35) = 0$; solving for y

$$y = \frac{-2 \pm \sqrt{2^2 - 4(-4x^2 + 24x - 35)}}{2}$$

$$= \frac{-2 \pm \sqrt{16x^2 - 96x + 144}}{2}$$

$$= -1 \pm \sqrt{4x^2 - 24x + 36}$$

(2) $2x^2 + 6y^2 - 3x - 34 = 0$

$6y^2 = -2x^2 + 3x + 34$

$y^2 = \dfrac{-2x^2 + 3x + 34}{6}$

$y = \dfrac{\pm\sqrt{-2x^2 + 3x + 34}}{\sqrt{6}}$

Graph these four equations to obtain (1.30, 2.40), (2.39, -2.23), (3.43, -1.86), (4.19, 1.38).

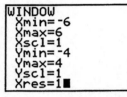 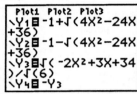 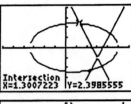

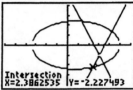 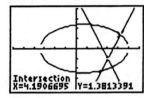 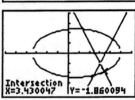

Exercise 10-5

2. $x = t^2$ This parametric equation gives half
$y = t^4 - 2$ of a parabola where $x \geq 0$, since $t^2 \geq 0$.

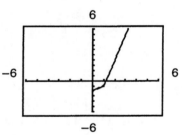

$y = x^2 - 2$ The quadratic equation gives the complete parabola with a domain $(-\infty, \infty)$.

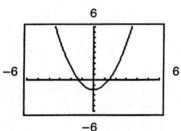

4. Eliminating the parameter gives $y = x + 1$.

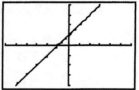

The graph is a straight line.

6. Eliminating the parameter gives $y = x + 1$, $x \geq 0$.

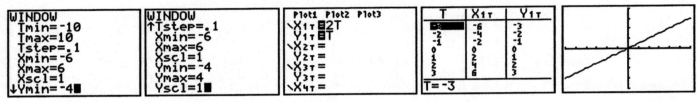

The graph is a ray (part of a straight line).

8. Eliminating the parameter gives $y = \dfrac{x}{2}$.

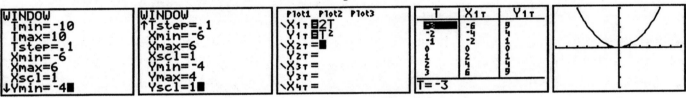

The graph is a straight line.

10. Eliminating the parameter gives $y = \dfrac{x^2}{4}$ $(x^2 = 4y)$.

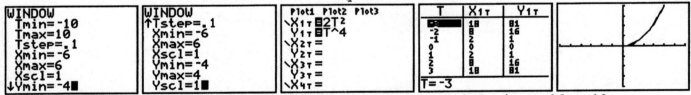

The graph is a parabola.

12. Eliminating the parameter gives $y = \dfrac{x^2}{4}$ $(x^2 = 4y)$, $x \geq 0$.

The graph is a parabola; the right half of the parabola in problem 10.

14. $x = t - 1$, $\quad y = 2t + 2$
$t = x + 1$ $\quad y = 2(x + 1) + 2$
$y = 2x + 4$; line

16. $x = \sqrt{t}$, $\quad y = t + 1$, $t \geq 0$
$t = x^2$ $\quad y = x^2 + 1$, $x \geq 0$, $y \geq 1$; parabola (right half)

18. $\quad x = -3\sqrt{t}$, $\quad y = \sqrt{25 - t}$, $0 \leq t \leq 25$
$\quad -\dfrac{1}{3}x = \sqrt{t}$ $\quad y = \sqrt{25 - \dfrac{x^2}{9}}$
$\qquad t = \dfrac{x^2}{9}$ $\quad y^2 = 25 - \dfrac{x^2}{9}$
$\qquad\qquad\qquad\qquad \dfrac{x^2}{9} + y^2 = 25$, $-15 \leq x \leq 0$, $0 \leq y \leq 5$, Ellipse (2nd quadrant portion)
$\qquad\qquad\qquad\qquad x^2 + 9y^2 = 225$

20. $x = \sqrt{2 - t}$, $y = -\sqrt{4 - t}$, $t \le 2$
$x^2 = 2 - t$ $y = -\sqrt{4 - (2 - x^2)}$
  $t = 2 - x^2$ $y^2 = 2 + x^2$
             $y^2 - x^2 = 2$, $x \ge 0$, $y \le -\sqrt{2}$, Hyperbola (4th quadrant portion)

22. $x = 3 \sin \theta$, $y = 3 \cos \theta$, $0 \le \theta \le 2\pi$
  $\sin \theta = \dfrac{x}{3}$ $\cos \theta = \dfrac{y}{3}$
  $\cos^2\theta + \sin^2\theta = 1$
        $\dfrac{y^2}{9} + \dfrac{x^2}{9} = 1$
        $x^2 + y^2 = 9$; circle

24. $x = 3 + 4 \sin \theta$, $y = 2 + 2 \cos \theta$, $0 \le \theta \le 2\pi$
  $\sin \theta = \dfrac{x - 3}{4}$ $\cos \theta = \dfrac{y - 2}{2}$
        $\cos^2\theta + \sin^2\theta = 1$
  $\dfrac{(y - 2)^2}{4} + \dfrac{(x - 3)^2}{16} = 1$
  $\dfrac{(x - 3)^2}{16} + \dfrac{(y - 2)^2}{4} = 1$; ellipse

26. $Cy^2 + Dx + Ey + F = 0$; Answers may vary.
  Let $y = t$. Then $Dx = -Ct^2 - Et - F$
        $x = \dfrac{-(Ct^2 + Et + F)}{D}$, $y = t$; parabola; $t \in (-\infty, \infty)$.

28. $x = 1 + 3 \sec t$, $y = -2 + 2 \tan 2$, $0 \le t \le 2\pi$, $t \ne \dfrac{\pi}{2}$, $\dfrac{3\pi}{2}$
  $\sec t = \dfrac{x - 1}{3}$ $\tan t = \dfrac{y + 2}{2}$
      $\sec^2 t - \tan^2 t = 1$
  $\dfrac{(x - 1)^2}{9} - \dfrac{(y + 2)^2}{4} = 1$; hyperbola with center $(1, -2)$.

30. $x = -4 + 5 \cos t$, $y = 1 + 8 \sin t$, $0 \le t \le 2\pi$
  $\cos t = \dfrac{x + 4}{5}$ $\sin t = \dfrac{y - 1}{8}$
        $\cos^2 t + \sin^2 t = 1$
  $\dfrac{(x + 4)^2}{25} + \dfrac{(y - 1)^2}{64} = 1$; ellipse with center $(-4, 1)$.

32. $x = \sqrt{t^2 + 4}$, $y = \sqrt{t^2 + 1}$;   since $t^2 \ge 0$, $x \ge 2$, $y \ge 1$
  $x^2 = t^2 + 4$ $y = \sqrt{(x^2 - 4) + 1}$
  $t^2 = x^2 - 4$ $y^2 = x^2 - 3$
                $y^2 - x^2 = -3$
                $x^2 - y^2 = 3$, part of a hyperbola $\left[\dfrac{x^2}{3} - \dfrac{y^2}{3} = 1\right]$

34. $x = \dfrac{3t}{\sqrt{t^2 + 1}}$, $y = \dfrac{3}{\sqrt{t^2 + 1}}$; since $t^2 \geq 0$, $0 < y \leq 3$

$x^2 = \dfrac{9t^2}{t^2 + 1}$ $y = \dfrac{3}{\sqrt{\dfrac{x^2}{9 - x^2} + 1}}$

$x^2 t^2 + x^2 = 9t^2$ $y^2 = \dfrac{9}{\dfrac{x^2 + 9 - x^2}{9 - x^2}}$

$t^2 = \dfrac{x^2}{9 - x^2}$ $y^2 = \dfrac{9(9 - x^2)}{9}$

$y^2 = 9 - x^2$

$x^2 + y^2 = 9$, semi circle, $-3 < x < 3$, $0 < y \leq 3$.

36. $x = \dfrac{4t}{t^2 + 1}$ (1), $y = \dfrac{4t^2}{t^2 + 1}$ (2)

Solve (2) for t^2: $yt^2 + y = 4t^2$

$y = 4t^2 - yt^2$

$\dfrac{y}{4 - y} = t^2$, $y \neq 4$

Substitute (2) $\to$ (1): $x = \dfrac{4\sqrt{\dfrac{y}{4 - y}}}{\dfrac{y}{4 - y} + 1}$

$\dfrac{xy}{4 - y} + x = 4\sqrt{\dfrac{y}{4 - y}}$

$\dfrac{xy + 4x - xy}{4 - y} = 4\sqrt{\dfrac{y}{4 - y}}$

$\dfrac{x}{4 - y} = \sqrt{\dfrac{y}{4 - y}}$

$\dfrac{x^2}{(4 - y)^2} = \dfrac{y}{4 - y}$

$\dfrac{x^2}{4 - y} = y$

$x^2 = 4y - y^2$

$x^2 + y^2 - 4y = 0$

$x^2 + (y - 2)^2 = 4$; circle with hole at $(0, 4)$.

38. $36x^2 + 360x + 4y^2 - 8y + 760 = 0$

$36(x^2 + 10x + 25) + 4(y^2 - 2y + 1) = -760 + 900 + 4$

$36(x + 5)^2 + 4(y - 1)^2 = 144$

$\dfrac{(x + 5)^2}{4} + \dfrac{(y - 1)^2}{36} = 1$; Ellipse, center at $(-5, 1)$

Let $\cos^2 t = \dfrac{(x + 5)^2}{4}$ and $\sin^2 t = \dfrac{(y - 1)^2}{36}$

$\cos t = \dfrac{x + 5}{2}$ $\sin t = \dfrac{y - 1}{6}$

$2 \cos t = x + 5$ $6 \sin t = y - 1$

$x = 2 \cos t - 5$ $y = 6 \sin t + 1$, $0 \leq t \leq 2\pi$

40. $16x^2 + 32x - 9y^2 - 36y - 164 = 0$

$16(x^2 + 2x + 1) - 9(y^2 + 4y + 4) = 164 + 16 - 36$

$16(x + 1)^2 - 9(y + 2)^2 = 144$

$\dfrac{(x + 1)^2}{9} - \dfrac{(y + 2)^2}{16} = 1$; Hyperbola, center at $(-1, -2)$

Let $\sec^2 t = \dfrac{(x + 1)^2}{9}$ and $\tan^2 t = \dfrac{(y + 2)^2}{16}$

$\sec t = \dfrac{x + 1}{3}$ $\tan t = \dfrac{y + 2}{4}$

$3 \sec t = x + 1$ $4 \tan t = y + 2$

$x = 3 \sec t - 1$ $y = 4 \tan t - 2,\ 0 < t < 2\pi,\ t \neq \dfrac{\pi}{2},\ \dfrac{3\pi}{2}$

42. (1) $x_1 = t,$ $y_1 = \log t,\ t > 0$

(2) $x_2 = \log t,\ y_2 = t,\ t > 0$

(A)

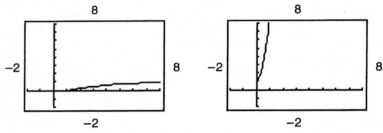

The graphs are inverses of each other and are symmetric about the line $y = x$.

(B) (1) $y_1 = \log x_1$ (2) $x_2 = \log y_2$

$y_2 = 10^{x_2}$

These functions are inverses of each other.

44. $y = a_0 + (\tan \alpha)x - \dfrac{4.9x^2}{(v_0)^2 \cos^2 \alpha}$ where $a_0 = 40,\ v_0 = 30,\ \alpha = 0°,\ y = 0$

$0 = 40 + (\tan 0°)x - \dfrac{4.9x^2}{30^2 (\cos 0°)^2}$

$\dfrac{4.9x^2}{900} = 40$

$4.9x^2 = 36000$

$x^2 = \dfrac{36000}{4.9}$

$x \approx 85.7$ m

46. $\alpha = 40°,\ v_0 = 300,\ a_0 = 0$:

The equations of motion are $x = 300 \cos 40° \cdot t$ and $y = -4.9t^2 + 300 \sin 40° \cdot t$.

(A) At impact $y = 0 = -4.9t^2 + 300 \sin 40° \cdot t$
from which $t \approx 39.354343 \approx 39.354$ sec.

(B) Range $\approx 300 \cos 40° \cdot 39.354 \approx 9044.153$ m ≈ 9.044 km

(C) Maximum height occurs at one half of the impact time.

Maximum height $= -4.9 \left(\dfrac{39.354}{2}\right)^2 + 300 \sin 40° \cdot \left(\dfrac{39.354}{2}\right) \approx 1897.236$ m

APPENDIX A
Exercise A-1

2. Since 6 is an element of {2, 4, 6} the statement $6 \in \{2, 4, 6\}$ is true.

4. Since 7 is not an element of {2, 4, 6} the statement $7 \notin \{2, 4, 6\}$ is true.

6. Since 2 and 6 are both elements of {2, 4, 6} the statement $\{2, 6\} \subset \{2, 4, 6\}$ is true.

8. Since {7, 3, 5} and {3, 5, 7} contain exactly the same elements the statement {7, 3, 5} = {3, 5, 7} is true.

10. The commutative property ($\cdot$) states that in general $uv = vu$. Comparing this with $uv = ?$ it follows that ? may be replaced with vu.

12. The associative property (+) states that in general $a + (b + c) = (a + b) + c$ from which $3 + (7 + y) = (3 + 7) + y$ and comparison to $3 + (7 + y) = ?$ gives $? = (3 + 7) + y$.

14. The identity property ($\cdot$) states that in general $1 \cdot a = a$ from which $1(u + v) = u + v$ and comparison to $1(u + v) = ?$ gives $? = u + v$.

16. Associative ($\cdot$). $7(3m) = (7 \cdot 3) \cdot m$ is a special case of $a(bc) = (ab)c$.

18. $-\dfrac{u}{-v} = \dfrac{u}{v}$ is a special case of Theorem 1 (#6) on the properties of negatives $\dfrac{-a}{-b} = -\dfrac{-a}{b} = -\dfrac{a}{-b} = \dfrac{a}{b}$, $b \neq 0$.

20. $8 - 12 = 8 + (-12)$ is an example of the general definition of subtraction as addition of opposites: $a - b = a + (-b)$.

22. $5 \div (-6) = 5\left(\dfrac{1}{-6}\right)$ is a special case of division $a \div b = a\left(\dfrac{1}{b}\right)$ with $a = 5$ and $b = -6$
$\dfrac{a}{b} \div \dfrac{c}{d} = \dfrac{a}{b} \cdot \dfrac{d}{c}$ with $a = 5$, $b = 1$, $c = -6$ and $d = 1$.

24. $ab(c + d) = abc + abd$ follows from the distributive property $x(y + z) = xy + xz$ with $x = ab$, $y = c$, and $z = d$.

26. $(x + y) \cdot 0 = 0$ follows from the property of zero $a \cdot 0 = 0$ where $a = x + y$.

28. $\{x \mid x$ is an odd integer between -4 and $6\}$ is the set $\{-3, -1, 1, 3, 5\}$.

30. $\{x \mid x$ is a letter in "consensus"$\} = \{c, o, n, s, e, u\}$

32. $\{x \mid x$ is a month with 32 days$\} = \emptyset$. There are no 32-day months.

34. $(5x)(7y) = 5[x(7y)]$ follows from associative ($\cdot$) $a(bc) = (ab)c$ with $a = 5$, $b = x$, and $c = 7y$.

36. $(x + 3)(x + 5) = (x + 3)x + (x + 3)5$ illustrates the distributive property $a(b + c) = ab + ac$ with $a = x + 3$, $b = x$ and $c = 5$.

38. $\dfrac{-7}{-(m - n)} = \dfrac{7}{m - n}$ illustrates the properties of negatives $\dfrac{-a}{-b} = \dfrac{a}{b}$ where $a = 7$ and $b = m - n$.

40. If $x(3x - 7) = 0$, then either $x = 0$ or $3x - 7 = 0$ is an example of the zero-product theorem which states $ab = 0$ if and only if $a = 0$ or $b = 0$ or both.

42. If $ab = 1$, does either a or b have to be 1? No, $\left(\dfrac{3}{5}\right)\left(\dfrac{5}{3}\right) = 1$ and neither $a = \dfrac{3}{5}$ or $b = \dfrac{5}{3}$ is 1.

44. (A) All integers are natural numbers is false since -1 is an integer but not a natural number.

(B) All rational numbers are real numbers is true.

(C) All natural numbers are rational numbers is true since $1 = \frac{1}{1}$, $2 = \frac{2}{1}$, $3 = \frac{3}{1}$, … for the natural numbers.

46. The $\sqrt{2}$ is an example of a real number that is not a rational number since $\sqrt{2}$ cannot be written as the ratio of two integers. π (pi) is also such a number. In fact, there are infinitely many such numbers.

48. (A) $8 \in N$, $8 \in Z$, $8 \in Q$, and $8 \in R$

(B) $\sqrt{2} \in R$

(C) $-1.414 \in Q$ and $-1.414 \in R$

(D) $\frac{-5}{2} \in Q$ and $\frac{-5}{2} \in R$

50. (A) $\frac{13}{6} = 2.1666…$

$= 2.1\overline{6}$

(B) $\sqrt{21} = 4.582575695…$

(C) $\frac{7}{16} = 0.437500…$

$= 0.4375$

(D) $\frac{29}{111} = 0.261261261…$

$= 0.\overline{261}$

52. (A) $(a + b) + c = a + (b + c)$ is T, associative (+)

(B) $(a - b) - c = a - (b - c)$ is F, since
$(8 - 4) - 2 = 4 - 2$ and $8 - (4 - 2) = 8 - 2$
$\qquad\qquad = 2 \qquad\qquad\qquad\qquad = 6$
There is no associative property for subtraction.

(C) $a(bc) = (ab)c$ is T, associative ($\cdot$)

(D) $(a \div b) \div c = a \div (b \div c)$ is F, since
$(8 \div 4) \div 2 = 2 \div 2$ and $8 \div (4 \div 2) = 8 \div 2$
$\qquad\qquad = 1 \qquad\qquad\qquad\qquad = 4$
There is no associative property for division.

54. $F = \{-2, 0, 2\}$; $G = \{-1, 0, 1, 2\}$

(A) $\{x \mid x \in F \text{ or } x \in G\} = \{-2, -1, 0, 1, 2\}$

(B) $\{x \mid x \in F \text{ and } x \in G\} = \{0, 2\}$

56. Let $x = 0.181818…$, then $100x = 18.181818…$ and $100x - x = 99x = 18$

$x = \frac{18}{99}$

$x = \frac{2}{11}$

58.

statement		reason
1. $(a + b) + (-a)$	$= (-a) + (a + b)$	1. commutative (+)
2.	$= [(-a) + a] + b$	2. associative (+)
3.	$= 0 + b$	3. inverse (+)
4.	$= b$	4. identity (+)

Exercise A-2

2. $2x^2 + x - 1$ is degree 2

4. $(2x^2 + x - 1) + (3x - 2) = 2x^2 + (1 + 3)x - 1 - 2$
$$= 2x^2 + 4x - 3$$

6. $(2x^2 + x - 1) - (3x - 2) = 2x^2 + x - 1 - 3x + 2$
$$= 2x^2 - 2x + 1$$

8. $(2x^2 + x - 1)(3x - 2) = 6x^3 - 4x^2 + 3x^2 - 2x - 3x + 2$
$$= 6x^3 - x^2 - 5x + 2$$

10. $2(u - 1) - (3u + 2) - 2(2u - 3) = 2u - 2 - 3u - 2 - 4u + 6$
$$= -5u + 2$$

12. $4a - 2a[5 - 3(a + 2)] = 4a - 2a[5 - 3a - 6]$
$$= 4a - 2a[-3a - 1]$$
$$= 4a + 6a^2 + 2a$$
$$= 6a^2 + 6a$$

14. $(a + b)(a - b) = a^2 - ab + ba - b^2$
$$= a^2 - b^2$$

16. $(3x - 5)(2x + 1) = 6x^2 + 3x - 10x - 5$
$$= 6x^2 - 7x - 5$$

18. $(2x - 3y)(x + 2y) = 2x^2 + 4xy - 3xy - 6y^2$
$$= 2x^2 + xy - 6y^2$$

20. $(3y + 2)(3y - 2) = 9y^2 - 6y + 6y - 4$
$$= 9y^2 - 4$$

22. $(3m + 7n)(2m - 5n) = 6m^2 - 15mn + 14mn - 35n^2$
$$= 6m^2 - mn - 35n^2$$

24. $(4m + 3n)(4m - 3n) = 16m^2 - 12mn + 12nm - 9n^2$
$$= 16m^2 - 9n^2$$

26. $(3u + 4v)^2 = (3u)^2 + 2(3u)(4v) + (4v)^2$
$$= 9u^2 + 24uv + 16v^2$$

28. $(a - b)(a^2 + ab + b^2) = a^3 + a^2b + ab^2 - a^2b - ab^2 - b^3$
$$= a^3 - b^3$$

30. $m - \{m - [m - (m - 1)]\} = m - \{m - [m - m + 1]\}$
$$= m - \{m - 1\}$$
$$= m - m + 1$$
$$= 1$$

32. $5b - 3\{-[2 - 4(2b - 1)] + 2(2 - 3b)\} = 5b - 3\{-[2 - 8b + 4] + 4 - 6b\}$
$$= 5b - 3\{-[6 - 8b] + 4 - 6b\}$$
$$= 5b - 3\{-6 + 8b + 4 - 6b\}$$
$$= 5b - 3\{2b - 2\}$$
$$= 5b - 6b + 6$$
$$= -b + 6$$

34. $(x^2 - 2xy + y^2)(x^2 + 2xy + y^2)$
$$= x^4 + 2x^3y + x^2y^2 - 2x^3y - 4x^2y^2 - 2xy^3 + x^2y^2 + 2xy^3 + y^4$$
$$= x^4 - 2x^2y^2 + y^4$$

36. $(n^2 + 2n + 1)(n^2 - 4n - 3) = n^4 - 4n^3 - 3n^2 + 2n^3 - 8n^2 - 6n + n^2 - 4n - 3$
$$= n^4 - 2n^3 - 10n^2 - 10n - 3$$

38. $(3a - b)(3a + b) - (2a - 3b)^2$
$$= 9a^2 - b^2 - (4a^2 - 12ab + 9b^2)$$
$$= 9a^2 - b^2 - 4a^2 + 12ab - 9b^2$$
$$= 5a^2 + 12ab - 10b^2$$

40. $(y - 2)(y + 1) + (y - 3)(y + 4)$
$$= y^2 - y - 2 + y^2 + y - 12$$
$$= 2y^2 - 14$$

42. $(3a + 2b)^3 = (9a^2 + 12ab + 4b^2)(3a + 2b)$
$= 27a^3 + 18a^2b + 36a^2b + 24ab^2 + 12ab^2 + 8b^3$
$= 27a^3 + 54a^2b + 36ab^2 + 8b^3$

44. $6(x + h) + 2 - (6x + 2) = 6x + 6h + 2 - 6x - 2$
$= 6h$

46. $4(x + h)^2 - 5(x + h) - (4x^2 - 5x) = 4(x^2 + 2xh + h^2) - 5x - 5h - 4x^2 + 5x$
$= 4x^2 + 8xh + 4h^2 - 5x - 5h - 4x^2 + 5x$
$= 8xh + 4h^2 - 5h$

48. $-(x + h)^2 + 4(x + h) - 9 - (-x^2 + 4x - 9)$
$= -(x^2 + 2xh + h^2) + 4x + 4h - 9 + x^2 - 4x + 9$
$= -x^2 - 2xh - h^2 + 4h + x^2$
$= -2xh - h^2 + 4h$

50. $2(x + h)^2 + 3(x + h) - (2x^2 + 3x) = 2(x^2 + 2xh + h^2) + 3x + 3h - 2x^2 - 3x$
$= 2x^2 + 4xh + 2h^2 + 3h - 2x^2$
$= 4xh + 2h^2 + 3h$

52. $(2x^2 - 4xy + y^2) + (3xy - y^2) - [(x^2 - 2xy - y^2) + (-x^2 + 3xy - 2y^2)]$
$= 2x^2 - 4xy + y^2 + 3xy - y^2 - [x^2 - 2xy - y^2 - x^2 + 3xy - 2y^2]$
$= 2x^2 - xy - [xy - 3y^2]$
$= 2x^2 - xy - xy + 3y^2$
$= 2x^2 - 2xy + 3y^2$

54. $(2x - 1)^3 - 2(2x - 1)^2 + 3(2x - 1) + 7$
$= (4x^2 - 4x + 1)(2x - 1) - 2(4x^2 - 4x + 1) + 6x - 3 + 7$
$= 8x^3 - 4x^2 - 8x^2 + 4x + 2x - 1 - 8x^2 + 8x - 2 + 6x + 4$
$= 8x^3 - 20x^2 + 20x + 1$

56. $2\{(x - 3)(x^2 - 2x + 1) - x[3 - x(x - 2)]\}$
$= 2\{x^3 - 2x^2 + x - 3x^2 + 6x - 3 - x[3 - x^2 + 2x]\}$
$= 2\{x^3 - 5x^2 + 7x - 3 - 3x + x^3 - 2x^2\}$
$= 2\{2x^3 - 7x^2 + 4x - 3\}$
$= 4x^3 - 14x^2 + 8x - 6$

58. Suppose $(a - b)^2 = a^2 - b^2$,
then $\qquad a^2 - 2ab + b^2 = a^2 - b^2$
$2ab - 2b^2 = 0$
$b(a - b) = 0$
$b = 0 \quad$ or $\quad a - b = 0$
$a = b$

Therefore, unless $b = 0$ or $a = b$, $(a - b)^2 = a^2 - b^2$ will not be true.
In general, $(a - b)^2 \neq a^2 - b^2$.

60. Let $a_n x^n$ be the term of highest degree in the first polynomial and $a_m x^m$ be the term of highest degree in the second polynomial, then $a_n a_m x^n x^m = a_n a_m x^{n+m}$ will be the term with the highest degree in the product; thus, the product is of degree $m + n$.

62. Answer does not change. The product is still of degree $m + n = m + m = 2m$.

64.

$A = \ell w$
$= (x + 8)x$
$= x^2 + 8x$

66. $\qquad x$ = number of quarters
$x + 4$ = number of dimes
Value $= 25x + 10(x + 4)$
$= 25x + 10x + 40$
$= 35x + 40$

68. The cube + coating has sides of length $x + 4$; then
$V = (x + 4)^3 - x^3$
$= (x^2 + 8x + 16)(x + 4) - x^3$
$= x^3 + 4x^2 + 8x^2 + 32x + 16x + 64 - x^3$
$= 12x^2 + 48x + 64$

Exercise A-3

2. $6m^4 - 9m^3 - 3m^2 = 3m^2(2m^2 - 3m - 1)$

4. $8u^3v - 6u^2v^2 + 4uv^3 = 2uv(4u^2 - 3uv + 2v^2)$

6. $7m(2m - 3) + 5(2m - 3) = (2m - 3)(7m + 5)$

8. $a(3c + d) - 4b(3c + d) = (3c + d)(a - 4b)$

10. $2y^2 - 6y + 5y - 15 = 2y(y - 3) + 5(y - 3)$
$$= (y - 3)(2y + 5)$$

12. $5x^2 - 40x - x + 8 = 5x(x - 8) - (x - 8)$
$$= (x - 8)(5x - 1)$$

14. $3a^2 - 12ab - 2ab + 8b^2 = 3a(a - 4b) - 2b(a - 4b)$
$$= (a - 4b)(3a - 2b)$$

16. $3pr - 2qs - qr + 6ps = 3pr - qr + 6ps - 2qs$
$$= r(3p - q) + 2s(3p - q)$$
$$= (3p - q)(r + 2s)$$

18. $3y^2 - y - 2 = (3y + 2)(y - 1)$ **20.** $u^2 - 2uv - 15v^2 = (u - 5v)(u + 3v)$

22. $m^2 - 6m - 3$ prime   **24.** $w^2x^2 - y^2 = (wx - y)(wx + y)$ difference of squares

26. $9m^2 - 6mn + n^2 = (3m - n)^2$ perfect square trinomial

28. $y^2 + 16$ prime. Sum of squares will not factor over the reals.

30. $4z^2 - 28z + 48 = 4(z^2 - 7z + 12)$ **32.** $2x^4 - 24x^3 + 40x^2 = 2x^2(x^2 - 12x + 20)$
$$= 4(z - 3)(z - 4) \qquad\qquad = 2x^2(x - 10)(x - 2)$$

34. $4xy^2 - 12xy + 9x = x(4y^2 - 12y + 9)$
$$= x(2y - 3)^2$$

36. $6m^2 - mn - 12n^2 = (2m - 3n)(3m + 4n)$ **38.** $4u^3v - uv^3 = uv(4u^2 - v^2)$
$$= uv(2u - v)(2u + v)$$

40. $2x^3 - 2x^2 + 8x = 2x(x^2 - x + 4)$

42. $r^3 - t^3 = (r - t)(r^2 + rt + t^2)$ difference of cubes

44. $a^3 + 1 = (a + 1)(a^2 - a + 1)$ sum of cubes

46. $2(x - 3)(4x + 7)^2 + 8(x - 3)^2(4x + 7) = 2(x - 3)(4x + 7)[(4x + 7) + 4(x - 3)]$
$$= 2(x - 3)(4x + 7)(4x + 7 + 4x - 12)$$
$$= 2(x - 3)(4x + 7)(8x - 5)$$

48. $3x^4(x - 7)^2 + 4x^3(x - 7)^3 = x^3(x - 7)^2[3x + 4(x - 7)]$
$$= x^3(x - 7)^2(3x + 4x - 28)$$
$$= x^3(x - 7)^2(7x - 28)$$
$$= 7x^3(x - 7)^2(x - 4)$$

50. $4(x - 3)^3(x^2 + 2)^3 + 6x(x - 3)^4(x^2 + 2)^2$

$\quad\quad\quad = 2(x - 3)^3(x^2 + 2)^2[2(x^2 + 2) + 3x(x - 3)]$

$\quad\quad\quad = 2(x - 3)^3(x^2 + 2)^2(2x^2 + 4 + 3x^2 - 9x)$

$\quad\quad\quad = 2(x - 3)^3(x^2 + 2)^2(5x^2 - 9x + 4)$

$\quad\quad\quad = 2(x - 3)^3(x^2 + 2)^2(5x - 4)(x - 1)$

52. $(x + 2)^2 - 9y^2 = [(x + 2) + 3y][(x + 2) - 3y]$

$\quad\quad\quad\quad\quad = (x + 3y + 2)(x - 3y + 2)$

54. $15ac - 20ad + 3bc - 4bd = 5a(3c - 4d) + b(3c - 4d)$

$\quad\quad\quad\quad\quad\quad\quad\quad = (3c - 4d)(5a + b)$

56. $5u^2 + 4uv - 2v^2$ is prime relative to the integers.

58. $x^3 - x^2 - x + 1 = x^2(x - 1) - (x - 1)$

$\quad\quad\quad\quad\quad = (x^2 - 1)(x - 1)$

$\quad\quad\quad\quad\quad = (x + 1)(x - 1)(x - 1)$

$\quad\quad\quad\quad\quad = (x + 1)(x - 1)^2$

60. $t^3 - 2t^2 + t - 2 = t^2(t - 2) + (t - 2)$

$\quad\quad\quad\quad\quad = (t - 2)(t^2 + 1)$

62. $6(x - y)^2 + 23(x - y) - 4 = [(x - y) + 4][6(x - y) - 1]$ \quad Use $6a^2 + 23a - 4$

$\quad\quad\quad\quad\quad\quad\quad\quad\quad\quad\quad\quad\quad$ where $a = (x - y)$

$\quad\quad\quad\quad\quad\quad\quad\quad = (x - y + 4)(6x - 6y - 1)$

64. $y^4 - 3y^2 - 4 = (y^2 - 4)(y^2 + 1)$

$\quad\quad\quad\quad\quad = (y - 2)(y + 2)(y^2 + 1)$

66. $27a^2 + a^5b^3 = a^2(27 + a^3b^3)$ sum of cubes

$\quad\quad\quad\quad = a^2(3 + ab)(9 - 3ab + a^2b^2)$

68. $y^2 - 2xy + x^2 - y + x = (y^2 - 2xy + x^2) - (y - x)$

$\quad\quad\quad\quad\quad\quad\quad = (y - x)^2 - (y - x)$

$\quad\quad\quad\quad\quad\quad\quad = (y - x)(y - x - 1)$

70. $25(4x^2 - 12xy + 9y^2) - 9a^2b^2 = 25(2x - 3y)^2 - 9a^2b^2$ \quad difference of squares

$\quad\quad\quad\quad\quad\quad\quad\quad\quad = [5(2x - 3y) + 3ab][5(2x - 3y) - 3ab]$

$\quad\quad\quad\quad\quad\quad\quad\quad\quad = [10x - 15y + 3ab][10x - 15y - 3ab]$

72. $a^4 + 2a^2b^2 + b^4 - a^2b^2 = (a^2 + b^2)^2 - a^2b^2$ \quad difference of squares

$\quad\quad\quad\quad\quad\quad\quad\quad = [(a^2 + b^2) - ab][(a^2 + b^2) + ab]$

$\quad\quad\quad\quad\quad\quad\quad\quad = (a^2 + b^2 - ab)(a^2 + b^2 + ab)$

74. (A) area $= 16 \cdot 9 - 4x^2 = 144 - 4x^2 = 4(6 - x)(6 + x)$

$\quad\quad$ (B) volume $= (16 - 2x)(9 - 2x) \cdot x = 2x(8 - x)(9 - 2x) = 4x^3 - 50x^2 + 144x$

Exercise   A-4

2. $\dfrac{d^5}{3a} \div \left(\dfrac{d^2}{6a^2} \cdot \dfrac{a}{4d^3}\right) = \dfrac{d^5}{3a} \div \left(\dfrac{1}{24ad}\right)$

$\qquad\qquad\qquad\qquad\quad = \dfrac{d^5}{3a} \cdot \dfrac{24ad}{1}$

$\qquad\qquad\qquad\qquad\quad = 8d^6$

4. $\dfrac{x^2}{12} + \dfrac{x}{18} - \dfrac{1}{30} = \dfrac{15x^2}{180} + \dfrac{10x}{180} - \dfrac{6}{180}$

$\qquad\qquad\qquad\qquad = \dfrac{15x^2 + 10x - 6}{180}$

6. $\dfrac{4m - 3}{18m^3} + \dfrac{3}{4m} - \dfrac{2m - 1}{6m^2} = \dfrac{2(4m - 3)}{36m^3} + \dfrac{9m^2(3)}{36m^3} - \dfrac{6m(2m - 1)}{36m^3}$

$\qquad\qquad\qquad\qquad\qquad\qquad = \dfrac{8m - 6 + 27m^2 - 12m^2 + 6m}{36m^3}$

$\qquad\qquad\qquad\qquad\qquad\qquad = \dfrac{15m^2 + 14m - 6}{36m^3}$

8. $\dfrac{x^2 - 9}{x^2 - 3x} \div (x^2 - x - 12) = \dfrac{(x + 3)(x - 3)}{x(x - 3)} \cdot \dfrac{1}{(x - 4)(x + 3)}$

$\qquad\qquad\qquad\qquad\qquad\qquad = \dfrac{1}{x(x - 4)}$

10. $\dfrac{x^2 - 6x + 9}{x^2 - x - 6} \div \dfrac{x^2 + 2x - 15}{x^2 + 2x} = \dfrac{(x - 3)^2}{(x - 3)(x + 2)} \cdot \dfrac{x(x + 2)}{(x + 5)(x - 3)}$

$\qquad\qquad\qquad\qquad\qquad\qquad = \dfrac{x}{x + 5}$

12. $\dfrac{3}{x^2 - 1} - \dfrac{2}{x^2 - 2x + 1} = \dfrac{3}{(x - 1)(x + 1)} - \dfrac{2}{(x - 1)(x - 1)}$

$\qquad\qquad\qquad\qquad\qquad = \dfrac{3(x - 1)}{(x - 1)^2(x + 1)} - \dfrac{2(x + 1)}{(x - 1)^2(x + 1)}$

$\qquad\qquad\qquad\qquad\qquad = \dfrac{3x - 3 - 2x - 2}{(x - 1)^2(x + 1)}$

$\qquad\qquad\qquad\qquad\qquad = \dfrac{x - 5}{(x - 1)^2(x + 1)}$

14. $\dfrac{x + 1}{x - 1} - 1 = \dfrac{x + 1}{x - 1} - \dfrac{x - 1}{x - 1}$

$\qquad\qquad\qquad = \dfrac{x + 1 - x + 1}{x - 1}$

$\qquad\qquad\qquad = \dfrac{2}{x - 1}$

16. $\dfrac{3}{a - 1} - \dfrac{2}{1 - a} = \dfrac{3}{a - 1} - \dfrac{-2}{a - 1}$

$\qquad\qquad\qquad\quad = \dfrac{3}{a - 1} + \dfrac{2}{a - 1}$

$\qquad\qquad\qquad\quad = \dfrac{5}{a - 1}$

18. $\dfrac{2x}{x^2 - y^2} + \dfrac{1}{x + y} - \dfrac{1}{x - y} = \dfrac{2x}{(x + y)(x - y)} + \dfrac{1(x - y)}{(x + y)(x - y)} - \dfrac{1(x + y)}{(x + y)(x - y)}$

$\qquad\qquad\qquad\qquad\qquad\qquad = \dfrac{2x + x - y - (x + y)}{(x + y)(x - y)}$

$\qquad\qquad\qquad\qquad\qquad\qquad = \dfrac{3x - y - x - y}{(x + y)(x - y)}$

$\qquad\qquad\qquad\qquad\qquad\qquad = \dfrac{2x - 2y}{(x + y)(x - y)}$

$\qquad\qquad\qquad\qquad\qquad\qquad = \dfrac{2(x - y)}{(x + y)(x - y)}$

$\qquad\qquad\qquad\qquad\qquad\qquad = \dfrac{2}{x + y}$

20. $\dfrac{1 + \frac{3}{x}}{x - \frac{9}{x}} \cdot \dfrac{x}{x} = \dfrac{x + 3}{x^2 - 9} = \dfrac{x + 3}{(x + 3)(x - 3)}$

$\qquad\qquad\qquad\qquad\qquad = \dfrac{1}{x - 3}$

22. $\dfrac{4x^4(x^2 + 3) - 3x^2(x^2 + 3)^2}{x^6} = \dfrac{x^2(x^2 + 3)[4x^2 - 3(x^2 + 3)]}{x^6}$

$\qquad\qquad\qquad\qquad\qquad\qquad = \dfrac{x^2(x^2 + 3)(x^2 - 9)}{x^6}$

$\qquad\qquad\qquad\qquad\qquad\qquad = \dfrac{x^2(x^2 + 3)(x + 3)(x - 3)}{x^6}$

$\qquad\qquad\qquad\qquad\qquad\qquad = \dfrac{(x^2 + 3)(x + 3)(x - 3)}{x^4}$

24. $\dfrac{2x(2x + 3)^4 - 8x^2(2x + 3)^3}{(2x + 3)^8} = \dfrac{2x(2x + 3)^3[(2x + 3) - 4x]}{(2x + 3)^8}$

$\qquad\qquad\qquad\qquad\qquad\qquad = \dfrac{2x(2x + 3)^3(3 - 2x)}{(2x + 3)^8}$

$\qquad\qquad\qquad\qquad\qquad\qquad = \dfrac{2x(3 - 2x)}{(2x + 3)^5}$

26. $\dfrac{3x^2(x + 1)^3 - 3(x^3 + 4)(x + 1)^2}{(x + 1)^6} = \dfrac{3(x + 1)^2[x^2(x + 1) - (x^3 + 4)]}{(x + 1)^6}$

$\qquad\qquad\qquad\qquad\qquad\qquad\qquad = \dfrac{3(x + 1)^2[x^3 + x^2 - x^3 - 4]}{(x + 1)^6}$

$\qquad\qquad\qquad\qquad\qquad\qquad\qquad = \dfrac{3(x + 1)^2(x^2 - 4)}{(x + 1)^6}$

$\qquad\qquad\qquad\qquad\qquad\qquad\qquad = \dfrac{3(x + 2)(x - 2)}{(x + 1)^4}$

28. $\dfrac{x^2}{x^2 + 2x + 1} + \dfrac{x - 1}{3x + 3} - \dfrac{1}{6} = \dfrac{x^2}{(x + 1)^2} + \dfrac{x - 1}{3(x + 1)} - \dfrac{1}{6}$

$\qquad\qquad\qquad\qquad\qquad = \dfrac{6x^2}{6(x + 1)^2} + \dfrac{2(x + 1)(x - 1)}{6(x + 1)^2} - \dfrac{(x + 1)^2}{6(x + 1)^2}$

$\qquad\qquad\qquad\qquad\qquad = \dfrac{6x^2 + 2x^2 - 2 - (x^2 + 2x + 1)}{6(x + 1)^2}$

$\qquad\qquad\qquad\qquad\qquad = \dfrac{7x^2 - 2x - 3}{6(x + 1)^2}$

30. $\dfrac{2 - x}{2x + x^2} \cdot \dfrac{x^2 + 4x + 4}{x^2 - 4} = \dfrac{-(x - 2)}{x(x + 2)} \cdot \dfrac{(x + 2)(x + 2)}{(x + 2)(x - 2)}$

$\qquad\qquad\qquad\qquad\qquad = -\dfrac{1}{x}$

32. $\dfrac{c + 2}{5c - 5} - \dfrac{c - 2}{3c - 3} + \dfrac{c}{1 - c} = \dfrac{c + 2}{5(c - 1)} - \dfrac{c - 2}{3(c - 1)} - \dfrac{c}{c - 1}$

$\qquad\qquad\qquad\qquad\qquad = \dfrac{3(c + 2)}{15(c - 1)} - \dfrac{5(c - 2)}{15(c - 1)} - \dfrac{15c}{15(c - 1)}$

$\qquad\qquad\qquad\qquad\qquad = \dfrac{3c + 6 - 5c + 10 - 15c}{15(c - 1)}$

$\qquad\qquad\qquad\qquad\qquad = \dfrac{-17c + 16}{15(c - 1)}$

34. $\left(\dfrac{x^3 - y^3}{y^3} \cdot \dfrac{y}{x - y}\right) \div \dfrac{x^2 + xy + y^2}{y^2} = \left(\dfrac{(x - y)(x^2 + xy + y^2)}{y^3} \cdot \dfrac{y}{x - y}\right) \cdot \dfrac{y^2}{(x^2 + xy + y^2)}$
$= 1$

36. $\left(\dfrac{x^2 - xy}{xy + y^2} + \dfrac{x^2 - y^2}{x^2 + 2xy + y^2}\right) \div \dfrac{x^2 - 2xy + y^2}{x^2y + xy^2} = \dfrac{x(x - y)}{y(x + y)} \cdot \dfrac{(x + y)^2}{(x + y)(x - y)} \cdot \dfrac{xy(x + y)}{(x - y)^2}$
$= \dfrac{x}{y} \cdot \dfrac{xy(x + y)}{(x - y)^2}$
$= \dfrac{x^2(x + y)}{(x - y)^2}$

38. $\left(\dfrac{3}{x - 2} - \dfrac{1}{x + 1}\right) \div \dfrac{x + 4}{x - 2} = \dfrac{3(x + 1) - 1(x - 2)}{(x - 2)(x + 1)} \cdot \dfrac{x - 2}{x + 4}$
$= \dfrac{3x + 3 - x + 2}{x + 1} \cdot \dfrac{1}{x + 4}$
$= \dfrac{2x + 5}{(x + 1)(x + 4)}$

40. $\dfrac{\frac{x}{y} - 2 + \frac{y}{x}}{\frac{x}{y} - \frac{y}{x}} \cdot \dfrac{xy}{xy} = \dfrac{x^2 - 2xy + y^2}{x^2 - y^2}$
$= \dfrac{(x - y)^2}{(x - y)(x + y)}$
$= \dfrac{x - y}{x + y}$

42. $\dfrac{\frac{1}{(x + h)^2} - \frac{1}{x^2}}{h} = \dfrac{x^2 - (x + h)^2}{x^2(x + h)^2} \cdot \dfrac{1}{h}$
$= \dfrac{x^2 - x^2 - 2xh - h^2}{x^2(x + h)^2} \cdot \dfrac{1}{h}$
$= \dfrac{-h(2x + h)}{x^2(x + h)^2} \cdot \dfrac{1}{h}$
$= \dfrac{-2x - h}{x^2(x + h)^2}$

44. $\dfrac{\frac{2x + 2h + 3}{x + h} - \frac{2x + 3}{x}}{h} \cdot \dfrac{x(x + h)}{x(x + h)} = \dfrac{2x^2 + 2xh + 3x - (2x + 3)(x + h)}{xh(x + h)}$
$= \dfrac{2x^2 + 2xh + 3x - 2x^2 - 2xh - 3x - 3h}{xh(x + h)}$
$= \dfrac{-3h}{xh(x + h)}$
$= \dfrac{-3}{x(x + h)}$

46. (A) Solution shown is incorrect. The two terms "-3" were canceled incorrectly. Only factors can be canceled.

(B) $\dfrac{x^2 - 2x - 3}{x - 3} = \dfrac{(x - 3)(x + 1)}{(x - 3)} = x + 1$

48. (A) Solution shown is incorrect. The term "+h" in the numerator was canceled incorrectly. Only factors can be canceled.

(B) $\dfrac{(x + h)^3 - x^3}{h} = \dfrac{x^3 + 3x^2h + 3xh^2 + h^3 - x^3}{h}$
$= \dfrac{h(3x^2 + 3xh + h^2)}{h}$
$= 3x^2 + 3xh + h^2$

50. (A) Solution shown is correct.

$$\frac{2}{x-1} - \frac{x+3}{x^2-1} = \frac{2(x+1) - (x+3)}{(x-1)(x+1)} = \frac{2x+2-x-3}{(x-1)(x+1)}$$

$$= \frac{(x-1)}{(x-1)(x+1)} = \frac{1}{x+1}$$

52. (A) Solution shown is incorrect. The two terms were combined incorrectly. The first term "x" must be built up as a fraction with a common denominator.

(B) $x + \dfrac{x-2}{x^2-3x+2} = \dfrac{x(x^2-3x+2) + x - 2}{x^2-3x+2}$

$$= \frac{x(x-2)(x-1) + (x-2)}{(x-2)(x-1)}$$

$$= \frac{(x-2)(x(x-1)+1)}{(x-2)(x-1)}$$

$$= \frac{x^2 - x + 1}{x-1}$$

54. $\dfrac{\frac{s^2}{s-t} - s}{\frac{t^2}{s-t} + t} \cdot \dfrac{s-t}{s-t} = \dfrac{s^2 - s(s-t)}{t^2 + t(s-t)}$

$$= \frac{s^2 - s^2 + st}{t^2 + st - t^2}$$

$$= \frac{st}{st}$$

$$= 1$$

56. $1 - \dfrac{1}{1 - \dfrac{1}{1 - \frac{1}{x} \cdot \frac{x}{x}}} = 1 - \dfrac{1}{1 - \frac{x}{x-1}} \cdot \dfrac{x-1}{x-1}$

$$= 1 - \frac{x-1}{x-1-x}$$

$$= 1 - \frac{x-1}{-1}$$

$$= 1 + x - 1$$

$$= x$$

58. $\dfrac{a}{b} + \dfrac{c}{b} = a\left(\dfrac{1}{b}\right) + c\left(\dfrac{1}{b}\right)$ definition of division

$$= (a + c)\left(\frac{1}{b}\right) \quad \text{distributive}$$

$$= \frac{a+c}{b} \qquad \text{definition of division}$$

Exercise A-5

2. $x^3 x^{-3} = x^{3-3}$
$= x^0$
$= 1$

4. $(2x^5)(3x^7)(4x^2) = 24x^{5+7+2}$
$= 24x^{14}$

6. $(2cd^2)^{-3} = \dfrac{1}{(2cd^2)^3}$

$$= \frac{1}{2^3 c^3 (d^2)^3}$$

$$= \frac{1}{8c^3 d^6}$$

8. $\left(\dfrac{x^2 y}{2w^2}\right)^3 = \dfrac{(x^2)^3 y^3}{2^3(w^2)^3}$

$$= \frac{x^6 y^3}{8w^6}$$

10. $\dfrac{10^{-13} \cdot 10^{-4}}{10^{-21} \cdot 10^3} = \dfrac{10^{-17}}{10^{-18}}$
$= 10^{-17 - (-18)}$
$= 10$

12. $\dfrac{2a^6 b^{-2}}{16a^{-3}b^2} = \dfrac{2a^6 a^3}{16b^2 b^2}$

$$= \frac{a^{6+3}}{8b^{2+2}}$$

$$= \frac{a^9}{8b^4}$$

14. $\left(\dfrac{x^{-1}}{x^{-8}}\right)^{-1} = \dfrac{x^{-1(-1)}}{x^{-8(-1)}}$

$$= \frac{x^1}{x^8}$$

$$= \frac{1}{x^7}$$

16. $\dfrac{18 \times 10^{12}}{6 \times 10^{-4}} = 3 \times 10^{12+4}$

$\qquad\qquad = 3 \times 10^{16}$

18. $4{,}930 = 4.93 \times 10^3$

20. $0.017 = 1.7 \times 10^{-2}$

22. $0.000592 = 5.92 \times 10^{-4}$

24. $4 \times 10^{-4} = 0.0004$

26. $6.5 \times 10^9 = 6{,}500{,}000{,}000$

28. $6.3 \times 10^{-6} = 0.0000063$

30. $\dfrac{32n^5 n^{-8}}{24m^{-7}m^7} = \dfrac{32n^5 m^7}{24n^8 m^7}$

$\qquad\qquad\quad = \dfrac{4}{3n^3}$

32. $\left(\dfrac{m^{-2}n^3}{m^4 n^{-1}}\right)^2 = \left(\dfrac{n^3 n^1}{m^4 m^2}\right)^2 = \left(\dfrac{n^4}{m^6}\right)^2$ simplify inside parentheses first

$\qquad\qquad = \dfrac{n^8}{m^{12}}$

34. $\left(\dfrac{6mn^{-2}}{3m^{-1}n^2}\right)^{-3} = \left(\dfrac{6mm}{3n^2 n^2}\right)^{-3}$

$\qquad\qquad\quad = \left(\dfrac{2m^2}{n^4}\right)^{-3}$

$\qquad\qquad\quad = \left(\dfrac{n^4}{2m^2}\right)^{3}$

$\qquad\qquad\quad = \dfrac{n^{12}}{8m^6}$

36. $\left[\left(\dfrac{x^{-2}y^3 t}{x^{-3}y^{-2}t^2}\right)^2\right]^{-1} = \left[\left(\dfrac{x^3 y^3 y^2 t}{x^2 t^2}\right)^2\right]^{-1}$

$\qquad\qquad\qquad\quad = \left[\left(\dfrac{xy^5}{t}\right)^2\right]^{-1}$

$\qquad\qquad\qquad\quad = \left[\dfrac{x^2 y^{10}}{t^2}\right]^{-1}$

$\qquad\qquad\qquad\quad = \dfrac{t^2}{x^2 y^{10}}$

38. $(a^2 - b^2)^{-1} = \dfrac{1}{a^2 - b^2}$

40. $\dfrac{1 - x}{x^{-1} - 1} = \dfrac{1 - x}{\frac{1}{x} - 1} \cdot \dfrac{x}{x}$

$\qquad\quad = \dfrac{x(1 - x)}{1 - x}$

$\qquad\quad = x$

42. $\dfrac{u + v}{u^{-1} + v^{-1}} = \dfrac{u + v}{\frac{1}{u} + \frac{1}{v}} \cdot \dfrac{uv}{uv}$

$\qquad\qquad = \dfrac{uv(u + v)}{v + u}$

$\qquad\qquad = uv$

44. $-2(x^2 + 3x)^{-3}(2x + 3) = \dfrac{-2(2x + 3)}{(x^2 + 3x)^3}$

46. $2^{(3^2)} = 2^9 = 512$, $(2^3)^2 = 8^2 = 64$
On a calculator 2^3^2 = 64, (2^3)^2 = 64 and 2^(3^2) = 512.

48. $a^{-n} \cdot a^n = a^n \cdot a^{-n} = a^{n + (-n)} = a^0 = 1$. The definition of reciprocal gives
$a^n \cdot \dfrac{1}{a^n} = 1$ and comparing with $a^n \cdot a^{-n} = 1$ helps motivate the definition
$a^{-n} = \dfrac{1}{a^n}$.

50. $\dfrac{6x^3 + 9x}{3x^3} = \dfrac{6x^3}{3x^3} + \dfrac{9x}{3x^3}$

$\qquad\qquad = 2 + 3x^{-2}$

52. $\dfrac{7x^5 - x^2}{4x^5} = \dfrac{7x^5}{4x^5} - \dfrac{x^2}{4x^5}$

$\qquad\qquad = \dfrac{7}{4} - \dfrac{1}{4}x^{-3}$

54. $\dfrac{3x^4 - 4x^2 - 1}{4x^3} = \dfrac{3x^4}{4x^3} - \dfrac{4x^2}{4x^3} - \dfrac{1}{4x^3}$

$\qquad\qquad\quad = \dfrac{3}{4}x - x^{-1} - \dfrac{1}{4}x^{-3}$

56. $\dfrac{(4,320)(0.000\ 000\ 000\ 704)}{(835)(635,000,000,000)} = \dfrac{(4.32 \times 10^3)(7.04 \times 10^{-10})}{(8.35 \times 10^2)(6.35 \times 10^{11})}$

$\approx 5.74 \times 10^{-21}$ using a calculator

58. $\dfrac{0.000\ 000\ 007\ 23}{(0.0933)(43,700,000,000)} = \dfrac{7.23 \times 10^{-9}}{(9.33 \times 10^{-2})(4.37 \times 10^{10})}$

$\approx 1.77 \times 10^{-18}$ using a calculator

60. $(-302)^7 \approx -2.2911 \times 10^{17}$ using calculator

62. $(23.8)^{-8} \approx 9.7137 \times 10^{-12}$ using calculator

64. $(0.000\ 000\ 000\ 482)^{-4} \approx 1.8527 \times 10^{37}$ using calculator

66. $\dfrac{4(x-3)^{-4}}{8(x-3)^{-2}} = \dfrac{1}{2(x-3)^2}$

68. $\dfrac{b^{-2} - c^{-2}}{b^{-3} - c^{-3}} = \dfrac{\frac{1}{b^2} - \frac{1}{c^2}}{\frac{1}{b^3} - \frac{1}{c^3}} \cdot \dfrac{b^3 c^3}{b^3 c^3}$

$= \dfrac{bc^3 - b^3 c}{c^3 - b^3}$

$= \dfrac{bc(c^2 - b^2)}{(c-b)(c^2 + bc + b^2)}$

$= \dfrac{bc(c-b)(c+b)}{(c-b)(c^2 + bc + b^2)}$

$= \dfrac{bc(c+b)}{c^2 + bc + b^2}$

70. $\left[\dfrac{u^{-2} - v^{-2}}{(u^{-1} - v^{-1})^2}\right]^{-1} = \left[\dfrac{\frac{1}{u^2} - \frac{1}{v^2}}{u^{-2} - 2u^{-1}v^{-1} + v^{-2}}\right]^{-1}$

$= \left[\dfrac{\frac{v^2 - u^2}{u^2 v^2}}{\frac{1}{u^2} - \frac{2}{uv} + \frac{1}{v^2}} \cdot \dfrac{u^2 v^2}{u^2 v^2}\right]^{-1}$

$= \left[\dfrac{v^2 - u^2}{v^2 - 2uv + u^2}\right]^{-1}$

$= \left[\dfrac{(v-u)(v+u)}{(v-u)(v-u)}\right]^{-1}$

$= \left[\dfrac{v+u}{v-u}\right]^{-1} = \dfrac{v-u}{v+u}$

72. weight in pounds = (weight per gram)(number of grams)

$= \dfrac{2.2 \times 10^{-3}\ \text{lb}}{\text{gram}} \cdot 1.5 \times 10^{21}\ \text{gram}$

$= 3.3 \times 10^{18}\ \text{lb}$

74. distance = (rate)(time)

$= \left(1.86 \times 10^5\ \dfrac{\text{mi}}{\text{sec}}\right)(10^{-10}\ \text{sec})$

$= 1.86 \times 10^{-5}\ \text{mi}$

$= 1.86 \times 10^{-5}\ \text{mi} \left(\dfrac{5280\ \text{ft}}{\text{mi}}\right)$

$\approx 9.82 \times 10^{-2}\ \text{ft}$

$\approx 9.82 \times 10^{-2}\ \text{ft} \left(\dfrac{12\ \text{in}}{\text{ft}}\right)$

$\approx 1.18\ \text{in}$

76. GNP per person $= \dfrac{\text{GNP}}{\text{population}}$

$= \dfrac{4,240,000,000,000}{242,000,000}$

$= \dfrac{4.24 \times 10^{12}}{2.42 \times 10^8}$

$\approx 1.75 \times 10^4$

$\approx \$17,500$ per person

Exercise A-6

2. $64^{1/3} = 4$

4. $16^{3/4} = (16^{1/4})^3$
$= 2^3$
$= 8$

6. $(32)^{3/5} = (32^{1/5})^3$
$= 2^3$
$= 8$

8. $(-32)^{3/5} = (-32^{1/5})^3$
$= (-2)^3$
$= -8$

10. $\left(\dfrac{8}{27}\right)^{2/3} = \left[\left(\dfrac{8}{27}\right)^{1/3}\right]^2$
$= \left[\dfrac{2}{3}\right]^2$
$= \dfrac{4}{9}$

12. $8^{-2/3} = \dfrac{1}{8^{2/3}}$
$= \dfrac{1}{(8^{1/3})^2}$
$= \dfrac{1}{2^2}$
$= \dfrac{1}{4}$

14. $x^{1/4}x^{3/4} = x^{1/4+3/4}$
$= x^1$
$= x$

16. $x^{1/4}x^{-3/4} = x^{1/4-3/4}$
$= x^{-2/4}$
$= \dfrac{1}{x^{1/2}}$

18. $(x^{-2/3})^{-6} = x^{(-2/3)(-6)}$
$= x^4$

20. $(4u^{-2}v^4)^{1/2} = 4^{1/2}u^{-2(1/2)}v^{4(1/2)}$
$= 2u^{-1}v^2$
$= \dfrac{2v^2}{u}$

22. $\left(\dfrac{m^{-2/3}}{n^{-1/2}}\right)^{-6} = \dfrac{m^{(-2/3)(-6)}}{n^{(-1/2)(-6)}}$
$= \dfrac{m^4}{n^3}$

24. $\left(\dfrac{w^4}{9x^{-2}}\right)^{-1/2} = \dfrac{w^{4(-1/2)}}{9^{-1/2}x^{-2(-1/2)}}$
$= \dfrac{w^{-2}}{\dfrac{1}{9^{1/2}}x}$
$= \dfrac{\dfrac{1}{w^2}}{\dfrac{x}{3}}$
$= \dfrac{1}{w^2}\cdot\dfrac{3}{x}$
$= \dfrac{3}{xw^2}$

26. $\left(\dfrac{25x^5y^{-1}}{16x^{-3}y^{-5}}\right)^{1/2} = \left(\dfrac{25x^8y^4}{16}\right)^{1/2}$
$= \dfrac{5x^{8(1/2)}y^{4(1/2)}}{4}$
$= \dfrac{5}{4}x^4y^2$

28. $\dfrac{6a^{3/4}}{15a^{-1/3}} = \dfrac{2}{5}a^{3/4-(-1/3)}$
$= \dfrac{2}{5}a^{(9/12+4/12)}$
$= \dfrac{2}{5}a^{13/12}$

30. $\left(\dfrac{x^{-1/3}y^{1/2}}{x^{-1/4}y^{1/3}}\right)^6 = \dfrac{x^{(-1/3)(6)}y^{(1/2)(6)}}{x^{(-1/4)(6)}y^{(1/3)(6)}}$
$= \dfrac{x^{-2}y^3}{x^{-3/2}y^2}$
$= x^{-2-(-3/2)}y^{3-2}$
$= x^{-1/2}y^1$
$= \dfrac{y}{x^{1/2}}$

32. $3x^{3/4}(4x^{1/4} - 2x^8) = 12x^{(3/4+1/4)} - 6x^{(3/4+8)}$
$= 12x - 6x^{35/4}$

34. $(3u^{1/2} - v^{1/2})(u^{1/2} - 4v^{1/2}) = 3u^{(1/2+1/2)} - 12u^{1/2}v^{1/2} - v^{1/2}u^{1/2} + 4v^{(1/2+1/2)}$
$= 3u - 13u^{1/2}v^{1/2} + 4v$

36. $(5m^{1/2} + n^{1/2})(5m^{1/2} - n^{1/2}) = (5m^{1/2})^2 - (n^{1/2})^2$
$= 25m - n$

38. $(3x^{1/2} - y^{1/2})^2 = (3x^{1/2})^2 - 2(3x^{1/2})(y^{1/2}) + (y^{1/2})^2$
$= 9x - 6x^{1/2}y^{1/2} + y$

40. $22^{3/2} \approx 103.2$ using a calculator   **42.** $827^{-3/8} \approx 0.08053$ using a calculator

44. $37.09^{7/3} \approx 4588$ using a calculator

46. $(491,300,000,000)^{7/4} \approx 2.883 \times 10^{20}$ using a calculator

48. For $x = 2$, $y = 3$: $(x^3 + y^3)^{1/3} = (2^3 + 3^3)^{1/3} = (8 + 27)^{1/3} = 35^{1/3} \approx 3.271$
while $(x + y) = 2 + 3 = 5$.

50. For $x = 2$, $y = 3$: $(x + y)^{-1/2} = (2 + 3)^{-1/2} = 5^{-1/2} = \dfrac{1}{\sqrt{5}} \approx 0.447$

while $\dfrac{1}{(x + y)^2} = \dfrac{1}{(2 + 3)^2} = \dfrac{1}{5^2} = \dfrac{1}{25} = 0.04$.

52. $\dfrac{x^{2/3} + 2}{2x^{1/3}} = \dfrac{x^{2/3}}{2x^{1/3}} + \dfrac{2}{2x^{1/3}}$

$= \dfrac{1}{2}x^{1/3} + x^{-1/3}$

54. $\dfrac{2x^{3/4} + 3x^{1/3}}{3x} = \dfrac{2x^{3/4}}{3x} + \dfrac{3x^{1/3}}{3x}$

$= \dfrac{2}{3}x^{-1/4} + x^{-2/3}$

56. $\dfrac{2x^{1/3} - x^{1/2}}{4x^{1/2}} = \dfrac{2x^{1/3}}{4x^{1/2}} - \dfrac{x^{1/2}}{4x^{1/2}}$ $\qquad \left(\dfrac{1}{3} - \dfrac{1}{2} = \dfrac{2 - 3}{6} = -\dfrac{1}{6}\right)$

$= \dfrac{1}{2}x^{-1/6} - \dfrac{1}{4}$

58. $(a^{n/2}b^{n/3})^{1/n} = (a^{n/2})^{1/n}(b^{n/3})^{1/n}$ $\qquad$ **60.** $(a^{m/3}b^{n/2})^{-6} = (a^{m/3})^{-6}(b^{n/2})^{-6}$

$\qquad = a^{(n/2)(1/n)}b^{(n/3)(1/n)}$ $\qquad\qquad\qquad = a^{(m/3)(-6)}b^{(n/2)(-6)}$

$\qquad = a^{1/2}b^{1/3}$ $\qquad\qquad\qquad\qquad\qquad = a^{-2m}b^{-3n}$

$\qquad\qquad\qquad\qquad\qquad\qquad\qquad = \dfrac{1}{a^{2m}b^{3n}}$

62. (A) let $x = 2$, then $(x^2)^{1/2} = (2^2)^{1/2} = (4^{1/2}) = 2 \neq -2$ which shows 2 is a real value of x such that $(x^2)^{1/2} \neq -x$

(B) let $x = -2$, then $(x^2)^{1/2} = ((-2)^2)^{1/2} = (4)^{1/2} = 2 = -(-2)$ which shows -2 is a real value of x such that $(x^2)^{1/2} = -x$

(C) $\qquad (x^3)^{1/3} = -x$
$\qquad\qquad\quad x^3 = (-x)^3$
$\qquad\qquad\quad x^3 = -x^3$
$\qquad\quad x^3 + x^3 = 0$
$\qquad\qquad\; 2x^3 = 0$
$\qquad\qquad\qquad x = 0$,
which shows $(x^3)^{1/3} = -x$ only for $x = 0$

64. For $b \geq 0$, $(b^m)^{1/n} = (b^{1/n})^m$. for $b < 0$, both $(b^m)^{1/n}$ and $(b^{1/n})^m$ are not real. No, it is not possible for one to be real and the other not.

66. $\dfrac{(x - 1)^{1/2} - x(\frac{1}{2})(x - 1)^{-1/2}}{(x - 1)} = \dfrac{(x - 1)^{1/2} - \frac{x}{2(x - 1)^{1/2}}}{x - 1} \cdot \dfrac{2(x - 1)^{1/2}}{2(x - 1)^{1/2}}$

$= \dfrac{2(x - 1) - x}{2(x - 1)^{3/2}}$

$= \dfrac{2x - 2 - x}{2(x - 1)^{3/2}}$

$= \dfrac{x - 2}{2(x - 1)^{3/2}}$

68. $\dfrac{(x + 2)^{2/3} - x(\frac{2}{3})(x + 2)^{-1/3}}{(x + 2)^{4/3}} = \dfrac{(x + 2)^{2/3} - \frac{2x}{3(x + 2)^{1/3}}}{(x + 2)^{4/3}} \cdot \dfrac{3(x + 2)^{1/3}}{3(x + 2)^{1/3}}$

$$= \frac{3(x + 2) - 2x}{3(x + 2)^{5/3}}$$

$$= \frac{3x + 6 - 2x}{3(x + 2)^{5/3}}$$

$$= \frac{(x + 6)}{3(x + 2)^{5/3}}$$

70. $N = 50x^{1/2}y^{1/2}$
$ = 50(256)^{1/2}(144)^{1/2}$
$ = 50(16)(12)$
$ = 9600$ units estimated units

72. $d = 0.0212v^{7/3}$
$ = 0.0212(50)^{7/3}$
$ \approx 195$ ft

Exercise A-7

2. $n^{4/5} = \sqrt[5]{n^4}$ **4.** $7y^{2/5} = 7\sqrt[5]{y^2}$ **6.** $(7x^2y)^{5/7} = \sqrt[7]{(7x^2y)^5}$

8. $x^{1/2} + y^{1/2} = \sqrt{x} + \sqrt{y}$ **10.** $\sqrt{c} = c^{1/2}$ **12.** $7m\sqrt[5]{n^2} = 7mn^{2/5}$

14. $\sqrt[9]{(3m^4n)^2} = (3m^4n)^{2/9}$ **16.** $\sqrt[3]{x + y} = (x + y)^{1/3}$

18. $\sqrt[3]{-27} = -3$ since $(-3)^3 = -27$ **20.** $\sqrt{16m^4y^8} = \sqrt{16}\sqrt{m^4}\sqrt{y^8} = (4^2)^{1/2}(m^4)^{1/2}(y^8)^{1/2}$
$\phantom{20. \sqrt{16m^4y^8} = \sqrt{16}\sqrt{m^4}\sqrt{y^8}} = 4m^2y^4$

22. $\sqrt[5]{32a^{15}b^{10}} = 32^{1/5}(a^{15})^{1/5}(b^{10})^{1/5}$
$\phantom{22. \sqrt[5]{32a^{15}b^{10}}} = 2a^3b^2$

24. $\sqrt{27m^2n^7} = \sqrt{9m^2n^6 \cdot 3n}$
$\phantom{24. \sqrt{27m^2n^7}} = 3mn^3\sqrt{3n}$

26. $\sqrt[4]{2^4x^5y^8} = \sqrt[4]{2^4x^4y^8 \cdot x}$
$\phantom{26. \sqrt[4]{2^4x^5y^8}} = 2xy^2\sqrt[4]{x}$

28. $\sqrt[10]{n^6} = n^{6/10}$
$\phantom{28. \sqrt[10]{n^6}} = n^{3/5}$
$\phantom{28. \sqrt[10]{n^6}} = \sqrt[5]{n^3}$

30. $\sqrt{\sqrt[4]{5x}} = ((5x)^{1/4})^{1/2}$ $(x \geq 0)$
$\phantom{30. \sqrt{\sqrt[4]{5x}}} = (5x)^{1/8}$
$\phantom{30. \sqrt{\sqrt[4]{5x}}} = \sqrt[8]{5x}$

32. $\sqrt{2x}\sqrt{8xy} = \sqrt{16x^2y}$ $(x \geq 0,\ y \geq 0)$
$\phantom{32. \sqrt{2x}\sqrt{8xy}} = 4x\sqrt{y}$

34. $\dfrac{1}{\sqrt{7}} = \dfrac{1}{\sqrt{7}} \cdot \dfrac{\sqrt{7}}{\sqrt{7}}$
$\phantom{34. \frac{1}{\sqrt{7}}} = \dfrac{\sqrt{7}}{7}$

36. $\dfrac{12y^2}{\sqrt{6y}} = \dfrac{12y^2}{\sqrt{6y}} \cdot \dfrac{\sqrt{6y}}{\sqrt{6y}}$
$\phantom{36. \frac{12y^2}{\sqrt{6y}}} = \dfrac{12y^2\sqrt{6y}}{6y}$
$\phantom{36. \frac{12y^2}{\sqrt{6y}}} = 2y\sqrt{6y}$

38. $\dfrac{4}{\sqrt{6}-2} = \dfrac{4}{\sqrt{6}-2} \cdot \dfrac{\sqrt{6}+2}{\sqrt{6}+2}$

$\qquad\qquad = \dfrac{4\sqrt{6}+8}{6-4}$

$\qquad\qquad = \dfrac{4\sqrt{6}+8}{2}$

$\qquad\qquad = 2\sqrt{6}+4$

40. $\dfrac{\sqrt{2}}{\sqrt{10}-2} = \dfrac{\sqrt{2}}{\sqrt{10}-2} \cdot \dfrac{\sqrt{10}+2}{\sqrt{10}+2}$

$\qquad\qquad = \dfrac{\sqrt{20}+2\sqrt{2}}{10-4}$

$\qquad\qquad = \dfrac{2\sqrt{5}+2\sqrt{2}}{6}$

$\qquad\qquad = \dfrac{\sqrt{5}+\sqrt{2}}{3}$

42. $2a\sqrt[3]{8a^8b^{13}} = 2a\sqrt[3]{2^3a^6b^{12}\cdot a^2b}$

$\qquad\qquad = 2a\cdot 2a^2b^4\sqrt[3]{a^2b}$

$\qquad\qquad = 4a^3b^4\sqrt[3]{a^2b}$

44. $\dfrac{\sqrt[5]{32u^{12}v^8}}{uv} = \dfrac{\sqrt[5]{2^5u^{10}v^5\cdot u^2v^3}}{uv}$

$\qquad\qquad = \dfrac{2u^2v\sqrt[5]{u^2v^3}}{uv}$

$\qquad\qquad = 2u\sqrt[5]{u^2v^3}$

46. $\sqrt[8]{3^6(u+v)^6} = 3^{6/8}\cdot(u+v)^{6/8}$

$\qquad\qquad = 3^{3/4}(u+v)^{3/4}$

$\qquad\qquad = \sqrt[4]{3^3(u+v)^3}$

48. $\sqrt{\sqrt[6]{x^8y^6}} = [(x^8y^6)^{1/6}]^{1/2}$

$\qquad\qquad = (x^{8/6}y^{6/6})^{1/2}$

$\qquad\qquad = (x^{4/3}y)^{1/2}$

$\qquad\qquad = x^{4/3\cdot 1/2}y^{1/2}$

$\qquad\qquad = x^{4/6}y^{3/6}$

$\qquad\qquad = \sqrt[6]{x^4y^3}$

50. $\sqrt[4]{4m^5n}\,\sqrt[4]{6m^3n^4} = \sqrt[4]{24m^8n^5}$

$\qquad\qquad = \sqrt[4]{m^8n^4\cdot 24n}$

$\qquad\qquad = m^2n\sqrt[4]{24n}$

52. $\sqrt{x^2+y^2}$ cannot be simplified further

54. $\dfrac{\sqrt{6}\,\sqrt{8c}}{\sqrt{18c}} \cdot \dfrac{\sqrt{2c}}{\sqrt{2c}} = \dfrac{\sqrt{6}\,\sqrt{16c^2}}{\sqrt{36c^2}}$

$\qquad\qquad = \dfrac{\sqrt{6}\cdot 4c}{6c}$

$\qquad\qquad = \dfrac{2\sqrt{6}}{3}$

56. $\dfrac{8x^3y^5}{\sqrt[3]{4x^2y}} \cdot \dfrac{\sqrt[3]{2xy^2}}{\sqrt[3]{2xy^2}} = \dfrac{8x^3y^5\sqrt[3]{2xy^2}}{\sqrt[3]{8x^3y^3}}$

$\qquad\qquad = \dfrac{8x^3y^5\sqrt[3]{2xy^2}}{2xy}$

$\qquad\qquad = 4x^2y^4\sqrt[3]{2xy^2}$

58. $\sqrt[5]{\dfrac{4x^2}{16y^3}} = \dfrac{\sqrt[5]{4x^2}}{\sqrt[5]{2^4y^3}} \cdot \dfrac{\sqrt[5]{2y^2}}{\sqrt[5]{2y^2}}$

$\qquad\qquad = \dfrac{\sqrt[5]{8x^2y^2}}{2y}$

60. $\dfrac{5\sqrt{x}}{3-2\sqrt{x}} \cdot \dfrac{3+2\sqrt{x}}{3+2\sqrt{x}} = \dfrac{15\sqrt{x}+10x}{9-4x}$

62. $\dfrac{3\sqrt{2} - 2\sqrt{3}}{3\sqrt{3} - 2\sqrt{2}} \cdot \dfrac{3\sqrt{3} + 2\sqrt{2}}{3\sqrt{3} + 2\sqrt{2}} = \dfrac{9\sqrt{6} + 12 - 18 - 4\sqrt{6}}{27 - 8}$

$$= \dfrac{5\sqrt{6} - 6}{19}$$

64. $\dfrac{-y^2}{2 - \sqrt{y^2 + 4}} \cdot \dfrac{2 + \sqrt{y^2 + 4}}{2 + \sqrt{y^2 + 4}} = \dfrac{-2y^2 - y^2\sqrt{y^2 + 4}}{4 - (y^2 + 4)}$

$$= \dfrac{-2y^2 - y^2\sqrt{y^2 + 4}}{-y^2}$$

$$= 2 + \sqrt{y^2 + 4}$$

66. $\dfrac{\sqrt{x} - \sqrt{y}}{\sqrt{x} + \sqrt{y}} \cdot \dfrac{\sqrt{x} + \sqrt{y}}{\sqrt{x} + \sqrt{y}} = \dfrac{x - y}{x + 2\sqrt{xy} + y}$

68. $\dfrac{\sqrt{2 + h} + \sqrt{2}}{h} \cdot \dfrac{\sqrt{2 + h} - \sqrt{2}}{\sqrt{2 + h} - \sqrt{2}} = \dfrac{2 + h - 2}{h\sqrt{2 + h} - h\sqrt{2}}$

$$= \dfrac{h}{h\sqrt{2 + h} - h\sqrt{2}}$$

$$= \dfrac{1}{\sqrt{2 + h} - \sqrt{2}}$$

70. $\sqrt{306.721} \approx 17.51$ using a calculator

72. $\sqrt[8]{0.070144} \approx 0.7174$ using a calculator

74. $\sqrt[12]{6,423,000,000,000} \approx 11.68$ using a calculator

76. $\sqrt[5]{4 + \sqrt[5]{4}} \approx 1.397$ using a calculator

78. $\sqrt[3]{\sqrt{5}} \approx 1.308$ using a calculator

$\sqrt[6]{5} \approx 1.308$ using a calculator

80. $\dfrac{1}{\sqrt[3]{5}} \approx 0.5848$ using a calculator

$\dfrac{\sqrt[3]{25}}{5} \approx 0.5848$ using a calculator

82. $\sqrt{x^2} = |x|$ from which $\sqrt{x^2} = x$ if and only if $|x| = x$ which is true for $x \geq 0$. Hence, $\sqrt{x^2} = x$ for $x \geq 0$.

84. $\sqrt[3]{x^3} = x$ from which $\sqrt[3]{x^3} = -x$ if and only if $x = -x$ which is true only for $x = 0$. Hence, $\sqrt[3]{x^3} = x$ for $x = 0$.

86. (A) $2\sqrt[3]{2 + \sqrt{5}} = 3.236067977\ldots$ (B) $\sqrt{8} = 2.828427125\ldots$

(C) $\sqrt{3} + \sqrt{7} = 4.377802119\ldots$ (D) $\sqrt{3 + \sqrt{8}} + \sqrt{3 - \sqrt{8}} = 2.828427125\ldots$

(E) $\sqrt{10 + \sqrt{84}} = 4.377802119\ldots$ (F) $1 + \sqrt{5} = 3.236067977\ldots$

(A) & (F), (B) & (D), and (C) & (E) have the same value on a calculator.

Let $x = 1 + \sqrt{5}$, then

$$x^3 = 1 + 3 \cdot 1^2 \cdot \sqrt{5} + 3 \cdot 1 \cdot \sqrt{5}^2 + \sqrt{5}^3$$
$$x^3 = 1 + 3\sqrt{5} + 3 \cdot 5 + 5\sqrt{5}$$
$$x^3 = 16 + 8\sqrt{5} = 8(2 + \sqrt{5})$$
$$x = 2\sqrt[3]{2 + \sqrt{5}} \text{ which shows (A) \& (F) are equal.}$$

Let $x = \sqrt{3 + \sqrt{8}} + \sqrt{3 - \sqrt{8}} > 0$, then

$$x^2 = 3 + \sqrt{8} + 2\sqrt{3 + \sqrt{8}}\sqrt{3 - \sqrt{8}} + 3 - \sqrt{8}$$
$$x^2 = 6 + 2\sqrt{3^2 - \sqrt{8}^2} = 6 + 2$$
$$x^2 = 8$$
$$x = \sqrt{8} \text{ since } x > 0, \text{ which shows (B) \& (D) are equal.}$$

Let $x = \sqrt{3} + \sqrt{7} > 0$, then

$$x^2 = 3 + 2\sqrt{3}\sqrt{7} + 7$$
$$x^2 = 10 + 2\sqrt{21} = 10 + \sqrt{4 \cdot 21}$$
$$x^2 = 10 + \sqrt{84}$$
$$x = \sqrt{10 + \sqrt{84}} \text{ since } x > 0, \text{ which shows (C) \& (E) are equal.}$$

88.
$$\frac{1}{\sqrt[3]{m} + \sqrt[3]{n}} = \frac{1}{m^{1/3} + n^{1/3}}$$

$$= \frac{1}{m^{1/3} + n^{1/3}} \cdot \frac{m^{2/3} - m^{1/3}n^{1/3} + n^{2/3}}{m^{2/3} - m^{1/3}n^{1/3} + n^{2/3}}$$

$$= \frac{m^{2/3} - m^{1/3}n^{1/3} + n^{2/3}}{m - m^{2/3}n^{1/3} + m^{1/3}n^{2/3} + m^{2/3}n^{1/3} - m^{1/3}n^{2/3} + n}$$

$$= \frac{m^{2/3} - (mn)^{1/3} + n^{2/3}}{m + n}$$

$$= \frac{\sqrt[3]{m^2} - \sqrt[3]{mn} + \sqrt[3]{n^2}}{m + n}$$

90.
$$\frac{1}{\sqrt{x} + \sqrt{y} - \sqrt{z}} \cdot \frac{(\sqrt{x} + \sqrt{y}) + \sqrt{z}}{(\sqrt{x} + \sqrt{y}) + \sqrt{z}} = \frac{\sqrt{x} + \sqrt{y} + \sqrt{z}}{(\sqrt{x} + \sqrt{y})^2 - z}$$

$$= \frac{\sqrt{x} + \sqrt{y} + \sqrt{z}}{x + 2\sqrt{x}\sqrt{y} + y - z}$$

$$= \frac{\sqrt{x} + \sqrt{y} + \sqrt{z}}{(x + y - z) + 2\sqrt{x}\sqrt{y}} \cdot \frac{(x + y - z) - 2\sqrt{x}\sqrt{y}}{(x + y - z) - 2\sqrt{x}\sqrt{y}}$$

$$= \frac{(\sqrt{x} + \sqrt{y} + \sqrt{z})(x + y - z - 2\sqrt{xy})}{(x + y - z)^2 - 4xy}$$

92. $\dfrac{\sqrt[3]{t} - \sqrt[3]{x}}{t - x} = \dfrac{t^{1/3} - x^{1/3}}{t - x} \cdot \dfrac{t^{2/3} + t^{1/3}x^{1/3} + x^{2/3}}{t^{2/3} + t^{1/3}x^{1/3} + x^{2/3}}$

$= \dfrac{t + t^{2/3}x^{1/3} + t^{1/3}x^{2/3} - t^{2/3}x^{1/3} - t^{1/3}x^{2/3} - x}{(t - x)(t^{2/3} + t^{1/3}x^{1/3} + x^{2/3})}$

$= \dfrac{t - x}{(t - x)(t^{2/3} + t^{1/3}x^{1/3} + x^{2/3})}$

$= \dfrac{1}{\sqrt[3]{t^2} + \sqrt[3]{tx} + \sqrt[3]{x^2}}$

94. $\sqrt[m]{\sqrt[n]{x}} = \sqrt[m]{x^{1/n}}$

$= (x^{1/n})^{1/m}$

$= x^{1/mn}$

$= \sqrt[mn]{x}$

96. $T = 2\pi\sqrt{\dfrac{L}{g}}$

$= 2\pi\sqrt{\dfrac{L}{g} \cdot \dfrac{g}{g}}$

$= 2\pi\sqrt{\dfrac{Lg}{g^2}}$

$= 2\pi\dfrac{\sqrt{Lg}}{\sqrt{g^2}}$

$= \dfrac{2\pi\sqrt{Lg}}{g}$

Exercise A-8

2. $x - 9 = -2$
$ \underline{+9 \quad +9}$
$ x = 7$

4. $7 - 3t = 1$
$\underline{-1 -7}$
$ -3t = -6$
$ \dfrac{-3t}{-3} = \dfrac{-6}{-3}$
$ t = 2$

6. $3y + 5 = 6y - 10$
$\underline{-3y + 10 - 3y + 10}$
$ 15 = 3y$
$ \dfrac{15}{3} = \dfrac{3y}{3}$
$ 5 = y$

8. $(-4, 8) \Rightarrow -4 < x < 8$;

10. $(-3, 3] \Rightarrow -3 < x \le 3$;

12. $(-\infty, 7) \Rightarrow x < 7$;

14. $-5 \le x \le 5 \Rightarrow [-5, 5]$;

16. $-4 \le x < 5 \Rightarrow [-4, 5)$;

18. $x > 3 \Rightarrow (3, \infty)$;

20. $[-5, 6]$ or $-5 \le x \le 6$

22. $(1, \infty)$ or $x > 1$

24. $4x + 8 \ge x - 1$
$ 3x > -9$
$ x > -3$; $[-3, \infty)$;

26. $2(x - 3) + 5 < 5 - x$
$2x - 6 + 5 < 5 - x$
$2x - 1 < 5 - x$
$3x < 6$
$x < 2; \ (-\infty, 2);$

28. $\dfrac{m}{-3} \le -2$

$m \ge 6; \ [6, \infty);$

30. $2(1 - u) \ge 5u$
$2 - 2u \ge 5u$
$-7u \ge -2$

$u \le \dfrac{2}{7}; \ \left(-\infty, \dfrac{2}{7}\right];$

32. $\dfrac{y - 3}{4} - 1 > \dfrac{y}{2}$
$y - 3 - 4 > 2y$
$y - 7 > 2y$
$-y > 7$
$y < -7; \ (-\infty, -7);$

34. $\dfrac{x - 2}{3} + 1 = \dfrac{x}{7}$
$7(x - 2) + 21(1) = 3x$
$7x - 14 + 21 = 3x$
$7x + 7 = 3x$
$4x = -7$
$x = -\dfrac{7}{4}$

36. $0.4(x + 5) - 0.3x = 17$
$4(x + 5) - 3x = 10(17)$
$4x + 20 - 3x = 170$
$x = 150$

38. $0.02x - 0.5(x - 2) = 5.32$
$2x - 50(x - 2) = 532$
$2x - 50x + 100 = 532$
$-48x = 432$
$x = -9$

40. $(-5, 5) \cap [4, 7]$

$\Rightarrow [4, 5)$

42. $[-1, 4) \cup (2, 6]$

$\Rightarrow [-1, 6]$

44. $(-\infty, 1) \cap (2, \infty)$

$\Rightarrow \varnothing,$ the empty set

46. $(1, 6] \cup [9, \infty)$

48. $[2, 3] \cap (1, 5)$

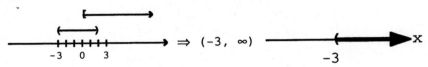

$\Rightarrow [2, 3]$

50. $(-3, 2) \cup [0, \infty)$

$\Rightarrow (-3, \infty)$

52. $\dfrac{p}{3} - \dfrac{p - 2}{2} \leq \dfrac{p}{4} - 4$ Multiply both sides by 12

$4p - 6(p - 2) \leq 3p - 12(4)$
$4p - 6p + 12 \leq 3p - 48$
$-2p + 12 \leq 3p - 48$
$-5p \leq -60$
$p \geq 12$

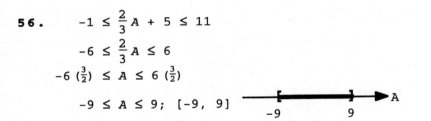

54. $\dfrac{2}{3}(x + 7) - \dfrac{x}{4} > \dfrac{1}{2}(3 - x) + \dfrac{x}{6}$ Multiply both sides by 12

$4(2(x + 7)) - 3x > 6(3 - x) + 2x$
$4(2x + 14) - 3x > 18 - 6x + 2x$
$8x + 56 - 3x > 18 - 4x$
$5x + 56 > 18 - 4x$
$9x > -38$
$x > -\dfrac{38}{9} \text{ or } x > -4\dfrac{2}{9}; \ (-4\dfrac{2}{9}, \infty);$

56. $-1 \leq \dfrac{2}{3}A + 5 \leq 11$

$-6 \leq \dfrac{2}{3}A \leq 6$

$-6\left(\dfrac{3}{2}\right) \leq A \leq 6\left(\dfrac{3}{2}\right)$

$-9 \leq A \leq 9; \ [-9, 9]$

58. $-1 \leq 9 - 2x < 5$
$-10 \leq -2x < -4$
$5 \geq x > 2$

$2 < x \leq 5; \ (2, 5]$

60. $15 \leq 7 - \dfrac{2}{5}x \leq 21$

$8 \leq -\dfrac{2}{5}x \leq 14$

$8\left(-\dfrac{5}{2}\right) \geq x \geq 14\left(-\dfrac{5}{2}\right)$

$-20 \geq x \geq -35$

$-35 \leq x \leq -20; \ [-35, -20]$

62. Assume that $m > n > 0$; then $n - m < 0$ and division by a negative quantity would reverse the inequality in line 4. The correct steps are:

$$mn > n^2$$
$$mn - m^2 > n^2 - m^2$$
$$m(n - m) > (n + m)(n - m)$$
$$m < n + m$$
$$0 < n \quad \text{which is true.}$$

64. a, b, c are real numbers.
If $a < b$: case 1, $c > 0$
$$a + c < b + c$$
case 2, $c < 0$
$$a + c < b + c$$

66. (A) If $a < b$, $c > 0$:
$$a\left(\tfrac{1}{c}\right) < b\left(\tfrac{1}{c}\right)$$
$$\frac{a}{c} < \frac{b}{c}$$

(B) If $a < b$, $c < 0$:
$$a\left(\tfrac{1}{c}\right) > b\left(\tfrac{1}{c}\right)$$
$$\frac{a}{c} > \frac{b}{c}$$

APPENDIX B

2. $$\frac{9x + 21}{(x + 5)(x - 3)} = \frac{A}{x + 5} + \frac{B}{x - 3} = \frac{A(x - 3) + B(x + 5)}{(x + 5)(x - 3)}$$

$$9x + 21 = A(x - 3) + B(x + 5)$$

$x = 3:\ \ 9(3) + 21 = 8B \Rightarrow B = 6$

$x = -5:\ 9(-5) + 21 = -8A \Rightarrow A = 3$

4. $$\frac{x - 11}{(3x + 2)(2x - 1)} = \frac{A}{3x + 2} + \frac{B}{2x - 1} = \frac{A(2x - 1) + B(3x + 2)}{(3x + 2)(2x - 1)}$$

$$x - 11 = A(2x - 1) + B(3x + 2)$$

$x = \dfrac{1}{2}:\ \ \dfrac{1}{2} - 11 = B\left(\dfrac{3}{2} + 2\right)$

$$-\frac{21}{2} = \frac{7}{2}B \Rightarrow B = -3$$

$x = -\dfrac{2}{3}:\ -\dfrac{2}{3} - 11 = A\left(-\dfrac{4}{3} - 1\right)$

$$-\frac{35}{3} = -\frac{7}{3}A \Rightarrow A = 5$$

6. $$\frac{x^2 - 6x + 11}{(x + 1)(x - 2)^2} = \frac{A}{x + 1} + \frac{B}{x - 2} + \frac{C}{(x - 2)^2}$$

$$= \frac{A(x - 2)^2 + B(x + 1)(x - 2) + C(x + 1)}{(x + 1)(x - 2)^2}$$

$$x^2 - 6x + 11 = A(x - 2)^2 + B(x + 1)(x - 2) + C(x + 1)$$

$x = -1:\ (-1)^2 - 6(-1) + 11 = A(-1 - 2)^2 \Rightarrow A = 2$

$x = 2:\ \ \ \ \ 2^2 - 6(2) + 11 = C(2 + 1) \Rightarrow C = 1$

$A = 2,\ C = 1,\ x = 0:\ 0^2 - 6(0) + 11 = 2(0 - 2)^2 + B(0 + 1)(0 - 2) + 1(0 + 1)$

$$11 = 8 - 2B + 1 \Rightarrow B = -1$$

8. $$\frac{5x^2 - 9x + 19}{(x - 4)(x^2 + 5)} = \frac{A}{x - 4} + \frac{Bx + C}{x^2 + 5} = \frac{A(x^2 + 5) + (Bx + C)(x - 4)}{(x - 4)(x^2 + 5)}$$

$$5x^2 - 9x + 19 = A(x^2 + 5) + (Bx + C)(x - 4)$$

$x = 4:\ 5(4)^2 - 9(4) + 19 = A(4^2 + 5) + (4B + C)(4 - 4)$

$$63 = 21A \Rightarrow A = 3$$

$$5x^2 - 9x + 19 = 3(x^2 + 5) + (Bx + C)(x - 4)$$

$x = 5:\ 5(5)^2 - 9(5) + 19 = 3(5^2 + 5) + (5B + C) \Rightarrow 5B + C = 9$

$x = 6:\ 5(6)^2 - 9(6) + 19 = 3(6^2 + 5) + (6B + C)(2) \Rightarrow 6B + C = 11$

which has $B = 2,\ C = -1$ as solutions

10. $\dfrac{3x^3 - 3x^2 + 10x - 4}{(x^2 - x + 3)^2} = \dfrac{Ax + B}{x^2 - x + 3} + \dfrac{Cx + D}{(x^2 - x + 3)^2}$

$\qquad\qquad\qquad\qquad = \dfrac{(Ax + B)(x^2 - x + 3) + Cx + D}{(x^2 - x + 3)^2}$

$3x^3 - 3x^2 + 10x - 4 = (Ax + B)(x^2 - x + 3) + Cx + D$

$x = 0$: $\qquad\qquad -4 = 3B + D$ $\qquad\qquad\qquad\qquad$ (1)

$x = 1$: $\qquad\qquad\ \ 6 = 3A + 3B + C + D$ $\qquad\qquad$ (2)

$x = 2$: $\qquad\qquad 28 = 10A + 5B + 2C + D$ $\qquad$ (3)

$x = -1$: $\qquad\quad -20 = -5A + 5B - C + D$ $\qquad$ (4)

from (3) & (4): $-12 = 15B + 3D$ which may be solved with (1) to obtain
$B = 0$, $D = -4$. Substitution into (2) and (3) gives

$\qquad\qquad 3A + C = 10$

$\qquad\qquad 10A + 2C = 32$ for which $A = 3$, $C = 1$

12. $\dfrac{-x - 21}{x^2 + 2x - 15} = \dfrac{-x - 21}{(x - 3)(x + 5)} = \dfrac{A}{x - 3} + \dfrac{B}{x + 5} = \dfrac{A(x + 5) + B(x - 3)}{(x - 3)(x + 5)}$

$\qquad\qquad -x - 21 = A(x + 5) + B(x - 3)$

$x = 3$: $\qquad -24 = 8A \Rightarrow A = -3$

$x = -5$: $\qquad -16 = -8B \Rightarrow B = 2$

$\dfrac{-x - 21}{x^2 + 2x - 15} = \dfrac{-3}{x - 3} + \dfrac{2}{x + 5}$

14. $\dfrac{11x - 11}{6x^2 + 7x - 3} = \dfrac{11x - 11}{(2x + 3)(3x - 1)} = \dfrac{A}{2x + 3} + \dfrac{B}{3x - 1} = \dfrac{A(3x - 1) + B(2x + 3)}{(2x + 3)(3x - 1)}$

$\qquad\qquad 11x - 11 = A(3x - 1) + B(2x + 3)$

$x = \dfrac{1}{3}$: $\qquad \dfrac{11}{3} - 11 = B\left(\dfrac{2}{3} + 3\right) \Rightarrow B = -2$

$x = -\dfrac{3}{2}$: $\qquad \dfrac{-33}{2} - 11 = A\left(-\dfrac{9}{2} - 1\right) \Rightarrow A = 5$

$\qquad \dfrac{11x - 11}{6x^2 + 7x - 3} = \dfrac{5}{2x + 3} + \dfrac{-2}{3x - 1}$

16. $\dfrac{5x^2 - 36x + 48}{x(x - 4)^2} = \dfrac{A}{x} + \dfrac{B}{x - 4} + \dfrac{C}{(x - 4)^2} = \dfrac{A(x - 4)^2 + Bx(x - 4) + Cx}{x(x - 4)^2}$

$5x^2 - 36x + 48 = A(x - 4)^2 + Bx(x - 4) + Cx$

$x = 0$: $\qquad\quad 48 = 16A \Rightarrow A = 3$

$x = 4$: $\qquad\ -16 = 4C \Rightarrow C = -4$

$A = 3$, $C = -4$, $x = 1$: $17 = 3(-3)^2 - 3B - 4 \Rightarrow B = 2$

$\qquad \dfrac{5x^2 - 36x + 48}{x(x - 4)^2} = \dfrac{3}{x} + \dfrac{2}{x - 4} + \dfrac{-4}{(x - 4)^2}$

18. $\dfrac{6x^2 - 15x + 16}{x^3 - 3x^2 + 4x} = \dfrac{6x^2 - 15x + 16}{x(x^2 - 3x + 4)} = \dfrac{A}{x} + \dfrac{Bx + C}{x^2 - 3x + 4}$

$\qquad\qquad\qquad\quad = \dfrac{A(x^2 - 3x + 4) + (Bx + C)x}{x(x^2 - 3x + 4)}$

$6x^2 - 15x + 16 = A(x^2 - 3x + 4) + (Bx + C)x$

$x = 0: \qquad 16 = 4A \Rightarrow A = 4$

$6x^2 - 15x + 16 = 4(x^2 - 3x + 4) + (Bx + C)x$

$x = 1: \qquad 7 = 8 + B + C \Rightarrow B + C = -1 \qquad (1)$

$x = 2: \qquad 10 = 8 + 4B + 2C \Rightarrow 4B + 2C = 2 \quad (2)$

Solving (1) and (2): $B = 2$, $C = -3$

$\dfrac{6x^2 - 15x + 16}{x^3 - 3x^2 + 4x} = \dfrac{4}{x} + \dfrac{2x - 3}{x^2 - 3x + 4}$

20. $\dfrac{-5x^2 + 7x - 18}{x^4 + 6x^2 + 9} = \dfrac{-5x^2 + 7x - 18}{(x^2 + 3)^2} = \dfrac{Ax + B}{x^2 + 3} + \dfrac{Cx + D}{(x^2 + 3)^2}$

$-5x^2 + 7x - 18 = (Ax + B)(x^2 + 3) + Cx + D$

$x = 0: \qquad -18 = 3B + D \qquad\qquad\qquad (1)$

$x = 1: \qquad -16 = 4A + 4B + C + D \qquad (2)$

$x = -1: \qquad -30 = -4A + 4B - C + D \qquad (3)$

add (2) and (3): $8B + 2D = -46$ which may be solved with

$\qquad\qquad (1) \quad 3B + D = -18$ to give $B = -5$, $D = -3$

then (2) becomes $\qquad\qquad 4A + C = 7$

$B = -5$, $D = -3$, $x = 2$: $\quad 7A + C = 7$ which has $A = 0$ and $C = 7$ as solutions.

$\dfrac{-5x^2 + 7x - 18}{x^4 + 6x^2 + 9} = \dfrac{-5}{x^2 + 3} + \dfrac{7x - 3}{(x^2 + 3)^2}$

22. $\dfrac{x^3 + x^2 - 13x + 11}{x^2 + 2x - 15}$

$$
\begin{array}{r}
x - 1 \\
x^2 + 2x - 15\overline{\smash{)}\, x^3 + x^2 - 13x + 11} \\
\underline{x^3 + 2x^2 - 15x} \\
-x^2 + 2x + 11 \\
\underline{-x^2 - 2x + 15} \\
4x - 4 \\
\end{array}
$$

$\dfrac{x^3 + x^2 - 13x + 11}{x^2 + 2x - 15} = x - 1 + \dfrac{4x - 4}{x^2 + 2x - 15}$

$\dfrac{4x - 4}{x^2 + 2x - 15} = \dfrac{4x - 4}{(x + 5)(x - 3)} = \dfrac{A}{x + 5} + \dfrac{B}{x - 3} = \dfrac{A(x - 3) + B(x + 5)}{(x + 5)(x - 3)}$

$4x - 4 = A(x - 3) + B(x + 5)$

$x = 3: \qquad\qquad 8 = 8B \Rightarrow B = 1$

$x = -5: \qquad -24 = -8A \Rightarrow A = 3$

$\dfrac{x^3 + x^2 - 13x + 11}{x^2 + 2x - 15} = x - 1 + \dfrac{3}{x + 5} + \dfrac{1}{x - 3}$

24. $\dfrac{4x^2 - 8x + 1}{x^3 - x + 6} = \dfrac{4x^2 - 8x + 1}{(x + 2)(x^2 - 2x + 3)} = \dfrac{A}{x + 2} + \dfrac{Bx + C}{x^2 - 2x + 3}$

$\qquad\qquad = \dfrac{A(x^2 - 2x + 3) + (Bx + C)(x + 2)}{(x + 2)(x^2 - 2x + 3)}$

(To factor the denominator, use your grapher to find the x-intercept of -2 for $x^3 - x - 6$; then divide.)

$\begin{aligned}
4x^2 - 8x + 1 &= A(x^2 - 2x + 3) + (Bx + C)(x + 2) \\
&= Ax^2 - 2Ax + 3A + Bx^2 + 2Bx + Cx + 2C \\
&= (A + B)x^2 + (-2A + 2B + C)x + (3A + 2C)
\end{aligned}$

x^2 terms: $4x^2 = (A + B)x^2 \Rightarrow 4 = A + B$ $\qquad\qquad$ (1)

x terms: $-8x = (-2A + 2B + C)x \Rightarrow -8 = -2A + 2B + C$ $\quad$ (2)

constants: $1 = 3A + 2C$ $\qquad\qquad\qquad\qquad$ (3)

Solve (1) for B and substitute into (2):

$\qquad -8 = -2A + 2(4 - A) + C$

$\qquad -16 = -4A + C$ $\qquad\qquad\qquad\qquad$ (4)

Solving (3) and (4) gives $A = 3$, $C = -4$

$\qquad\qquad B = 4 - A \Rightarrow B = 1$

$\dfrac{4x^2 - 8x + 1}{x^3 - x + 6} = \dfrac{3}{x + 2} + \dfrac{x - 4}{x^2 - 2x + 3}$

26. $\dfrac{5x^2 - 18x + 1}{x^3 - x^2 - 8x + 12} = \dfrac{5x^2 - 18x + 1}{(x + 3)(x - 2)^2} = \dfrac{A}{x + 3} + \dfrac{B}{x - 2} + \dfrac{C}{(x - 2)^2}$

$\qquad\qquad = \dfrac{A(x - 2)^2 + B(x + 3)(x - 2) + C(x + 3)}{(x + 3)(x - 2)^2}$

(To factor the denominator, use your grapher to find the x-intercepts of 2 and -3 for $x^3 - x^2 - 8x + 12$; then divide.)

$\qquad 5x^2 - 18x + 1 = A(x - 2)^2 + B(x + 3)(x - 2) + C(x + 3)$

$x = 2$: $\qquad\quad -15 = 5C \Rightarrow C = -3$

$x = -3$: $\qquad\quad 100 = 25A \Rightarrow A = 4$

$\qquad 5x^2 - 18x + 1 = 4(x - 2)^2 + B(x + 3)(x - 2) - 3(x + 3)$

$x = 1$: $\qquad\quad -12 = -4B - 8 \Rightarrow B = 1$

$\dfrac{5x^2 - 18x + 1}{x^3 - x^2 - 8x + 12} = \dfrac{4}{x + 3} + \dfrac{1}{x - 2} + \dfrac{-3}{(x - 2)^2}$

28. $\dfrac{-2x^3 + 12x^2 - 20x - 10}{x^4 - 7x^3 + 17x^2 - 21x + 18}$

$$= \dfrac{-2x^3 + 12x^2 - 20x - 10}{(x - 3)^2(x^2 - x + 2)}$$

$$= \dfrac{A}{x - 3} + \dfrac{B}{(x - 3)^2} + \dfrac{Cx + D}{x^2 - x + 2}$$

$$= \dfrac{A(x - 3)(x^2 - x + 2) + B(x^2 - x + 2) + (Cx + D)(x - 3)^2}{(x - 3)^2(x^2 - x + 2)}$$

(To factor the denominator, use your grapher to find the x-intercept of 3 for $x^4 - 7x^3 + 17x^2 - 21x + 18$; then divide.)

$-2x^3 + 12x^2 - 20x - 10 = A(x - 3)(x^2 - x + 2) + B(x^2 - x + 2) + (Cx + D)(x - 3)^2$

$x = 3$: $-16 = 8B \Rightarrow B = -2$

$-2x^3 + 12x^2 - 20x - 10 = A(x - 3)(x^2 - x + 2) - 2(x^2 - x + 2) + (Cx + D)(x - 3)^2$

$-2x^3 + 12x^2 - 20x - 10 = x^3(A + C) + x^2(-4A - 2 - 6C + D) + x(5A + 2 + 9C - 6D)$
$$+ (-6A - 4 + 9D)$$

x^3 terms: $A + C = -2$ (1)
x^2 terms: $-4A - 6C + D - 2 = 12$ (2)
x terms: $5A + 9C - 6D + 2 = -20$ (3)
constants: $-6A - 4 + 9D = -10$ (4)

(1) $\rightarrow$ (2): $-4A - 6(-2 - A) + D = 14 \Rightarrow 2A + D = 2$ (5)

(5) $+ \frac{1}{3}$(4): $D = 0$, $A = 1$, so $C = -3$

$$\dfrac{-2x^3 + 12x^2 - 20x - 10}{x^4 - 7x^3 + 17x^2 - 21x + 18} = \dfrac{1}{x - 3} + \dfrac{-2}{(x - 3)^2} + \dfrac{-3x}{x^2 - x + 2}$$

30. $\dfrac{6x^5 - 13x^4 + x^3 - 8x^2 + 2x}{6x^4 - 7x^3 + x^2 + x - 1} = x - 1 + \dfrac{-7x^3 - 8x^2 + 4x - 1}{6x^4 - 7x^3 + x^2 + x - 1}$ by long division

$\dfrac{-7x^3 - 8x^2 + 4x - 1}{6x^4 - 7x^3 + x^2 + x - 1}$

$$= \dfrac{-7x^3 - 8x^2 + 4x - 1}{(2x + 1)(x - 1)(3x^2 - 2x + 1)}$$

$$= \dfrac{A}{2x + 1} + \dfrac{B}{x - 1} + \dfrac{Cx + D}{3x^2 - 2x + 1}$$

$$= \dfrac{A(x - 1)(3x^2 - 2x + 1) + B(2x + 1)(3x^2 - 2x + 1) + (Cx + D)(2x + 1)(x - 1)}{(2x + 1)(x - 1)(3x^2 - 2x + 1)}$$

(To factor the donominator, use your grapher to find the x-intercepts of $6x^4 - 7x^3 + x^2 + x - 1$; then divide.)

$-7x^3 - 8x^2 + 4x - 1 = A(x - 1)(3x^2 - 2x + 1) + B(2x + 1)(3x^2 - 2x + 1)$
$$+ (Cx + D)(2x + 1)(x - 1)$$

$x = 1$: $-12 = 6B \Rightarrow B = -2$

$-7x^3 - 8x^2 + 4x - 1 = A(x - 1)(3x^2 - 2x + 1) - 2(2x + 1)(3x^2 - 2x + 1)$
$$+ (Cx + D)(2x + 1)(x - 1)$$

$x = 0$: $\Rightarrow A + D = -1$
$x = -1$: $\Rightarrow 12A + 2C - 2D = 18$ $\Big\} \Rightarrow A = 1$, $C = 1$, $D = -2$
$x = -2$: $\Rightarrow 51A + 18C - 9D = 87$

$$\dfrac{6x^5 - 13x^4 + x^3 - 8x^2 + 2x}{6x^4 - 7x^3 + x^2 + x - 1} = x - 1 + \dfrac{1}{2x + 1} + \dfrac{-2}{x - 1} + \dfrac{x - 2}{3x^2 - 2x + 1}$$

PART II
ANSWERS

CHAPTER 1

Exercise 1-1

1.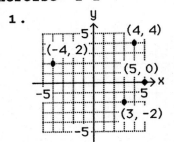

(4, 4)
(-4, 2)
(5, 0)
(3, -2)

2.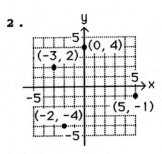

(0, 4)
(-3, 2)
(5, -1)
(-2, -4)

3.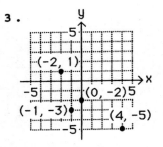

(-2, 1)
(0, -2)
(-1, -3)
(4, -5)

4.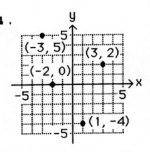

(-3, 5)
(3, 2)
(-2, 0)
(1, -4)

5. $A(2, 4)$, $B(3, -1)$, $C(-4, 0)$, $D(-5, 2)$ **6.** $A(0, 3)$, $B(-4, -5)$, $C(4, 1)$, $D(1, -3)$

7. $A(-3, -3)$, $B(0, 4)$, $C(-3, 2)$, $D(5, -1)$ **8.** $A(4, 2)$, $B(-2, -4)$, $C(-4, 3)$, $D(5, 0)$

9. $\sqrt{145}$ **10.** $d = \sqrt{146}$ **11.** $\sqrt{68}$

12. $d = \sqrt{85}$ **13.** $x^2 + y^2 = 49$ **14.** $x^2 + y^2 = 25$

15. $(x - 2)^2 + (y - 3)^2 = 36$ **16.** $(x - 5)^2 + (y - 6)^2 = 4$

17. $(x + 4)^2 + (y - 1)^2 = 7$ **18.** $(x + 5)^2 + (y - 6)^2 = 11$

19. $(x + 3)^2 + (y + 4)^2 = 2$ **20.** $(x - 4)^2 + (y + 1)^2 = 5$

20. (A) -4   (B) 5   (C) -3, 1   (D) -2, 0

21.

x	y
-3	-2
-2	-1
-1	0
0	1
1	2
2	3
3	4

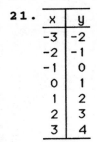

22.

x	y
-3	5
-2	4
-1	3
0	2
1	1
2	0
3	-1

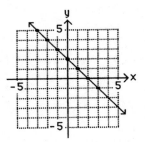

23.

x	y
-3	4
-2	-1
-1	-4
0	-5
1	-4
2	-1
3	4

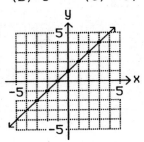

24.

x	y
-3	-5
-2	0
-1	3
0	4
1	3
2	0
3	-5

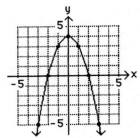

25.

x	y
-3	-4.5
-2	-1
-1	1.5
0	3
1	3.5
2	3
3	1.5

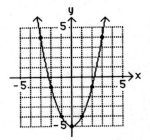

26.

x	y
-3	2.5
-2	4
-1	4.5
0	4
1	2.5
2	0
3	-3.5

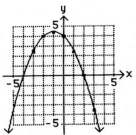

27. (A) 6   (B) -5   (C) -1   (D) 8   (E) -5   (F) 5

28. (A) 5   (B) -8   (C) 6   (D) -2, 4   (E) -4, 6   (F) -3, 5

29. (A) 6   (B) 4   (C) 4   (D) 8   (E) -8, 0, 6   (F) -7, -2, 7

30. (A) −3　　(B) 1　　(C) 4　　(D) 3, 6　　(E) −6, −4, 2, 7　　(F) −5, 2, 7

31. A right triangle　**32.** A right triangle　**33.** 18.11　　　　**34.** 18.62

35.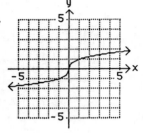

36.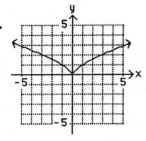

37.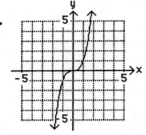

38.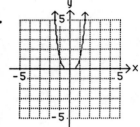

39.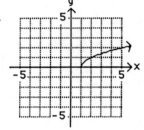

40.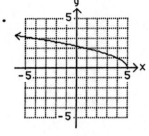

41.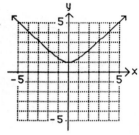

42.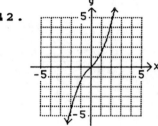

43.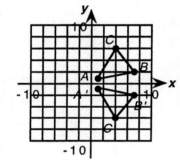

44.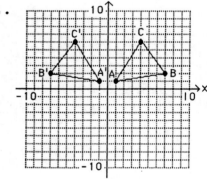

45.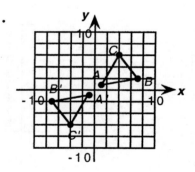

46.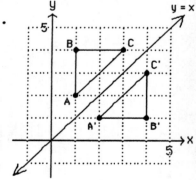

49. $(x - 4)^2 + (y - 2)^2 = 34$　　　**50.** $(x - 2)^2 + (y + 1)^2 = 34$

51. $(x - 2)^2 + (y - 2)^2 = 50$　　　**52.** $(x + 5)^2 + (y - 4)^2 = 98$

53. (A) 3,000 cases　　(B) Demand decreases by 400 cases
(C) Demand increases by 600 cases　(D) Demand increases with decreasing price
and decreases with increasing price.

54. (A) 3,000 cases　　(B) Supply increases by 300 cases
(C) Supply decreases by 400 cases　(D) When the price increases, the supply
will increase.

55. (A) 53°F　　(B) 68°F at 3 PM　　(C) 1 AM, 7 AM, 11 PM

56. (A) 60°F   (B) 44°F at 5 AM   (C) 9 AM, 10 PM

57.
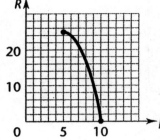

58.
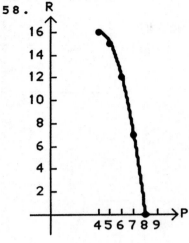

59. (A)
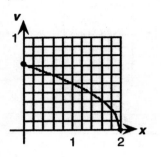

60. (A)
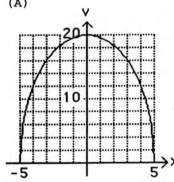

Exercise 1-2

1. Yes   **2.** Yes   **3.** No   **4.** No   **5.** Yes   **6.** No

7. (A) Xmin = -7, Xmax = 6, Ymin = -9, Ymax = 14

8. (A) Xmin = -4, Xmax = 7, Ymin = -4, Ymax = 3

9.
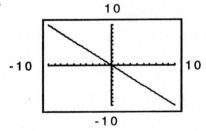

10.
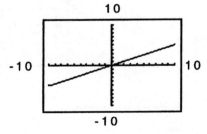

11.
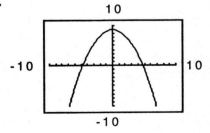

12.
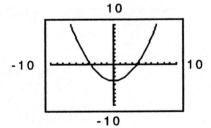

13.

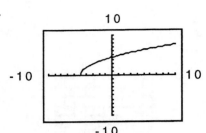

14.

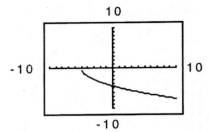

15.

x	$y = 4 + 4x - x^2$
-2	-8
0	4
2	8
4	4
6	-8

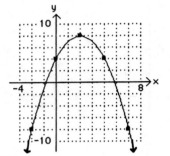

16.

x	-7	-5	-3	-1	1
y	19	-5	-13	-5	19

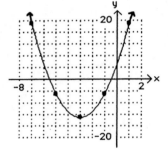

17.

x	$y = 2\sqrt{2x + 10}$
-5	0
-3	4
-1	5.7
1	6.9
3	8
5	8.9

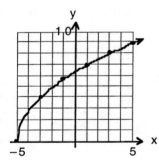

18.

x	-4	-2	0	2	4
y	4	3.5	2.8	2	0

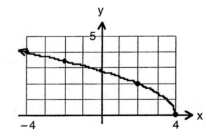

19.

x	$y = 0.5x(4 - x)(x + 2)$
−3	10.5
−1	−2.5
1	4.5
3	7.5
5	−17.5

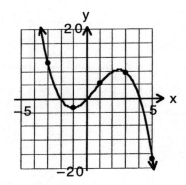

20.

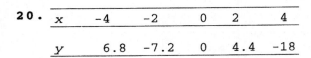

x	−4	−2	0	2	4
y	6.8	−7.2	0	4.4	−18

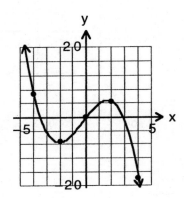

21. (A) −6.37   (B) 0.63   (C) −1.63   **22.** (A) 5.95   (B) −7.39   (C) 3.58

23. (A) 0.92   (B) −3.93   (C) −2.09   **24.** (A) −3.23   (B) 3.72   (C) 2.11

25.

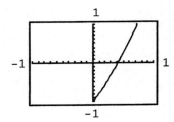
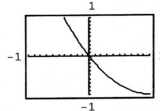
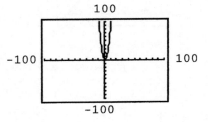

Best view

26.

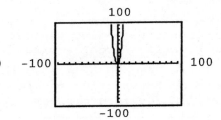

Best view

27.

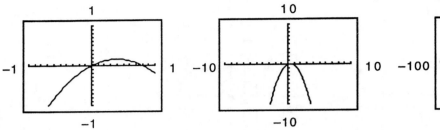

Best view

28.

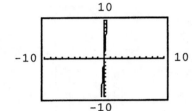 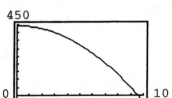 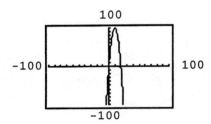

Best view

29. −0.57, 0.76, 2.31   **30.** −0.59, 0.81, 2.11   **31.** ±6.32, ±2.24

32. ±7.07, ±2.45   **33.** 1.4142   **34.** 1.5874

39. 9.5 sec   **40.** 3.6 sec

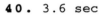 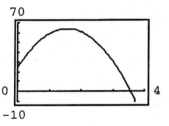

41. A 0.89 in. square or a 2.40 in. square can be cut out.
Dimension for smaller square: 0.89" × 9.22" × 6.72"
Dimension for larger square: 2.40" × 6.20" × 3.70"

42. A 1.06 in. square or a 2.42 in. square can be cut out.
Dimension for smaller square: 1.06" × 9.88" × 6.88"
Dimension for larger square: 2.42" × 7.16" × 4.16"

43. A 0.93 in. square or a 3.92 in. square can be cut out.
Dimension for smaller square: 0.93" × 10.14" × 10.61"
Dimension for larger square: 3.92" × 4.16" × 6.12"

44. A 1.21 in. square or a 2.65 in. square can be cut out.
Dimension for smaller square: 1.21" × 7.58" × 8.19"
Dimension for larger square: 2.65" × 4.70" × 6.03"

45. (A)

x	17,800	15,600	13,600
y	20	25	30

(B) Demand decreases 2,000 cases

(C) Demand increases 2,200 cases

46. (A)

x	11,700	10,000	8,400
y	35	40	45

(B) Demand decreases 1,600 cases

(C) Demand increases 1,700 cases

47. (A)

y	20	25	30
R	356,000	390,000	408,000

(B) Revenue increases $18,000

(C) Revenue decreases $34,000

(D) The company should raise the price $5 to increase the revenue.

48. (A)

y	35	40	45
R	409,500	400,000	378,000

(B) Revenue decreases $22,000

(C) Revenue increases $9,500

(D) The company should lower the price $5 to increase the revenue.

Exercise 1-3

1. A function   **2.** A function   **3.** Not a function

4. Not a function   **5.** A function   **6.** A function

7. A function; Domain = {2, 3, 4, 5}; Range = {4, 6, 8, 10}

8. A function; Domain = {-1, 0, 1, 2}; Range = {4, 3, 2, 1}

9. Not a function

10. A function; Domain = {-10, -5, 0, 5, 10}; Range = {0, 5, 10}

11. A function; Domain = {0, 1, 2, 3, 4, 5}; Range = {1, 2}

12. Not a function   **13.** A function   **14.** A function   **15.** Not a function

16. A function   **17.** Not a function   **18.** Not a function   **19.** -8

20. -2   **21.** -6   **22.** 17   **23.** 1   **24.** -9   **25.** 10   **26.** -24

27. $-\dfrac{30}{17}$ **28.** Not defined   **29.** 3   **30.** -1

31. Domain: all real numbers or $(-\infty, \infty)$

32. Domain: all real numbers or $(-\infty, \infty)$

33. Domain: all real numbers except 4 or $(-\infty, -4) \cup (4, \infty)$

34. Domain: all real numbers except 3 or $(-\infty, 3) \cup (3, \infty)$

35. Domain: $x \geq 0$ or $[0, \infty)$ **36.** Domain: $x \geq 0$ or $[0, \infty)$

37. Domain: $x \leq 0$ or $(-\infty, 0]$ **38.** Domain: $x \leq 0$ or $(-\infty, 0]$

39. Domain: all real numbers except -1 and 1 or $(-\infty, -1) \cup (-1, 1) \cup (1, \infty)$

40. Domain: all real numbers except -3 and 2 or $(-\infty, -3) \cup (-3, 2) \cup (2, \infty)$

41. Domain: $x \geq 0$, $x \neq 5$ or $[0, 5) \cup (5, \infty)$

42. Domain: $x \leq 0$, $x \neq -4$ or $(-\infty, -4) \cup (-4, 0]$

43. $f(x) = 2x - 3$ **44.** $f(x) = 5x^2 - 6$ **45.** $f(x) = 4x^2 - 2x + 9$

46. $f(x) = -8 + 5x - 2x^2$ **47.** 3   **48.** -4   **49.** $-6 - h$ **50.** $8 + 2h$

51. $11 - 2h$ **52.** $-3h + 2$ **53.** $g(x) = 3x + 1$

54. $f(x) = 7x + 5x^3$ **55.** $F(x) = \dfrac{x}{8 + \sqrt{x}}$ **56.** $G(x) = \sqrt{4 + x^2}$

57. Function f multiplies the domain element by 2 and then subtracts the product of 3 and the square of the domain element.

58. Function g multiplies the cube of the domain element by 5 and then subtracts the product of 8 and the domain element.

59. Function F takes the square root of the sum of the fourth power of the domain element and 9.

60. Function G divides the domain element by a denominator formed by multiplying the domain element by 3 and subtracting 6.

61. $f(x) = 2x^2 - 4x + 6$

62. $g(x) = 5 - 7x^2 + 8x$

63. $m(x) = 4x - 3\sqrt{x} + 9$

64. $s(x) = 2\sqrt[3]{x} - 6x - 5$

65. (A) 3 (B) 3

66. (A) -2 (B) -2

67. (A) $2x + h$ (B) $x + a$

68. (A) $2x + h + 1$ (B) $x + a + 1$

69. (A) $-6x - 3h + 9$ (B) $-3x - 3a + 9$

70. (A) $-2x - h - 2$ (B) $-x - a - 2$

71. (A) $3x^2 + 3xh + h^2$ (B) $x^2 + ax + a^2$

72. (A) $3x^2 + 3xh + h^2 + 1$ (B) $x^2 + ax + a^2 + 1$

73. 2

74. 3

75. (A) $s(0) = 0$, $s(1) = 16$, $s(2) = 64$, $s(3) = 144$ (B) $64 + 16h$
(C) Value of expression tends to 64; this number appears to be the speed of the object at the end of 2 s.

76. (A) $S(8) = 640$, $S(9) = 810$, $S(10) = 1000$, $S(11) = 1210$ (B) $220 + 10h$

(C) $220 + h \to 220$ as h tends to 0. This is the speed of the automobile at the instant $t = 11$ sec.

77. (A)

x	0	5,000	10,000	15,000	20,000	25,000	30,000
$B(x)$	212	203	194	185	176	167	158

(B) The boiling point drops 9°F for each 5,000 foot increase in altitude.

78. (A)

x	0	1	2	3	4	5
$A(x)$	25	16	7	-2	-11	-20

(B) The air temperature drops 9°C for each kilometer increase in altitude.

79. The rental charges are $20 per day plus $0.25 per mile driven.

80. The installation charges are $15 for travel to the installation site plus $0.70 per minute spent at the site.

81. (A)

t	0	1	2	3	4
Sales	5.9	6.5	7.7	8.6	9.7
$S(t)$	5.7	6.7	7.7	8.6	9.6

(B)

(C) $10.6 billion, $17.4 billion

(D) Between 1988 and 1992, the company's sales increased from $5.9 billion to $9.7 billion.

82. (A)

t	0	1	2	3	4
Net Income	1.2	1.5	1.8	2.1	2.4
$I(t)$	1.2	1.5	1.8	2.1	2.4

(B)

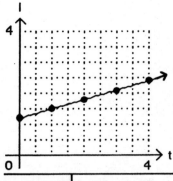

(C) $2.7 billion,
$4.8 billion

(D) From 1988 to 1992, the company's income rose at a yearly (linear) rate of 30% (.3t).

83. (A)

r (R&D)	0.66	0.75	0.85	0.99	1.1
Sales	5.9	6.5	7.7	8.6	9.7
S(r)	5.9	6.6	7.5	8.7	9.7

(B)

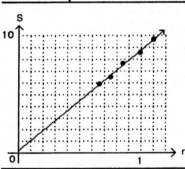

(C) $13.1 billion,
$17.4 billion

84. (A)

r (R&D)	0.66	0.75	0.85	0.99	1.1
Net Income	1.2	1.5	1.8	2.1	2.4
I(r)	1.3	1.5	1.8	2.2	2.5

(B)

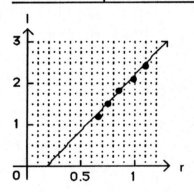

(C) $3.6 billion,
$4.9 billion

Exercise 1-4

1. (A) [-4, 4)　　(B) [-3, 3)　　(C) 0　　(D) 0　　(E) [-4, 4)　　(F) None
(G) None　　(H) None

2. (A) (-5, 5]　　(B) [-4, 4)　　(C) 0　　(D) 0　　(E) None　　(F) (-5, 5]
(G) None　　(H) None

3. (A) (-∞, ∞)　　(B) [-4, ∞)　　(C) -3, 1　　(D) -3　　(E) [-1, ∞)　　(F) (-∞, -1]
(G) None　　(H) None

4. (A) $(-\infty, \infty)$ (B) $(-\infty, 3]$ (C) 0, 4   (D) 0   (E) $(-\infty, 2]$
(F) $[2, \infty)$ (G) none   (H) none

5. (A) $(-\infty, 2) \cup (2, \infty)$ (The function is not defined at $x = 2$.)
(B) $(-\infty, -1) \cup [1, \infty)$ (C) None   (D) 1   (E) None   (F) $(-\infty, -2] \cup (2, \infty)$
(G) $[-2, 2)$ (H) $x = 2$

6. (A) $(-\infty, -3) \cup (-3, \infty)$ (B) $(-\infty, -2) \cup [2, \infty)$ (C) none   (D) 2
(E) $(-\infty, -3) \cup [3, \infty)$ (F) none   (G) $(-3, 3]$ (H) $x = -3$

7. Increasing: $[-2, 10]$, decreasing: $[-10, -2]$

8. Increasing: $[-10, 3]$, decreasing: $[3, 10]$

9. Increasing: $[-3, 10]$, constant: $[-10, -3]$

10. Decreasing: $[-10, 2]$, constant: $[2, 10]$

11. Decreasing: $[-4, 3]$, constant: $[-10, -4]$, $[3, 10]$

12. Increasing: $[-5, 2]$, constant: $[-10, -5]$, $[2, 10]$

13. Increasing: $[1, 10]$, decreasing: $[-10, -3]$, constant: $[-3, 1]$

14. Increasing: $[-4, 10]$, decreasing: $[-10, -2]$, constant: $[-2, 4]$

15. Increasing: $[-4, 0]$, $[4, 10]$, decreasing: $[-10, -4]$, $[0, 4]$

16. Increasing: $[-10, -5] \cup [0, 3]$, decreasing: $[-5, 0] \cup [3, 10]$

17. One possible answer: **18.** One possible answer: **19.** One possible answer:

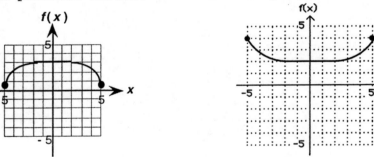
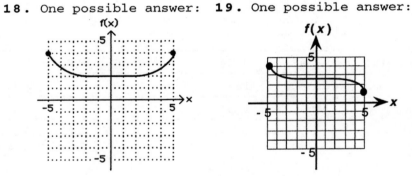

20. One possible answer: **21.** One possible answer: **22.** One possible answer:

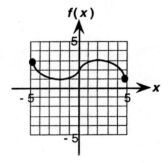
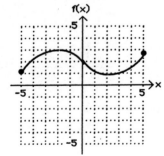

23. $f(3.6) = -5.9$ is a local minimum; x intercepts: 0.7, 6.5

24. $f(-1.7) \approx 5.8$ is a local maximum; x intercepts: -6.1, 2.7

25. $f(3.1) = 6.1$ is a local maximum; x intercepts: 0, 12.3

26. $f(1.8) \approx -5.3$ is a local minimum; x intercepts: 0, 7.1

27. $f(0.8) = -7.1$ is a local minimum; x intercepts: -0.7, 3.1

28. $f(0.5) \approx 3.1$ is a local maximum; x intercepts: -0.5, 5.5

29. Domain: $[-1, 1]$;
Range: $[0, 1]$

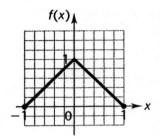

30. Domain: $[-2, 2]$;
Range: $[-2, 1]$

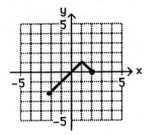

31. Domain: $[-3, -1) \cup (-1, 2]$
Range: $\{-2, 4\}$ (a set, not an interval)
Discontinuous: at $x = -1$

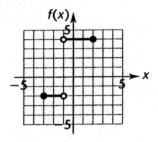

32. Domain: $[-2, 2) \cup (2, 5]$;
Range: $\{-3, 1\}$
Discontinuous at $x = 2$

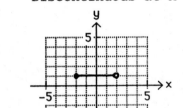

33. Domain: All real numbers
Range: All real numbers
Discontinuous at $x = -1$

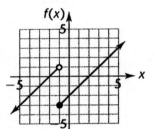

34. Domain: all real numbers
Range: all real numbers
Discontinuous at $x = 2$

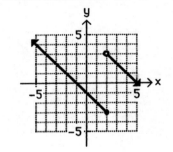

35. Domain: $(-\infty, 0) \cup (0, \infty)$
Discontinuous at $x = 0$
Range: $(-\infty, -1) \cup (1, \infty)$

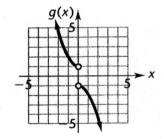

36. Domain: $x \neq 0 \Leftrightarrow$
$(-\infty, 0) \cup (0, \infty)$
Range: $(-\infty, -2) \cup (2, \infty)$
Discontinuous at $x = 0$

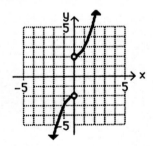

37. The graph of f decreases on $[-10, -2.15]$ to a local minimum value, $f(-2.15) = -36.62$, and then increases on $[-2.15, 10]$.

38. The graph of g increases on $[-10, 3.45]$ to a local maximum value, $f(3.45) \approx 36.90$, and then decreases on $[3.45, 10]$.

39. The graph of h increases on $[-10, -4.64]$ to a local maximum value, $f(-4.64) \approx 281.93$, decreases on $[-4.64, 5.31]$ to a local minimum value, $f(5.31) \approx -211.41$, and then increases on $[5.31, 10]$.

40. The graph of k decreases on $[-10, -4.91]$ to a local minimum value, $f(-4.91) \approx -285.14$, increases on $[-4.91, 5.57]$ to a local maximum value, $f(5.57) \approx 289.96$, and then decreases on $[5.57, 10]$.

41. The graph of p decreases on [-10, -3.77] to a local minimum value, $f(-3.77) \approx 0$, increases on [-3.77, 0.50] to a local maximum value, $f(0.50) \approx 18.25$, decreases on [0.50, 4.77] to a local minimum value, $f(4.77) \approx 0$, and then increases on [4.77, 10].

42. The graph of q decreases on [-10, -4.57] to a local minimum value, $f(-4.57) \approx 0$, increases on [-4.57, 1] to a local maximum value, $f(1) = 31$, decreases on [1, 6.57] to a local minimum value, $f(6.57) \approx 0$, and then increases on [6.57, 10].

43. One possible answer:

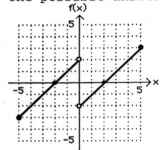

44. One possible answer:

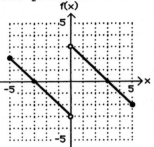

45. One possible answer:

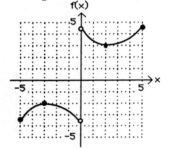

46. One possible answer:

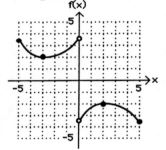

47. One possible answer:

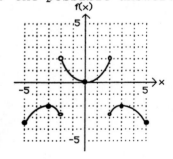

48. One possible answer:

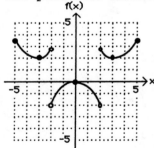

49. Domain: All real numbers except $x = 2$;
Range: {-5, 5} (A set, not an interval);
Discontinuous at $x = 2$

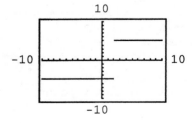

50. Domain: All real numbers except $x = -3$;
Range: {-4, 4} (A set, not an interval);
Discontinuous at $x = -3$

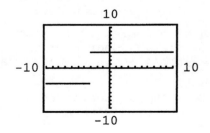

51. Domain: All real numbers
except $x = 1$;
Range: $(-\infty, -3) \cup (5, \infty)$;
Discontinuous at $x = 1$

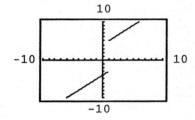

52. Domain: All real numbers
except $x = -1$;
Range: $(-\infty, -3) \cup (1, \infty)$;
Discontinuous at $x = -1$

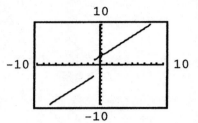

53. Domain: All real numbers
except $x = 3$;
Range: $(0, \infty)$;
Discontinuous at $x = 3$

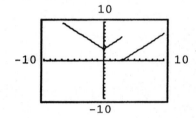

54. Domain: All real numbers
except $x = -2$;
Range: $(0, \infty)$;
Discontinuous at $x = -2$

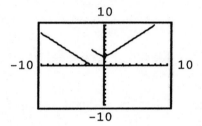

55. Domain: All real numbers
Range: All integers
Discontinuous at the even integers

$$f(x) = \begin{cases} \vdots & & \vdots \\ -2 & \text{if} & -4 \le x < -2 \\ -1 & \text{if} & -2 \le x < 0 \\ 0 & \text{if} & 0 \le x < 2 \\ 1 & \text{if} & 2 \le x < 4 \\ 2 & \text{if} & 4 \le x < 6 \\ \vdots & & \vdots \end{cases}$$

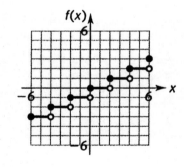

56. $f(x) = \begin{cases} -2 & \text{if} & -6 \le x < -3 \\ -1 & \text{if} & -3 \le x < 0 \\ 0 & \text{if} & 0 \le x < 3 \\ 1 & \text{if} & 3 \le x < 6 \\ 2 & \text{if} & 6 \le x < 9 \end{cases}$

Domain: all real numbers
Range: all integers
Discontinuous at all integers
divisible by 3

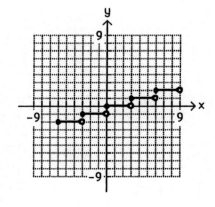

57. Domain: All real numbers
Range: All integers
Discontinuous at rational numbers of the form $\frac{k}{3}$ where k is an integer

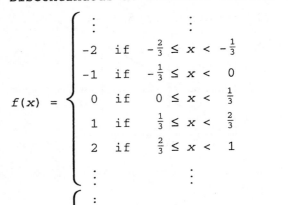

$$f(x) = \begin{cases} \vdots & \vdots \\ -2 & \text{if } -\frac{2}{3} \le x < -\frac{1}{3} \\ -1 & \text{if } -\frac{1}{3} \le x < 0 \\ 0 & \text{if } 0 \le x < \frac{1}{3} \\ 1 & \text{if } \frac{1}{3} \le x < \frac{2}{3} \\ 2 & \text{if } \frac{2}{3} \le x < 1 \\ \vdots & \vdots \end{cases}$$

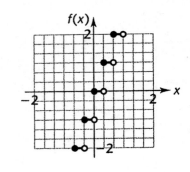

58. $f(x) = \begin{cases} \vdots \\ -2 \text{ if } -1 \le x < -\frac{1}{2} \\ -1 \text{ if } -\frac{1}{2} \le x < 0 \\ 0 \text{ if } 0 \le x < \frac{1}{2} \\ 1 \text{ if } \frac{1}{2} \le x < 1 \\ 2 \text{ if } 1 \le x < \frac{3}{2} \\ \vdots \end{cases}$

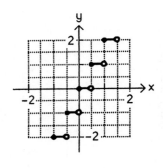

Domain: all real numbers
Range: all integers
Discontinuous at all rational numbers of the form $\frac{k}{2}$ where k is an integer.

59. Domain: all real numbers; Range: [0, 1)
Discontinuous at all integers.

$$f(x) = \begin{cases} \vdots & \vdots \\ x + 2 & \text{if } -2 \le x < -1 \\ x + 1 & \text{if } -1 \le x < 0 \\ x & \text{if } 0 \le x < 1 \\ x - 1 & \text{if } 1 \le x < 2 \\ x - 2 & \text{if } 2 \le x < 3 \\ \vdots & \vdots \end{cases}$$

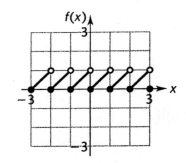

60. $f(x) = \begin{cases} \vdots \\ -2 - x \text{ if } -2 \le x < -1 \\ -1 - x \text{ if } -1 \le x < 0 \\ 0 - x \text{ if } 0 \le x < 1 \\ 1 - x \text{ if } 1 \le x < 2 \\ 2 - x \text{ if } 2 \le x < 3 \\ \vdots \end{cases}$

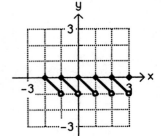

Domain: all real numbers
Range: (-1, 0]
Discontinuous at all integers.

61. (A) One possible answer:

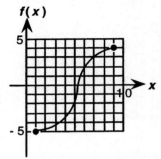

(B) The graph must cross the *x* axis exactly once.

62. (A) One possible answer:

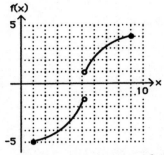

(B) The graph can cross the *x* axis at most one time.

63. (A) One possible answer:

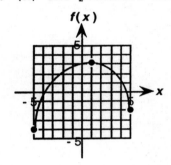

(B) This graph crosses the *x* axis twice. To meet the conditions specified a graph must cross the *x* axis at least twice. If it crossed fewer times the function would have to be discontinuous somewhere. However, the graph could cross more times; in fact there is no upper limit on the number of times it can cross the *x* axis.

64. (A) One possible answer:

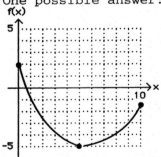

(B) The graph crosses the *x*-axis three times. Yes, it could cross an infinite number of times. It could not cross fewer than three times.

65. (A) One possible answer:

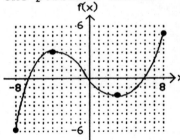

(B) The graph can cross the axis 0, 1, or 2 times.

66. (A) One possible answer:

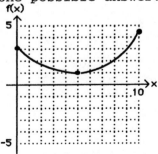

(B) The graph cannot cross the *x* axis.

67. (A) $C(x) = \begin{cases} 15 & 0 < x \leq 1 \\ 18 & 1 < x \leq 2 \\ 21 & 2 < x \leq 3 \\ 24 & 3 < x \leq 4 \\ 27 & 4 < x \leq 5 \\ 30 & 5 < x \leq 6 \end{cases}$

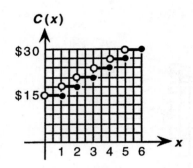

(B) No, since $f(x) \neq C(x)$ at $x = 1, 2, 3, 4, 5,$ or 6

68. (A) $C(x) = \begin{cases} 4 & 0 < x \leq 1 \\ 6 & 1 < x \leq 2 \\ 8 & 2 < x \leq 3 \\ 10 & 3 < x \leq 4 \\ 12 & 4 < x \leq 5 \\ 14 & 5 < x \leq 6 \end{cases}$

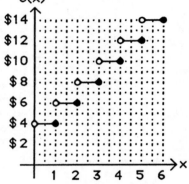

(B) No, since $f(x) \neq C(x)$ at $x = 1, 2, 3, 4, 5,$ or 6

69. $E(x) = \begin{cases} 200 & \text{if } 0 \leq x \leq 3,000 \\ 80 + 0.04x & \text{if } 3,000 < x < 8,000 \\ 180 + 0.04x & \text{if } 8,000 \leq x \end{cases}$

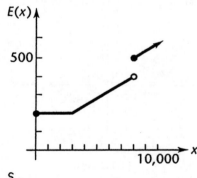

$E(5,750) = \$310;\ E(9,200) = \$548$
discontinuous at $x = 8,000$

70. $S(x) = \begin{cases} 2x \text{ if } 0 \leq x \leq 30 \\ 2(30) + 1(x - 30) = x + 30 \text{ if } x > 30 \end{cases}$

No points of discontinuity.
$S(25) = 50;\ S(45) = 75$

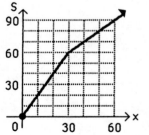

71.

$$f(4) = 10[\![0.5 + 0.4]\!] = 10(0) = 0$$
$$f(-4) = 10[\![0.5 - 0.4]\!] = 10(0) = 0$$
$$f(6) = 10[\![0.5 + 0.6]\!] = 10(1) = 10$$
$$f(-6) = 10[\![0.5 - 0.6]\!] = 10(-1) = -10$$
$$f(24) = 10[\![0.5 + 2.4]\!] = 10(2) = 20$$
$$f(25) = 10[\![0.5 + 2.5]\!] = 10(3) = 30$$
$$f(247) = 10[\![0.5 + 24.7]\!] = 10(25) = 250$$
$$f(-243) = 10[\![0.5 - 24.3]\!] = 10(-24) = -240$$
$$f(-245) = 10[\![0.5 - 24.5]\!] = 10(-24) = -240$$
$$f(-246) = 10[\![0.5 - 24.6]\!] = 10(-25) = -250$$

f rounds numbers to the tens place

72.

x	40	-40	60	-60	740	750	7,551	-601	-649	-651
$f(x)$	0	0	100	-100	700	800	7,600	-600	-600	-700

$f(x)$ rounds to the nearest hundred.

73. $f(x) = [\![100x + 0.5]\!]/100$

74. $f(x) = \dfrac{1}{1000}[\![0.5 + 1000x]\!]$

75. (A) Estimated maximum revenue is $25,650 when 900 car seats are sold.

(B) The maximum revenue is $25,714.28 when 857 car seats are sold.

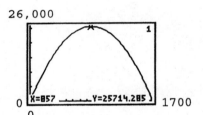

76. (A) Estimated maximum profit is $6,250 when 500 car seats are sold.

(B) The maximum profit is $6,314.29 when 543 car seats are sold.

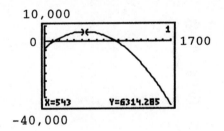

77. (A) The estimated maximum volume is 648 in³ when the side of the cut-out square is 3 in.

(B) The maximum volume is approximately 654.98 in³ when the side of the cut-out square is approximately 3.39 in.

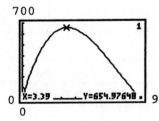

78. (A) The estimated maximum volume is 672 in³ when the side of the cut-out square is 4 in.

(B) The maximum volume is approximately 673.84 in³ when the side of the cut-out square is approximately 3.77 in.

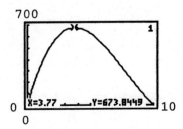

79. (A) The estimated minimal cost is $301,000 when the land portion of the pipe is 15 miles long.

(B) The minimal cost is approximately $300,000 when the land portion of the pipe is approximately 13.6 miles long.

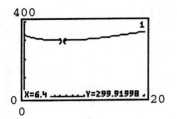

80. (A) The estimated minimal time is 104 minutes when the land portion of the trip is 20 miles.

(B) The minimal time is approximately 102 minutes when the land portion of the trip is approximately 17.9 miles.

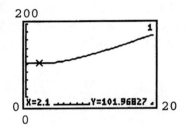

81. (A)

x	28	30	32	34	36
Mileage	45	52	55	51	47
$f(x)$	45.3	51.8	54.2	52.4	46.5

(B)

```
y
60 │ ·············
   │ ·············
50 │ ···●●●···
   │ ···●·····●···
40 │ ●···········
   │ ·············
30 │ ·············
   │ ·············
20 │ ·············
   │ ·············
10 │ ·············
   │ ·············
   └──────────────→ x
    28   32   36
```

(C) $f(31) \approx 53.50$ thousand miles
$f(35) \approx 49.95$ thousand miles

82. (A)

x	0	1	2	3	4
Production	4.7	4.1	3.5	3.7	5.0
$f(x)$	4.8	3.8	3.5	3.9	4.9

(B)

```
y
5 │●···········●
  │ ···········
4 │ ·●·······●··
  │ ·····●●·····
3 │ ···········
  │ ···········
2 │ ···········
  │ ···········
1 │ ···········
  └────────────→ x
            4
```

(C) 1994: f(5) ≈ 6.55 million vehicles;
1995: f(6) ≈ 8.88 million vehicles

Exercise 1-5

1. odd **2.** odd **3.** even **4.** even **5.** neither

6. neither **7.** even **8.** even **9.** neither **10.** neither

11.
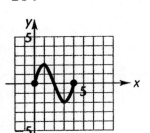

12.
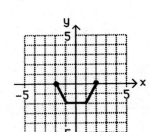

13.
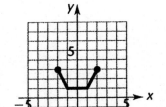

14.
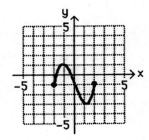

15.
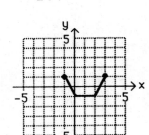

16.
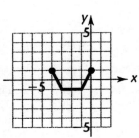

17.
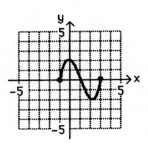

18.
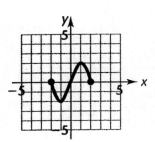

19.
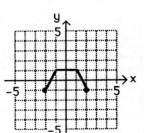

20.
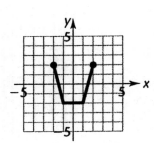

21.
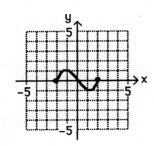

22.

23. The graph of $y = x^2$ is shifted 2 units to the right; $y = (x - 2)^2$.

24. The graph of $y = |x|$ is shifted 1 unit to the left; $y = |x + 1|$.

25. The graph of $y = x^3$ is shifted down 2 units; $y = x^3 - 2$.

26. The graph of $y = \sqrt[3]{x}$ is shifted up 3 units; $y = \sqrt[3]{x} + 3$.

27. The graph of $y = |x|$ is contracted by a factor of 0.25; $y = 0.25|x|$.

28. The graph of $y = \sqrt[3]{x}$ is expanded by a factor of 3: $y = 3\sqrt[3]{x}$.

29. The graph of $y = x^3$ is reflected in the x axis (or the y axis); $y = -x^3$.

30. The graph of $y = x^2$ is reflected in the x axis; $y = -x^2$.

31. $g(x) = \sqrt[3]{x + 4} - 5$ **32.** $g(x) = (x - 5)^3 + 4$ **33.** $g(x) = -0.5(6 + \sqrt{x})$

34. $g(x) = -4(\sqrt{x} - 2)$ **35.** $g(x) = -2(x + 4)^2 - 2$ **36.** $g(x) = -0.5|x - 3| + 4$

37. The graph of $y = x^2$ is shifted 7 units left and 9 units up.

38. The graph of $y = x^2$ is shifted 4 units right and 6 units down.

39. The graph of $y = |x|$ is shifted 8 units right and reflected in the x axis.

40. The graph of $y = |x|$ is shifted 5 units left and reflected in the x axis.

41. The graph of $y = \sqrt{x}$ is reflected in the x axis and shifted 3 units up.

42. The graph of $y = \sqrt{x}$ is shifted 3 units to the left and 2 units down.

43. The graph of $y = x^2$ is expanded by a factor of 4 and reflected in the x axis.

44. The graph of $y = |x|$ is contracted by a factor of 0.5 and reflected in the x axis.

45. $y = |x + 2| + 2$ **46.** $y = (x - 2)^2 - 4$ **47.** $y = 4 - \sqrt{x}$

48. $y = \sqrt{x} - 2$ **49.** $y = 4 - (x - 1)^2$ **50.** $y = 5 - |x + 2|$

51. $y = 0.5(x - 3)^3 + 1$ **52.** $y = 2\sqrt[3]{x - 1} + 2$

53. Reversing the order does not change the result.

54. Reversing the order does not change the result.

55. Reversing the order can change the result.

56. Reversing the order can change the result.

57. Reversing the order can change the result.

58. Reversing the order does not change the result.

59. 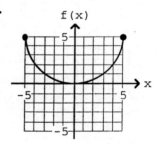 **60.** 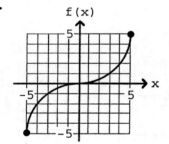 **61.**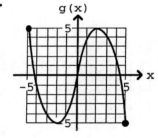

62.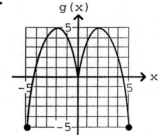

63. Conclusion: Any function can be written as the sum of two other functions, one even and the other odd.

64. (A) If f is even, g is odd. (B) If f is odd, g is even.

65. Graph of $f(x)$ Graph of $|f(x)|$ Graph of $-|f(x)|$

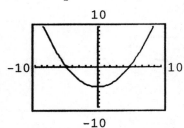 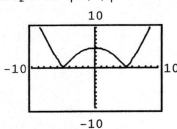 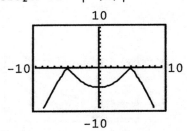

66. Graph of $f(x)$ Graph of $|f(x)|$ Graph of $-|f(x)|$

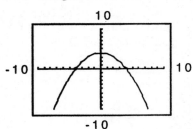 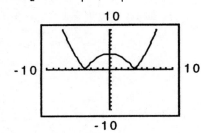 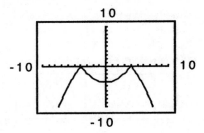

67. Graph of $f(x)$ Graph of $|f(x)|$ Graph of $-|f(x)|$

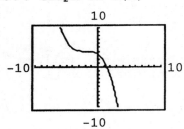 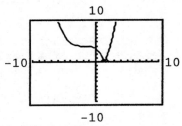 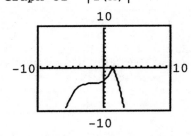

68. Graph of $f(x)$ Graph of $|f(x)|$ Graph of $-|f(x)|$

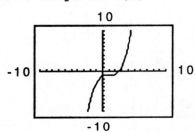 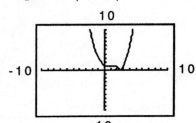 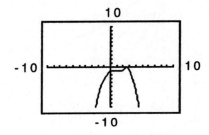

69. The graph of $y = |f(x)|$ is the same as the graph of $y = f(x)$ whenever $f(x) \geq 0$ and is the reflection of the graph of $y = f(x)$ with respect to the x axis whenever $f(x) < 0$.

70. For $x \leq 0$ the graph of $-|f(x)|$ is the same as the graph of $f(x)$.
For $x > 0$ the graph of $-|f(x)|$ is the reflected graph of $|f(x)|$ in the x-axis.

72. $F(x) = 0.75f(x)$
$F(x)$ will be the graph of $f(x)$ contracted by a factor of 0.75; that is, all y-values will be multiplied by 0.75, giving the points (200, 30,000), (600, 45,000) and (1000, 90,000).

73. Each graph is a vertical translation of the graph of $y = 0.004(x - 10)^3$.

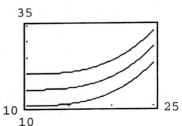

74. Each graph is an expansion of the graph of $y = \sqrt{x}$.

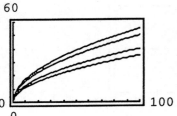

75. Each graph is a contraction followed by a vertical translation of the graph of $y = x^2$.

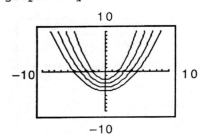

76. Each graph is a reflection followed by an expansion and then a vertical translation of the graph of $y = x^2$

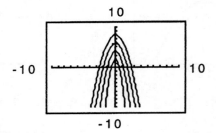

77. Each graph is a portion of the graph of a horizontal translation followed by a contraction (except for $C = 8$) of the graph of $y = t^2$.

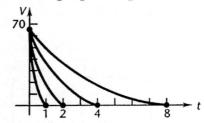

78. Each graph is a portion of the graph of a horizontal translation followed by a contraction of the graph of $y = t^2$.

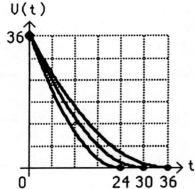

CHAPTER 1 REVIEW

1.

(graph with points $(0, 3)$, $(-4, 0)$, $(-3, -4)$, $(4, -2)$)

(1-1)

2. (A) $x^2 + y^2 = 7$
(B) $(x - 3)^2 + (y + 2)^2 = 7$ *(1-1)*

3. Xmin = -4, Xmax = 9, Ymin = -6, Ymax = 7   *(1-2)*

4. (A) Function; domain = { 1, 2, 3}, range = {1, 4, 9}
   (B) Not a function
   (C) Function; domain = {-2, -1, 0, 1 ,2}, range = {2}   *(1-3)*

5. (A) Not a function   (B) A function   (C) A function   (D) Not a function *(1-3)*

6. (A) -1   (B) 24   (C) 0   (D) 0   *(1-3)*

7. (A) Odd   (B) Even   (C) Neither   *(1-5)*

8. $f(-4) = 4$, $f(0) = -4$, $f(3) = 0$, $f(5)$ is not defined *(1-1, 1-3, 1-4)*

9. $x = -2$, $x = 1$ *(1-1, 1-3, 1-4)*

10. Domain: [-4, 5), range: [-4, 4]   *(1-4)*

11. Increasing: [0, 5), decreasing: [-4, 0]   *(1-4)*

12. $x = 0$ *(1-4)*

13.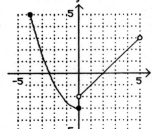
   (1-5)

14.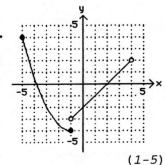
   (1-5)

15.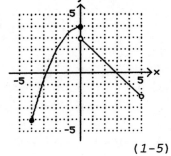
   (1-5)

16.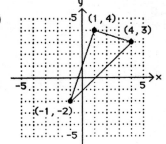
   (1-5)

17. (A) g (B) m (C) n (D) f *(1-5)*

18. (A) 0   (B) 1   (C) 2   (D) 0   *(1-4)*

19. (A) -2, 0   (B) -1 and 1   (C) No solution   (D) $x = 3$ and $x < -2$ *(1-4)*

20. Domain = $(-\infty, \infty)$, range = $(-3, \infty)$ *(1-4)*

21. [-2, -1], [1, ∞) *(1-4)*   **22.** [-1, 1) *(1-4)*

23. $(-\infty, -2)$ *(1-4)*   **24.** $x = -2$, $x = 1$ *(1-4)*

25. (A)

(B) 16.56

(C) A right triangle *(1-1)*

26. (A)

x	0	1	2	3	4	5	6
y	-4	1	4	5	4	1	-4

(B)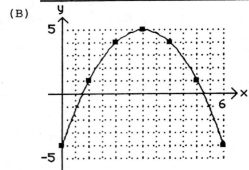

27. (A) All real numbers   (B) All real numbers except $t = 5$
(C) $w \geq 0$ or $[0, \infty)$ *(1-3)*

28. $5 + 2h$ *(1-3)*

29. $f(x) = 4x^3 - \sqrt{x}$ *(1-3)*

30. The function f multiplies the square of the domain element by 3, adds 4 times the domain element, and then subtracts 6.   *(1-3)*

31. $c = 1.3$, $f(1.3) = 5.2$, x intercepts: $x = 0$, $x = 3.3$ *(1-4)*

32. (A)

(B) Domain: $[-4, 5]$, range: $(-5, -1] \cup [1, 5]$

(C) $x = 0$

(D) Decreasing on $[-5, 0)$,
increasing on $[0, 5]$ *(1-4)*

33. The graph of f increases on $[-10, -4.47]$ to a local maximum value, $f(-4.47) \approx 22.89$, decreases on $[-4.47, 4.47]$ to a local minimum value, $f(4.47) \approx -12.89$, and then increases on $[4.47, 10]$.   *(1-4)*

34. (A) Reflected across x axis   (B) Shifted down 3 units
(C) Shifted left 3 units   *(1-5)*

35. (A) $-(x - 2)^2 + 4$ (B) $4 - 4\sqrt{x}$ *(1-5)*

36. $g(x) = 8 - 3|x - 4|$

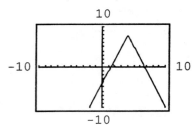

(1-5)

37. Center: $(-2, 2)$, radius: 2

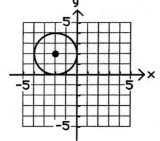

(1-1)

38. Domain: $x \geq 0$, $x \neq 9$ or $[0, 9) \cup (9, \infty)$ *(1-3)*

39. (A) One possible answer: (B) One possible answer:

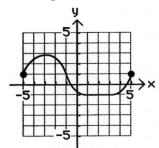 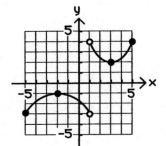

(*1-4*)

40. $g(t) = 2t^2 - 4t + 5$ (*1-3*)

41. Domain: $x \neq 2$ or $(-\infty, 2) \cup (2, \infty)$
range: $y > -3$ or $(-3, \infty)$;
discontinuous at $x = 2$

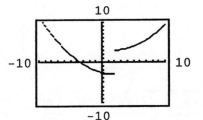

(*1-4*)

42. (A)   (B)

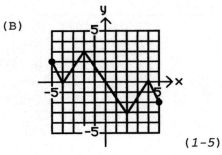

(*1-5*)

43. $(x - 4)^2 + (y + 3)^2 = 34$ (*1-1*)

44. (A) $6x - 5 + 3h$ (B) $3x + 3a - 5$ (*1-3*)

45. (A) The graph must cross the x axis exactly once.
(B) The graph can cross the x axis once or not at all.   (*1-4*)

46. (A) $f(x) = \begin{cases} 2 & \text{for } -3 < x \le -2 \\ 1 & \text{for } -2 < x \le -1 \\ 0 & \text{for } -1 < x < 1 \\ 1 & \text{for } 1 \le x < 2 \\ 2 & \text{for } 2 \le x < 3 \end{cases}$

(B)

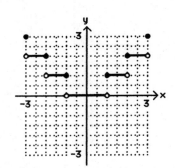

(C) Range: Nonnegative integers (D) Discontinuous at all integers except 0
(E) Even

(*1-4, 1-5*)

47. (A) 3,800 bottles   (B) The demand decreases by 400 bottles.
(C) The demand increases by 500 bottles.   (*1-1*)

48. (A) 3,970 bottles   (B) The demand decreases by 490 bottles.
(C) The demand increases by 520 bottles.   (*1-2*)

49. (A)

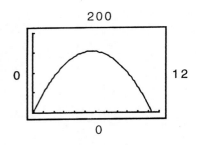

(B) 11.3 sec

(C) 155 m

(1-2, 1-4)

50. (A) The estimated maximum volume is 10,472 in³ when the flap is 7 in wide.

(B) The maximum volume is approximately 10,480 in³ when the flap is 6.8 in wide.

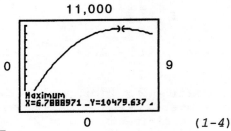

(1-4)

51. (A)

x	0	5	10	15	20
Consumption	309	276	271	255	233
$f(x)$	303	286	269	252	234

(B)

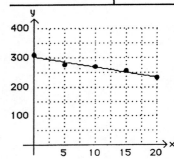

(C) 217 in 1995, 200 in 2000

(D) $y = -3.46x + 303.4$, which is the same as the modeling function f.

(E) Per capita egg consumption is dropping about 17 eggs every five years. *(1-3)*

52. (A)

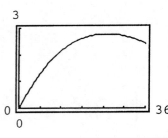

(B) The function increases on [0, 24.8] to a local maximum of 2.8 cc/sec, and then decreases on [24.8, 36]. *(1-4)*

53. (A)

$$C(x) = \begin{cases} 0.49x & \text{for } 0 \leq x < 36 \\ 0.44x & \text{for } 36 \leq x < 72 \\ 0.39x & \text{for } 72 \leq x \end{cases}$$

Discontinuous at $x = 36$ and $x = 72$.

(B)

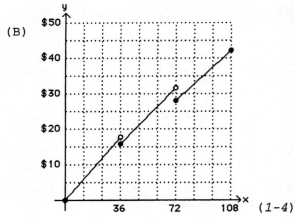

(1-4)

54. (A) 0   (B) 1   (C) 2   (D) 0   (E) 1   (F) 0   *(1-5)*

CHAPTER 2

Exercise 2-1

1. *x* intercept = -2; *y* intercept = 2; slope = 1

2. *x* intercept = 1; *y* intercept = 1; slope = -1

3. *x* intercept = -2; *y* intercept = -4; slope = -2

4. *x* intercept = -1; *y* intercept = -3; slope = -3

5. *x* intercept = 3; *y* intercept = -1; slope = $\frac{1}{3}$

6. *x* intercept = 4; *y* intercept = -2; slope = $\frac{1}{2}$

7. Not linear   **8.** Not linear   **9.** Linear   **10.** Linear

11. Linear   **12.** Linear   **13.** Linear   **14.** Linear

15. Not linear   **16.** Not linear

17. *x* intercept: $\frac{20}{3}$;
y intercept: 4;
slope: $-\frac{3}{5}$

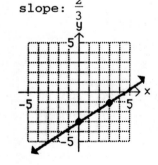

18. *x* intercept: 4;
y intercept: 6;
slope: $-\frac{3}{2}$

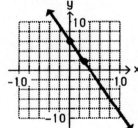

19. *x* intercept: 0;
y intercept: 0;
slope: $-\frac{3}{4}$

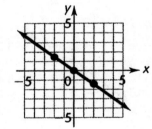

20. *x* intercept: $\frac{9}{2}$;
y intercept: -3;
slope: $\frac{2}{3}$

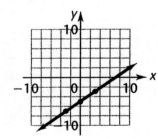

21. *x* intercept: $\frac{15}{2}$;
y intercept: -5;
slope: $\frac{2}{3}$

22. *x* intercept: 6;
y intercept: 8;
slope: $-\frac{4}{3}$

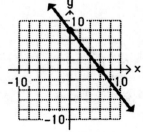

23. *x* intercept: -4;
y intercept: 8;
slope: 2

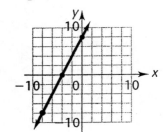

24. *x* intercept: -5;
y intercept: 6;
slope: $\frac{6}{5}$

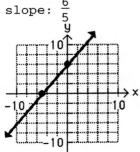

25. *x* intercept: -3;
y intercept: none;
slope is not defined

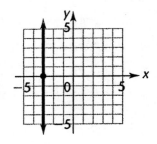

26. *x* intercept: none;
y intercept: -2;
slope: 0

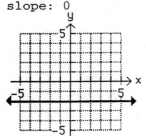

27. *x* intercept: none;
y intercept: 3.5;
slope: 0

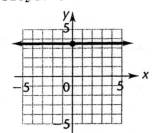

28. *x* intercept: 2.5;
y intercept: none;
slope is not defined

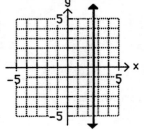

29. $y = x$

30. $y = -x + 7$

31. $y = -\frac{2}{3}x - 4$

32. $y = \frac{5}{3}x + 6$

33. $y = -3x + 4$

34. $y = 2x - 4$

35. $y = -\frac{2}{5}x + 2$

36. $y = \frac{1}{2}x$

37. $y = -2x + 8$

38. $y = -\frac{1}{3}x + 3$

39. $y = -\frac{4}{3}x + \frac{8}{3}$

40. $y = \frac{3}{4}x - \frac{5}{2}$

41. $y = 4$

42. $y = -2$

43. $x = 4$

44. $x = -3$

45. $y = \frac{3}{4}x + 3$

46. $y = -\frac{5}{4}x - 5$

47. $3x - y = -13$

48. $2x + y = -8$

49. $3x - y = 9$

50. $3x + 2y = -14$

51. $x = 2$

52. $y = 3$

53. $x = 3$

54. $y = -3$

55. $3x - 2y = 15$

56. $3x + 4y = 29$

57. $3x - y = 4$

58. $5x - 4y = -26$

61. slope $AB = -\frac{3}{4}$ = slope DC **62.** $m_{DA} = \frac{4}{3}$; $m_{CB} = \frac{4}{3}$ which shows $DA \parallel CB$.

63. (slope AB)(slope BC) = $\left(-\frac{3}{4}\right)\left(\frac{4}{3}\right)$ = -1

64. $m_{AD} = \frac{4}{3}$; $m_{DC} = -\frac{3}{4}$ from which $m_{AD} \cdot m_{DC}$ = -1 which shows $AD \perp DC$.

65. $6x + 8y = -9$ **66.** $8x - 6y = 13$

67. $3x + 4y = 25$

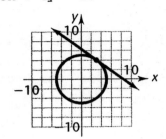

68. $4x - 3y = -50$

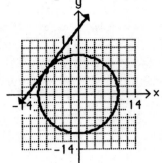

69. $x - y = 10$

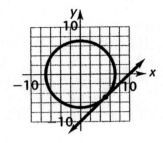

70. $x + 2y = -20$

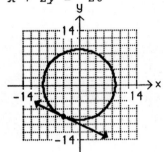

71. $232 = 5x - 12y$

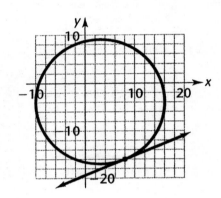

72. $8x + 15y = -194$

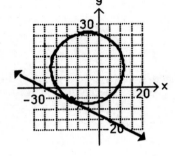

73. (A)

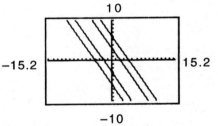

(B) Varying C produces a family of parallel lines.

74. (A)

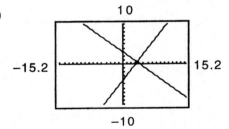

(B)

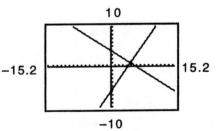

(C) The lines are perpendicular to each other.

75. The function g is never linear.   **76.** The function g is never linear.

79. (A) $F = \dfrac{9}{5}C + 32$ (B) 68°F, 30°C   (C) $\dfrac{9}{5}$

80. (A) $s = 0.4w$ (B) $w = 9$ lbs.   (C) slope = 0.4

81. (A) $V = -1,600t + 8,000,\ 0 \le t \le 5$ (B) $V = \$3,200$ (C) $-1,600$

82. (A) $R = 1.5C + 3$, $(C > 10)$ (B) $158
(C) slope = 1.5; the retail price rises $1.50 for each $1 in cost

83. (A) $T = -5A + 70$, $A \geq 0$ (B) $A = 14$ thousand feet
(C) slope = -5; the temperature changes $-5°F$ for each 1,000 foot rise in altitude.

84. (A) $T = 4A + 200$, $(A \geq 0)$ (B) $T = 226$ mph
(C) slope = 4 which indicates that true air speed increases 4 mph for each one thousand foot increase in altitude.

85. (A) $h = 1.13t + 12.8$ (B) $t = 32.9$ hours

86. (A) $p = \dfrac{5}{11}d + 15$ (B) $d = 55$ ft

87. (A) $R = 0.00152C - 0.159$, $C \geq 210$ (B) $R = 0.236$
(C) slope = 0.00152; coronary risk increases 0.00152 per unit increase in cholesterol above the 210 cholesterol level.

88. (A) $N = -\dfrac{113}{4500}t + 4.76$ $(t \geq 0)$ (B) $N \approx 2.25$ people per household

89. (A) $C(x) = 128x + 375$
(B) The fixed costs are $375, the variable costs are $128x$, and the cost of producing an additional surfboard is $128.
(C) $3,571

90. (A) $C(x) = 38x + 491$
(B) The fixed costs are $491, the variable costs are $38x$, and the cost of producing an additional pair of skates is $38.
(C) $7,154

91. (A) $C(x) = -1.2x + 97.4$ (B) 64%, 32%   (C) 1979

92. (A) $0.81x - 3.8$ (B) 22%, 42%   (C) 2028

Exercise 2-2

1. $x = c$, $x = f$ **2.** $x = a$, $x = d$ **3.** $x = b$, $x = e$ **4.** $x = b$, $x = e$

5. (c, f) **6.** $(-\infty, a] \cup [d, \infty)$ **7.** $(-\infty, b] \cup [e, \infty)$ **8.** (a, d)

9. 18   **10.** 4   **11.** 9   **12.** 1   **13.** $\dfrac{11}{2}$ or 5.5   **14.** 9.5

15. $x < 5$ or $(-\infty, 5)$; x

16. $x \geq -3$; $[-3, \infty)$;   x

17. $t > 2$ or $(2, \infty)$; t

18. $n \leq -3$; $(-\infty, -3]$;   n

19. $-2 < t \leq 3$ or $(-2, 3]$; t **20.** $3 \leq m < 7$; $[3, 7)$;   m

21. $y = 2, 8$ **22.** $x = -6$ or 4   **23.** $-2 \leq t \leq 0.8$; $[-2, 0.8]$

24. $1.5 < w < 7.5$; $(1.5, 7.5)$ **25.** 3   **26.** -4

27. $-30 \leq x < 18$ or $[-30, 18)$ **28.** $41 \leq x < 59$ or $[41, 59)$ x

29. $t = 1.5, 4.5$ **30.** $s = -6, 1.2$

31. $x < -7.5$ and $x > 1.25$; $(-\infty, -7.5) \cup (1.25, \infty)$

32. $x \leq 2.6$ or $x \geq 6.2$ **33.** $x = 3.4$ **34.** $x = -\dfrac{22}{5}$

35. $-5.5 < x < 2.5$ and $3.5 < x < 6.5$ **36.** $-7.5 < x < 0.625$ or $x > 7.5$

37. $d = \dfrac{a_n - a_1}{n - 1}$ **38.** $C = \dfrac{5}{9}(F - 32)$ **39.** $f = \dfrac{d_1 d_2}{d_2 + d_1}$ **40.** $R_1 = \dfrac{RR_2}{R_2 - R_1}$

41. $a = \dfrac{A - 2bc}{2b + 2c}$ **42.** $c = \dfrac{A - 2ab}{2a + 2b}$ **43.** $x = \dfrac{5y + 3}{2 - 3y}$ **44.** $y = \dfrac{3x + 2}{x - 3}$

45. The graphs are identical for $x \geq 0$. For $x < 0$, each is the reflection of the other in the x axis.

46. The graphs are identical for all values of x.

47. (A) and (C), $a > 0$ and $b > 0$, or $a < 0$ and $b < 0$
(B) and (D), $a > 0$ and $b < 0$, or $a < 0$ and $b > 0$

48. (A) two of three numbers must be negative and one positive or all three must be positive

(B) two of three numbers must be positive and one negative or all three must be negative

(C) two of three numbers must be negative and one positive or all three must be positive

(D) a can be either positive or negative, and b and c must have opposite signs.

49. >   **50.** <   **51.** >   **52.** <

53. $(2.9, 3) \cup (3, 3.1)$;

54. $(4.99, 5) \cup (5, 5.01)$;

55. $(c - d, c) \cup (c, c + d)$;

56. $(4 - d, 4) \cup (4, 4 + d)$;

57. ± 1 **58.** ± 1 **59.** \$19,750

60. (A) \$39,900
(B) They are never the same. Employees should always choose the first method.

61. $|A - 12.436| < 0.001$, $(12.435, 12.437)$

62. $|V - 6.94| < 0.02$, $(6.92, 6.96)$

63. (A) $x > 40,625$ (B) $x = 40,625$ **64.** (A) $x > 27,500$ (B) 27,500

65. (B) $x > 52,000$ (C) Raise wholesale price \$3.50 to \$66.50

66. (B) $x > 33,000$ (C) Raise wholesale price \$140 to \$144

67. $|N - 2.37| \leq 0.005$ **68.** $|N - 3.65 \times 10^{-3}| \leq 5 \times 10^{-6}$

69. \$2,060 $\leq$ Benefit reduction $\leq$ \$3,560

70. \$1,373.33 $\leq$ Benefit reduction $\leq$ \$2,373.33

71. 16°C to 27°C   **72.** 68°F to 86°F

73. (A) $T = 30 + 25(x - 3)$ (B) 330°C
     (C) $9.8 \leq x \leq 13.8$ (from 9.8 km to 13.8 km)

74. (A) $V = V_S(1 + 0.03A)$ (B) 143 mph   (C) 99.6 mph   (D) 4,940 ft.

Exercise 2-3

1. $f(x) = (x - 2)^2 + 1$ **2.** $g(x) = -(x + 1)^2 - 2$ **3.** $h(x) = -(x + 1)^2$

4. $k(x) = (x - 2)^2$ **5.** $m(x) = (x - 2)^2 - 3$ **6.** $n(x) = -(x + 1)^2 + 4$

7. The graph of f is the graph of $y = x^2$ shifted to the right 2 units and up 1 unit.

8. The graph of $g(x)$ is the graph of $y = x^2$ reflected in the x axis and then shifted to the left 1 unit and down 2 units.

9. The graph of h is the graph of $y = x^2$ reflected in the x axis and shifted to the left 1 unit.

10. The graph of $k(x)$ is the graph of $y = x^2$ shifted to the right 2 units.

11. The graph of m is the graph of $y = x^2$ shifted to the right 2 units and down 3 units.

12. The graph of $n(x)$ is the graph of $y = x^2$ reflected in the x axis and then shifted to the left 1 unit and up 4 units.

13. k **14.** f **15.** m **16.** n **17.** h **18.** g

19.

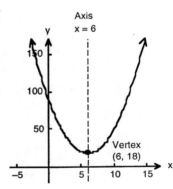

20.

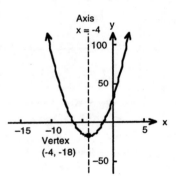

21.

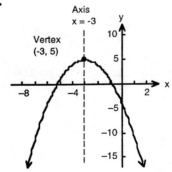

22.

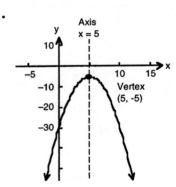

23.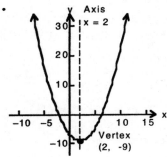

24.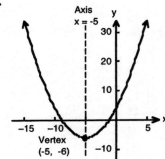

25. Increasing: $[2.25, \infty)$; decreasing: $(-\infty, 2,25]$; range: $[4.75, \infty)$

26. Increasing: $[-2.9, \infty)$; decreasing: $(-\infty, -2.9]$; range: $[-59.05, \infty)$

27. Increasing: $(-\infty, 2.2]$; decreasing: $[2.2, \infty)$; range: $(-\infty, 60.4]$

28. Increasing: $(-\infty, -1.25]$; decreasing: $[-1.25, \infty)$; range: $(-\infty, 28.5]$

29. $y = 2x^2 - 4x - 2$ **30.** $y = 3x^2 + 12x + 8$ **31.** $y = -0.5x^2 - x + 3.5$

32. $y = -\frac{1}{3}x^2 + 2x$ **33.** $y = -2x^2 + 16x - 24$ **34.** $y = 3x^2 + 12x$

35. $y = -0.5x^2 - 4x + 4$ **36.** $y = -0.4x^2 + 4x - 2$ **37.** $y = 5x^2 + 50x + 100$

38. $y = 10x^2 - 120x + 300$ **43.** Center: $(3, 2)$; radius: 7

44. Center: $(1, 5)$; radius: 9 **45.** Center: $(-4, 1)$; radius: 5

46. Center: $(2, -6)$; radius: 8

48. (A) $x = \dfrac{-b}{2a}$ (B) $\left(\dfrac{-b}{2a}, \dfrac{4ac - b^2}{4a}\right)$

(C) $\dfrac{4ac - b^2}{4a}$ is the minimum value if $a > 0$ and the maximum value if $a < 0$.

49. $y = 2x - 1$ 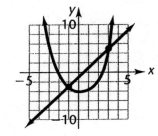   **50.** $y = -2x + 1$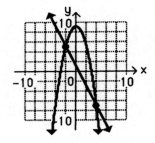

51. (A) $1 + h$ (B)

h	$slope = 1 + h$
1	2
0.1	1.1
0.01	1.01
0.001	1.001

; The slope seems to be approaching 1.

52. $f(x) = x^2 + 2x - 6$
(A) $h + 6$

(B)

h	1	0.1	0.01	0.001
m_{SL}	7	6.1	6.01	6.001

Slope seems to be approaching 6.

53. The minimum product is -225 for the numbers 15 and -15. There is no maximum product.

54. The maximum product is 900 when both numbers are 30. There is no minimum product.

55. (A) $A(x) = -x^2 + 50x + 5000$, $0 \leq x \leq 100$ (B) $x = 25$ (C) 75 ft × 75 ft

56. (A) $A(x) = x^2 - 5x + 2250$, $0 \leq x \leq 45$ (B) $x = 0$
(C) 50 ft (barn side) × 45 ft

57. (A) $d(t) = -16t^2 + 176t$, $0 \leq t \leq 11$ (B) 1.68 sec; 9.32 sec

58. (A) $d(t) = -16t^2 + 144t$, $0 \leq t \leq 9$ (B) 2.35 sec; 6.65 sec

59. (A) $h(x) = -0.14x^2 + 14$, $-10 \leq x \leq 10$ (B) No   (C) 11.76 ft   (D) 7.56 ft

60. (A) $d(x) = 0.005x^2 + 10$ (B) 157.5 ft

61. (A)
```
QuadReg
y=ax²+bx+c
a=-.3228219836
b=640.014462
c=-16529.02301
```
(B)
```
LinReg
y=ax+b
a=85.79752367
b=118918.4268
```
(C) 295 mowers;
1,422 mowers

62. (A) 455 mowers; 1,261 mowers   (B) 858 lawn mowers; maximum profit is \$102,421

63. (A)
```
QuadReg
y=ax²+bx+c
a=-.080952381
b=3.442857143
c=61.38095238
```

64. (A)
```
QuadReg
y=ax²+bx+c
a=-.0704761905
b=2.814285714
c=52.69047619
```

(B) 2003

(B) 2000

Exercise 2-4

1. $7 + 5i$ **2.** $7 + 3i$ **3.** $5 + 3i$ **4.** $14 - 5i$

5. $2 + 4i$ **6.** $4 + 2i$ **7.** $5 + 9i$ **8.** $-3 - 2i$

9. $4 - 3i$ **10.** $9 - 4i$ **11.** -24 or $-24 + 0i$

12. -24 or $-24 + 0i$ **13.** $-12 - 6i$ **14.** $-6 - 10i$ **15.** $15 - 3i$

16. $-21 + i$ **17.** $-4 - 33i$ **18.** $8 + i$ **19.** 65 or $65 + 0i$

20. 34 or $34 + 0i$ **21.** $\frac{2}{5} - \frac{1}{5}i$ **22.** $\frac{3}{10} + \frac{1}{10}i$ **23.** $\frac{3}{13} + \frac{11}{13}i$

24. $\frac{4}{13} - \frac{7}{13}i$ **25.** $5 + 3i$ **26.** $3 + 3i$ **27.** $7 - 5i$

28. $-5 + 3i$ **29.** $-3 + 2i$ **30.** $-6 - 13i$ **31.** $8 + 25i$

32. $13 + i$ **33.** $\frac{5}{7} - \frac{2}{7}i$ **34.** $3 - 4i$ **35.** $\frac{2}{13} + \frac{3}{13}i$

36. $\frac{3}{25} + \frac{4}{25}i$ **37.** $-\frac{2}{5}i$ or $0 - \frac{2}{5}i$ **38.** $-\frac{1}{3}i$ or $0 - \frac{1}{3}i$ **39.** $\frac{3}{2} - \frac{1}{2}i$

40. $-\frac{1}{3} - \frac{2}{3}i$ **41.** $-6i$ or $0 - 6i$ **42.** $4 - 7i$

45. $i^{18} = -1$, $i^{32} = 1$, $i^{67} = -i$ **46.** i, $-i$, 1

47. $x = 3$, $y = -2$ **48.** $x = 1$, $y = 3$ **49.** $x = 2$, $y = 3$ **50.** $x = -4$, $y = 1$

51. $0.6 + 1.2i$ **52.** $-0.7 + 0.1i$ **53.** $1.5 + 0.5i$ **54.** $-0.6 + 1.2i$

56. $1/i = -i$ **57.** $(a + c) + (b + d)i$ **58.** $(a - c) + (b - d)i$

59. $a^2 + b^2$ or $(a^2 + b^2) + 0i$ **60.** $u^2 + v^2$ or $(u^2 + v^2) + 0i$

61. $(ac - bd) + (ad + bc)i$ **62.** $\frac{ac + bd}{c^2 + d^2} + \frac{(bc - ad)}{c^2 + d^2}i$

63. $i^{4k} = (i^4)^k = (i^2 \cdot i^2)^k = [(-1)(-1)]^k = 1^k = 1$

67. $3 + i$ or $-3 - i$ **68.** $1 + i$, $-1 - i$

71. (1) Definition of addition; (2) Commutative (+) property for R;
(3) Definition of addition

72. (1) Definition of multiplication; (2) Commutative ($\cdot$);
(3) Definition of multiplication

Exercise 2-5

1. $u = 0$, 2 **2.** $A = 0$, -4 **3.** $y = \frac{2}{3}$ (double root)

4. $x = -\frac{1}{4}$ (double root)   **5.** $x = \frac{3}{2}$, 4 **6.** $x = -4$, $\frac{2}{3}$ **7.** $m = \pm 2\sqrt{3}$

8. $y = \pm 3\sqrt{5}$ **9.** $x = \pm 5i$ **10.** $x = \pm 4i$ **11.** $y = \pm\frac{4}{3}$

12. $x = \pm\frac{3}{2}$ **13.** $x = \pm\frac{5i}{2}$ or $\pm\frac{5}{2}i$ **14.** $a = \pm\frac{3}{4}i$ **15.** $n = -2$, -8

16. $m = -2$, 8 **17.** $d = 3 \pm 2i$ **18.** $t = -1 \pm 3i$ **19.** $x = 5 \pm 2\sqrt{7}$

20. $x = 3 \pm 2\sqrt{3}$ **21.** $x = 2 \pm 2i$ **22.** $y = 1 \pm i\sqrt{2}$ **23.** $x = \frac{2 \pm \sqrt{2}}{2}$

24. $m = \frac{3 \pm \sqrt{3}}{2}$ **25.** $x = \frac{1}{5} \pm \frac{3}{5}i$ **26.** $x = -\frac{3}{7} \pm \frac{\sqrt{19}}{7}i$

27. $(-5, 2)$. $-5 < x < 2$.

28. $(-4, 3)$. $-4 < x < 3$.

29. $(-\infty, 3) \cup (7, \infty)$. $x < 3$ or $x > 7$.

30. $(-\infty, -5) \cup (-2, \infty)$. $x < -5$ or $x > -2$.

31. $[0, 8]$. $0 \le x \le 8$. x

32. $(-\infty, -6] \cup [0, \infty)$. $x \le -6$ or $x \ge 0$. x

33. $[-5, 0]$. $-5 \le x \le 0$. x

34. $[0, 4]$. $0 \le x \le 4$. x

35. $x = 3 \pm 2\sqrt{3}$

36. $y = 5 \pm 2\sqrt{7}$

37. $y = \dfrac{3 \pm \sqrt{3}}{2}$

38. $d = \dfrac{2 \pm \sqrt{2}}{2}$

39. $x = \dfrac{1 \pm \sqrt{7}}{3}$

40. $x = \dfrac{-5 \pm \sqrt{73}}{6}$

41. $x = -\dfrac{5}{4}, \dfrac{2}{3}$

42. $x = -\dfrac{4}{3}, \dfrac{1}{3}$

43. $x = \dfrac{3 \pm \sqrt{13}}{2}$

44. $x = -1 \pm \sqrt{3}$

45. $t = \sqrt{\dfrac{2s}{g}}$

46. $a = \sqrt{c^2 - b^2}$

47. $I = \dfrac{E + \sqrt{E^2 - 4RP}}{2R}$

48. $r = \sqrt{\dfrac{A}{P}} - 1$

49. $x < 0.48$ or $x > 1.35$

50. $0.77 < x < 6.25$

51. $-1.05 \le x \le 0.63$

52. $x \le -1.87$ or $x \ge 0.45$

53. $(-\infty, -3] \cup [3, \infty)$

54. $[-2, 2]$

55. $(-\infty, -2] \cup [1.5, \infty)$

56. $\left(-\infty, -\dfrac{2}{3}\right] \cup [3, \infty)$

57. $(3 - \sqrt{5}, 3 + \sqrt{5})$

58. $(4 - \sqrt{2}, 4 + \sqrt{2})$

59. If $c < 4$ there are two distinct real roots, if $c = 4$ there is one real double root, and if $c > 4$ there are two distinct imaginary roots.

60. If $c < 1$ there are two distinct real roots, if $c = 1$ there is one real double root, and if $c > 1$ there are two complex roots (conjugates).

61. If $a > 0$, the solution set is $(-\infty, r_1) \cup (r_2, \infty)$. If $a < 0$, the solution set is (r_1, r_2).

62. If $a > 0$, the solution set is $[r_1, r_2]$. If $a < 0$, the solution set is $(-\infty, r_1] \cup [r_2, \infty)$.

63. If $a > 0$, the solution set is R, the set of real numbers. If $a < 0$, the solution set is $\{r\}$.

64. If $a > 0$, the solution set is $\varnothing$, the empty set. If $a < 0$, the solution set is $(-\infty, r) \cup (r, \infty)$.

65. $x^2 \ge 0$

66. $x^2 < 0$

67. $x = -i, -2i$

68. $x = 2i, 5i$

69. $x = \sqrt{2} - i, -\sqrt{2} - i$

70. $x = 3i$ and $x = -i$

71. $x = 1, -\dfrac{1}{2} \pm \dfrac{1}{2}i\sqrt{3}$

72. $x = 1, x = -1, x = i, x = -i$

74. No

76. $-\dfrac{b}{a}$

77. The $\pm$ in front still yields the same two numbers even if a is negative.

78. $(a - b)^2 = (b - a)^2$ does not imply $a - b = b - a$

79. 8, 13 **80.** $x = 0, 2$ **81.** 12, 14 **82.** 24, 25

83. $33 < x < 122$ **84.** $50 \le x \le 106$ **85.** At 8:06 AM

86. (A) $0 \le t \le 11$ (B) $1.29 < t < 9.71$ **87.** 2.19 ft

88. No, the walkway in Problem 87 requires 200 square feet of bricks. A walkway of width 1.72 feet can be built with 160 square feet of bricks.

89. (A) $A(w) = 400w - 2w^2$, $0 \le w \le 200$
(B) $50 \le w \le 150$
(C) No, the maximum cross-sectional area is 20,000 square feet when $w = 100$ feet.

90. (A) $A(w) = -0.8w^2 + 4w$, $0 \le w \le 5$
(B) $1.5 \le w \le 3.5$
(C) This restricts w to $0 \le w \le 2.5$.

91. 52 mi **92.** straightaways: 348 ft; diameters: 198 ft

Exercise 2-6

1. T **2.** F **3.** F **4.** T **5.** F **6.** T **7.** $x = 22$

8. $x = 19$ **9.** $n = 8$ **10.** $m = 18$ **11.** no solution

12. no solution **13.** $x = 0, 4$ **14.** $w = 9$ **15.** $y = \pm 2, \pm i\sqrt{2}$

16. $x = \pm 3, \pm i\sqrt{2}$ **17.** $x = \pm\frac{1}{2}i$ **18.** $x = \pm\frac{3}{2}i$ **19.** $x = \frac{1}{8}, -8$

20. $x = 125, -8$ **21.** $m = 3, -2, \frac{1}{2} \pm \frac{\sqrt{7}}{2}i$ **22.** $x = 1, -3, -1 \pm i$

23. no solution **24.** no solution **25.** $y = 1$ **26.** $x = 5, 13$

27. $x = 2$ **28.** $x = 4$ **29.** $x = -\frac{3}{2} + \frac{1}{2}i$ **30.** $x = \frac{5}{2} \pm \frac{1}{2}i$

31. $n = -\frac{3}{4}, \frac{1}{5}$ **32.** $x = -\frac{3}{2}, \frac{2}{3}$ **33.** $y = \pm 3, \pm 1$ **34.** $x = \pm\frac{1}{2}, \pm 2$

35. $y = 1, 16$ **36.** $x = 16, \frac{1}{4}$ **37.** $m = 3, 7, 2, 8$

38. $x = 4, 2, 3 \pm 2i$ **39.** $x = -2$ **40.** $x = 3$

41. $y = \pm\sqrt{\dfrac{3 \pm \sqrt{3}}{2}}$ (four roots) **42.** $m = \pm\sqrt{\dfrac{2 \pm \sqrt{2}}{2}}$ (four roots)

43. $m = 9, 16$ **44.** $y = 4$ **45.** $t = 4, 81$ **46.** $x = 9$

47. $x = -4, 39,596$ **48.** $x = 2, 3,482$ **49.** $x = \left(\dfrac{4}{5 \pm \sqrt{17}}\right)^5 \approx 0.016203, 1974.98$

50. $x = \left(\dfrac{2}{3 \pm \sqrt{5}}\right)^5 \approx 0.008131, 122.991869$ **51.** 13.1 in. by 9.1 in.

52. 5.3 in. by 2.8 in. **53.** 1.65 ft or 3.65 ft **54.** $r = 3.73$ cm

CHAPTER 2 REVIEW

1. slope: $-\dfrac{3}{2}$

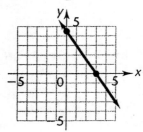

$(2\text{-}1)$

2. $2x + 3y = 12$ $\quad (2\text{-}1)$ $\quad$ **3.** $y = -\dfrac{2}{3}x + 2$ $\quad (2\text{-}1)$

4. *vertical:* $x = -3$, slope not defined; *horizontal:* $y = 4$, slope $= 0$ $\qquad (2\text{-}1)$

5. (A) $x = 21$ $\quad$ (B) $x = \dfrac{30}{11}$ $\quad (2\text{-}2)$

6. (A) $f(x) = -(x + 1)^2 + 4$
(B) It is the same as the graph of $y = x^2$ reflected in the *x* axis, shifted left 1 unit, and up 4 units.
(C) $x = -3, 1$ $\qquad (2\text{-}3, 2\text{-}5)$

7. (A) $f(x) = \left(x - \dfrac{3}{2}\right)^2 - \dfrac{17}{4}$

(B) It is the same as the graph of $y = x^2$ shifted right $\dfrac{3}{2}$ units, and

down $\dfrac{17}{4}$ units.

(C) $x = \dfrac{3 \pm \sqrt{17}}{2}$ $\qquad (2\text{-}3, 2\text{-}5)$

8. (A) $3 - 6i$ $\quad$ (B) $15 + 3i$ $\quad$ (C) $2 + i$ $\qquad (2\text{-}4)$ $\qquad$ **9.** $x = 2$ $\quad (2\text{-}1, 2\text{-}5)$

10. $x = \pm\dfrac{\sqrt{14}}{2}$ $\quad (2\text{-}5)$ $\qquad$ **11.** $x = 0, 2$ $\quad (2\text{-}5)$ $\qquad$ **12.** $x = \dfrac{1}{2}, 3$ $\quad (2\text{-}5)$

13. $m = -\dfrac{1}{2} \pm \dfrac{\sqrt{3}}{2}i$ $\quad (2\text{-}5)$ $\qquad$ **14.** $y = \dfrac{3 \pm \sqrt{33}}{4}$ $\quad (2\text{-}5)$ $\qquad$ **15.** $x = 2, 3$ $\quad (2\text{-}6)$

16. $x \geq 1$; $[1, \infty)$ $\longrightarrow x$ $\qquad (2\text{-}2)$

17. $(-5, 4)$; $-5 < x < 4$. $\longrightarrow x$ $\qquad (2\text{-}5)$

18. $x < -2$ or $x > 6$; $(-\infty, -2) \cup (6, \infty)$. $\longleftrightarrow x$ $\qquad (2\text{-}5)$

20. $3x + 2y = -6$ $\quad (2\text{-}1)$ $\qquad$ **21.** (A) $y = -2x - 3$ $\quad$ (B) $y = \dfrac{1}{2}x + 2$ $\quad (2\text{-}1)$

22. $-14 < y < -4$; $(-14, -4)$ $\quad (2\text{-}2)$ $\qquad$ **23.** $x \leq 2.5$ or $5.5 \leq x$ $\quad (2\text{-}2)$

24. $-1 \leq m \leq 2$ $\quad (2\text{-}2)$

25. (A) $(-\infty, 2]$ $\quad$ (B) $[-1 - \sqrt{5}, -1 + \sqrt{5}]$ $\quad$ (C) $(-\infty, 3 - \sqrt{3}) \cup (3 + \sqrt{3}, \infty)$
$\qquad (2\text{-}2, 2\text{-}5)$

26. (A)

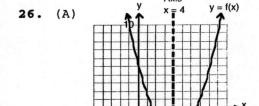

(B) Increasing: $[4, \infty)$;
decreasing $(-\infty, 4]$;
Range: $[-3, \infty)$

(2-3)

27. $y = 2x + 2$; $f(x) = -0.5x^2 + x + 1.5$ *(2-1, 2-3)*

28. (A) $5 + 4i$ (B) $-i$ *(2-4)*

29. (A) $-1 + i$ (B) $\frac{4}{13} - \frac{7}{13}i$ (C) $\frac{5}{2} - 2i$ *(2-4)* **30.** $x = \frac{-5 \pm \sqrt{5}}{2}$ *(2-5)*

31. $u = 1 \pm i\sqrt{2}$ *(2-5)* **32.** $\frac{1}{2} - \frac{3}{2}i$ *(2-6)* **33.** $x = -\frac{27}{8}, 64$ *(2-6)*

34. $m = \pm 3i, \pm 2$ *(2-6)* **35.** $y = \frac{9}{4}, 3$ *(2-6)* **38.** $x < 1.98$ *(2-2)*

39. $x < -0.67$ or $x > 3.07$ *(2-5)*

40. If $c < 9$ there are two distinct real roots, if $c = 9$ there is one real double root, and if $c > 9$ there are two distinct imaginary roots. *(2-5)*

41. $M = \frac{P}{1 - dt}$ *(2-2)* **42.** $I = \frac{E \pm \sqrt{E^2 - 4PR}}{2R}$ *(2-5)*

43. True for all real b and all negative a. *(2-2)* **44.** $\frac{a}{b}$ is less than 1. *(2-2)*

45. $6 - d < x < 6 + d$, $x \neq 6$. $(6 - d, 6) \cup (6, 6 + d)$![number line] x *(2-2)*
$6 - d \quad 6 \quad 6 + d$

46. 1 *(2-4)* **47.** Perpendicular *(2-1)* **48.** Center: $(2, 1)$; radius: $2\sqrt{2}$ *(2-3)*

49. $y = -x + 7$

50. $x = 1, 243$ *(2-6)*

51. $x = -1$; $\frac{1 \pm i\sqrt{3}}{2}$ *(2-5)*

52. (A) 4,750 calculators; $7,437.50
(B) 2,614 or 6,886 calculators
(C) None *(2-3)*

53. 3,240 or 9,260 calculators *(2-3)*

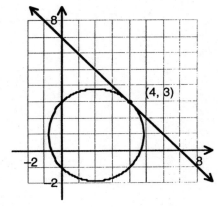

(1-1, 2-1)

54. Profit: $3,240 < x < 9,260$
Loss: $0 \leq x < 3,240$ or $x > 9,260$ *(2-3)*

55. (A) $V = -1,250t + 12,000$ (B) $V = \$5,750$ (2-1)

56. (A) $R = 1.6C$ (B) $R = \$168$ (2-1)

57. $E(x) = \begin{cases} 200 & \text{if } 0 \le x \le 3,000 \\ 0.1x - 100 & \text{if } x > 3,000 \end{cases}$; $E(2,000) = 200$, $E(5,000) = 400$ (2-1)

58. (A) $A(x) = 60x - \frac{3}{2}x^2$ (B) $0 < x < 40$ (C) $x = 20$, $y = 15$ (2-3)

59. (A) $H = 0.7(220 - A)$ (B) $H = 140$ beats per minute   (C) $A = 40$ years old   (2-1)

60. 20 cm by 24 cm   (2-5)   **61.** $B = 14.58$ ft or 6.58 ft   (2-6)

62. 6.6 ft.   (2-5)

63. (A)
```
QuadReg
 y=ax²+bx+c
 a=.074496337
 b=-3.312225275
 c=51.05448718
```

(B) 2005   (2-3)

64. (A)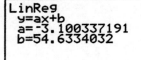
```
LinReg
 y=ax+b
 a=-3.100337191
 b=54.6334032
```

(B) 45.33%   (2-1)

CUMULATIVE REVIEW EXERCISE (Chapters 1 and 2)

1. (A)

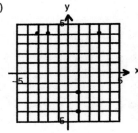

(B) Xmin = -3, Xmax = 3,
Ymin = -4, Ymax = 4

(C) No

(1-1, 1-2, 1-3)

2. (A) $2\sqrt{5}$ (B) $y = 2x - 4$ (C) $y = -\frac{1}{2}x + \frac{17}{2}$

(D) $(x - 3)^2 + (y - 2)^2 = 20$

(E)

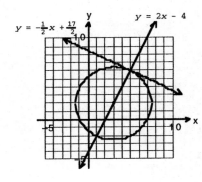

(1-1, 2-1)

3. slope: $\frac{2}{3}$ y intercept: -2

x intercept: 3

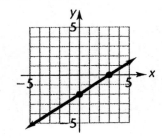

(2-1)

4. (A) 2 (B) 4 (C) $\frac{-2}{5}$ *(1-3)*

5. (A) Expanded by a factor of 2 (B) Shifted right 2 units
(C) Shifted down 2 units *(1-5)*

6. Domain: [-2, 3]; Range: [-1, 2] *(1-3)*

7. Neither *(1-5)*

8. (A) (B)

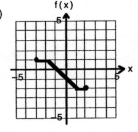 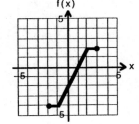

(1-5)

9. $x = \frac{5}{2}$ *(2-2)*   **10.** $x = 0, -4$ *(2-5)*   **11.** $x = \pm\sqrt{5}$ *(2-5)*

12. $x = 3 \pm \sqrt{7}$ *(2-5)*   **13.** $x = 3$ *(2-6)*

14. $y \geq 5$; $[5, \infty)$

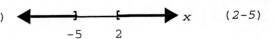

(2-2)

15. $-5 < x < 9$; $(-5, 9)$

(2-2)

16. $x \leq -5$ or $x \geq 2$; $(-\infty, -5] \cup [2, \infty)$

(2-5)

17. (A) $f(x) = (x - 2)^2 - 5$
   (B) It is the same as the graph of $y = x^2$ shifted to the right 2 units and down 5 units.
   (C) $x = 2 \pm \sqrt{5}$ *(2-3, 2-5)*

18. (A) $7 - 10i$ (B) $23 + 7i$ (C) $1 - i$ *(2-4)*

19. (A) All real numbers $(-\infty, \infty)$ (B) $\{-2\} \cup [1, \infty)$ (C) 1
   (D) $[-3, -2]$ and $[2, \infty)$ (E) $-2, 2$ *(1-4)*

20. (A) $y = -\frac{3}{2}x - 8$ (B) $y = \frac{2}{3}x + 5$ *(2-1)*

21. Range: $[-9, \infty)$

$\text{Min } f(x) = f\left(-\frac{b}{2a}\right) = -9$

y intercept: $f(0) = -8$
x intercepts: $x = 4$ and $x = -2$

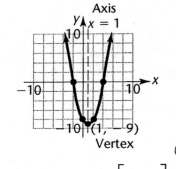

(2-3)

22. $x < \frac{3}{2}$ or $x > 3$; $\left(-\infty, \frac{3}{2}\right) \cup (3, \infty)$

(2-2)

23. $\frac{2}{3} \leq m \leq 2$; $\left[\frac{2}{3}, 2\right]$

(2-2)

24. $\left(-\infty, \frac{9}{7}\right)$ *(2-2)*   **25.** $\left[\frac{7}{2} - \frac{\sqrt{5}}{2}, \frac{7}{2} + \frac{\sqrt{5}}{2}\right]$ *(2-5)*

26. (A) $0 + 0i$ or 0 (B) $\frac{6}{5}$ (C) $i^{35} = i^{32}i^3 = (i^4)^8(-i) = 1^8(-i) = -i$ *(2-4)*

27. (A) $3 + 18i$ (B) $-2.9 + 10.7i$ (C) $-4 - 6i$ *(2-4)*

28. Domain: all real numbers
   Range: $(-\infty, -1) \cup [1, \infty)$
   Discontinuous at: $x = 0$

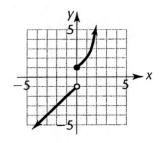

(1-4)

29. Center: (3, -1);

Radius: $\sqrt{10}$

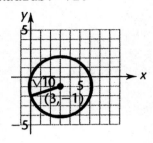

$(1\text{-}1, \ 2\text{-}3)$

30. The graph of $y = |x|$ is contracted by $\frac{1}{2}$, reflected in the x axis, shifted two units to the right and three units up; $y = -\frac{1}{2}|x - 2| + 3$. $(1\text{-}5)$

31. $y = (x + 2)^2 - 3$ $(2\text{-}3)$ **32.** $y = 3 \pm \sqrt{-5}$, $y = 3 \pm i\sqrt{5}$ $(2\text{-}6)$

33. $x = \frac{27}{8}, \ -\frac{1}{8}$ $(2\text{-}6)$ **34.** $u = \pm 2i$, $\pm\sqrt{3}$ $(2\text{-}6)$

35. $t = \frac{9}{4}$ $(2\text{-}6)$ **36.** $x = \frac{4}{3}i$ $(2\text{-}6)$

37. $-18.36 \le x < 16.09$ or $[-18.36, \ 16.09)$ $(2\text{-}2)$ **38.** $-5.68, \ 1.23$ $(2\text{-}5)$

39. If $b < -2$ or $b > 2$ there are two distinct real roots; if $b = -2$ or $b = 2$, there is one real double root; and if $-2 < b < 2$ there are two distinct imaginary roots. $(2\text{-}5)$

42. $-5 - 2h$ $(1\text{-}3)$ **43.** $y = 2\sqrt[3]{x + 1} - 1$ $(1\text{-}5)$

44. (A) $h = \dfrac{A - 2\pi r^2}{2\pi r}$

(B) $r = -\dfrac{h}{2} + \sqrt{\dfrac{h^2}{4} + \dfrac{A}{2\pi}}$

The negative root is discarded since r must be positive. $(2\text{-}2, \ 2\text{-}5)$

45. 0 $(2\text{-}4)$ **46.** All a and b such that $a < b$. $(2\text{-}2)$

47. $\dfrac{a^2 - b^2}{a^2 + b^2} + \dfrac{2ab}{a^2 + b^2}i$ $(2\text{-}4)$ **48.** $x = \dfrac{\sqrt{2} \pm i}{3}$ $(2\text{-}5)$

49. $x = \pm 2i, \ \pm 3i$ $(2\text{-}6)$ **50.** $x = -1.5 + 0.5i$ $(2\text{-}6)$

51. $x = \left(\dfrac{6}{1 \pm \sqrt{13}}\right)^5$ $(2\text{-}6)$ **53.** (A) $x + 0.5h - 3$ (B) $0.5x + 0.5a - 3$ $(1\text{-}3)$

55. $f(x) = \begin{cases} -2x & \text{if } x < -2 \\ 4 & \text{if } -2 \le x \le 2 \\ 2x & \text{if } x > 2 \end{cases}$

Domain: all real numbers; Range $[4, \infty)$

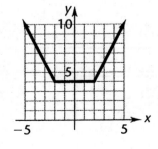

$(1\text{-}4)$

56. $f(x) = \begin{cases} \vdots & \vdots \\ 2x + 2 & \text{if } -1 \le x < -\frac{1}{2} \\ 2x + 1 & \text{if } -\frac{1}{2} \le x < 0 \\ 2x & \text{if } 0 \le x < \frac{1}{2} \\ 2x - 1 & \text{if } \frac{1}{2} \le x < 1 \\ 2x - 2 & \text{if } 1 \le x < \frac{3}{2} \\ 2x - 3 & \text{if } \frac{3}{2} \le x < 2 \\ \vdots & \vdots \end{cases}$

Domain: All real numbers
Range: [0, 1)
Discontinous at $x = k/2$, k an integer

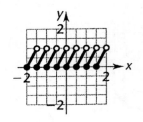

(1-4)

57. $x = 2, -1 + i\sqrt{3}$ *(2-5)*   **58.** $x = 8,800$ books *(2-2)*   **59.** $|p - 200| \le 10$ *(2-2)*

60. (A) Profit: $5.5 < p < $8 or ($5.5, $8)
(B) Loss: $0 \le p < $5.5 or $p > $8. [$0, $5.5) ∪ ($8, ∞)   *(2-3)*

61. 40 mi from A to B and 75 mi from B to C *or* 75 mi from A to B and 40 mi from B to C *(2-5)*

62. $x = -900(3.29) + 4,571$; 1,610 bottles   *(2-2)*

63. $C(x) = \begin{cases} 0.06x & \text{if } 0 \le x \le 60 \\ 0.05x + 0.6 & \text{if } 60 < x \le 150 \\ 0.04x + 2.1 & \text{if } 150 < x \le 300 \\ 0.03x + 5.1 & \text{if } 300 < x \end{cases}$

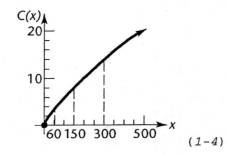

(1-4)

64. (A) $A(x) = 80x - 2x^2$
(B) $0 < x < 40$
(C) 20 feet by 40 feet

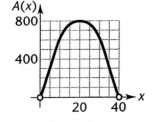

(1-4, 2-3)

65. (A) $f(1) = 1$; $f(2) = 0$; $f(3) = 1$; $f(4) = 0$
(B) $f(n) = \begin{cases} 1 \text{ if } n \text{ is an odd integer} \\ 0 \text{ if } n \text{ is an even integer} \end{cases}$ *(1-4)*

66. (A) 30,000 bushels
(B) The demand decreases to 20,000 bushels
(C) The demand increases to 40,000 bushels

(E)

q	20	25	30	35	40
p	340	332	325	320	315

```
QuadReg
 y=ax²+bx+c
 a=.0228571429
 b=-2.611428571
 c=383.0285714
```

(1-1, 1-2, 2-1)

67. (A)

```
LinReg
 y=ax+b
 a=.798
 b=-3.93
```

(B)

```
QuadReg
 y=ax²+bx+c
 a=.011
 b=.303
 c=1.295
```

(C) The quadratic model is a better fit.

MPH	Linear Model	Quadratic Model
15	8.0	8.3
20	12.0	11.8
25	16.0	15.7
30	20.0	20.3

(D) Range at 17 MPH: 19 hours and 320 miles
     Range at 28 MPH: 10 hours and 280 miles   (*2-1, 2-3*)

CHAPTER 3

Exercise 3-1

1. c **2.** a **3.** d **4.** b **5.** h **6.** f **7.** h, k

8. g **9.** $2m + 1$, R = 0   **10.** $y - 3$ **11.** $4x - 5$, R = 11

12. $4x + 1$, R = -4   **13.** $x^2 + x + 1$, R = 0   **14.** $a^2 - 3a + 9$

15. $2y^2 - 5y + 13$, R = -27   **16.** $x^2 + 3x + 8$, R = 27

17. $\dfrac{x^2 + 3x - 7}{x - 2} = x + 5 + \dfrac{3}{x - 2}$ **18.** $(x^2 + 3x - 3) \div (x - 3) = x + 6 + \dfrac{15}{x - 3}$

19. $\dfrac{4x^2 + 10x - 9}{x + 3} = 4x - 2 - \dfrac{3}{x + 3}$ **20.** $(2x^2 + 7x - 5) \div (x + 4) = 2x - 1 + \dfrac{-1}{x + 4}$

21. $\dfrac{2x^3 - 3x + 1}{x - 2} = 2x^2 + 4x + 5 + \dfrac{11}{x - 2}$

22. $(x^3 + 2x^2 - 3x - 4) \div (x + 2) = x^2 - 3 + \dfrac{2}{x + 2}$

23. 4   **24.** -2   **25.** 3   **26.** -25   **27.** -6   **28.** 19

29. $3x^3 - 3x^2 + 3x - 4$, R = 0   **30.** $5x^3 + 5x^2 + 3x + 3$, R = 0

31. $x^4 - x^3 + x^2 - x + 1$, R = 0   **32.** $x^3 + 2x^2 + 4x + 8$, R = 0

33. $3x^3 - 7x^2 + 21x - 67$, R = 200   **34.** $x^3 + x^2 - x + 2$, R = 5

35. $2x^5 - 3x^4 - 15x^3 + 2x + 10$, R = 0   **36.** $4x^5 - 4x^4 - 3x + 5$, R = 0

37. $4x^3 - 6x - 2$, R = 2   **38.** $2x^2 - 4x + 4$, R = 5

39. $4x^2 - 2x - 4$, R = 0   **40.** $3x^2 - 3x + 3$, R = 0

41. $3x^3 - 0.8x^2 + 1.68x - 2.328$, R = 0.0688

42. $4x^3 - 0.2x^2 + 4.86x + 10.402$, R = 1.2814

43. $3x^4 - 0.4x^3 + 5.32x^2 - 4.256x - 3.5952$, R = -0.12384

44. $7x^4 - 7.3x^3 + 9.57x^2 - 10.613x + 9.5517$, R = -13.59653

45. (A) $P(x) \to \infty$ as $x \to \infty$ and $P(x) \to -\infty$ as $x \to -\infty$; three intercepts and two local extrema

(B) x intercepts: -0.86, 1.68, 4.18; local maximum: $P(0.21) \approx 6.21$; local minimum: $P(3.12) \approx -6.06$

46. (A) $P(x) \to -\infty$ as $x \to \infty$ and $P(x) \to \infty$ as $x \to \infty$; three intercepts and two local extrema

(B) x intercepts: -3.25, -0.52, 1.77; local maximum: $P(-2.12) \approx 7.06$; local minimum: $P(0.79) \approx -5.21$

47. (A) $P(x) \to -\infty$ as $x \to \infty$ and $P(x) \to \infty$ as $x \to -\infty$; three intercepts and two local extrema

(B) x intercept: 4.47; local minimum: $P(-0.12) \approx 4.94$; local maximum: $P(2.79) \approx 17.21$

48. (A) $P(x) \to -\infty$ as $x \to \infty$ and $P(x) \to \infty$ as $x \to -\infty$; three intercepts and two local extrema

(B) x intercept: -4.18; local minimum: $P(-2.53) \approx -17.13$; local maximum: $P(0.53, -2.87)$

49. (A) $P(x) \to \infty$ as $x \to \infty$ and as $x \to -\infty$; four intercepts and three local extrema

(B) x intercepts: none; local minimum: $P(-1.87) \approx 5.81$; local maximum: $P(-0.28) \approx 12.43$; local minimum: $P(1.41) \approx 4.59$

50. (A) $P(x) \to -\infty$ as $x \to \infty$ and as $x \to -\infty$; four intercepts and three local extrema

(B) x intercepts: none; local maximum: $P(-1.85) \approx -1.63$; local minimum: $P(0.26) \approx -16.38$; local maximum: $P(1.59) \approx -11.99$

51. $P(x) = x^3$ **52.** $P(x) = x^4 + 1$ **53.** No such polynomial exists

54. No such polynomial exists   **55.** $2x^2 - 3x + 2$, R = 0

56. $4x^2 - 2x - 1$, R = -2   **57.** $x^2 + (-3 + i)x - 3i$, R = 0

58. $x^2 + (-2 - i)x + 2i$, R = 0   **59.** (A) -5   (B) $-40i$ (C) 0   (D) 0

60. (A) $40i$ (B) -8   (C) 0   (D) 0

61. x intercepts: -12.69, -0.72, 4.41; local maximum: $P(2.07) \approx 96.07$; local minimum: $P(-8.07) \approx -424.07$

62. x intercepts: -12.76, -4.55, -0.69; local maximum: $P(-9.56) \approx 142.16$; local minimum: $P(-2.44) \approx -38.16$

63. x intercepts: -16.06, 0.50, 15.56; local maximum: $P(-9.13) \approx 65.86$; local minimum: $P(9.13) \approx -55.86$

64. x intercepts: -17.25, 1.08, 16.17; local maximum: $P(9.66) \approx 15.03$; local minimum: $P(-9.66) \approx -21.03$

65. x intercepts: -16.15, -2.53, 1.56, 14.12; local minimum: $P(-11.68) \approx -1,395.99$; local maximum: $P(-0.50) \approx 95.72$; local minimum: $P(9.92) \approx -1,140.27$

66. x intercepts: -15.07, -1.89, 2.92, 12.04; local minimum: $P(-10.73) \approx -1,191.45$; local maximum: $P(0.45) \approx 103.82$; local minimum: $P(8.77) \approx -485.79$

67. x intercepts: 1, 1.09; local minimum: $P(1.05) \approx -0.20$; local maximum: $P(6.01) \approx 605.01$; local minimum: $P(10.94) \approx 9.70$

68. x intercepts: -1, -0.97; local minimum: $P(-8.98) \approx 15.98$; local maximum: $P(-5.03) \approx 264.03$; local minimum: $P(-0.98) \approx -0.02$

69. (A) In both cases the coefficient of x is a_2, the constant term $a_2r + a_1$, and the remainder is $(a_2r + a_1)r + a_0$.
(B) The remainder expanded is $a_2r^2 + a_1r + a_0 = P(r)$.

70. (A) In both cases: the coefficient of x^2 is a_3, of x is $a_3r + a_2$, and the constant term is $(a_3r + a_2)r + a_1$. The remainder is $[(a_3r + a_2)r + a_1]r + a_0$.
(B) $P(r) = a_3r^3 + a_2r^2 + a_1r + a_0 = $ remainder

71. $P(-2) = 81$; $P(1.7) = 6.2452$ or 6.2   **72.** $P(-2) = -12$; $P(1.3) = -1.6347$

73. (A) $R(x) = 0.0004x^3 - x^2 + 569x$

(B) 364 air conditioners; price: \$258; max revenue: \$93,911

74. (A) $P(x) = 0.0004x^3 - x^2 + 479x - 10,000$

(B) 290 air conditioners; price: \$313; max profit: \$54,566

75. (A) $V = 28x + 28x^2 + 8x^3$ (B) 0.097 ft

76. (A) $V(x) = (2 + 2x)^2(3 + 2x) - 12$ (B) 0.0031 ft

77. (A)
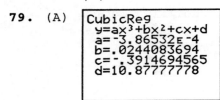
```
CubicReg
y=ax³+bx²+cx+d
a=.0246666667
b=-.0973333333
c=3.076190476
d=26.79761905
```

(B) $1,072.8 billion

78. (A)
```
CubicReg
y=ax³+bx²+cx+d
a=.0726666667
b=.179047619
c=10.82619048
d=141.5952381
```

(B) $3,855

79. (A)
```
CubicReg
y=ax³+bx²+cx+d
a=-3.86532ᴇ-4
b=.0244083694
c=-.3914694565
d=10.87777778
```

(B) 7.5 marriages per 1,000 population

80. (A)
```
CubicReg
y=ax³+bx²+cx+d
a=-3.313131ᴇ-4
b=.019974026
c=-.220981241
d=2.709090909
```

(B) 3.0 divorces per 1,000 population

Exercise 3-2

1. -8 (multiplicity 3), 6 (multiplicity 2); degree of $P(x)$ is 5

2.
root	multiplicity
5	1
-7	2

deg of $P(x) = 3$

3. -4 (multiplicity 3), 3 (multiplicity 2); -1; degree of $P(x)$ is 6

4.
root	multiplicity
2	3
-3	2
1	1

deg of $P(x) = 6$

5. $P(x) = (x - 3)^2(x + 4)$; degree 3   **6.** $P(x) = (x + 2)^3(x - 1)^2$, deg $P(x) = 5$

7. $P(x) = (x + 7)^3[x - (-3 + \sqrt{2})][x - (-3 - \sqrt{2})]$; degree 5

8. $P(x) = \left(x - \frac{1}{3}\right)^2[x - (5 + \sqrt{7})][x - (5 - \sqrt{7})]$, deg $P(x) = 4$

9. $P(x) = [x - (2 - 3i)][x - (2 + 3i)](x + 4)^2$; degree 4

10. $P(x) = (x - i\sqrt{3})^2(x + i\sqrt{3})^2(x - 4)^3$, deg $P(x) = 7$

11. $(x + 2)(x - 1)(x - 3)$, degree 3   **12.** $(x + 2)(x + 1)(x - 1)(x - 3)$, degree 4

13. $(x + 2)^2(x - 1)^2$, degree 4   **14.** $(x - 1)^2(x + 3)$, degree 3

15. $(x + 3)(x + 2)x(x - 1)(x - 2)$, degree 5

16. $(x + 2)^2x(x - 2)^2$, degree 5   **17.** Yes   **18.** Yes   **19.** Yes   **20.** Yes

21. ±1, ±2, ±3, ±6

22. ±1, ±2, ±4, ±8

23. ±1, ±2, ±4, $\pm\frac{1}{3}$, $\pm\frac{2}{3}$, $\pm\frac{4}{3}$

24. ±1, ±3, $\pm\frac{1}{2}$, $\pm\frac{3}{2}$

25. ±1, ±3, $\pm\frac{1}{2}$, $\pm\frac{3}{2}$, $\pm\frac{1}{3}$, $\pm\frac{1}{4}$, $\pm\frac{3}{4}$, $\pm\frac{1}{6}$, $\pm\frac{1}{12}$

26. ±1, ±5, $\pm\frac{1}{2}$, $\pm\frac{5}{2}$

27. $P(x) = (x - 1)(x + 4)(x + 4)$

28. $P(x) = (x - 3)(x - 3)(x + 2)$

29. $P(x) = (x - 1)(x + 1)(x - i)(x + i)$

30. $P(x) = (x - i)(x - i)(x + i)(x + i)$

31. $P(x) = (2x - 1)[x - (4 + 5i)][x - (4 - 5i)]$

32. $P(x) = (3x + 2)[x - (2 - 3i)][x - (2 + 3i)]$

33. $\frac{1}{2}$, $1 \pm \sqrt{2}$ **34.** 1, $2 \pm \sqrt{2}$ **35.** -2 (double), $\pm\sqrt{5}$

36. -1 (double root), $1 \pm \sqrt{2}$ **37.** ± 2, $1 \pm \sqrt{2}$ **38.** -1, 3, $-1 \pm 2i$

39. ± 1, $\frac{3}{2}$, $\pm i$ **40.** ± 2, $-\frac{1}{2}$, $\pm i$ **41.** 2, 3, -5 **42.** -2, 3, 6

43. 0, 2, $-\frac{2}{5}$, $\frac{1}{2}$ **44.** $-\frac{5}{3}$, -1, 0, $\frac{3}{2}$ **45.** 2 (double), $\frac{1}{2} \pm \frac{1}{2}\sqrt{3}$

46. -1 (double zero), $1 \pm \frac{\sqrt{5}}{2}$ **47.** -1 (double), $-\frac{1}{3}$, $2 \pm i$

48. 1 (double zero), $-\frac{5}{2}$, $1 \pm i$ **49.** $P(x) = (x + 2)(3x + 2)(2x - 1)$

50. $P(x) = (x - 3)(3x - 1)(2x + 1)$ **51.** $P(x) = (x + 4)[x - (1 + \sqrt{2})][x - (1 - \sqrt{2})]$

52. $P(x) = (x - 4)[x - (2 + \sqrt{3})][x - (2 - \sqrt{3})]$

53. $P(x) = (x - 2)(x + 1)(2x - 1)(2x + 1)$

54. $P(x) = (x + 2)(x + 1)(2x - 1)(x - 1)$

55. $x^2 - 8x + 41$ **56.** $x^2 - 4x + 13$ **57.** $x^2 - 6x + 25$

58. $x^2 - 10x + 29$ **59.** $x^2 - 2ax + a^2 + b^2$ **60.** $x^2 + b^2$

61. -1 and $3 + i$ **62.** zeros: $1 - i$, $1 + i$, -3 **63.** $5i$ and 3

64. $\pm 4i$, -2 **65.** $2 + i$, $2 - i$, $\sqrt{2}$, $-\sqrt{2}$ **66.** zeros: $\pm 3i$, $1 \pm \sqrt{3}$

67. $\sqrt{6}$ is a zero of $P(x) = x^2 - 6$, but $P(x)$ has no rational zeros.

68. $\sqrt{12}$ is a zero of $P(x) = x^2 - 12$, but $P(x)$ has no rational zeros.

69. $\sqrt[3]{5}$ is a zero of $P(x) = x^3 - 5$, but $P(x)$ has no rational zeros.

70. $\sqrt[5]{8}$ is a zero of $P(x) = x^5 - 8$, but $P(x)$ has no rational zeros.

71. $\frac{1}{3}$, $6 \pm 2\sqrt{3}$ **72.** $\frac{5}{2}$, $1 \pm \sqrt{7}$ **73.** $\frac{3}{2}$, $-\frac{5}{2}$, $\pm 4i$

74. $-\frac{9}{2}$, $\frac{8}{3}$, $-2 \pm i$ **75.** $\frac{3}{2}$ (double), $4 \pm \sqrt{6}$ **76.** 2 (triple zero), $\pm\sqrt{6}$

77. (A) 3 (B) $-\frac{1}{2} + \frac{\sqrt{3}}{2}i$ and $-\frac{1}{2} - \frac{\sqrt{3}}{2}i$

78. (A) 3 (B) $-1 \pm i\sqrt{3}$ **79.** maximum of n; minimum of 1 **80.** n, 0

81. No, since $P(x)$ is not a polynomial with real coefficients (the coefficient of x is the imaginary number $2i$).

82. They must be identities; hence, are equal for <u>all</u> values of x (real or complex).

83. 2 feet   **84.** 1 foot   **85.** 0.5×0.5 inches or 1.59×1.59 inches

86. 1 ft × 1 ft or 2 ft × 2 ft

Exercise 3-3

  1. There is at least one x intercept in each of the intervals $(-5, -1)$, $(-1, 3)$, and $(5, 8)$

  2. There is at least one x intercept in each of the intervals $(-8, -2)$, $(2, 4)$, and $(4, 9)$.

  3. There is at least one x intercept in each of the intervals $(-6, -4)$, $(-4, 0)$, $(2, 4)$, and $(4, 7)$

  4. There is at least one x intercept in each of the intervals $(-1, 0)$, $(0, 2)$, and $(2, 5)$.

  5. Zeros in $(0, 1)$, $(3, 4)$, and $(4, 5)$ **6.** Zeros in $(2, 3)$, $(3, 4)$, and $(6, 7)$

  7. Zeros in $(-3, -2)$, $(-2, -1)$, and $(1, 2)$

  8. Zeros in $(-3, -2)$, $(-1, 0)$, and $(1, 2)$

  9. Upper bound: 2; lower bound: -2   **10.** Upper bound: 4; lower bound: -1

  11. Upper bound: 3; lower bound: -2   **12.** Upper bound: 4; lower bound: -1

  13. Upper bound: 2; lower bound: -3   **14.** Upper bound: 3; lower bound: -1

  15. (A) Upper bound: 4; lower bound: -2; real zeros in $(-2, -1)$, $(0, 1)$, and $(3, 4)$
  (B) 5 intervals, 3.2

  16. (A) Upper bound: 2; lower bound: -3; real zeros in $(-3, -2)$, $(-1, 0)$, and $(1, 2)$
  (B) 5 intervals, 1.7

  17. (A) Upper bound: 3; lower bound: -2; real zero in $(-2, -1)$
  (B) 6 intervals, -1.4

  18. (A) Upper bound: 4; lower bound: -1; real zero in $(3, 4)$ (B) 6 intervals, 3.5

  19. (A) Upper bound: 4; lower bound: -3; real zeros in $(-3, -2)$, $(-1, 0)$, $(1, 2)$, and $(3, 4)$ (B) 4 intervals, 3.1

  20. (A) Upper bound: 4; lower bound: -3; real zeros in $(-3, -2)$, $(-1, 0)$, $(1, 2)$, and $(2, 3)$ (B) 6 intervals, 2.9

  21. (A) Upper bound: 3; lower bound: -2; real zeros in $(-2, -1)$ and $(-1, 0)$
  (B) 5 intervals, -0.5

  22. (A) Upper bound: 4; lower bound: -1; real zeros in $(1, 2)$ and $(2, 3)$
  (B) 7 intervals, 2.9

  23. (A) Upper bound: 3; lower bound: -1   (B) 2.25

  24. (A) Upper bound: 1; lower bound: -3   (B) -2.21

  25. (A) Upper bound: 3; lower bound: -4   (B) -3.51, 2.12

  26. (A) Upper bound: 5; lower bound: -3   (B) -2.29, 4.07

  27. (A) Upper bound: 2; lower bound: -3   (B) -2.09, 0.75, 1.88

  28. (A) Upper bound: 3; lower bound: -1   (B) 2.12

  29. (A) Upper bound: 1; lower bound: -1   (B) 0.83

  30. (A) Upper bound: 3; lower bound: -2   (B) -1.35 0.72, 2.92

  34. maximum routine at $x = 1$; minimum routine at $x = 3$; results will depend on the graphing utility

  35. -1.83 (double zero); 3.83 (double zero)

  36. -3.24 (double zero); 1.24 (double zero)

  37. -1.24 (double zero); 2 (simple zero); 3.24 (double zero)

38. -2 (simple zero); 0.27 (double zero); 3.73 (double zero)

39. -0.22 (double zero); 2 (simple zero); 2.22 (double zero)

40. -4.12 (double zero); -4 (simple zero); 0.12 (double zero)

41. (A) Upper bound: 30; lower bound: -10   (B) -1.29, 0.31, 24.98

42. (A) Upper bound: 40; lower bound: -10   (B) 0.35, 1.63, 35.02

43. (A) Upper bound: 30; lower bound: -40   (B) -36.53, -2.33, 2.40, 24.46

44. (A) Upper bound: 30; lower bound: -20   (B) -14.70, -4.46, 3.92, 27.25

45. (A) Upper bound: 20; lower bound: -10   (B) -7.47, 14.03

46. (A) Upper bound: 20; lower bound: -10   (B) No real zeros

47. (A) Upper bound: 30; lower bound: -20   (B) -17.66, 2.5 (double zero), 22.66

48. (A) Upper bound: 20; lower bound: -30   (B) -23.22, -3.67 (double zero), 17.22

49. (A) Upper bound: 40; lower bound: -40   (B) -30.45, 9.06, 39.80

50. (A) Upper bound: 20; lower bound: -20   (B) -3.5 (double zero), 17.69

51. $x^4 - 3x^2 - 2x + 4 = 0$; (1, 1) and (1.659, 2.752)

52. $x^4 - x^2 - 4x + 4 = 0$; (1, 1) and (1.315, 1.729)

53. $4x^3 - 84x^2 + 432x - 600 = 0$; 2.319 in or 4.590 in

54. $3x^3 - 70x^2 + 400x - 500 = 0$; 1.741 in or 6.234 in

55. $x^3 - 15x^2 + 30 = 0$; 1.490 ft

56. $8x^3 - 20x^2 + 8 = 0$; 0.758 × 0.758 × 3.481 ft or 2.313 × 2.313 × 0.374 ft

Exercise 3-4

1. $g(x)$ **2.** $k(x)$ **3.** $h(x)$ **4.** $f(x)$

5. Domain: $(-\infty, -1) \cup (-1, \infty)$; x intercept: 2

6. Domain: all x except 1 or $(-\infty, 1) \cup (1, \infty)$; $x = -2$, x intercept

7. Domain: $(-\infty, -4) \cup (-4, 4) \cup (4, \infty)$; x intercepts: -1, 1

8. Domain: all x except ±5 or $(-\infty, -5) \cup (-5, 5) \cup (5, \infty)$; $x = \pm6$, x intercepts

9. Domain: $(-\infty, -3) \cup (-3, 4) \cup (4, \infty)$; x intercepts: -2, 3

10. Domain: all x except -3 and 2 or $(-\infty, -3) \cup (-3, 2) \cup (2, \infty)$;
    -4, 3: x intercepts

11. Domain: all real numbers; x intercept: 0

12. Domain: all real numbers; x intercept: 0

13. Vertical asymptote: $x = 4$; horizontal asymptote: $y = 2$

14. Vertical asymptote: $x = -5$; horizontal asymptote: $y = 3$

15. Vertical asymptote: $x = -4$, $x = 4$; horizontal asymptote: $y = \frac{2}{3}$

16. Vertical asymptote: $x = \pm5$; horizontal asymptote: $y = \frac{5}{2}$

17. No vertical asymptotes; horizontal asymptote: $y = 0$

18. Vertical asymptote: $x = \frac{1}{2}$ and $x = -2$; no horizontal asymptote

19. Vertical asymptotes: $x = -1$, $x = \frac{5}{3}$; no horizontal asymptote

20. No vertical asymptote; horizontal asymptote: $y = 0$

21.　　**22.**　　**23.**　　**24.**

25.　　**26.**　　**27.**　　**28.**

29.　　**30.**　　**31.**　　**32.**

33.　　**34.**　　**35.**　　**36.**

37.　　**38.**　　**39.**　　**40.**

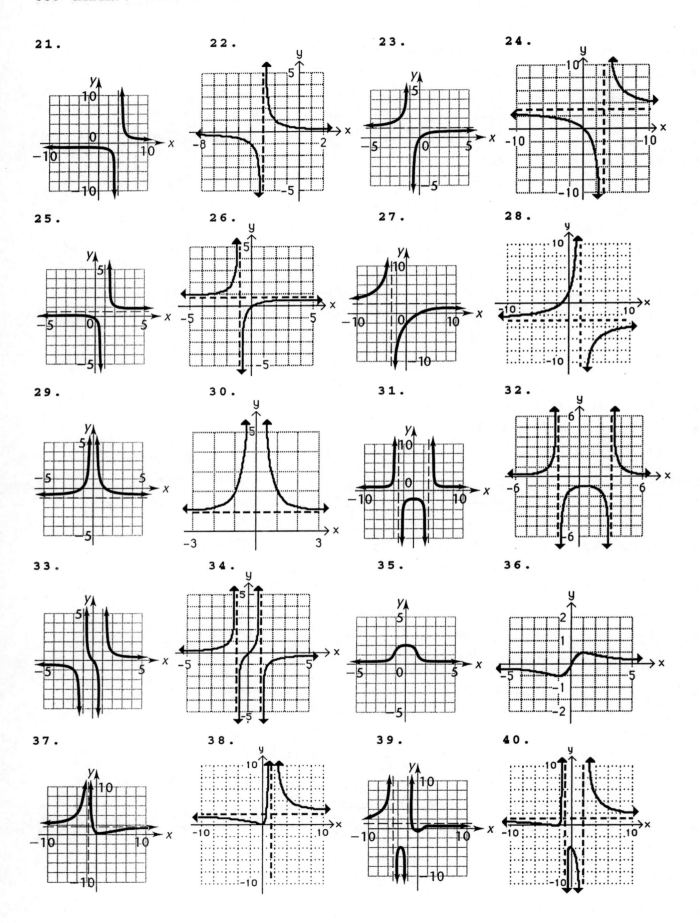

41. The maximum number of x intercepts is 2 and the minimum number is 0. For example, $\dfrac{x^2 - 1}{x^2}$ has two x intercepts and $\dfrac{x^2 + 1}{x^2}$ has none.

42. The maximum number of vertical asymptotes is 2 as in $\dfrac{x^2}{x^2 - 1}$ and the minimum number is 0 as in $\dfrac{x^2}{x^2 + 1}$.

43. Vertical asymptote: $x = 1$; oblique asymptote: $y = 2x + 2$

44. $x = -2$ vertical asymptote; $y = 3x - 6$ is an oblique asymptote

45. Oblique asymptote: $y = x$

46. $x = 2$ vertical asymptote

47. Vertical asymptote: $x = 0$; oblique asymptote: $y = 2x - 3$

48. $x = 0$ vertical asymptote; $y = -3x + 5$; oblique asymptote

49. $f(x) \to 5$ as $x \to \infty$ and $f(x) \to -5$ as $x \to -\infty$; the lines $y = 5$ and $y = -5$ are horizontal asymptotes

50. $f(x) \to 2$ as $x \to \infty$ and $f(x) \to -2$ as $x \to -\infty$; the lines $y = \pm 2$ are horizontal asymptotes

51. $f(x) \to 4$ as $x \to \infty$ and $f(x) \to -4$ as $x \to -\infty$; the lines $y = 4$ and $y = -4$ are horizontal asymptotes

52. $f(x) \to 3$ as $x \to \infty$ and $f(x) \to -3$ as $x \to -\infty$; the lines $y = \pm 3$ are horizontal asymptotes

53.

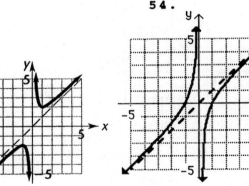

54.

55.

56.

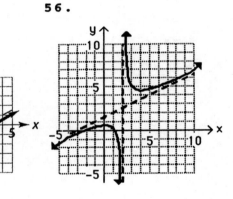

57.

58.

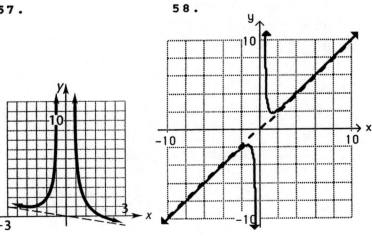

59. Let $p(x) = x^2 - 1$; $[f(x) - p(x)] \to 0$ as $x \to \infty$ and as $x \to -\infty$

60. $p(x) = x^3 - x$, $[f(x) - p(x)] \to 0$ as $x \to \pm\infty$

61. $p(x) = x^3 + x$; $[f(x) - p(x)] \to 0$ as $x \to \infty$ and as $x \to -\infty$

62. $p(x) = x^2$, $[f(x) - p(x)] \to 0$ as $x \to \pm\infty$

63. Domain: $x \neq 2$, or $(-\infty, 2) \cup (2, \infty)$;
$f(x) = x + 2$

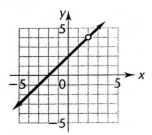

64. $g(x) = x - 1$ for $x \neq -1$;
Domain: $x \neq -1$ or $(-\infty, -1) \cup (-1, \infty)$

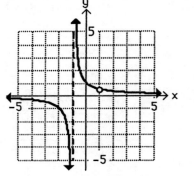

65. Domain: $x \neq 2, -2$ or
$(-\infty, -2) \cup (-2, 2) \cup (2, \infty)$;
$r(x) = \dfrac{1}{x - 2}$

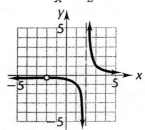

66. $S(x) = \dfrac{1}{x + 1}$, $x \neq \pm 1$;
Domain: $x \neq \pm 1$ or
$(-\infty, -1) \cup (-1, 1) \cup (1, \infty)$

67. As $t \to \infty$, $N \to 50$

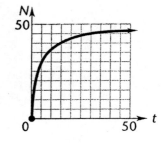

68.

$$S(w) = \dfrac{26}{w} + 0.06 \to 0.06 \text{ as } w \to \infty$$

69. As $t \to \infty$, $N \to 5$

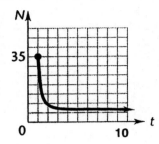

70. $f(x) \to 50$ as $x \to \infty$

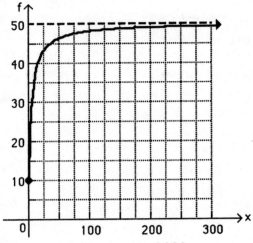

71. (A) $\overline{C}(n) = 25n + 175 + \dfrac{2,500}{n}$

(B) 10 yr

(C)

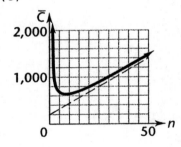

72. (A) $\overline{C}(x) = \dfrac{1}{5}x + 2 + \dfrac{2000}{x}$

(B) 100 units

(C)

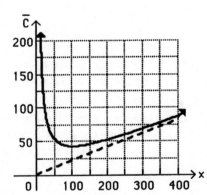

73. (A) $L(x) = 2x + \dfrac{450}{x} = \dfrac{2x^2 + 450}{x}$

(B) $(0, \infty)$

(C) 15 ft by 15 ft

(D)

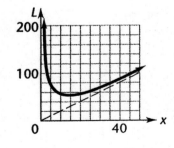

74. (A) $L(x) = 3x + \dfrac{450}{x}$ (B) $(0, \infty)$

(C) $x = 12.247$ ft by $\ell = 18.372$ ft will require the least amount of fencing, 73.485 ft

(D)

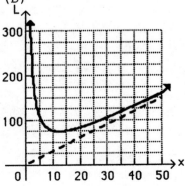

CHAPTER 3 REVIEW

1. $2x^3 + 3x^2 - 1 = (x + 2)(2x^2 - x + 2) - 5$ *(3-1)*

2. $P(3) = -8$ *(3-1, 3-2)*   **3.** 2, -4, -1 *(3-2)*   **4.** $1 - i$ is a zero *(3-2)*

5. (A) $P(x) = (x + 2)x(x - 2) = x^3 - 4x$
  (B) $P(x) \to \infty$ as $x \to \infty$ and $P(x) \to -\infty$ as $x \to -\infty$ *(3-1, 3-2)*

6. Lower bounds: -2, -1; upper bound: 4   *(3-3)*

7. $P(1) = -5$ and $P(2) = 1$ are of opposite sign.   *(3-2)*

8. ±1, ±2, ±3, ±6   *(3-2)*   **9.** -1, 2, 3   *(3-2)*

10. (A) Domain is $(-\infty, -4) \cup (-4, \infty)$; x intercept is $\frac{3}{2}$
  (B) Domain is $(-\infty, -2) \cup (-2, 3) \cup (3, \infty)$; x intercept is 0   *(3-4)*

11. (A) Horizontal asymptote: $y = 2$; Vertical asymptote: $x = -4$
  (B) Horizontal asymptote: $y = 0$; Vertical asymptotes: $x = -2$, $x = 3$ *(3-4)*

12. (A) The graph of $P(x)$
  has three x intercepts
  and two turning points;
  $P(x) \to \infty$ as $x \to \infty$ and
  $P(x) \to -\infty$ as $x \to -\infty$

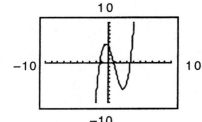

  (B) 3.53   *(3-1, 3-3)*

13. $P(x) = \left(x - \frac{1}{4}\right)(8x^3 - 12x^2 - 16x - 8) + 5$; $P\left(\frac{1}{4}\right) = 5$ *(3-1)*

14. -4   *(3-1)*   **15.** $P(x) = [x - (1 + \sqrt{2})][x - (1 - \sqrt{2})]$ *(3-2)*

16. Yes, since $P(-1) = 0$, $x - (-1) = x + 1$ must be a factor.   *(3-2)*

17. 4, $-\frac{1}{2}$, -2   *(3-2)*   **18.** $(x - 4)(2x + 1)(x + 2)$ *(3-2)*

19. no rational zeros   *(3-2)*   **20.** -1, $\frac{1}{2}$, and $\frac{1 \pm i\sqrt{3}}{2}$ *(3-2)*

21. $(x + 1)(2x - 1)\left(x - \frac{1 + i\sqrt{3}}{2}\right)\left(x - \frac{1 - i\sqrt{3}}{2}\right)$ *(3-2)*

22. (A) -0.24 (double zero); 2 (simple zero); 4.24 (double zero)
  (B) -0.24 can be approximated with a maximum routine; 2 can be approximated
  with the bisection; 4.24 can be approximated with a minimum routine   *(3-3)*

23. (A) Upper bound: 7; lower bound: -5   (B) 4 intervals   (C) -4.67, 6.62 *(3-3)*

24. (A) Domain is $(-\infty, -1) \cup (-1, \infty)$;
  x intercept: $x = 1$; y intercept: $y = -\frac{1}{2}$
  (B) Vertical asymptote: $x = -1$.
  Horizontal asymptote: $y = \frac{1}{2}$

(C)

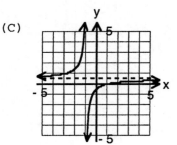

    (3-4)

25. $P(x) = [x^2 + (1 + i)x + (3 + 2i)][x - (1 + i)] + 3 + 5i$ (3-1)

26. $P(x) = \left(x + \dfrac{1}{2}\right)^2 (x + 3)(x - 1)^3$. The degree is 6.   (3-2)

27. $P(x) = (x + 5)[x - (2 - 3i)][x - (2 + 3i)]$. The degree is 3.   (3-2)

28. $\dfrac{1}{2}$, ± 2, $1 \pm \sqrt{2}$ (3-2)

29. $(x - 2)(x + 2)(2x - 1)[x - (1 - \sqrt{2})][x - (1 + \sqrt{2})]$ (3-2)

30. zeros: 0.91, 1; local minimum: $P(-8.94) \approx 9.7$;
local maximum: $P(-4.01) \approx 605.01$; local minimum: $P(0.95) \approx -0.20$ (3-1)

31. Since $P(x)$ changes sign three times, the minimal degree is 3.   (3-3)

32. $P(x) = a(x - r)(x^2 - 2x + 5)$ and since the constant term, $-5ar$, must be an integer, r must be a rational number.   (3-2)

33. (A) 3   (B) $-\dfrac{3}{2} \pm \dfrac{3i}{2}\sqrt{3}$ (3-2)

34. (A) Upper bound: 30; lower bound: -30   (B) -23.54, 21.57   (3-3)

35.

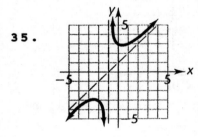

(3-4)

36. $y = 2$ and $y = -2$ (3-4)

37. $2x^3 - 32x + 48 = 0$, 4×12 ft or 5.2×9.2 ft   (3-2)

38. $x^3 + 27x^2 - 729 = 0$, 4.789 ft   (3-3)

39. $4x^3 - 70x^2 + 300x - 300$, 1.450 in or 4.465 in   (3-3)

40. $x^4 - 7x^2 - 2x + 8$, (-2, 4), (-1.562, 2.440), (1, 1), (2.562, 6.564)   (3-2)

41. (A)   (B) 339 refrigerators   (C) 36 ads

```
CubicReg
 y=ax³+bx²+cx+d
 a=⁻.0102791694
 b=.8486894107
 c=⁻2.575453575
 d=221.667258
```

(3-1)

42. (B)   (C) 25 yr, 41 yr, 55 yr

```
CubicReg
 y=ax³+bx²+cx+d
 a=⁻.0048619529
 b=.5893160173
 c=⁻22.74548148
 d=341.7396941
```

(3-1)

CHAPTER 4

Exercise 4-1

1.

x	-3	-2	-1	0	1	2	3
$f(x)$	1	0	-1	-2	-3	-2	-1
$g(x)$	2	3	2	1	0	-1	-2
$(f + g)(x)$	3	3	1	-1	-3	-3	-3

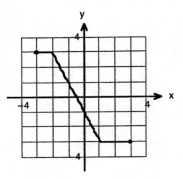

2.

x	-3	-2	-1	0	1	2	3
$(g - f)(x)$	1	3	3	3	3	3	-1

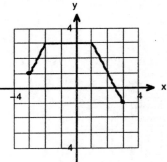

3. -2   4. -1   5. 1   6. 2   7. -2   8. -3   9. 3   10. 0

11. $(f + g)(x) = 5x + 1$; $(f - g)(x) = 3x - 1$; $(fg)(x) = 4x^2 + 4x$

$\left(\dfrac{f}{g}\right)(x) = \dfrac{4x}{x + 1}$; Domain $f + g$, $f - g$, $fg = (-\infty, \infty)$;

Domain of $f/g = (-\infty, -1) \cup (-1, \infty)$

12. $(f + g)(x) = 4x - 2$; $(f - g)(x) = 2x + 2$; $(fg)(x) = f(x)g(x) = 3x^2 - 6x$;

$\left(\dfrac{f}{g}\right)(x) = \dfrac{3x}{x - 2}$; Domain $f + g$, $f - g$, fg: $(-\infty, \infty)$

Domain $\dfrac{f}{g}$: $(-\infty, 2) \cup (2, \infty)$

13. $(f + g)(x) = 3x^2 + 1$; $(f - g)(x) = x^2 - 1$; $(fg)(x) = 2x^4 + 2x^2$;

$\left(\dfrac{f}{g}\right)(x) = \dfrac{2x^2}{x^2 + 1}$; Domain of each function: $(-\infty, \infty)$

14. $(f + g)(x) = x^2 + 3x + 4$; $(f - g)(x) = f(x) - g(x) = -x^2 + 3x - 4$;

$(fg)(x) = 3x^3 + 12x$; $\left(\dfrac{f}{g}\right)(x) = \dfrac{3x}{x^2 + 4}$; Domain $f + g$, $f - g$, fg, $\dfrac{f}{g}$: $(-\infty, \infty)$

15. $(f + g)(x) = x^2 + 3x + 4$; $(f - g)(x) = -x^2 + 3x + 6$;

$(fg)(x) = 3x^3 + 5x^2 - 3x - 5$; $\left(\dfrac{f}{g}\right)(x) = \dfrac{3x + 5}{x^2 - 1}$; Domain $f + g$, $f - g$, fg: $(-\infty, \infty)$

Domain of f/g: $(-\infty, -1) \cup (-1, 1) \cup (1, \infty)$

16. $(f + g)(x) = -x^2 + 2x + 2$; $(f - g)(x) = x^2 + 2x - 16$;

$(fg)(x) = -2x^3 + 7x^2 + 18x - 63$; $\left(\dfrac{f}{g}\right)(x) = \dfrac{2x - 7}{9 - x^2}$

Domain $f + g$, $f - g$, fg: $(-\infty, \infty)$; Domain $\dfrac{f}{g}$: $(-\infty, -3) \cup (-3, 3) \cup (3, \infty)$

17. $(f \circ g)(x) = (x^2 - x + 1)^3$; Domain: $(-\infty, \infty)$; $(g \circ f)(x) = x^6 - x^3 + 1$;
Domain: $(-\infty, \infty)$

18. $(f \circ g)(x) = (x^3 + 2x + 4)^2$; $(g \circ f)(x) = g(f(x)) = x^6 + 2x^2 + 4$
Domain $f \circ g$, $g \circ f$: $(-\infty, \infty)$

19. $(f \circ g)(x) = |2x + 4|$; Domain: $(-\infty, \infty)$; $(g \circ f)(x) = 2|x + 1| + 3$; Domain: $(-\infty, \infty)$

20. $(f \circ g)(x) = |3x - 2|$; $(g \circ f)(x) = 3|x - 4| + 2$; Domain $f \circ g$, $g \circ f$: $(-\infty, \infty)$

21. $(f \circ g)(x) = (2x^3 + 4)^{1/3}$; Domain: $(-\infty, \infty)$; $(g \circ f)(x) = 2x + 4$; Domain: $(-\infty, \infty)$

22. $(f \circ g)(x) = (8 - x^3)^{2/3}$; $(g \circ f)(x) = 8 - x^2$; Domain $f \circ g$, $g \circ f$: $(-\infty, \infty)$

23. $(f \circ g)(x) = (g \circ f)(x) = x$

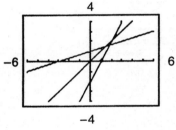

24. $(f \circ g)(x) = (g \circ f)(x) = x$

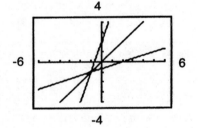

25. $(f \circ g)(x) = (g \circ f)(x) = x$
symmetric with respect to
the line $y = x$

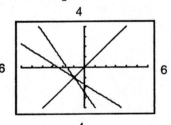

26. $(f \circ g)(x) = (g \circ f)(x) = x$

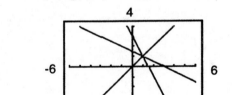

27. $(f + g)(x) = \sqrt{2 - x} + \sqrt{x + 3}$; $(f - g)(x) = \sqrt{2 - x} - \sqrt{x + 3}$;

$(fg)(x) = \sqrt{6 - x - x^2}$; $\left(\dfrac{f}{g}\right)(x) = \sqrt{\dfrac{2 - x}{x + 3}}$

The domain of the functions $f + g$, $f - g$, and fg is $[-3, 2]$.
The domain of $\dfrac{f}{g}$ is $(-3, 2]$.

28. $(f + g)(x) = \sqrt{x + 4} + \sqrt{3 - x}$; $(f - g)(x) = \sqrt{x + 4} - \sqrt{3 - x}$;

$(fg)(x) = \sqrt{12 - x - x^2}$; $\left(\dfrac{f}{g}\right)(x) = \sqrt{\dfrac{x + 4}{3 - x}}$;

Domain $f + g$, $f - g$, fg: $[-4, 3]$; Domain $\dfrac{f}{g}$: $[-4, 3)$

29. $(f + g)(x) = = 2\sqrt{x} - 2$; $(f - g)(x) = 6$; $(fg)(x) = x - 2\sqrt{x} - 8$;

$\left(\dfrac{f}{g}\right)(x) = \dfrac{\sqrt{x} + 2}{\sqrt{x} - 4}$; The domain of $f + g$, $f - g$, and fg is $[0, \infty)$.

Domain of $\dfrac{f}{g} = [0, 16) \cup (16, \infty)$.

30. $(f + g)(x) = 3 - 2\sqrt{x}$; $(f - g)(x) = -1$; $(fg)(x) = 2 - 3\sqrt{x} + x$;

$\left(\dfrac{f}{g}\right)(x) = \dfrac{1 - \sqrt{x}}{2 - \sqrt{x}}$; Domain $f + g$, $f - g$, fg: $[0, \infty)$; Domain $\dfrac{f}{g}$: $[0, 4) \cup (4, \infty)$

31. $(f + g)(x) = \sqrt{x^2 + x - 6} + \sqrt{7 + 6x - x^2}$;
$(f - g)(x) = \sqrt{x^2 + x - 6} - \sqrt{7 + 6x - x^2}$;
$(fg)(x) = \sqrt{-x^4 + 5x^3 + 19x^2 - 29x - 42}$;

$\left(\dfrac{f}{g}\right)(x) = \sqrt{\dfrac{x^2 + x - 6}{7 + 6x - x^2}}$

The domain of the functions $f + g$, $f - g$, and fg is $[2, 7]$.
The domain of $\dfrac{f}{g}$ is $[2, 7)$.

32. $(f + g)(x) = \sqrt{8 + 2x - x^2} + \sqrt{x^2 - 7x + 10}$;
$(f - g)(x) = \sqrt{8 + 2x - x^2} - \sqrt{x^2 - 7x + 10}$;

$(fg)(x) = \sqrt{-x^4 + 9x^3 - 16x^2 - 36x + 80}$; $\left(\dfrac{f}{g}\right)(x) = \sqrt{\dfrac{8 + 2x - x^2}{x^2 - 7x + 10}}$

Domain $f + g$, $f - g$, fg: $[-2, 2]$; Domain $\dfrac{f}{g}$: $[-2, 2)$

33. $(f \circ g)(x) = \sqrt{x - 4}$; Domain: $[4, \infty)$; $(g \circ f)(x) = \sqrt{x} - 4$;
Domain: $[0, \infty)$

34. $(f \circ g)(x) = \sqrt{2x + 5}$; Domain $f \circ g$: $\left[-\dfrac{5}{2}, \infty\right)$

$(g \circ f)(x) = 2\sqrt{x} + 5$; Domain $g \circ f$: $[0, \infty)$

35. $(f \circ g)(x) = \dfrac{1}{x} + 2$; Domain: $(-\infty, 0) \cup (0, \infty)$

$(g \circ f)(x) = \dfrac{1}{x + 2}$; Domain: $(-\infty, -2) \cup (-2, \infty)$

36. $(f \circ g)(x) = \dfrac{1}{x^2} - 3$; Domain $f \circ g$: $(-\infty, 0) \cup (0, \infty)$

$(g \circ f)(x) = \dfrac{1}{(x - 3)^2}$; Domain $g \circ f$: $(-\infty, 3) \cup (3, \infty)$

37. $(f \circ g)(x) = \dfrac{1}{|x - 1|}$; Domain: $(-\infty, 1) \cup (1, \infty)$

$(g \circ f)(x) = \dfrac{1}{|x| - 1}$; Domain of $g \circ f$: $(-\infty, -1) \cup (-1, 1) \cup (1, \infty)$

38. $(f \circ g)(x) = \left|\dfrac{1}{x} - 1\right|$; Domain $f \circ g$: $(-\infty, 0) \cup (0, \infty)$

$(g \circ f)(x) = \dfrac{1}{|x - 1|}$; Domain $g \circ f$: $(-\infty, 1) \cup (1, \infty)$

39. (e)   **40.** (d)   **41.** (a)   **42.** (b)   **43.** (c)   **44.** (f)

45. $g(x) = 2x - 7;\ f(x) = x^4;\ h(x) = (f \circ g)(x)$

46. $f(x) = x^7;\ g(x) = 3 - 5x;\ h(x) = (f \circ g)(x)$

47. $g(x) = 4 + 2x;\ f(x) = x^{1/2};\ h(x) = (f \circ g)(x)$

48. $f(x) = x^{1/2};\ g(x) = 3x - 11;\ h(x) = (f \circ g)(x)$

49. $f(x) = x^7;\ g(x) = 3x - 5;\ h(x) = (g \circ f)(x)$

50. $g(x) = 5x + 3;\ f(x) = x^6;\ h(x) = (g \circ f)(x)$

51. $f(x) = x^{-1/2};\ g(x) = 4x + 3;\ h(x) = (g \circ f)(x)$

52. $g(x) = -2x + 1;\ f(x) = x^{-1/2};\ h(x) = (g \circ f)(x)$

57. $(f + g)(x) = 2x;\ (f - g)(x) = \dfrac{2}{x};\ (fg)(x) = x^2 - \dfrac{1}{x^2};\ \left(\dfrac{f}{g}\right)(x) = \dfrac{x^2 + 1}{x^2 - 1}$

The domain of $f + g,\ f - g,$ and $fg\ = (-\infty,\ 0) \cup (0,\ \infty)$.

The domain of $\dfrac{f}{g}$ is $(-\infty,\ -1) \cup (-1,\ 0) \cup (0,\ 1) \cup (1,\ \infty)$.

58. $(f + g)(x) = 2x - 1 - \dfrac{6}{x - 1};\ (f - g)(x) = -1 + \dfrac{6}{x - 1};\ (fg)(x) = x^2 - x - 6$

$\left(\dfrac{f}{g}\right)(x) = \dfrac{(x - 1)^2}{(x - 3)(x + 2)}$

Domain $f + g,\ f - g,\ fg$: $(-\infty,\ 1) \cup (1,\ \infty)$

Domain $\dfrac{f}{g}$: $(-\infty,\ -2) \cup (-2,\ 1) \cup (1,\ 3) \cup (3,\ \infty)$

59. $(f + g)(x) = 2;\ (f - g)(x) = \dfrac{-2x}{|x|};\ (fg)(x) = 0;\ \left(\dfrac{f}{g}\right)(x) = 0$

The domain of $f + g,\ f - g,$ and fg is $(-\infty,\ 0) \cup (0,\ \infty)$. Domain of $\dfrac{f}{g}$ is $(0,\ \infty)$.

60. $(f + g)(x) = 2x;\ (f - g)(x) = 2|x|;\ (fg)(x) = 0;\ \left(\dfrac{f}{g}\right)(x) = 0$

Domain $f + g,\ f - g,\ fg$: $(-\infty,\ \infty)$; Domain $\dfrac{f}{g}$: $(-\infty,\ 0)$

61. $(f \circ g)(x) = \sqrt{4 - x^2}$; Domain of $f \circ g = [-2,\ 2]$
$(g \circ f)(x) = 4 - x$; Domain of $g \circ f$ is $(-\infty,\ 4]$

62. $(f \circ g)(x) = \sqrt{x^2 - 1};\ (g \circ f)(x) = x - 1$
Domain $f \circ g$: $(-\infty,\ -1] \cup [1,\ \infty)$; Domain $g \circ f$: $[1,\ \infty)$

63. $(f \circ g)(x) = \dfrac{6x - 10}{x}$; Domain of $f \circ g$ is $(-\infty,\ 0) \cup (0,\ 2) \cup (2,\ \infty)$

$(g \circ f)(x) = \dfrac{x + 5}{5 - x}$; Domain of $g \circ f$ is $(-\infty,\ 0) \cup (0,\ 5) \cup (5,\ \infty)$

64. $(f \circ g)(x) = \dfrac{2x - 4}{x - 4};\ (g \circ f)(x) = \dfrac{4 - 2x}{x}$
Domain $f \circ g$: $(-\infty,\ 0) \cup (0,\ 4) \cup (4,\ \infty)$; Domain $g \circ f$: $(-\infty,\ 0) \cup (0,\ 1) \cup (1,\ \infty)$

65. $(f \circ g)(x) = \sqrt{16 - x^2}$; Domain of $f \circ g$ is $[-4, 4]$

$(g \circ f)(x) = \sqrt{34 - x^2}$; Domain of $g \circ f$ is $[-5, 5]$

66. $(f \circ g)(x) = \sqrt{x^2 + 16}$; $(g \circ f)(x) = \sqrt{x^2 + 16}$
Domain $f \circ g$: $(-\infty, \infty)$; Domain $g \circ f$: $(-\infty, -3] \cup [3, \infty)$

67. $(f \circ g)(x) = \sqrt{2 + x}$; Domain of $f \circ g$ is $[-2, 3]$; The first graph is correct.

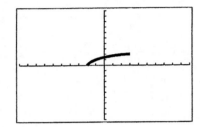 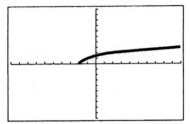

68. $(f \circ g)(x) = \sqrt{7 - x}$; Domain $f \circ g$: $[1, 7]$; The first graph is correct.

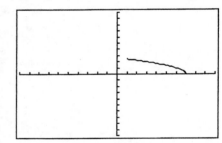 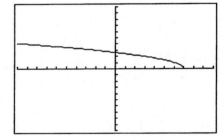

69. $(f \circ g)(x) = \sqrt{x^2 + 1}$; Domain of $f \circ g$ is $(-\infty, -2] \cup [2, \infty)$; The first graph is correct.

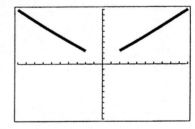 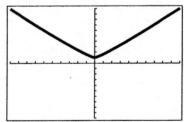

70. $(f \circ g)(x) = \sqrt{-x^2 + 9}$; Domain $f \circ g$: $[-2, 2]$; The first graph is correct.

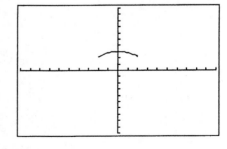 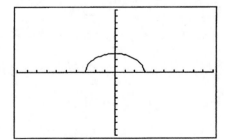

71. $(f \circ g)(x) = \sqrt{16 - x^2}$; Domain of $f \circ g$ is $[-3, 3]$; The first graph is correct.

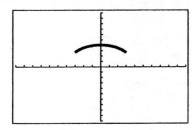
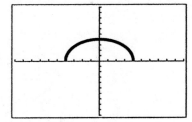

72. $(f \circ g)(x) = \sqrt{x^2 - 2}$; Domain $f \circ g$: $(-\infty, -3] \cup [3, \infty)$. The first graph is correct.

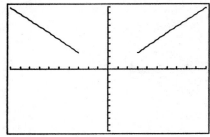
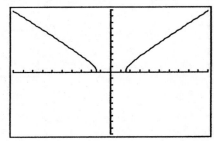

73. $P(p) = -70,000 + 6,000p - 200p^2$ **74.** $P(p) = -100p^2 + 7000p - 140,000$

75. $V(t) = 0.016\pi t^{2/3}$ **76.** (A) $d = \sqrt{h^2 + 100^2}$ (B) $d = 5\sqrt{t^2 + 400}$

77. (A) $r(h) = \frac{1}{2}h$ (B) $V(h) = \frac{1}{12}\pi h^3$ (C) $V(t) = \frac{0.125}{12}\pi t^{3/2}$

78. (A) $w(h) = 2h$ (B) $V = 6h^2$ (C) $V(t) = 6(2 - 0.2\sqrt{t})^2$

Exercise 4-2

1. one-to-one   **2.** not one-to-one   **3.** not one-to-one   **4.** one-to-one

5. one-to-one   **6.** not one-to-one   **7.** not one-to-one   **8.** one-to-one

9. one-to-one   **10.** not one-to-one   **11.** not one-to-one   **12.** one-to-one

13. one-to-one   **14.** not one-to-one   **15.** one-to-one   **16.** one-to-one

17. one-to-one   **18.** one-to-one   **19.** not one-to-one   **20.** one-to-one

21. one-to-one   **22.** not one-to-one

23. one-to-one   **24.** not one-to-one

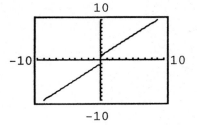
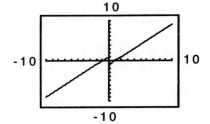

25. not one-to-one

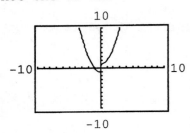

26. one-to-one

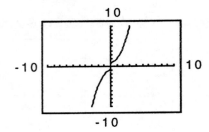

27. not one-to-one

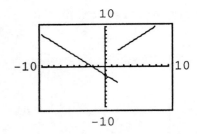

28. not one-to-one

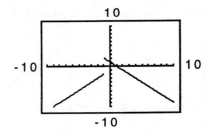

29. one-to-one

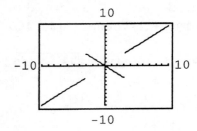

30. one-to-one

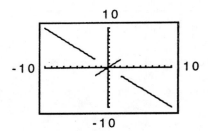

31. Range of f^{-1} = [-4, 4];
Domain of f^{-1} = [1, 5]

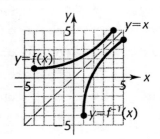

32. $D_{f^{-1}}$: $-4 \le x \le 3$; $R_{f^{-1}}$: $-2 \le y \le 5$

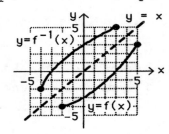

33. Range of f^{-1} = [-5, 3];
Domain of f^{-1} = [-3, 5]

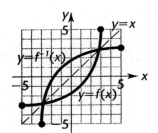

34. $D_{f^{-1}}$: -5 ≤ x ≤ 5;
$R_{f^{-1}}$: 0 ≤ y ≤ 5

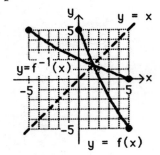

35.

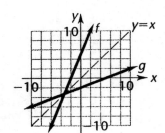

36.

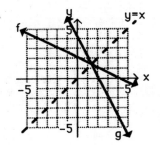

37.

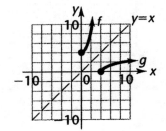

38.

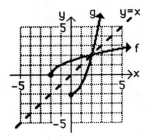

39.

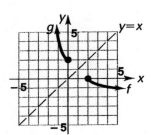

40.

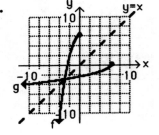

41. $f^{-1}(x) = \dfrac{1}{3}x$

42. $f^{-1}(x) = 2x$

43. $f^{-1}(x) = \dfrac{x + 3}{4}$

44. $f^{-1}(x) = -3x + 5$

45. $f^{-1}(x) = 10x - 6$

46. $f^{-1}(x) = -\dfrac{1}{2}x - \dfrac{7}{2}$

47. $f^{-1}(x) = \dfrac{x + 2}{x}$

48. $f^{-1}(x) = \dfrac{3 - 4x}{x}$

49. $f^{-1}(x) = \dfrac{2x}{1 - x}$

50. $f^{-1}(x) = \dfrac{3}{1 - x}$

51. $f^{-1}(x) = \dfrac{4x + 5}{3x - 2}$

52. $f^{-1}(x) = \dfrac{7x - 5}{4x - 3}$

53. $f^{-1}(x) = \sqrt[3]{x - 1}$

54. $f^{-1}(x) = \sqrt[5]{x + 2}$

55. $f^{-1}(x) = (4 - x)^5 - 2$

56. $f^{-1}(x) = (x + 2)^3 - 3$

57. $f^{-1}(x) = 16 - 4x^2,\ x \geq 0$

58. $f^{-1}(x) = 36 - 9x^2$ where $x \leq 0$

59. $f^{-1}(x) = (3 - x)^2 + 2,\ x \leq 3$

60. $f^{-1}(x) = 5 - (x - 4)^2$ where $x \geq 4$

61. The x intercept of f is the y intercept of f^{-1} and the y intercept of f is the x intercept of f^{-1}.

62. A constant function cannot have an inverse because it is not 1-1.

63. $f^{-1}(x) = 1 + \sqrt{x - 2}$

64. $f^{-1}(x) = 5 - \sqrt{3 - x}$

65. $f^{-1}(x) = -1 - \sqrt{x + 3}$

66. $f^{-1}(x) = \sqrt{9 + x} - 4$

67. $f^{-1}(x) = \sqrt{9 - x^2}$;
Domain of
$\quad f^{-1} = [-3, 0]$;
Range of $f^{-1} = [0, 3]$

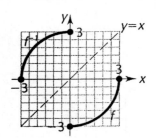

68. $f^{-1}(x) = \sqrt{9 - x^2}$;
Domain of
$\quad f^{-1}: 0 \leq x \leq 3$;
Range of $f^{-1}: 0 \leq y \leq 3$

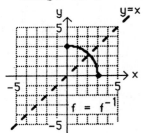

69. $f^{-1}(x) = -\sqrt{9 - x^2}$;
Domain: $f^{-1} = [0, 3]$;
Range of $f^{-1} = [-3, 0]$

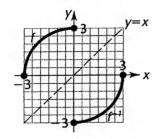

70. $f^{-1}(x) = -\sqrt{9 - x^2}$;
Domain of f^{-1}:
$\quad -3 \leq x \leq 0$;
Range of $f^{-1}: -3 \leq y \leq 0$

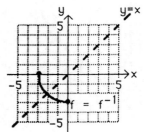

71. $f^{-1}(x) = \sqrt{2x - x^2}$;
Domain of
$\quad f^{-1} = [1, 2]$;
Range of $f^{-1} = [0, 1]$

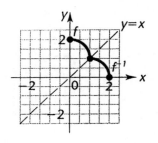

72. $f^{-1}(x) = \sqrt{2x - x^2}$;
Domain of $f^{-1}: 0 \leq x \leq 1$;
Range of $f^{-1}: 0 \leq y \leq 1$

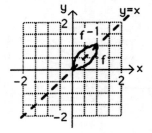

73. $f^{-1}(x) = -\sqrt{2x - x^2}$;
Domain of $f^{-1} = [0, 1]$;
Range of $f^{-1} = [-1, 0]$

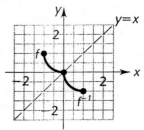

74. $f^{-1}(x) = -\sqrt{2x - x^2}$;
Domain of $f^{-1}: 1 \leq x \leq 2$;
Range of $f^{-1}: -1 \leq y \leq 0$

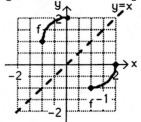

75. $f^{-1}(x) = \dfrac{x - b}{a}$

76. $f^{-1}(x) = \sqrt{a^2 - x^2}$, $0 \leq x \leq a$

77. $a = 1$ and $b = 0$ or $a = -1$ and b arbitrary.

78. The graph must be symmetric with respect to the line $y = x$.

81. (A) $f^{-1}(x) = 2 - \sqrt{x}$ (B) $f^{-1}(x) = 2 + \sqrt{x}$

82. (A) $f^{-1}(x) = -\sqrt{x} - 1$ (B) $f^{-1}(x) = \sqrt{x} - 1$

83. (A) $f^{-1}(x) = 2 - \sqrt{4 - x^2}$, $0 \leq x \leq 2$ (B) $f^{-1}(x) = 2 + \sqrt{4 - x^2}$, $0 \leq x \leq 2$

84. (A) $f^{-1}(x) = 3 - \sqrt{9 - x^2}$, $0 \leq x \leq 3$ (B) $f^{-1}(x) = 3 + \sqrt{9 - x^2}$, $0 \leq x \leq 3$

85. (A) $200 \leq q \leq 1,000$

(B) $p = \dfrac{15,000}{q} - 5$; domain: $200 \leq q \leq 1,000$; range: $10 \leq p \leq 70$

86. (A) $300 \leq q \leq 700$

(B) $p = \dfrac{20q}{900 - q}$; domain: $300 \leq q \leq 700$; range: $10 \leq p \leq 70$

87. (A) $r = 1.25w + 2.45$ (C) $w = 0.8r - 1.96$

88. (A) $t = -5a + 63$ (B) $a = -0.2t + 12.6$

Exercise 4-3

1. (A) g (B) n (C) f (D) m

2. (A) m (B) f (C) n (D) g

3. 16.24   **4.** $3^{-\sqrt{2}} = 0.2115$ **5.** 5.047   **6.** $\pi^{-\sqrt{3}} = 0.1377$

7. 4.469   **8.** $\dfrac{3^{\pi} - 3^{-\pi}}{2} = 15.76$

9. Increasing; y intercept: 1; horizontal asymptote: $y = 0$

10. Increasing; y intercept: 1; horizontal asymptote: $y = 0$

11. Decreasing; y intercept: 1; horizontal asymptote: $y = 0$

12. Decreasing; y intercept: 1; horizontal asymptote: $y = 0$

13. Increasing; y intercept: -1; horizontal asymptote: $y = 0$

14. Decreasing; y intercept: -1; horizontal asymptote: $y = 0$

15. Increasing; y intercept: 5; horizontal asymptote: $y = 0$

16. Increasing; y intercept: 4; horizontal asymptote: $y = 0$

17. Increasing; y intercept: 22; horizontal asymptote: $y = -5$

18. Increasing; y intercept: 29; horizontal asymptote: $y = 4$

19. 10^{2x+3} **20.** 4^{6xy} **21.** 3^{2x-1} **22.** 5

23. $\dfrac{4^{3xz}}{5^{3yz}}$ **24.** $2^{xz}3^{yz}$ **25.** $x = 2$ **26.** $x = 1$

27. $x = -1, 3$ **28.** $x = 6, -1$ **29.** $x = \dfrac{2}{3}$ **30.** $x = 3$

31. $x = -2$ **32.** $x = 2$ **33.** $x = \dfrac{1}{2}$ **34.** $x = -\dfrac{1}{2}$

35. $x = \dfrac{1}{2}, 1$ **36.** $x = -1, \dfrac{3}{2}$ **37.** $a = 1$ or $a = -1$ **38.** $a = 2$, $b = -2$, for example

41.

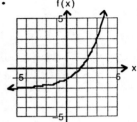

42.

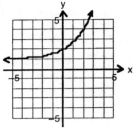

43.

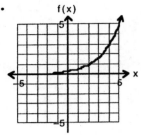

44.

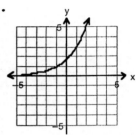

45.

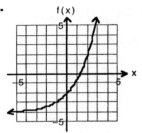

46.

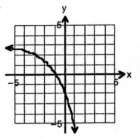

47.

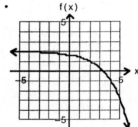

48.

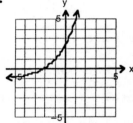

49.

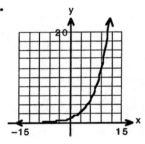

50.

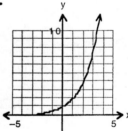

51.

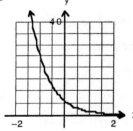

52.

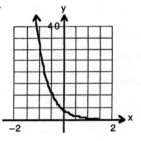

53.

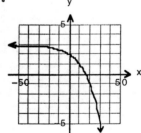

54.

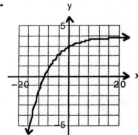

55.

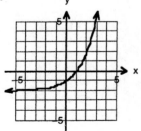

56.

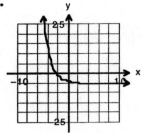

57. $6^{2x} - 6^{-2x}$ **58.** $3^{2x} - 3^{-2x}$ **59.** 4   **60.** $2(3^{2x}) + 2(3^{-2x})$

61. Local maximum: $m(0.91) \approx 2.67$; x intercept: -0.55; horizontal asymptote: $y = 2$

62. Local maximum: $h(1.44) \approx 0.59$; x intercept: 0.46, 3.31; horizontal asymptote: $y = -1$

63. Local minimum: $f(0) = 1$; no x intercepts; no horizontal asymptotes

64. Local minimum: $g(0) = 1$; no x intercepts; no horizontal asymptotes

65.

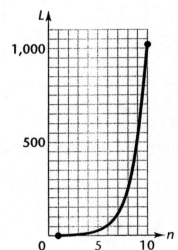

66. $N = N_0 2^{t/d} = 100 \cdot 2^{t/(1/2)}$
$= 100 \cdot 2^{2t}$

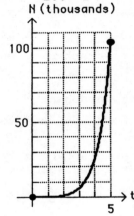

67. (A) 76 flies   (B) 570 flies   **68.** (A) 43,000,000   (B) 90,000,000

69. (A) 19 pounds   (B) 7.9 pounds   **70.** (A) 8.49 mg   (B) 0.750 mg

71. (A) $4,225.92   (B) $12,002.75   **72.** (A) $2633.56   (B) $7079.54

73. $9,841   **74.** $9,217

75. Yes, after 6,217 days   **76.** Yes, after 1,056 weeks

77. No   **78.** $r \geq 0.125973313$, about 12.6%

79.

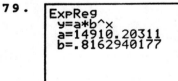
```
ExpReg
 y=a*b^x
 a=14910.20311
 b=.8162940177
```

Estimated purchase price: $14,910; estimated value after 10 years: $1,959

80.
```
ExpReg
 y=a*b^x
 a=30363.17638
 b=.7896877851
```

Estimated purchase price: $30,363; estimated value after 10 years: $2,864

Exercise 4-4

1. (A) m (B) f (C) n (D) g **2.** (A) g (B) n (C) f (D) m

3. 7.524   **4.** 2.350   **5.** 1.649   **6.** 4.113   **7.** 15.15   **8.** 0.06599

9. e^{-x} **10.** e^{-4x} **11.** e^{3x} **12.** e^{2x}

13. e^{3x-1} **14.** e^{2x+2} **15.** (B) e **16.** (B) e

17. Decreasing; no x intercept; y intercept: -1, horizontal asymptote: x axis

18. Increasing; no x intercept; y intercept: -1, horizontal asymptote: x axis

19. Increasing; no x intercept; y intercept: 10, horizontal asymptote: x axis

20. Increasing; no x intercept; y intercept: 100, horizontal asymptote: x axis

21. Decreasing; no x intercept; y intercept: 100, horizontal asymptote: x axis

22. Decreasing; no x intercept; y intercept: 10, horizontal asymptote: x axis

23. Increasing; x intercept: -0.69; y intercept: 1, horizontal asymptote: $y = 2$

24. Increasing; x intercept: 0.55; y intercept: -2, horizontal asymptote: $y = -3$

25. Increasing; x intercept: 0.23; y intercept: -1, horizontal asymptote: $y = -2$

26. Decreasing; no x intercept; y intercept: 4, horizontal asymptote: $y = 3$

27. The graph of g is the same as the graph of f shifted to the right 2 units.

28. The graph of g is the same as the graph of f shifted to the left 3 units.

29. The graph of g is the same as the graph of f shifted upward 2 units.

30. The graph of g is the same as the graph of f shifted downward 1 unit.

31. The graph of g is the same as the graph of f reflected in the y axis, shifted to the left 2 units, and expanded vertically.

32. The graph of g is the same as the graph of f reflected in the y axis, shifted to the right 1 unit and contracted vertically.

33. $\dfrac{e^{-2x}(-2x - 3)}{x^4}$ **34.** $\dfrac{e^{5x}(5x - 4)}{x^5}$ **35.** $2e^{2x} + 2e^{-2x}$ **36.** $e^x - e^{-x}$

37. $2e^{2x}$ **38.** $\dfrac{2}{e^{2x}}$ **39.** $x = 0$

40. $(x - 3)e^x = 0 \Rightarrow x - 3 = 0,\ e^x = 0,$ no solution, $e^x > 0$
$$x = 3$$

41. $x = 0, 5$ **42.** $x = 0, -3$

43. No local extrema; no x intercept: y intercept: 2.14; horizontal asymptote: $y = 2$

44. No local extrema; x intercept: 0.10; y intercept: -0.28; horizontal asymptote: $y = -3$

45. Local minimum: $m(0) = 1$; no x intercepts; y intercept: 1; no horizontal asymptotes

46. Local maximum: $n(0) = 1$; no x intercepts; y intercept: 1; horizontal asymptote: x axis

47. Local maximum: $s(0) = 1$; no x intercepts; y intercept: 1; horizontal asymptote: x axis

48. Local minimum: $r(0) = 1$; no x intercepts; y intercept: 1; no horizontal asymptotes

49. No local extrema; no x intercept; y intercept: 50; horizontal asymptotes: x axis and $y = 200$

50. No local extrema; no x intercept; y intercept: 50; horizontal asymptotes: x axis and $y = 100$

51. $f(x) \rightarrow 2.718 \approx e$ as $x \rightarrow 0$ **52.** $f(x) \rightarrow 1$ as $x \rightarrow \infty$

53.

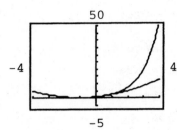

54.

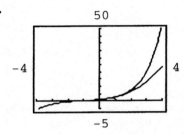

55.

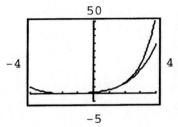

56.

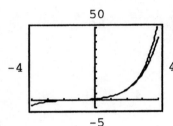

57. As $x \rightarrow \infty$, $f_n(x) \rightarrow 0$; The line $y = 0$ is a horizontal asymptote.
As $x \rightarrow -\infty$, $f_1(x) \rightarrow -\infty$ and $f_3(x) \rightarrow -\infty$, while $f_2(x) \rightarrow \infty$. As $x \rightarrow -\infty$, $f_n(x) \rightarrow \infty$ if n is even and $f_n(x) \rightarrow -\infty$ if n is odd.

58. as $x \rightarrow \infty$, $g(x) \rightarrow \infty$, as $x \rightarrow -\infty$, $g(x) \rightarrow 0$. $y = 0$ is an horizontal asymptote.

59. 7.1 billion   **60.** 120 million   **61.** 2006   **62.** 2009

63.

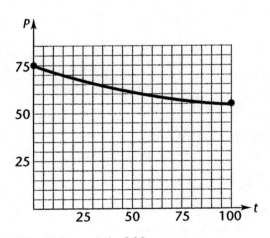

64.

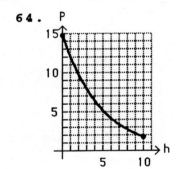

65. (A) 62%   (B) 39%   **66.** (A) 10%   (B) 1%

67. (A) $10,691.81   (B) $36,336.69   **68.** (A) $11,871.65   (B) $20,427.93

69. Gill Savings: $1,230.60; Richardson S & L: $1,231.00; U.S.A. Savings: $1,229.03

70. Alamo: $10,850.88; Lamar: $10,838.29   **71.** $12,197.09

72. $P = P_0 e^{rt} \Rightarrow 50,000 = P_0 e^{0.1(5.5)} \Rightarrow P_0 = \$28,847.49$

73. (A) 15 million   (B) 30 million

74. (A) 59.87... million   (B) 128.02... million

75. (A) 12 boards, 18 boards   (B) 8 days
(C) N approaches 40, the upper limit for the number of boards an average employee can produce.

76. (A) 143,000 viewers, 338,000 viewers   (B) 19 days
(C) N approaches 2 million viewers, the upper limit for the number of potential viewers.

77. $T = 50°F$ **78.** $T = 44°F$

79. q approaches 0.0009 coulombs, the upper limit for the charge on the capacitor.

80. q approaches 0.000008 coulombs, the upper limit for the charge on the capacitor.

81. (A) 25 deer, 37 deer   (B) 10 years
(C) N approaches 100 deer, the upper limit for the number of deer the island can support.

82. (A) 10 computers, 13 computers   (B) 21 days
(C) N approaches 50 computers, the upper limit for the number of computers an average trainee can be expected to test per day.

Exercise 4-5

1. $81 = 3^4$ **2.** $125 = 5^3$ **3.** $0.001 = 10^{-3}$ **4.** $1000 = 10^3$

5. $3 = 81^{1/4}$ **6.** $4^{1/2} = 2$ **7.** $16 = \left(\frac{1}{2}\right)^{-4}$ **8.** $27 = \left(\frac{1}{3}\right)^{-3}$

9. $\log_{10} 0.0001 = -4$ **10.** $\log_{10} 10,000 = 4$ **11.** $\log_4 8 = \frac{3}{2}$

12. $\log_{27} 9 = \frac{2}{3}$ **13.** $\log_{32} \frac{1}{2} = -\frac{1}{5}$ **14.** $\log_2 \frac{1}{8} = -3$ **15.** $\log_{49} 7 = \frac{1}{2}$

16. $\log_{64} 4 = \frac{1}{3}$ **17.** 0   **18.** 0   **19.** 1

20. 1   **21.** 4   **22.** 5   **23.** $\log_{10} 10^{-2} = -2$

24. 2   **25.** $\frac{1}{3}$ **26.** $\frac{3}{2}$ **27.** $\sqrt{x}$

28. $x - 1$ **29.** x^2 **30.** u^{-3} **31.** $x = 2^2 = 4$

32. $x = 27$ **33.** $y = 2$ **34.** $y = 2$ **35.** $b = 4$

36. $b = 10$ **37.** b is any positive real number except 1

38. any $b > 0$ and $b \neq 1$ **39.** $x = 2$ **40.** $x = 2$

41. $\log_{1/3} 9 = -2$ **42.** $y = -\frac{1}{2}$ **43.** $b = 100$ **44.** $b = 8$

45. $2 \log_b u + 7 \log_b v$ **46.** $\frac{1}{2} \log_b u + \frac{1}{3} \log_b v$

47. $\frac{2}{3} \log_b m - \frac{1}{2} \log_b n$ **48.** $3 \log_b u - 5 \log_b v$

49. $\log_b u - \log_b v - \log_b w$ **50.** $\log_b u + \log_b v - \log_b w$

51. $-2 \log_b a$ **52.** $0 - 5 \log_b M = -5 \log_b M$

53. $\frac{1}{3} \log_b(x^2 - y^2)$

54. $\frac{1}{2} \log_b(u^2 + 1)$

55. $\frac{1}{3} \log_b N - 2 \log_b p - 3 \log_b q$

56. $5 \log_b m + 3 \log_b n - \frac{1}{2} \log_b p$

57. $\frac{1}{4}(2 \log_b x + 3 \log_b y - \frac{1}{2} \log_b z)$

58. $\frac{3}{5}[\log_b x - 4 \log_b y - 9 \log_b z]$

59. $\log_b \frac{x^2}{y}$ **60.** $\log_b \frac{m}{\sqrt{n}}$

61. $\log_b \frac{w}{xy}$ **62.** $\log_b \frac{wx}{y}$

63. $\log_b \frac{x^3 y^2}{z^{1/4}}$ **64.** $\log_b \frac{\sqrt[3]{w}}{x^3 y^5}$

65. $\log_b \left(\frac{u^{1/2}}{v^2}\right)^5$ **66.** $\log_b (m^4 \sqrt[3]{n})^7$

67. $\log_b \sqrt[5]{x^2 y^3}$ **68.** $\log_b \sqrt[3]{\frac{x^4}{y^2}}$

69. $5 \log_b(x + 3) + 2 \log_b(2x - 7)$

70. $3 \log_b(5x - 4) + 4 \log_b(3x + 2)$

71. $7 \log_b(x + 10) - 2 \log_b(1 + 10x)$

72. $5 \log_b(x - 3) - 3 \log_b(5 + x)$

73. $2 \log_b x - \frac{1}{2} \log_b(x + 1)$

74. $\frac{1}{2} \log_b(x - 1) - 3 \log_b x$

75. $2 \log_b x + \log_b(x + 5) + \log_b(x - 4)$

76. $3 \log_b x + \log_b(x + 7) + \log_b(x - 2)$ **77.** $x = 4$

78. $x = -3$ **79.** $x = \frac{1}{3}$ **80.** $x = 3$ **81.** $x = \frac{8}{7}$

82. $x = 1$ **83.** $x = 2$ **84.** $x = 1$ **85.** $x = 2$

86. $x = 8$ **87.** 3.40   **88.** 2.48   **89.** -0.92

90. 0.51   **91.** 3.30   **92.** 2.76   **93.** 0.23

94. 0.55   **95.** -0.05   **96.** $0.13\overline{6}$

97. (A)

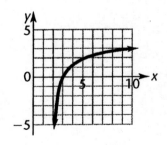

(B) $f^{-1}(x) = 2^x + 2$

98. (A)

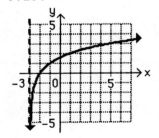

(B) $f^{-1}(x) = 2^x - 3$

99. (A)

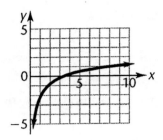

(B) $f^{-1}(x) = 2^{x+2}$

100. (A)

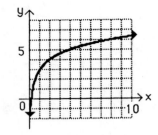

(B) $f^{-1}(x) = 2^{x-3}$

(B) Domain $f = (-\infty, \infty)$ = Range f^{-1}
Range $f = (0, \infty)$ = Domain f^{-1}

(C) $f^{-1}(x) = \log_{1/2} x = -\log_2 x$

101. (A)

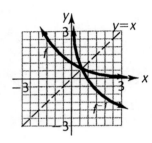

102. (A)

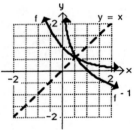

(B) domain of $f(x) = (-\infty, \infty)$ = range of $f^{-1}(x)$,
range of $f(x) = (0, \infty)$ = domain of $f^{-1}(x)$

(C) $f^{-1}(x) = -\log_3 x = \log_{1/3} x$

103. $f^{-1}(x) = \dfrac{1}{3}[1 + \log_5(x - 4)]$

104. $f^{-1}(x) = \dfrac{1}{2}[\log_3(x + 2) + 3]$

105. $g^{-1}(x) = \dfrac{1}{5}(e^{x/3} + 2)$

106. $f^{-1}(x) = \dfrac{1}{5}(e^{x-2} + 3)$

107. The reflection is not a function since $y = 3^{x^2}$ is not one-to-one.

108. The reflection is not a function since $y = 2^{|x|}$ is not one-to-one.

109. $x = 100e^{-0.08t}$

110. $x = Ce^{-kt}$

111. $\log_b M/N = u - v = \log_b M - \log_b N$

112. $\log_b m^p = p \log_b m$

Exercise 4-6

1. 4.9177	**2.** 5.9260	**3.** -2.8419	**4.** -1.4485
5. 3.7623	**6.** 14.8604	**7.** -2.5128	**8.** -10.3374
9. 200,800	**10.** 82.57	**11.** 0.0006648	**12.** 0.009097
13. 47.73	**14.** 162.1	**15.** 0.6760	**16.** 0.01644
17. 4.959	**18.** 6.116	**19.** 7.861	**20.** 7.604
21. 3.301	**22.** 921.034	**23.** 4.561	**24.** 7.644

25. $x = 12.725$ **26.** 17.322 **27.** -25.715 **28.** -17.027

29. $x = 1.1709 \times 10^{32}$ **30.** 1.8551×10^{-13}

31. 4.2672×10^{-7} **32.** 1.6007×10^{8} **33.** $f^{-1}(x) = e^{x/2} - 2$

34. $f^{-1}(x) = e^{0.5(x-2)}$ **35.** $f^{-1}(x) = e^{(x+3)/4}$ **36.** $f^{-1}(x) = e^{x/4} + 3$

37. Domain: $(-\infty, \infty)$; range: $(-\infty, \infty)$; x intercepts: ± 2.53; y intercept: -2

38. Domain: $(-\infty, \infty)$; range: $(-\infty, 2]$; x intercepts: ± 6.39; y intercept: 2; no asymptotes

39. Domain: $(-1, 1)$: range: $(-\infty, 1]$; x intercepts: ± 0.80; y intercept: 1

40. Domain: $(-\infty, -1) \cup (-1, 1) \cup (1, \infty)$; range: $(-\infty, \infty)$; x intercepts: ± 1.93; y intercept: -1; vertical asymptotes: $x = \pm 1$

41. The inequality sign in the last step reverses because $\log \frac{1}{3}$ is negative.

42. $\log \frac{1}{2} = -0.3010 < 0$, thus when $3 > 2$ is multiplied on both sides by $\log \frac{1}{2}$ (a negative number) the order of the inequality should be reversed: $3 \log \frac{1}{2} < 2 \log \frac{1}{2}$ rather than $3 \log \frac{1}{2} > 2 \log \frac{1}{2}$ as shown.

43. (B) Domain = $(1, \infty)$; Range = $(-\infty, \infty)$ **44.** (B) Domain = $(1, \infty)$; Range = $(-\infty, \infty)$

45. $(0.90, -0.11)$, $(38.51, 3.65)$ **46.** $(1.93, 0.28)$

47. $(6.41, 1.86)$, $(93.35, 4.54)$ **48.** $(3.06, 0.19)$

49.

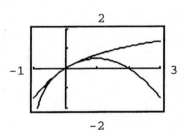

50.

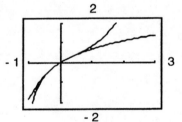

51.

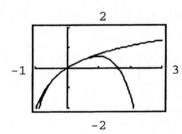

52.

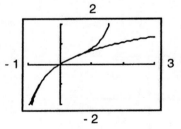

53. (A) 0 decibels (B) 120 decibels   **54.** (A) 65 decibels (B) 150 decibels

55. 30 decibels   **56.** 40 decibels   **57.** 8.6   **58.** 8.3

59. 1000 times as powerful   **60.** $E_1 \approx 32,000$

61. 7.67 km/s   **62.** $9.49 \dfrac{km}{sec}$

63. (A) 8.3, basic (B) 3.0, acidic   **64.** (A) 6.5 acidic (B) 5.4 acidic

65. 6.3×10^{-6} moles per liter   **66.** 2×10^{-6} moles per liter

Exercise 4-7

1. 1.46

2. 1.16

3. 0.321

4. 0.908

5. 1.29

6. 4.25

7. 3.50

8. -0.610

9. 1.80

10. 1.26

11. 2.07

12. 2.37

13. 20

14. 80

15. $x = 5$

16. $x = 10$

17. $x = \dfrac{11}{9}$

18. $x = \dfrac{21}{8}$

19. 14.2

20. 18.9

21. -1.83

22. 20.2

23. 11.7

24. 3.14

25. ±1.21

26. ±2.20

27. $x = 5$

28. $x = \dfrac{2}{3}$

29. $2 + \sqrt{3}$

30. $x = 1 + \sqrt{2}$

31. $\dfrac{1 + \sqrt{89}}{4}$

32. $x = 3$

33. $1, e^2, e^{-2}$

34. $x = 1, x = 10^{\pm 2}$

35. $x = e^e$

36. $x = 10^{10}$

37. $x = 100, 0.1$

38. $x = 10^{(\log 3)/(\log 3 - 1)}$

39. (B) 2   **40.** (B) 1   **41.** (B) -1.252, 1.707   **42.** (B) 1.248, 10.738

43. 3.6776

44. 2.2618

45. -1.6094

46. -7.5224

47. -1.7372

48. 2.4455

49. $r = \dfrac{1}{t} \ln \dfrac{A}{P}$

50. $t = \dfrac{\ln \frac{A}{P}}{n \ln(1 + \frac{r}{n})}$ **51.** $I = I_0(10^{D/10})$

52. $A = A_0 e^{-kt}$

53. $I = I_0[10^{(6-M)/2.5}]$

54. $D = 10^{(L-8.8)/5.1}$

55. $t = -\dfrac{L}{R} \ln\left(1 - \dfrac{RI}{E}\right)$

56. $n = \dfrac{\ln(\frac{Si}{R} + 1)}{\ln(1 + i)}$

57. $x = \ln(y \pm \sqrt{y^2 - 1})$

58. $x = \ln[y + \sqrt{y^2 + 1}]$

59. $x = \dfrac{1}{2} \ln \dfrac{1 + y}{1 - y}$

60. $x = \dfrac{1}{2} \ln \dfrac{y + 1}{y - 1}$

61.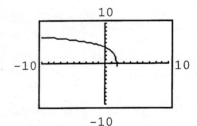

62.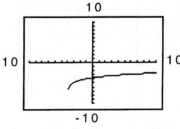

63.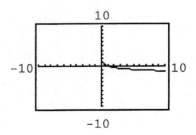

64.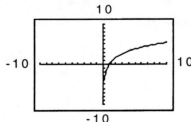

65. 0.38

66. 0.25

67. 0.55

68. 0.64

69. 0.57

70. 0.43

71. 0.85

72. 0.35

73. 0.43

74. 0.65

75. 0.27

76. 0.57

77. n = 5 years to the nearest year

78. 8 yrs. to nearest year

79. r = 0.0916 or 9.16%

80. 5.22 years

81. (A) m = 6   (B) 100 times brighter

82. (A) 12.8   (B) 206 in.

83. t = 35 years to the nearest year

84. 533 years

85. t = 18,600 years old

86. 5590 years

87. t = 7.52 seconds

88. 43 days

89. k = 0.40, t = 2.9 hours

90. k = 0.0485, d = 95.0 ft.

91. (A) 1996: 123.0 bush./acre;
2010: 141.4 bush./acre

```
LnReg
  y=a+blnx
  a=-492.8690524
  b=134.9522575
```

92. (A) 1996: 8,192 million bush.;
2010: 9,423 million bush.

```
LnReg
  y=a+blnx
  a=-33.05995492
  b=9.037919003
```

CHAPTER 4 REVIEW

1.

x	-3	-2	-1	0	1	2	3
$f(x)$	3	2	1	0	1	2	3
$g(x)$	-4	-3	-2	-1	0	1	2
$(f - g)(x)$	7	5	3	1	1	1	1

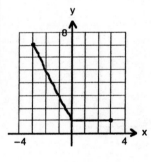

(4-1)

2. 2   *(4-1)*

3. 1   *(4-1)*

4. 0   *(4-1)*

5. 2   *(4-1)*

6. No   *(4-2)*

7. Yes   *(4-2)*

8. (A) m (B) f (C) n (D) g *(4-2, 4-3, 4-5)*

9. $\log m = n$ *(4-5)*

10. $\ln x = y$ *(4-5)*

11. $x = 10^y$ *(4-5)*

12. $y = e^x$ *(4-5)*

13. 7^{2x} *(4-3)*

14. e^{2x^2} *(4-3)*

15. $x = 8$ *(4-5)*

16. $x = 5$ *(4-5)*

17. $x = 3$ *(4-5)*

18. $x = 1.24$ *(4-6)*

19. $x = 11.9$ *(4-6)*

20. $x = 0.984$ *(4-6)*

21. $x = 103$ *(4-6)*

22. 1.145   *(4-5)*

23. Not defined   *(4-5)*

24. 2.211   *(4-5)*

25. 11.59   *(4-5)*

26. (A) $(f/g)(x) = (x^2 - 4)/(x + 3)$; Domain of $f/g = (-\infty, -3) \cup (-3, \infty)$
(B) $(g/f)(x) = (x + 3)/(x^2 - 4)$; Domain of $g/f = (-\infty, -2) \cup (-2, 2) \cup (2, \infty)$
(C) $(f \circ g)(x) = x^2 + 6x + 5$; Domain of $f \circ g = (-\infty, \infty)$
(D) $(g \circ f)(x) = x^2 - 1$; Domain of $g \circ f = (-\infty, \infty)$ *(4-1)*

27. $x = 4$ *(4-5)*   **28.** $x = 2$ *(4-5)*

29. $x = 3, -1$ *(4-4)*   **30.** $x = 1$ *(4-3)*

31. $x = 3, -3$ *(4-4)*   **32.** $x = -2$ *(4-5)*

33. $x = \dfrac{1}{3}$ *(4-5)*   **34.** $x = 64$ *(4-5)*

35. $x = e$ *(4-5)*   **36.** $x = 33$ *(4-5)*

37. $x = 1$ *(4-5)*   **38.** $x = 41.8$ *(4-3)*

39. $x = 1.95$ *(4-5)*   **40.** $x = 0.0400$ *(4-5)*

41. $x = -6.67$ *(4-5)*   **42.** $x = 1.66$ *(4-5)*

43. $x = 2.32$ *(4-7)*   **44.** $x = 3.92$ *(4-7)*

45. $x = 92.1$ *(4-7)*   **46.** $x = 2.11$ *(4-7)*

47. $x = 0.881$ *(4-7)*

48. (A) $(f \circ g)(x) = \sqrt{|x|} - 8$; $(g \circ f)(x) = |\sqrt{x} - 8|$
(B) Domain of $f \circ g$ is the set of all real numbers.
The domain of $(g \circ f)$ is $[0, \infty)$ *(4-1)*

49. (A) $(f \circ g)(x) = e^{\ln(x+1)-1}$; $(g \circ f)(x) = \ln(e^{x-1} + 1)$
(B) Domain of $f \circ g = (-1, \infty)$; Domain of $g \circ f = (-\infty, \infty)$ *(4-1)*

50. Functions f, h, F, and H are one-to-one   *(4-2)*

51. $f^{-1}(x) = (x + 7)/3$;
Domain of f^{-1} = Range of f^{-1}
= $(-\infty, \infty)$

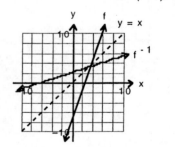

                                        (4-2)

52. $f^{-1}(x) = x^2 + 1$;
Domain of $f^{-1} = [0, \infty)$;
Range of $f^{-1} = [1, \infty)$

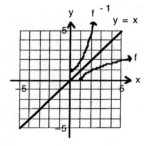

                                        (4-2)

53. $f^{-1}(x) = \sqrt{x + 1}$;
Domain of $f^{-1} = [-1, \infty)$;
Range of $f^{-1} = [0, \infty)$

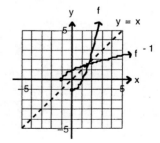

                                        (4-2)

54. $f^{-1}(x) = \ln(x - 1)$;
Domain of $f^{-1} = [1, \infty)$;
Range of $f^{-1} = (-\infty, \infty)$

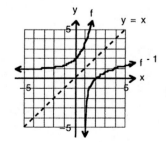

                                        (4-2)

55. $f^{-1}(x) = e^{x/2} + 1$;
Domain of $f^{-1} = (-\infty, \infty)$;
Range of $f^{-1} = (1, \infty)$

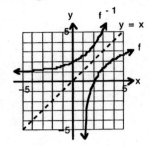

$(4-2)$

56. $x = 300$ $(4-7)$ **57.** $x = 2$ $(4-7)$

58. $x = 1$ $(4-7)$ **59.** $x = \dfrac{3 + \sqrt{13}}{2}$ $(4-7)$

60. $x = 1,\ 10^3,\ 10^{-3}$ $(4-7)$ **61.** $x = 10^e$ $(4-7)$

62. $e^{-x} - 1$ $(4-4)$ **63.** $2 - 2e^{-2x}$ $(4-4)$

64. Domain $= (-\infty, \infty)$; range $= (0, \infty)$; y intercept: 0.5; horizontal asymptote: $y = 0$
$(4-3)$

65. Domain $= (-\infty, \infty)$; range $= (0, \infty)$; y intercept: 10; horizontal asymptote: $y = 0$
$(4-4)$

66. Domain $= (1, \infty)$; range $= (-\infty, \infty)$; x intercept: 2; vertical asymptote: $x = 1$
$(4-6)$

67. Domain $= (-\infty, \infty)$; range $= (0, 100)$; y intercept: 25;
horizontal asymptotes: $y = 0$ and $y = 100$
$(4-4)$

68. $y = -e^x$; $y = e^{-x}$ or $y = \dfrac{1}{e^x}$ or $y = \left(\dfrac{1}{e}\right)^x$ $(4-5)$

69. (A) $y = e^{-x/3}$ is decreasing while $y = 4 \ln(x + 1)$ is increasing without bound.
(B) 0.258 $(4-5)$

70. 0.018, 2.187 $(4-5)$

71. (1.003, 0.010), (3.653, 4.502) $(4-6)$

72. (A) $(fg)(x) = x^2\sqrt{1 - x}$; domain is $(-\infty, 1]$

(B) $\left(\dfrac{f}{g}\right)(x) = \dfrac{x^2}{\sqrt{1 - x}}$; domain of $\dfrac{f}{g}$ is $(-\infty, 1)$

(C) $(f \circ g)(x) = 1 - x$; domain of $f \circ g$ is $(-\infty, 1]$

(D) $(g \circ f)(x) = \sqrt{1 - x^2}$; domain of $g \circ f$ is $[-1, 1]$
$(4-1)$

73. $I = I_0(10^{D/10})$ $(4-7)$ **74.** $x = \pm\sqrt{-2\ \ln(\sqrt{2\pi}\,y)}$ $(4-7)$

75. $I = I_0(e^{-kx})$ $(4-7)$ **76.** $n = -\dfrac{\ln\left(1 - \frac{Pi}{r}\right)}{\ln(1 + i)}$ $(4-7)$

77. $f^{-1}(x) = \dfrac{3x + 2}{x - 1}$ $(4-2)$

78. $f^{-1}(x) = \ln(x + \sqrt{x^2 + 1})$ $(4-2,\ 4-7)$

79. $y = ce^{-5t}$ *(4-5, 4-7)*

80. Domain $f = (0, \infty)$ = Range f^{-1}
Range $f = (-\infty, \infty)$ = Domain f^{-1}

81. If $\log_1 x = y$, then we would have to have $1^y = x$; that is, $1 = x$ for arbitrary positive x, which is impossible.   *(4-5)*

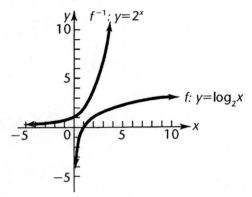

83. (A) [1, 3]
(B) $q = d^{-1}(p) = 4,500/p - 500$;
domain = [1, 3];
range = [1,000, 4,000]   *(4-5)*

(4-2, 4-5)

84. $P(p) = -14,000 + 700p - 10p^2$ *(4-1)*

85. $t = 23.4$ years *(4-7)*

86. $t = 23.1$ years   *(4-7)*

87. $t = 37,100$ years   *(4-7)*

88. (A) $N = 2^{2t}$ (or $N = 4^t$)   (B) $t = 15$ days   *(4-7)*

89. $A = 1.1 \times 10^{26}$ dollars   *(4-4)*

90. (A)

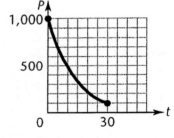

(B) 0

(4-4)

91. $M = 6.6$ *(4-6)*

92. $E = 10^{16.85}$ or 7.08×10^{16} joules   *(4-6)*

93. The level of the louder sound is 50 decibels more.   *(4-4)*

94. $k = 0.00942$, $d = 489$ feet   *(4-4)*

95. $t = 3$ years   *(4-7)*

96. (A) 1996: $207 billion;
2010: $886 billion

```
ExpReg
 y=a*b^x
  a=39.23474084
  b=1.109502846
```

(B) Midway through 2004   *(4-3)*

97. (A) 1996: 1,724 million bush.;
2010: 2,426 million bush.

```
LnReg
 y=a+blnx
  a=-21796.9294
  b=5153.244133
```

(4-7)

CUMULATIVE REVIEW EXERCISE (Chapters 3 and 4)

1. (A) $P(x) = (x + 1)^2 (x - 1)(x - 2)$
(B) $P(x) \to \infty$ as $x \to \infty$ and as $x \to -\infty$ *(3-1)*

2. (A) m (B) g (C) n (D) f *(4-1, 4-3)*

3. $3x^3 + 5x^2 - 18x - 3 = (x + 3)(3x^2 - 4x - 6) + 15$ *(3-1)*

4. -2, 3, 5   *(3-2)*   **5.** $P(1) = -5$ and $P(2) = 5$ are of opposite sign.   *(3-3)*

6. 1, 2, -4   *(3-2)*

7. (A) $x = \log y$ (B) $x = e^y$ *(4-6)*   **8.** (A) $8e^{3x}$ (B) e^{5x} *(4-4)*

9. (A) 9   (B) 4   (C) $\frac{1}{2}$ *(4-5)*   **10.** (A) 0.371   (B) 11.4   (C) 0.0562   (D) 15.6 *(4-6)*

11. $(f \circ g)(x) = \dfrac{x}{3 - x}$; Domain: $(-\infty, 0) \cup (0, 3) \cup (3, \infty)$ *(4-1)*

12. $f^{-1}(x) = \dfrac{x - 5}{2}$ or $\dfrac{1}{2}x - \dfrac{5}{2}$ *(4-2)*   **13.** $f(x) = 3 \ln x - \sqrt{x}$ *(4-5)*

14. The function f multiplies the base e raised to power of one-half the domain element by 100 and then subtracts 50.   *(4-4)*

15. (A) Domain: $x \neq -2$;
x intercept: $x = -4$;
y intercept: $y = 4$

     (B) *Vertical asymptote:* $x = -2$
        Horizontal asymptote: $y = 2$

(C)
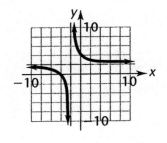

(3-4)

16. (A) $f^{-1}(x) = x^2 - 4$,   Domain: $x \geq 0$

     (B) Domain of $f = [-4, \infty)$ = Range of f^{-1}
        Range of $f = [0, \infty)$ = Domain of f^{-1}

     (C)

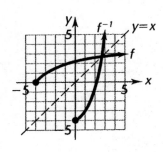

(4-2)

17. f and h are one-to-one
                 (4-2)

18. $P\left(\dfrac{1}{2}\right) = \dfrac{5}{2}$ *(3-2)*

19. (B)   *(3-1)*

20. (A) The graph of $P(x)$ has four x intercepts and three turning points; $P(x) \to \infty$ as $x \to \infty$ and as $x \to -\infty$

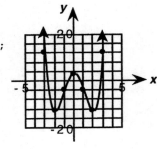

(3-1, 3-3)

     (B) 2.76

21. -0.56 and 3.56 must be double zeros and 2 must be a simple zero. *(3-3)*

22. (A) Upper bound: 4; lower bound: -6 (B) 4 intervals (C) -5.68, 3.80 *(3-3)*

23. 3, $1 \pm \frac{1}{2}i$ *(3-2)*

24. $P(x) = (x + 1)(x + 4)(x^2 - 3) = (x + 1)(x + 4)(x - \sqrt{3})(x + \sqrt{3})$.
The four zeros are -1, -4, $\pm\sqrt{3}$. *(3-2)*

25. $x = 4, -2$ *(4-4)* **26.** $\frac{1}{2}, -1$ *(4-5)*

27. $x = 2.5$ *(4-5)* **28.** $x = 10$ *(4-5)*

29. $x = \frac{1}{27}$ *(4-7)* **30.** $x = 5$ *(4-7)*

31. $x = 7$ *(4-7)* **32.** $x = 5$ *(4-6)*

33. $x = e^{0.1}$ *(4-7)* **34.** $x = 1, e^{0.5}$ *(4-7)*

35. $x = 3.38$ *(4-6)* **36.** $x = 4.26$ *(4-6)*

37. $x = 2.32$ *(4-7)* **38.** $x = 3.67$ *(4-7)*

39. $x = 0.549$ *(4-7)*

40. Domain: $(-\infty, \infty)$; range: $(0, \infty)$; y intercept: 3; horizontal asymptote: $y = 0$
(4-3)

41. Domain: $(-\infty, 2)$; range: $(-\infty, \infty)$; x intercept: 1; y intercept: ln 2;
vertical asymptote: $x = 2$ *(4-6)*

42. Domain: $(-\infty, \infty)$; range: $(0, \infty)$; y intercept: 100; horizontal asymptote: $y = 0$
(4-4)

43. Domain: $(-\infty, \infty)$; range: $(-\infty, 3)$; x intercept: -0.41; y intercept: 1;
horizontal asymptote: $y = 3$ *(4-4)*

44. Domain: $(-\infty, \infty)$; range: $(0, 3)$; y intercept: 2;
horizontal asymptotes: $y = 0$ and $y = 3$ *(4-4)*

45. A reflection in the x axis transforms the graph of $y = \ln x$ into the graph of
$y = -\ln x$. A reflection in the y axis transforms the graph of $y = \ln x$ into the
graph of $y = \ln(-x)$. *(4-5)*

46. (A) For $x > 0$, $y = e^{-x}$ decreases from 1 to 0 while ln x increases from $-\infty$ to ∞.
Consequently, the graphs can intersect at exactly one point.

(B) 1.31 *(4-4)*

47. (A) Domain g: $[-2, 2]$

(B) $\left(\dfrac{f}{g}\right)(x) = \dfrac{x^2}{\sqrt{4 - x^2}}$; domain of f/g is $(-2, 2)$

(C) $(f \circ g)(x) = 4 - x^2$; domain of $f \circ g$ is $[-2, 2]$ *(4-1)*

48. (A) $f^{-1}(x) = 1 + \sqrt{x + 4}$

(B) Domain of f^{-1} is $[-4, \infty)$
Range of f^{-1} = Domain of f
is $[1, \infty)$

(C)

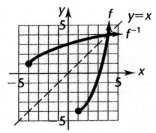

$(4-2)$

49. *Vertical asymptote: x = -2*
Oblique asymptote: y = x + 2

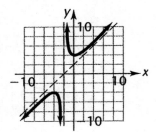

$(3-4)$

50. zeros: 2.97, 3; local minimum: $P(2.98) \approx -0.02$; local maximum: $P(7.03) \approx 264.03$;
local minimum: $P(10.98) \approx 15.98$ $(3-1)$

51. $P(x) = (x + 1)^2 x^3 (x - 3 - 5i)(x - 3 + 5i)$; degree 7 $(3-2)$

52. Yes, for example:
$P(x) = (x + i)(x - i)(x + \sqrt{2})(x - \sqrt{2}) = x^4 - x^2 - 2$ $(3-2)$

53. (A) Upper bound: 20; lower bound: -30   (B) -26.68, -6.22, 7.23, 16.67 $(3-3)$

54. 2, -1 (double), and $2 \pm i\sqrt{2}$;
$P(x) = (x - 2)(x + 1)^2 (x - 2 - i\sqrt{2})(x - 2 + i\sqrt{2})$ $(3-2)$

55. -2(double), -1.88, 0.35, 1.53 $(3-3)$

56. (A) $f^{-1}(x) = e^{x/3} + 2$ (C)

(B) Domain of $f = (2, \infty)$ = Range of f^{-1}
Range of $f = (-\infty, \infty)$ = Domain of f^{-1}

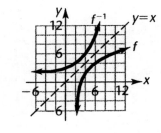

$(4-1, 4-7)$

57. $n = \dfrac{\ln(1 + \frac{Ai}{P})}{\ln(1 + i)}$ $(4-7)$ **58.** $y = Ae^{5x}$ $(4-7)$ **59.** $x = \ln(y + \sqrt{y^2 + 2})$ $(4-7)$

60. $V(t) = 0.036\pi t^{3/4}$ $(4-1)$

61. (A) $v = -2,000t + 20,000$ (B) $t = -0.0005v + 10$ $(4-2)$

62. $x = 2$ feet and $y = 2$ feet, or $x = 1.28$ feet and $y = 4.88$ feet $(3-2)$

63. 1.79 feet by 3.35 feet $(3-2)$

64. (A) 46.8 million   (B) 103 million $(4-3)$

65. $t = 10.2$ years $(4-7)$ **66.** $t = 9.90$ years $(4-7)$

67. 63.1 times as powerful $(4-6)$ **68.** $I = 6.31 \times 10^{-4}$ w/m^2 $(4-6)$

69. (A) 79.3   (B) 75.4   (C) 77.8   (D) 79.5 $(3-1, 4-3)$

70. Cubic regression $(3-1, 4-3)$

CHAPTER 5

Exercise 5-1

1. $(-1, 0)$ **2.** $(1, 0)$ **3.** $(1, 0)$ **4.** $(-1, 0)$

5. $(-1, 0)$ **6.** $(-1, 0)$ **7.** $(0, -1)$ **8.** $(0, 1)$

9. $(0, -1)$ **10.** $(0, 1)$ **11.** $(0, -1)$ **12.** $(0, 1)$

13. $\left(\dfrac{1}{\sqrt{2}}, \dfrac{1}{\sqrt{2}}\right)$ **14.** $\left(\dfrac{1}{2}, \dfrac{\sqrt{3}}{2}\right)$ **15.** $\left(\dfrac{\sqrt{3}}{2}, \dfrac{1}{2}\right)$ **16.** $\left(\dfrac{\sqrt{3}}{2}, -\dfrac{1}{2}\right)$

17. $\left(\dfrac{1}{2}, -\dfrac{\sqrt{3}}{2}\right)$ **18.** $\left(\dfrac{\sqrt{2}}{2}, \dfrac{-\sqrt{2}}{2}\right)$ **19.** $\left(-\dfrac{1}{2}, \dfrac{\sqrt{3}}{2}\right)$ **20.** $\left(\dfrac{\sqrt{3}}{2}, -\dfrac{1}{2}\right)$

21. $\left(-\dfrac{1}{\sqrt{2}}, -\dfrac{1}{\sqrt{2}}\right)$ **22.** $\left(-\dfrac{\sqrt{3}}{2}, \dfrac{1}{2}\right)$ **23.** $\left(-\dfrac{1}{\sqrt{2}}, -\dfrac{1}{\sqrt{2}}\right)$ **24.** $\left(-\dfrac{1}{2}, \dfrac{\sqrt{3}}{2}\right)$

25. a, $-$; b, $+$ **26.** a, $+$; b, $+$ **27.** a, $-$; b, $+$ **28.** a, $-$; b, $-$

29. a, $+$; b, $-$ **30.** a, $+$; b, $+$ **31.** a, $-$; b, $-$ **32.** a, $-$; b, $+$

33. a, $+$; b, $+$ **34.** a, $-$; b, $-$ **35.** 0; $2k\pi$, k any integer

36. π; $\pi + 2k\pi$, k any integer **37.** $3\pi/4$; $3\pi/4 + 2k\pi$, k any integer

38. $7\pi/4$; $7\pi/4 + 2k\pi$, k any integer

39. $W(x)$ is the coordinates of a point on a unit circle that is $|x|$ units from $(1, 0)$, in a counterclockwise direction if x is positive and in a clockwise direction if x is negative. $W(x + 4\pi)$ has the same coordinates as $W(x)$, since we return to the same point every time we go around the unit circle any integer multiple of 2π units (the circumference of the circle) in either direction.

40. $W(x)$ is the coordinates of a point on a unit circle that is $|x|$ units from $(1, 0)$, in a counterclockwise direction if x is positive and in a clockwise direction if x is negative. $W(x - 6\pi)$ has the same coordinates as $W(x)$, since we return to the same point every time we go around the unit circle any integer multiple of 2π units (the circumference of the circle) in either direction.

41. T **42.** F **43.** F **44.** T

45. T **46.** F **47.** $x = \dfrac{-7\pi}{4}$ and $\dfrac{\pi}{4}$

48. $x = -\dfrac{11\pi}{6}, \dfrac{\pi}{6}$ **49.** $x = \dfrac{-4\pi}{3}$ and $\dfrac{2\pi}{3}$ **50.** $x = -\dfrac{\pi}{3}, \dfrac{5\pi}{3}$

51. $x = \dfrac{-5\pi}{6}$ and $\dfrac{7\pi}{6}$ **52.** $x = -\dfrac{5\pi}{4}, \dfrac{3\pi}{4}$ **53.** $x = \dfrac{\pi}{4} + 2k\pi$, k any integer

54. $x = \dfrac{2\pi}{3} + 2k\pi$, k an integer

Exercise 5-2

1. (A) a (B) $\dfrac{1}{b}$ (C) $\dfrac{a}{b}$ (D) $\dfrac{1}{a}$ (E) $\dfrac{b}{a}$ (F) b

2. (A) $\sin x$ (B) $\sec x$ (C) $\tan x$ (D) $\csc x$ (E) $\cos x$ (F) $\cot x$

3. 1 **4.** 0 **5.** $\dfrac{1}{2}$ **6.** $\dfrac{\sqrt{3}}{2}$

7. 1   **8.** 0   **9.** $\sqrt{3}$ **10.** $\frac{1}{2}$

11. not defined   **12.** not defined   **13.** 1   **14.** 1

15. $\sqrt{2}$ **16.** $\frac{2}{\sqrt{3}}$ **17.** 1   **18.** 0

19. not defined   **20.** $\sqrt{3}$ **21.** quadrants II and III

22. quadrants I or III   **23.** quadrants I and II

24. quadrants I or IV   **25.** quadrants II and IV

26. quadrants III or IV   **27.** −0.6573   **28.** 0.03758

29. −14.60   **30.** 63.31   **31.** 1.000   **32.** 1.000

33. −1   **34.** −1   **35.** 0   **36.** 0

37. $\frac{1}{\sqrt{2}}$ **38.** $-\frac{1}{2}$ **39.** not defined   **40.** not defined

41. $-\frac{1}{\sqrt{3}}$ **42.** $-\frac{1}{\sqrt{3}}$ **43.** $\frac{\sqrt{3}}{2}$ **44.** $-\frac{1}{\sqrt{2}}$

45. 2   **46.** $-\frac{2}{\sqrt{3}}$ **47.** 1   **48.** 1

49. (A) sin 0.4 = 0.4 (B) cos 0.4 = 0.9 (C) tan 0.4 = 0.4

50. (A) sin 0.8 = 0.7 (B) cos 0.8 = 0.7 (C) cot 0.8 = 1

51. (A) sec 2.2 = −2 (B) tan 5.9 = −0.4 (C) cot 3.8 = 1

52. (A) csc 2.5 = 2 (B) cot 5.6 = −1 (C) tan 4.3 = 2

53. sin x < 0 in quadrants III and IV; cot x < 0 in quadrants II and IV; therefore, both are true in quadrant IV.

54. cos x > 0 in quadrants I and IV; tan x < 0 in quadrants II and IV; therefore, both are true in quadrant IV

55. cos x < 0 in quadrants II and III; sec x > 0 in quadrants I and IV; therefore, it is not possible to have both true for the same value of x.

56. sin x > 0 and csc x < 0 is never true because sin $x = \dfrac{1}{\csc x} \Rightarrow$ they have same sign.

57. none   **58.** none   **59.** $\frac{\pi}{2}$ and $\frac{3\pi}{2}$ **60.** 0, π, 2π

61. $\frac{\pi}{2}$ and $\frac{3\pi}{2}$ **62.** 0, π, 2π

63. (A) 0 to 1   (B) 1 to 0   (C) 0 to −1   (D) −1 to 0

64. (A) 1 to 0   (B) 0 to −1   (C) −1 to 0   (D) 0 to 1

65. 0.8138   **66.** −0.3847   **67.** 0.5290   **68.** −1.669

69. $\frac{1}{2}$ **70.** $-\frac{1}{2}$ **71.** $\sqrt{3}$ **72.** 1

73. −5   **74.** 1

75. $\sin x = -\dfrac{\sqrt{3}}{2}$, $\tan x = -\sqrt{3}$, $\cot x = -\dfrac{1}{\sqrt{3}}$, $\csc x = -\dfrac{2}{\sqrt{3}}$, $\sec x = 2$

76. $\cos x = -\dfrac{1}{2}$, $\tan x = -\sqrt{3}$, $\cot x = -\dfrac{1}{\sqrt{3}}$, $\csc x = \dfrac{2}{\sqrt{3}}$, $\sec x = -2$

77. $\cos x = -\dfrac{1}{\sqrt{2}}$, $\tan x = 1$, $\cot x = 1$, $\csc x = -\sqrt{2}$, $\sec x = -\sqrt{2}$

78. $\cos x = \dfrac{1}{2}$, $\sin x = -\dfrac{\sqrt{3}}{2}$, $\tan x = -\sqrt{3}$, $\cot x = -\dfrac{1}{\sqrt{3}}$, $\csc x = -\dfrac{2}{\sqrt{3}}$

79. $\cos x = -\dfrac{1}{2}$, $\sin x = \dfrac{-\sqrt{3}}{2}$, $\cot x = \dfrac{1}{\sqrt{3}}$, $\csc x = -\dfrac{2}{\sqrt{3}}$, $\sec x = -2$

80. $\tan x = -1$, $\sin x = \dfrac{1}{\sqrt{2}}$, $\cos x = -\dfrac{1}{\sqrt{2}}$, $\csc x = \sqrt{2}$, $\sec x = -\sqrt{2}$

81. π **82.** $\dfrac{4\pi}{3}$ **83.** $\dfrac{5\pi}{6}$ **84.** $\dfrac{3\pi}{4}$

85. $\dfrac{5\pi}{6}$ **86.** $\dfrac{5\pi}{4}$

87. (A) Identity (5)   (B) Identity (9)   (C) Identity (1)

88. (A) 4   (B) 9   (C) 2

89. 75 square meters   **90.** 18 square inches

91. $12\sqrt{3} \approx 20.78$ square inches   **92.** $200\sqrt{2} \approx 282.8$ square centimeters

93. $a_1 = 0.5$, $a_2 = 1.377583$, $a_3 = 1.569596$, $a_4 = 1.570796$, $a_5 = 1.570796$;
$\dfrac{\pi}{2} = 1.570796$

94. $a_1 = 1$, $a_2 \approx 1.540302$, $a_3 \approx 1.570792$, $a_4 \approx 1.570796$, $a_5 \approx 1.570796$;
$\dfrac{\pi}{2} \approx 1.570796$

Exercise 5-3

1. 40°   **2.** 72°   **3.** 270°   **4.** 135°

5. 405°   **6.** 420°   **7.** 6   **8.** $\theta = 2$

9. 2.5   **10.** $\theta = 1.5$ **11.** $\dfrac{\pi}{4}$ **12.** $\dfrac{\pi}{3}$

13. $\dfrac{3\pi}{2}$ **14.** $\dfrac{5\pi}{6}$ **15.** $\dfrac{13\pi}{6}$ **16.** $\dfrac{11\pi}{4}$

17. $\dfrac{\pi}{6}$, $\dfrac{\pi}{3}$, $\dfrac{\pi}{2}$, $\dfrac{2\pi}{3}$, $\dfrac{5\pi}{6}$, π **18.** $\dfrac{\pi}{3}$, $\dfrac{2\pi}{3}$, π, $\dfrac{4\pi}{3}$, $\dfrac{5\pi}{3}$, 2π

19. $-\dfrac{\pi}{4}$, $-\dfrac{\pi}{2}$, $-\dfrac{3\pi}{4}$, $-\pi$ **20.** $-\dfrac{\pi}{2}$, $-\pi$, $-\dfrac{3\pi}{2}$, -2π

21. 60°, 120°, 180°, 240°, 300°, 360°   **22.** 30°, 60°, 90°, 120°, 150°, 180°

23. -90°, -180°, -270°, -360°   **24.** -45°, -90°, -135°, -180°

25. 5.859°   **26.** 14.310°   **27.** 354.141°   **28.** 184.519°

29. 3°2'31"   **30.** 49°42'54"   **31.** 403°13'23"   **32.** 156°48'29"

33. 1.117
34. 0.436
35. 1.892
36. 3.545

37. 0.234
38. 0.981
39. 53.29°
40. 4.58°

41. 64.74°
42. 175.90°
43. -134.65°
44. -98.55°

45. Quadrant III
46. Quadrant II
47. Quadrant II
48. Quadrant IV

49. Quadrant III
50. Quadrant II
51. Quadrantal angle

52. Quadrantal angle
53. Quadrant IV
54. Quadrant I
55. Quadrant IV

56. Quadrant II
57. Quadrant II
58. Quadrant III

59. Quadrantal angle
60. Quadrantal angle
61. Quadrant II
62. Quadrant II

63. Quadrant III
64. Quadrant IV

65. A central angle of radian measure 1 is an angle subtended by an arc of the same length as the radius of the circle.

66. For an angle to have degree measure 1, the terminal side of the angle is rotated through 1/360th of a complete revolution.

67. coterminal
68. not coterminal
69. coterminal
70. coterminal

71. coterminal
72. coterminal
73. not coterminal
74. not coterminal

75. coterminal
76. coterminal
77. coterminal
78. coterminal

79. 24,000 mi
80. 25,000 mi

81. The 7.5° angle and θ have a common side. (An extended vertical pole in Alexandria will pass through the center of the earth.) The sun's rays are essentially parallel when they arrive at the earth. Thus, the other two sides of the angles are parallel, since a sun ray to the bottom of the well, when extended, will pass through the center of the earth. From geometry we know that the alternate interior angles made by a line intersecting two parallel lines are equal. Therefore, θ = 7.5°.

82. Since the circumference of the earth is given by $C = 2\pi r$, if C is known, then r can be found by using $r = C/2\pi$. Once the radius is known, the surface area and volume can be found using the formulas $S = 4\pi r^2$ and $V = 4\pi r^3/3$, respectively.

83. $\frac{7\pi}{4}$ radians
84. $\frac{3\pi}{4}$
85. 200 radians
86. 16 rad

87. $\frac{\pi}{26} \approx 0.12$ rad
88. $\frac{3\pi}{4}$ rad ≈ 2.36 rad
89. 12
90. $\theta = 10$ rad

91. 865,000 mi
92. 3,500 km
93. 33 ft
94. 70 ft

Exercise 5-4

1. $\sin \theta = \frac{4}{5}$, csc $\theta = \frac{5}{4}$, cos $\theta = \frac{3}{5}$, sec $\theta = \frac{5}{3}$, tan $\theta = \frac{4}{3}$, cot $\theta = \frac{3}{4}$

2. $\sin \theta = \frac{4}{5}$, cos $\theta = -\frac{3}{5}$, tan $\theta = -\frac{4}{3}$, csc $\theta = \frac{5}{4}$, sec $\theta = -\frac{5}{3}$, cot $\theta = -\frac{3}{4}$

3. $\sin \theta = \frac{\sqrt{3}}{2}$, csc $\theta = \frac{2}{\sqrt{3}}$, cos $\theta = -\frac{1}{2}$, sec $\theta = -2$, tan $\theta = -\sqrt{3}$, cot $\theta = -\frac{1}{\sqrt{3}}$

4. $\sin \theta = \frac{1}{2}$, cos $\theta = \frac{\sqrt{3}}{2}$, tan $\theta = \frac{1}{\sqrt{3}}$, csc $\theta = 2$, sec $\theta = \frac{2}{\sqrt{3}}$, cot $\theta = \sqrt{3}$

5. 0.4226
6. 57.29
7. -1.573
8. 2.380

9. 0.8439 **10.** 2.465 **11.** -0.3363 **12.** -2.601

13. 0.9174 **14.** -0.5705 **15.** 0 **16.** 1

17. $\sqrt{3}$ **18.** $\dfrac{\sqrt{3}}{2}$ **19.** $\dfrac{1}{\sqrt{2}}$ **20.** $\dfrac{2}{\sqrt{3}}$

21. $\sqrt{2}$ **22.** 1 **23.** Not defined **24.** 0

25. Not defined **26.** 1 **27.** 60° **28.** $\alpha = 45°$

29. $\dfrac{\pi}{6}$ **30.** $\alpha = \dfrac{\pi}{4}$ **31.** $\dfrac{\pi}{3}$ **32.** $\alpha = \dfrac{\pi}{4}$

33. $-\dfrac{1}{2}$ **34.** $\dfrac{1}{2}$ **35.** 0 **36.** 1

37. $-\dfrac{1}{\sqrt{3}}$ **38.** $\dfrac{2}{\sqrt{3}}$ **39.** $\dfrac{\sqrt{3}}{2}$ **40.** -1

41. $\dfrac{1}{\sqrt{2}}$ **42.** $-\dfrac{1}{2}$ **43.** 2 **44.** 1

45. $-\sqrt{3}$ **46.** $\dfrac{2}{\sqrt{3}}$ **47.** $-\dfrac{\sqrt{3}}{2}$ **48.** $-\dfrac{1}{\sqrt{3}}$

49. Defined for all θ, since cos $\theta = a/r$ and r is never zero.

50. 90° and 270°, since sec $\theta = r/a$ and $a = 0$ at $\theta = 90°$ and 270°.

51. 90° and 270°, since tan $\theta = b/a$ and $a = 0$ at $\theta = 90°$, 270°.

52. 0° and 180°, since cot $\theta = a/b$ and $b = 0$ at $\theta = 0°$ and 180°.

53. 0° and 180°, since csc $\theta = r/b$ and $b = 0$ at $\theta = 0°$ and 180°.

54. Defined for all θ, since sin $\theta = b/r$ and r is never zero.

55. 120° or $\dfrac{2\pi}{3}$ radians **56.** 240° or $\dfrac{4\pi}{3}$ radians

57. 210° or $\dfrac{7\pi}{6}$ radians **58.** 120° or $\dfrac{2\pi}{3}$ radians

59. 240° or $\dfrac{4\pi}{3}$ radians **60.** 135° or $\dfrac{3\pi}{4}$ radians

61. cos $\theta = -\dfrac{4}{5}$, tan $\theta = -\dfrac{3}{4}$, sec $\theta = -\dfrac{5}{4}$, cot $\theta = -\dfrac{4}{3}$, csc $\theta = \dfrac{5}{3}$

62. tan $\theta = -\dfrac{4}{3}$, sin $\theta = -\dfrac{4}{5}$, cos $\theta = \dfrac{3}{5}$, cot $\theta = -\dfrac{3}{4}$, csc $\theta = -\dfrac{5}{4}$, sec $\theta = \dfrac{5}{3}$

63. sin $\theta = -\dfrac{2}{3}$, sec $\theta = -\dfrac{3}{\sqrt{5}}$, tan $\theta = \dfrac{2}{\sqrt{5}}$, cot $\theta = \dfrac{\sqrt{5}}{2}$, csc $\theta = -\dfrac{3}{2}$

64. cos $\theta = -\dfrac{\sqrt{5}}{3}$, sin $\theta = -\dfrac{2}{3}$, tan $\theta = \dfrac{2}{\sqrt{5}}$, sec $\theta = -\dfrac{3}{\sqrt{5}}$, csc $\theta = -\dfrac{3}{2}$, cot $\theta = \dfrac{\sqrt{5}}{2}$

65. In these situations $P(a, b)$ is restricted so that $a = 0$. In this case, functions for which a is in the denominator are not defined. These functions are tangent and secant.

66. When the terminal side of an angle lies along the horizontal axis, $y = 0$ which implies csc $\theta = \frac{r}{b}$ and cot $\theta = \frac{a}{b}$ are not defined.

67. 150°, 210° **68.** 120°, 300° **69.** $\frac{\pi}{4}$, $\frac{5\pi}{4}$ **70.** $\frac{3\pi}{4}$, $\frac{5\pi}{4}$

71. (A) 1.75 radians (B) (−0.713, 3.936) **72.** (A) 4 radians (B) (−1.307, −1.514)

73. 2π units **74.** $s = \frac{4\pi}{3}$

75. k, 0.866k, 0.5k **76.** 0.93969k, 0.642787k, 0

78. 3.33

79. (A) 3.31371, 3.14263, 3.14160, 3.14159 (B) π = 3.1415926…

80. (A) 2.82843, 3.13953, 3.14157, 3.14159 (B) π = 3.1415926…

81. (A) 44.07; −0.32 (B) $y = -0.93x + 1.28$

82. (A) 0.09; −23.86 (B) $y = -3.49x + 16.94$

Exercise 5-5

1. b/c **2.** $\frac{a}{b}$ **3.** c/b **4.** $\frac{a}{c}$

5. b/a **6.** $\frac{c}{a}$ **7.** cos θ **8.** tan θ

9. sec θ **10.** sin θ **11.** cot θ **12.** csc θ

13. 60.55° **14.** θ = 4.93° **15.** 82.90° **16.** 59.36°

17. 37.09° **18.** θ = 63.35°

19. α = 72.2°, a = 3.28, b = 1.05 **20.** α = 56.30°, $a \approx$ 33.6, $c \approx$ 40.4

21. α = 46°40', b = 116, c = 169 **22.** α = 27°30', $a \approx$ 19.6, $b \approx$ 37.7

23. β = 67°0', b = 127, c = 138 **24.** β = 36°, $a \approx$ 3.5, $b \approx$ 2.5

25. β = 36.79°, a = 31.85, c = 39.77 **26.** β = 54.27°, $a \approx$ 4.663, $c \approx$ 7.985

27. β = 54.7° or 54°40', α = 35°20', c = 10.4

28. c = 51.2, β = 64°30', α = 25°30'

29. β = 52.5° or 52°30', α = 37°30', a = 7.67

30. $a \approx$ 157, α = 72°20', β = 17°40'

31. (A) cos θ = $OA/1$ = OA (B) Angle OED = θ; cot θ = $DE/1$ = DE
(C) sec θ = $OC/1$ = OC

32. (A) sin θ = $AD/1$ = AD (B) tan θ = $DC/1$ = DC
(C) csc θ = csc $\angle OED$ = $OE/1$ = OE

33. (A) As θ approaches 90°, OA = cos θ approaches 0.
(B) As θ approaches 90°, DE = cot θ approaches 0.
(C) As θ approaches 90°, OC = sec θ increases without bound.

34. (A) As $\theta \to$ 90°, sin $\theta \to$ 1 (B) As $\theta \to$ 90°, tan $\theta \to \infty$ (increases without bound)
(C) As $\theta \to$ 90°, csc $\theta \to$ 1

35. (A) As θ approaches 0°, AD = sin θ approaches 0.
(B) As θ approaches 0°, CD = tan θ approaches 0.
(C) As θ approaches 0°, OE = csc θ increases without bound.

36. (A) As $\theta \to 0°$, $\cos \theta \to 1$ (B) As $\theta \to 0°$, $\cot \theta \to \infty$ (increases without bound)
(C) As $\theta \to 0°$, $\sec \theta \to 1$

39. 228 ft   **40.** 315 m   **41.** 127.5 ft   **42.** 6 min

43. 2,225 mi   **44.** 870,000 mi   **45.** 44°   **46.** 2.78 in

47. 9.8 m/sec^2 **48.** 32.3 ft/sec^2

49. (B)

θ	$C(\theta)$
10°	$368,222
20°	$363,435
30°	$360,622
40°	$360,146
50°	$363,050

50. (B)

θ	$C(\theta) = 120{,}000 \sec \theta - 80{,}000 \tan \theta + 400{,}000$
10°	$507,745
20°	$498,584
30°	$492,376
40°	$489,521
50°	$491,347

51. 0.77 m   **52.** 1.2 in

Exercise 5-6

1. 2π, π, 2π **2.** 2π, π, 2π

3. (A) 1 unit   (B) Indefinitely far   (C) Indefinitely far

4. (A) 1 unit   (B) Indefinitely far   (C) Indefinitely far

5. (A) -2π, $-\pi$, 0, π, 2π (B) $-3\pi/2$, $-\pi/2$, $\pi/2$, $3\pi/2$ (C) No x intercepts

6. (A) $-3\pi/2$, $-\pi/2$, $\pi/2$, $3\pi/2$ (B) -2π, $-\pi$, 0, π, 2π (C) No x intercepts

7. (A) None   (B) $-3\pi/2$, $-\pi/2$, $\pi/2$, $3\pi/2$ (C) -2π, $-\pi$, 0, π, 2π

8. (A) None   (B) -2π, $-\pi$, 0, π, 2π (C) $-3\pi/2$, $-\pi/2$, $\pi/2$, $3\pi/2$

9. (A) No vertical asymptotes   (B) $-3\pi/2$, $-\pi/2$, $\pi/2$, $3\pi/2$ (C) -2π, $-\pi$, 0, π, 2π

10. (A) No vertical asymptotes   (B) -2π, $-\pi$, 0, π, 2π (C) $-3\pi/2$, $-\pi/2$, $\pi/2$, $3\pi/2$

11. (A) $y = \cos x$ (B) $y = \tan x$ (C) $y = \csc x$

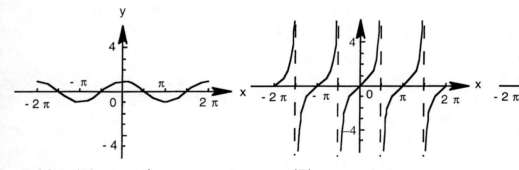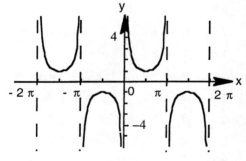

12. (A) $y = \sin x$ (B) $y = \cot x$ (C) $y = \sec x$

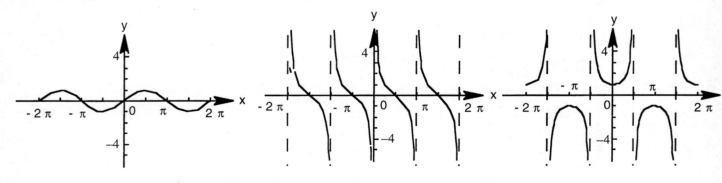

13. (A) A shift of $\pi/2$ to the left will transform the cosecant graph into the secant graph. [The answer is not unique—see part (B).] (B) The graph of $y = -\csc(x - \pi/2)$ is a $\pi/2$ shift to the right and a reflection in the x axis of the graph of $y = \csc x$. The result is the graph of $y = \sec x$.

14. (A) A shift of $\pi/2$ to the right will transform the secant graph into the cosecant graph. [The answer is not unique—see part (B).]

(B) The graph of $y = -\sec(x + \pi/2)$ is a $\pi/2$ shift to the left and a reflection in the x axis of the graph of $y = \sec x$. The result is the graph of $y = \csc x$.

15. (A)

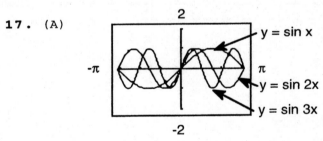

(B) No

(C) 1 unit; 2 units; 3 units

(D) The deviation of the graph from the x axis is changed by changing A. The deviation appears to be $|A|$.

16. (A)

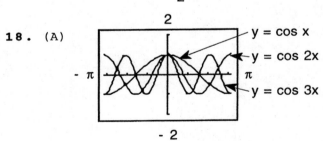

(B) No

(C) 1 unit; 3 units; 2 units

(D) The deviation of the graph from the x axis is changed by changing A. The deviation appears to be $|A|$.

17. (A)

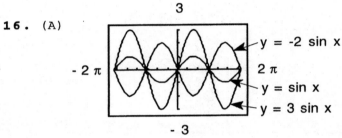

(B) 1; 2; 3

(C) n

18. (A)

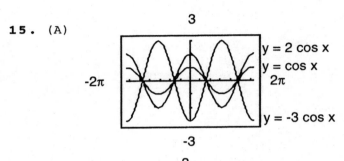

(B) 1; 2; 3

(C) n

19. (A)

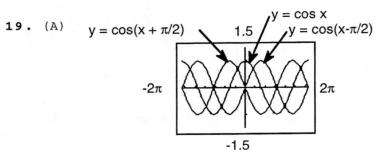

$y = \cos x$
$y = \cos(x + \pi/2)$ 1.5 $y = \cos(x - \pi/2)$
-2π 2π
-1.5

(B) The graph of $y = \cos x$ is shifted $|C|$ units to the right if $C < 0$ and $|C|$ units to the left if $C > 0$.

20. (A) $y = \sin(x + \pi/2)$ 1.5 $y = \sin x$ $y = \sin(x - \pi/2)$
-2π 2π
-1.5

(B) The graph of $y = \sin(x + C)$ is shifted C units to the left for $C > 0$ and $|C|$ units to the right for $C < 0$.

21. For each case, the number is not in the domain of the function and an error message of some type will appear.

22. In all three cases the calculator gives a division by zero error.
(A) $\csc \pi = \dfrac{1}{\sin \pi} = \dfrac{1}{0}$ (B) $\tan \dfrac{\pi}{2} = \dfrac{1}{0}$ (C) $\cot 0 = \dfrac{1}{0}$

23. (A) Both graphs are almost indistinguishable the closer x is to the origin.

(B)

x	−0.3	−0.2	−0.1	0.0	0.1	0.2	0.3
$\sin x$	−0.296	−0.199	−0.100	0.000	0.100	0.199	0.296

24.

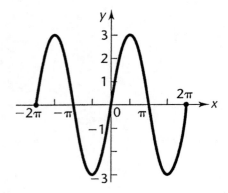

X	Y₁	Y₂
-.3	-.3093	-.3
-.2	-.2027	-.2
-.1	-.1003	-.1
0	0	0
.1	.10033	.1
.2	.20271	.2
.3	.30934	.3

X= -.3

For x close to zero the two graphs are almost identical.

Exercise 5-7

1. $A = 3$, $P = 2\pi$

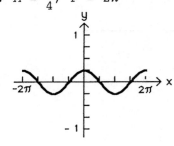

2. $A = \dfrac{1}{4}$, $P = 2\pi$

3. $|A| = \frac{1}{2}$, $P = 2\pi$

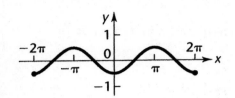

4. $A = 2$, $P = 2\pi$

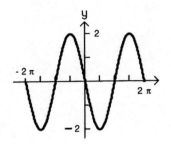

5. $A = 1$, $P = \frac{2\pi}{3}$

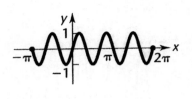

6. $y = \cos 2x$, $-\pi \le x \le \pi$
Amplitude = 1
Period = $\frac{2\pi}{2} = \pi$

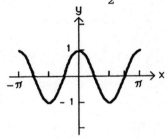

7. $A = 1$, $P = 2\pi \div \left(\frac{1}{2}\right) = 4\pi$

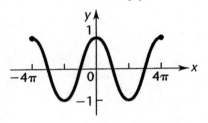

8. $y = \sin\left(\frac{x}{3}\right)$, $-6\pi \le x \le 6\pi$

Amplitude = 1; Period = $\frac{2\pi}{\frac{1}{3}} = 6\pi$

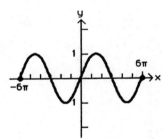

9. $A = 1$, $P = \frac{2\pi}{\pi} = 2$

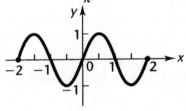

10. $y = \cos(\pi x)$, $-2 \le x \le 2$
Amplitude = 1
Period = $\frac{2\pi}{\pi} = 2$

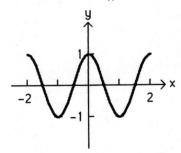

11. $A = 3$, $P = \frac{2\pi}{2} = \pi$

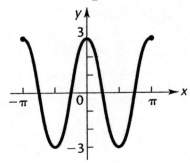

12. $y = 2 \sin 4x$, $-\pi \leq x \leq \pi$

Amplitude $= 2$

Period $= \dfrac{2\pi}{4} = \dfrac{\pi}{2}$

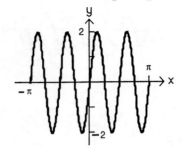

13. $A = \dfrac{1}{2}$, $P = \dfrac{2\pi}{2\pi} = 1$

The graph of $-\dfrac{1}{2} \sin 2\pi x$ is the graph of $\dfrac{1}{2} \sin 2\pi x$ turned upside down.

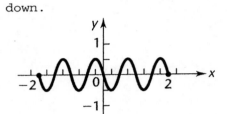

14. $y = -\dfrac{1}{3} \cos 2\pi x$, $-2 \leq x \leq 2$

Amplitude $= \dfrac{1}{3}$

Period $= \dfrac{2\pi}{2\pi} = 1$

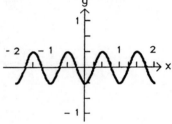

15. $A = 3$, $P = 2\pi \div \left(\dfrac{1}{2}\right) = 4\pi$

The graph of $-3 \cos \dfrac{x}{2}$ is the graph of $3 \cos \dfrac{x}{2}$ turned upside down.

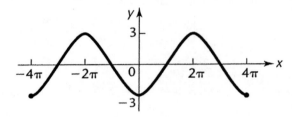

16. $y = -\dfrac{1}{4} \sin \left(\dfrac{x}{2}\right)$, $-4\pi \leq x \leq 4\pi$

Amplitude $= \dfrac{1}{4}$

Period $= \dfrac{2\pi}{\frac{1}{2}} = 4\pi$

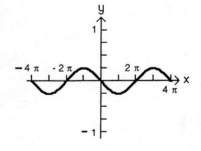

17. The graph is the same as the graph of $y = 2 \sin \dfrac{\pi x}{2}$ shifted 2 units up.

$A = 2$, $P = 4$

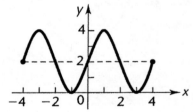

18. $y = 3 + 3\cos\left(\dfrac{\pi x}{2}\right),\ -4 \le x \le 4$

Amplitude = 3

Period = $\dfrac{2\pi}{\frac{\pi}{2}} = 4$

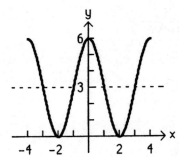

19. The graph is the same as the graph of $y = 2\cos\dfrac{x}{2}$, turned upside down and shifted up 4 units.

$A = 2,\ P = 2\pi \div \dfrac{1}{2} = 4\pi$

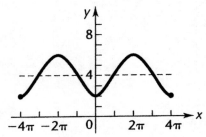

20. $y = 3 - 2\sin\left(\dfrac{x}{2}\right),\ -4\pi \le x \le 4\pi$

Amplitude = 2

Period = $\dfrac{2\pi}{\frac{1}{2}} = 4\pi$

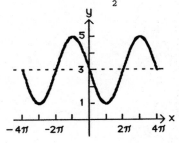

21. $A = 3,\ P = \dfrac{\pi}{2} = \dfrac{2\pi}{4};\ B = 4,\ y = 3\sin 4x,\ -\dfrac{\pi}{4} \le x \le \dfrac{\pi}{2}$

22. Amplitude = $\dfrac{1}{4}$ and period = $8\pi \Rightarrow y = \dfrac{1}{4}\sin\left(\dfrac{x}{4}\right),\ -4\pi \le x \le 8\pi$

23. $|A| = 10,\ P = 2 = \dfrac{2\pi}{\pi};\ B = \pi,\ A = -10,\ y = -10\sin \pi x\quad -1 \le x \le 2$

24. Amplitude = $\dfrac{1}{2}$ and period = $4 \Rightarrow y = -\dfrac{1}{2}\sin\left(\dfrac{\pi x}{2}\right),\ -2 \le x \le 4$

25. $A = 5,\ P = 8\pi = 2\pi \cdot 4 = 2\pi \div \dfrac{1}{4};\ B = \dfrac{1}{4},\ y = 5\cos\dfrac{1}{4}x\quad -4\pi \le x \le 8\pi$

26. Amplitude = 0.1 and period = $\dfrac{\pi}{4} \Rightarrow y = 0.1\cos 8x,\ -\dfrac{\pi}{8} \le x \le \dfrac{\pi}{4}$

27. $|A| = 0.5,\ P = 8 = 2\pi \cdot \dfrac{4}{\pi} = 2\pi \div \dfrac{\pi}{4};\ B = \dfrac{\pi}{4},\ A = -0.5,\ y = -0.5\cos\dfrac{\pi x}{4},\ -4 \le x \le 8$

28. Amplitude = 1 and period = $\dfrac{1}{2} \Rightarrow y = -\cos(4\pi x),\ -0.25 \le x \le 0.5$

29. $y = \cos 2x$ **30.** $y = \frac{1}{2} \sin 2x$ **31.** $y = 1 - \cos 2x$ **32.** $y = 1 + \cos 2x$

33. $A = 1$, $P = 2\pi$, Phase shift $= -\pi$

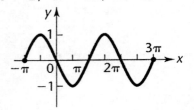

34. $A = 1$, $P = 2\pi$, Phase shift $= \pi$

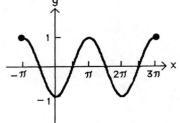

35. $A = \frac{1}{2}$, $P = 2\pi$, Phase shift $= \frac{\pi}{4}$

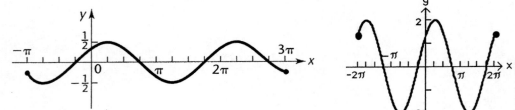

36. $A = 2$, $P = 2\pi$, Phase Shift $= -\frac{\pi}{4}$

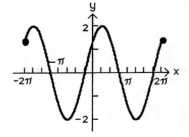

37. $A = 1$, $P = 2$, Phase shift $= 1$

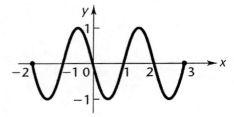

38. $A = 1$, $P = 1$, Phase shift $= \frac{1}{2}$

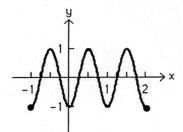

39. $A = 3$, $P = 2$, Phase shift $= -\frac{1}{2}$

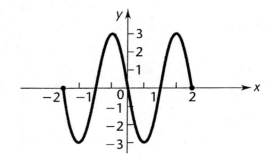

40. $A = 2$, $P = 2$, Phase shift $= \frac{1}{4}$

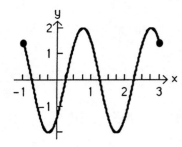

41. $A = 4$, $P = \pi$, Phase shift $= \dfrac{\pi}{2}$

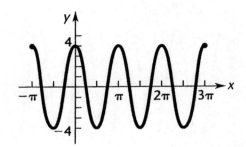

42. $A = 2$, $P = \dfrac{\pi}{2}$, Phase shift $= -\dfrac{\pi}{4}$

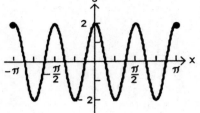

43.

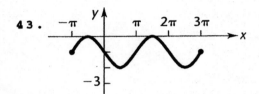

44.

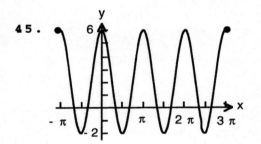

45.

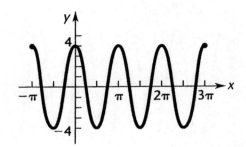

46.

47. $y = -4 \sin\left(\dfrac{\pi}{2}x - \dfrac{\pi}{2}\right)$

48. $y = 4 \sin\left(\dfrac{\pi}{2}x + \dfrac{\pi}{2}\right)$

49. $y = \dfrac{1}{2}\cos\left(\dfrac{1}{4}x - \dfrac{3\pi}{4}\right)$

50. $y = -\dfrac{1}{2}\cos\left(\dfrac{x}{4} + \dfrac{\pi}{4}\right)$

51. $A = 3.5$, $P = 4$, Phase shift $= -0.5$

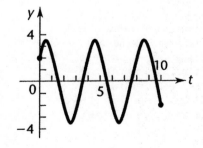

52. $A = 5.4$, $P = 5$, Phase shift $= 1$

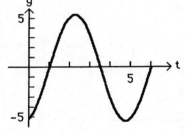

53. $A = 50$, $P = 1$, Phase shift = 0.25

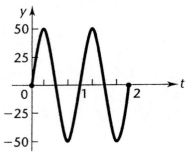

54. $A = 25$, $P = \dfrac{2}{5}$, Phase shift = 0.1

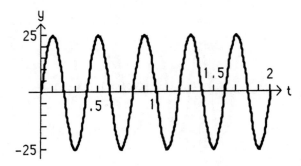

55. $y = 2 \sin(x + 0.785)$

56. $y = 2 \sin(x - \pi/4)$

57. $y = 2 \sin(x - 0.524)$

58. $y = 2 \sin(x + \pi/3)$

59. $y = 5 \sin(2x - 0.284)$

60. $y = 5 \sin(2x + 1.288)$

61.

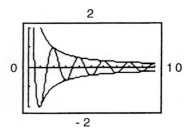

The amplitude is decreasing with time. This is often referred to as a *damped sine wave*. Examples are the vertical motion of a car after going over a bump (which is damped by the suspension system) and the slowing down of a pendulum that is released away from the vertical line of suspension (air resistance and friction).

62.

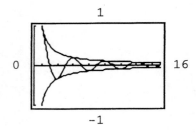

The amplitude is decreasing with time. This is often referred to as a **damped sine wave**. Examples are a car's vertical motion, which is damped by the suspension system after the car goes over a bump, and the slowing down of a pendulum that is released away from the vertical line of suspension (air resistance and friction).

63.

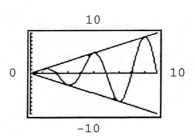

The amplitude is increasing with time. In physical and electrical systems this is referred to as *resonance*. Some examples are the swinging of a bridge during high winds and the movement of tall buildings during an earthquake. Some bridges and buildings are destroyed when the resonance reaches the elastic limits of the structure.

64.

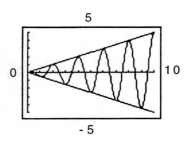

The amplitude is increasing with time. In physical and electrical systems this is referred to as **resonance**. Some examples are the swinging of a bridge during high winds and the movement of tall buildings during an earthquake. Some bridges and buildings are destroyed when the resonance reaches the elastic limits of the structure.

65.

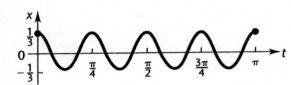

66.

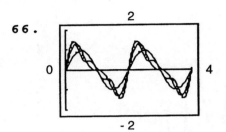

67. $A = \dfrac{1}{3}$

$P = \dfrac{2\pi}{8} = \dfrac{\pi}{4}$

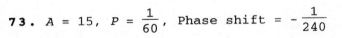

68. $I = 30 \sin 120t$

$A = 30$, $P = \dfrac{2\pi}{120} = \dfrac{\pi}{60}$, $f = \dfrac{60}{\pi}$ Hz

69. $y = -8 \cos 4\pi t$

70. $A = 110$, $P = \dfrac{1}{60} = \dfrac{2\pi}{B} \Rightarrow B = 120\pi$

$E = 110 \cos(120\pi t)$

71. The graph shows the seasonal changes of sulfur dioxide pollutant in the atmosphere; more is produced during winter months because of increased heating.

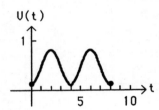

72. The graph shows the volume of air in the lungs t seconds after exhaling.

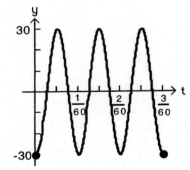

73. $A = 15$, $P = \dfrac{1}{60}$, Phase shift $= -\dfrac{1}{240}$

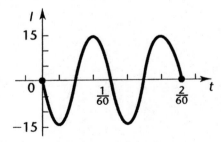

74. $A = 30$, $P = \dfrac{1}{60}$, Phase shift $= \dfrac{1}{120}$

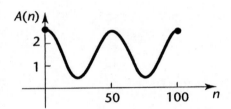

75.

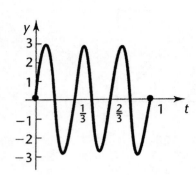

76.

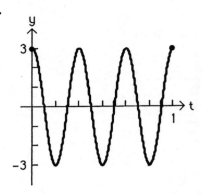

77. (A)

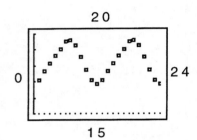

(B) $y = 18.22 + 1.37 \sin(\frac{\pi x}{6} - 1.75)$

(C)

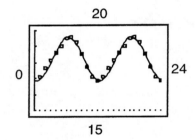

78. (A)

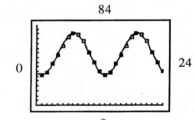

(B) $y = 53.5 + 22.5 \sin(\pi x/6 - 2.1)$

(C)   (D)

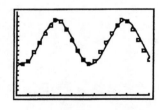

Exercise 5-8

1.

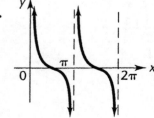

2.

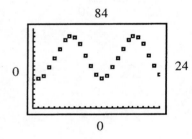

3.

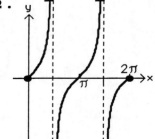

4.

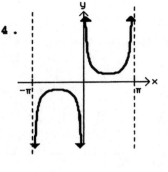

5. Period = $\dfrac{\pi}{4}$

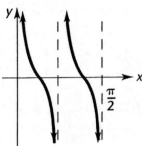

6. Period = $\dfrac{\pi}{2}$

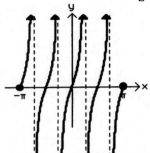

7. Period = $\dfrac{1}{8}$

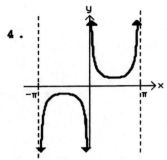

8. Period = $\dfrac{1}{2}$

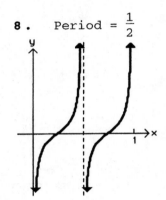

9. Period = 4π

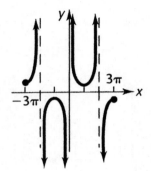

10. Period = 2

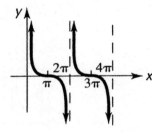

11. Period = 2π

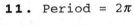

12. Period = 2π

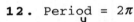

13. Period = 2

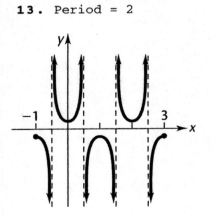

14. Period = 4π

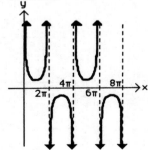

15. Period = π, Phase shift = $-\dfrac{\pi}{2}$

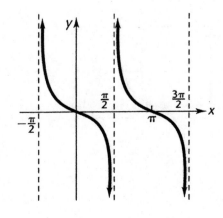

16. Period = π,
  Phase shift = $\dfrac{\pi}{2}$

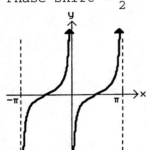

17. Period = $\dfrac{\pi}{2}$,
  Phase shift = $-\dfrac{\pi}{2}$

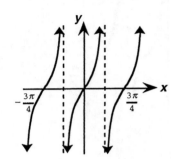

18. Period = $\dfrac{\pi}{2}$,
  Phase shift = $\dfrac{\pi}{2}$

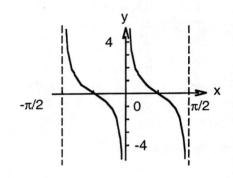

19. Period = 2, Phase shift = $-\dfrac{1}{2}$

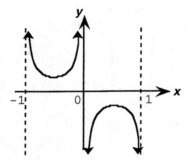

20. Period = 2, Phase shift = $\dfrac{1}{2}$

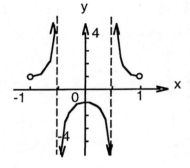

21. $y = 2 \cot 2x$

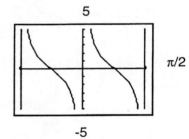

22. $y = 2 \csc 2x$

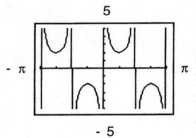

23. $y = \cot(x/2)$

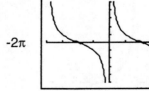

24. $y = \tan(x/2)$

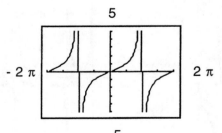

25. Period = 4π, Phase shift = π

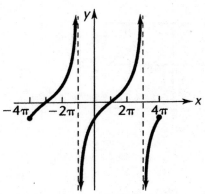

26. Period = $\dfrac{\pi}{2}$, Phase shift = $-\dfrac{\pi}{2}$

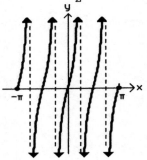

27. Period = 4, Phase shift = 1

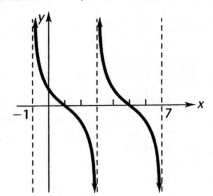

28. Period = 1, Phase shift = 1

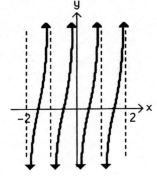

29. Period = 4, Phase shift = -1

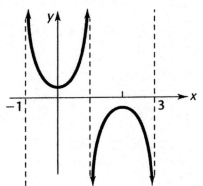

30. Period = 2, Phase shift = $\dfrac{1}{2}$

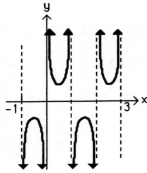

31. $y = \csc 3x$

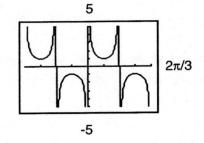

32. $y = \sec 2x$

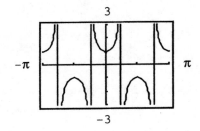

33. $y = \tan 2x$

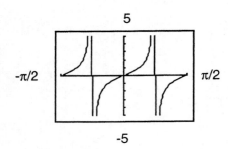

34. $y = \cot 3x$

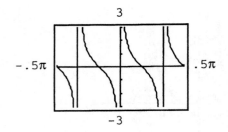

35. (A) $c = 20 \sec(\pi t/2)$, $[0, 1)$
(B)

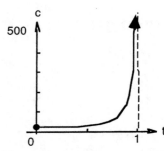

(C) The length of the light beam starts at 20 ft and increases slowly at first, then increases rapidly without end.

36. (A) $a = 20 \tan(\pi t/2)$, $[0, 1)$
(B)

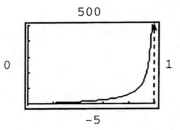

(C) Initially the distance from N is zero. The distance increases slowly at first, then begins to increase rapidly without end.

Exercise 5-9

1. $\dfrac{\pi}{2}$ **2.** 0 **3.** $\dfrac{\pi}{3}$ **4.** $\dfrac{\pi}{6}$ **5.** $\dfrac{\pi}{3}$ **6.** $\dfrac{\pi}{4}$ **7.** $\dfrac{\pi}{4}$

8. $\dfrac{\pi}{3}$ **9.** 0 **10.** $\dfrac{\pi}{6}$ **11.** $\dfrac{\pi}{6}$ **12.** 0 **13.** 1.144 **14.** 1.155

15. 1.561 **16.** 1.548 **17.** Not defined   **18.** Not defined   **19.** $-\dfrac{\pi}{4}$

20. $\dfrac{2\pi}{3}$ **21.** $-\dfrac{\pi}{3}$ **22.** $-\dfrac{\pi}{4}$ **23.** π **24.** $-\dfrac{\pi}{3}$ **25.** $-\dfrac{\pi}{2}$ **26.** $\dfrac{5\pi}{6}$

27. 25 **28.** -0.6 **29.** 2.3 **30.** -1.5 **31.** $\dfrac{1}{2}$ **32.** $\sqrt{3}$ **33.** $-\sqrt{2}$

34. $\dfrac{\sqrt{2}}{2}$ **35.** -1.472 **36.** -1.328 **37.** -0.9810 **38.** 1.001

39. 2.645 **40.** 2.456 **41.** $-45°$ **42.** $120°$ **43.** $-60°$ **44.** $-45°$

45. $180°$ **46.** $-90°$ **47.** $43.51°$ **48.** $85.40°$ **49.** $-21.48°$

50. $157.01°$ **51.** $-89.93°$ **52.** $-45.00°$

53. $\sin^{-1}(\sin 2) = 1.1416 \neq 2$. For the identity $\sin^{-1}(\sin x) = x$ to hold, x must be in the restricted domain of the sine function; that is, $-\dfrac{\pi}{2} \le x \le \dfrac{\pi}{2}$. The number 2 is not in the restricted domain.

54. $\cos^{-1}[\cos(-0.5)] = 0.5$. For the identity $\cos^{-1}(\cos x) = x$ to hold, x must be in the restricted domain of the cosine function; that is, $0 \le x \le \pi$. The number -0.5 is not in the restricted domain.

55.

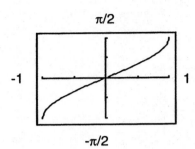

56.

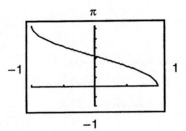

57.

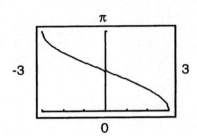

58.

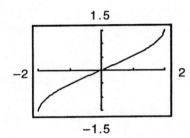

59.

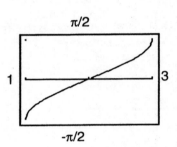

60.

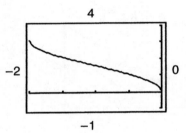

61.

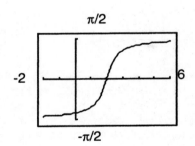

62.

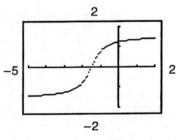

63. (A)

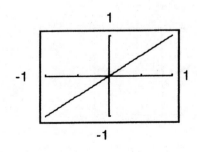

(B) The domain of $\cos^{-1}$ is restricted to $-1 \leq x \leq 1$; hence no graph will appear for other x.

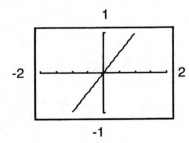

64. (A)

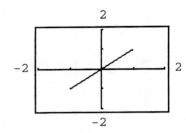

(B) The graph is the same. The domain of the inverse sine is the interval [-1, 1].

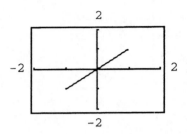

65. $\sqrt{1 - x^2}$ **66.** $\sqrt{1 - x^2}$ **67.** $\dfrac{1}{\sqrt{1 + x^2}}$ **68.** $\dfrac{x}{\sqrt{1 - x^2}}$

69. $f^{-1}(x) = 3 + \cos^{-1}\dfrac{x - 4}{2}$; $2 \le x \le 6$

70. $f^{-1}(x) = 1 + \sin^{-1}\dfrac{x - 3}{5}$; $-2 \le x \le 8$

71. (A)

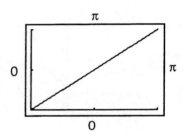

(B) The domain for cos x is $(-\infty, \infty)$ and the range is [-1, 1], which is the domain for $\cos^{-1} x$. Thus, $y = \cos^{-1}(\cos x)$ has a graph over the interval $(-\infty, \infty)$, but $\cos^{-1}(\cos x) = x$ only on the restricted domain of cos x, $[0, \pi]$.

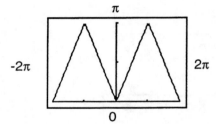

72. (A)

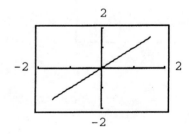

(B) The domain for sin x is $(-\infty, \infty)$ and the range is [-1, 1], which is the domain for $\sin^{-1} x$. Thus, $y = \sin^{-1}(\sin x)$ has a graph over the interval $(-\infty, \infty)$, but $\sin^{-1}(\sin x) = x$ only on the restricted domain of sin x, $[-\pi/2, \pi/2]$.

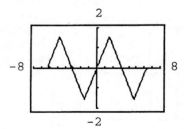

73. 75.38°; 24.41°   **74.** 103.68°; 34.35°

75. (A)

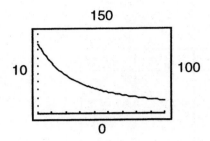

(B) 59.44 mm

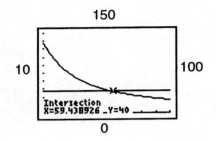

76. (A)

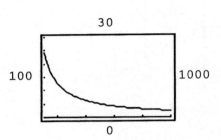

(B)

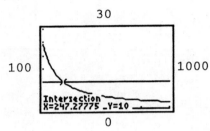

77. 21.59 inches   **78.** 35.81 inches

79. (A)

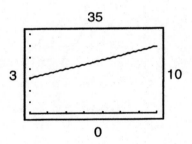

(B) 7.22 inches

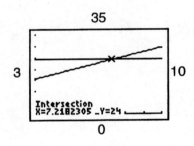

80. (A)

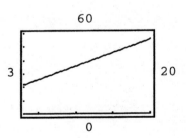

(B) 10.10 inches

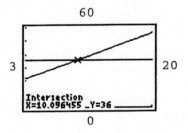

81. (B) 76.10 feet   **82.** 46.36 feet

CHAPTER 5 REVIEW

1. 2.5 radians *(5-3)*

2. 7.5 centimeters *(5-3)*

3. $\alpha = 54.8°$, $a = 16.5$ ft, $b = 11.6$ ft *(5-5)*

4. (A) $\frac{\pi}{3}$ (B) 60° (C) $\frac{\pi}{6}$ (D) 30° *(5-4)*

5. (A) III, IV (B) II, III (C) II, IV *(5-2, 5-4)*

6. $\sin \theta = -\dfrac{3}{5}$, $\sec \theta = \dfrac{5}{4}$, $\cot \theta = -\dfrac{4}{3}$ *(5-4)*

7.

$\theta°$	θ rad	$\sin \theta$	$\cos \theta$	$\tan \theta$	$\csc \theta$	$\sec \theta$	$\cot \theta$
0°	0	0	1	0	ND*	1	ND
30°	$\pi/6$	$1/2$	$\sqrt{3}/2$	$1/\sqrt{3}$	2	$2/\sqrt{3}$	$\sqrt{3}$
45°	$\pi/4$	$1/\sqrt{2}$	$1/\sqrt{2}$	1	$\sqrt{2}$	$\sqrt{2}$	1
60°	$\pi/3$	$\sqrt{3}/2$	$1/2$	$\sqrt{3}$	$2/\sqrt{3}$	2	$1/\sqrt{3}$
90°	$\pi/2$	1	0	ND	1	ND	0
180°	π	0	-1	0	ND	-1	ND
270°	$3\pi/2$	-1	0	ND	-1	ND	0
360°	2π	0	1	0	ND	1	ND

*ND = not defined   *(5-2, 5-4)*

8. (A) 2π (B) 2π (C) π *(5-6)*

9. (A) Domain = $(-\infty, \infty)$, range = $[-1, 1]$

(B) Domain is set of all real numbers except $x = \dfrac{2k + 1}{2}\pi$, k an integer, Range = all real numbers *(5-6)*

10.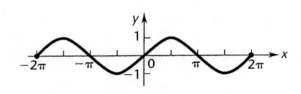
(5-6)

11.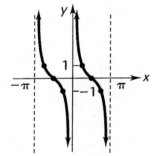
(5-6)

12. The central angle in a circle subtended by an arc of half the length of the radius. *(5-3)*

13. If the graph of $y = \sin x$ is shifted $\dfrac{\pi}{2}$ units to the left, the result will be the graph of $y = \cos x$. *(5-6, 5-7)*

14. 78.50° *(5-3)*

15. $\alpha = 49.7°$; $\beta = 40.3°$; $c = 20.6$ cm *(5-5)*

16. (A) II (B) Quadrantal (C) III *(5-3)*

17. (A) and (C) *(5-3)*   **18.** (B) and (C) *(5-4)*

19. (A) $\dfrac{\pi}{2}$, $\dfrac{3\pi}{2}$ (B) 0, π (C) 0, π *(5-3, 5-4)*

20. Since the coordinates of a point on a unit circle are given by $P(a, b) = P(\cos x, \sin x)$, we evaluate $P(\cos(-8.305), \sin(-8.305))$--using a calculator set in radian mode--to obtain $P(-0.436, -0.900)$. Note that $x = -8.305$, since P is moving clockwise. The quadrant in which $P(a, b)$ lies can be determined by the signs of a and b. In this case P is in the third quadrant, since a is negative and b is negative. *(5-1, 5-2)*

21. 0 *(5-2, 5-4)*   **22.** Not defined *(5-2, 5-4)*   **23.** 0 *(5-2, 5-9)*

24. $-\dfrac{1}{\sqrt{2}}$ or $-\dfrac{\sqrt{2}}{2}$ *(5-2, 5-4)* **25.** $\dfrac{\pi}{4}$ *(5-2, 5-9)* **26.** $-\dfrac{2}{\sqrt{3}}$ or $\dfrac{-2\sqrt{3}}{3}$ *(5-2, 5-4)*

27. $\frac{\pi}{3}$ *(5-2, 5-9)*   **28.** $-\frac{1}{2}$ *(5-2, 5-4)*   **29.** $-\frac{\pi}{4}$ *(5-2, 5-9)*

30. $-\frac{1}{\sqrt{3}}$ or $-\frac{\sqrt{3}}{3}$ *(5-2, 5-4)*   **31.** $-\frac{\pi}{6}$ *(5-2, 5-9)*   **32.** $\frac{5\pi}{6}$ *(5-2, 5-9)*

33. 0.33   *(5-2, 5-9)*   **34.** $-\sqrt{2}$ *(5-2, 5-9)*   **35.** $\frac{\sqrt{3}}{2}$ *(5-2, 5-9)*

36. $-\frac{4}{3}$ *(5-2, 5-9)*   **37.** 0.4431   *(5-4)*   **38.** -15.17   *(5-4)*

39. -2.077   *(5-2)*   **40.** -0.9750   *(5-5, 5-9)*   **41.** Not defined   *(5-5, 5-9)*

42. 1.557   *(5-5, 5-9)*   **43.** 1.095   *(5-9)*   **44.** Not defined   *(5-9)*

45. (A) $\theta = -30°$ (B) $\theta = 120°$ *(5-9)*

46. (A) $\Theta = 151.20°$ (B) $\Theta = 82.28°$ *(5-9)*

47. $\cos^{-1}[\cos(-2)] = 2$. For the identity $\cos^{-1}(\cos x) = x$ to hold, x must be in the restricted domain of the cosine function; that is, $0 \le x \le \pi$. The number -2 is not in the restricted domain.   *(5-9)*

48. $A = 2$, $P = 2$

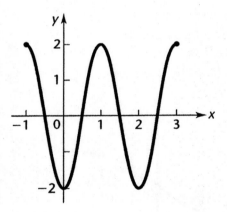

(5-7)

49.

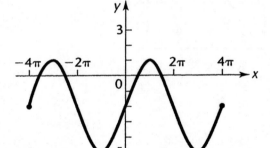

(5-7)

50. $y = 6 \cos 2x$; $-\frac{\pi}{2} \le x \le \pi$ *(5-7)*   **51.** $y = -0.5 \sin \pi x$; $-1 \le x \le 2$ *(5-7)*

52. If the graph of $y = \tan x$ is shifted $\frac{\pi}{2}$ units to the right and reflected in the x axis, the result will be the graph of $y = \cot x$.   *(5-6, 5-7)*

53. (A) $\cos x$ (B) $\tan^2 x$ *(5-2)*

54.

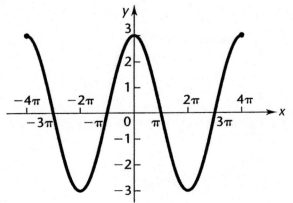

(5-7)

55. $A = 2$, $P = 4$,
Phase shift $= \frac{1}{2}$ *(5-7)*

56. Domain = [-1, 1]

Range = [0, π]

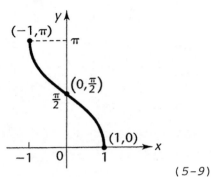

(5-9)

57. $y = \frac{1}{2} \cos 2x + \frac{1}{2}$

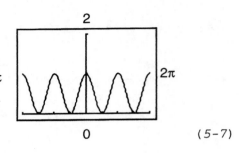

(5-7)

58. (A) $y = \tan x$

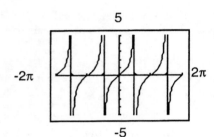

(B) $y = \cot x$

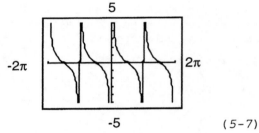

(5-7)

59. (A) 2.5 rad   (B) (-6.41, 4.79)   (5-1, 5-3)

60. (A) $\frac{2\pi}{3}$ (B) $\frac{5\pi}{4}$ (5-2)

61.

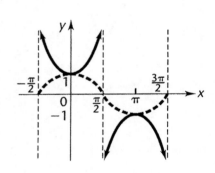

(5-6)

62.

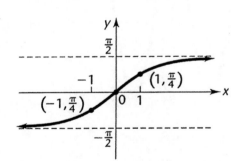

Domain = all real numbers

Range = $\left(-\frac{\pi}{2}, \frac{\pi}{2}\right)$ (5-9)

63. Phase Shift = $-\frac{1}{2}$; Period $P = 1$ (5-8)   **64.** Phase shift = $\frac{\pi}{2}$; Period = 4π (5-8)

65. (A) sine has origin symmetry   (B) cosine has y axis symmetry
(C) tangent has origin symmetry   (5-6)

66. $\dfrac{1}{\sqrt{1 - x^2}}$ (5-9)

67. For each case, the number is not in the domain of the function and an error message of some type will appear.   (5-2, 5-9)

68. $y = 2 \sin\left(\pi x + \dfrac{\pi}{4}\right)$ (5-7)

69. $y = 2 \sin(2x + 0.928)$

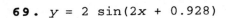
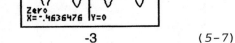
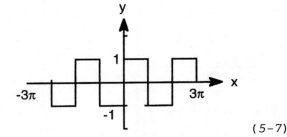

(5-7)

70. (A)

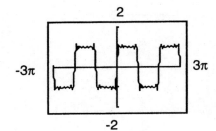

(B)

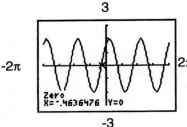

(5-7)

71. $\frac{2\pi}{5}$ radians (5-3)   **72.** 28.3 cm (5-5)   **73.** $I = 30 \cos 120\pi t$ (5-7)

74. (A) $L = 10 \csc \theta + 15 \sec \theta; \ 0 < \theta < \frac{\pi}{2}$

(B)
θ radians	0.4	0.5	0.6	0.7	0.8	0.9	1.0
L feet	42.0	38.0	35.9	35.1	35.5	36.9	39.6

35 feet is the length of the longest log that can make the corner.

(C) Length of longest log that can make the corner is 35.1 feet.

(D) Length L increases without bound.

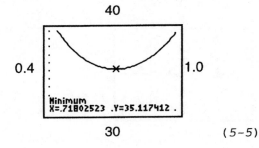

(5-5)

75. (A) $R(t) = 4 - 3 \cos \frac{\pi}{6} t$.

(B) The graph shows the seasonal changes in soft drink consumption. Most is consumed in August and the least in February.   (5-7)

76. (A)

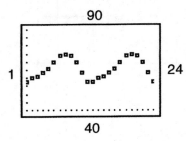

(C)

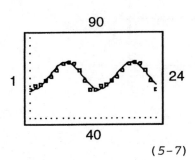

(5-7)

(B) $y = 66.5 + 8.5 \sin\left(\frac{\pi}{6} x - 2.4\right)$

CHAPTER 6

Exercise 6-1

27.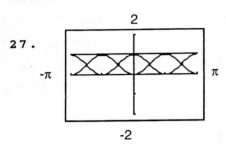

28.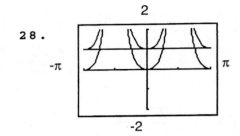

29.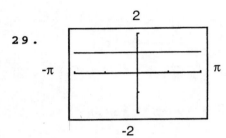

30.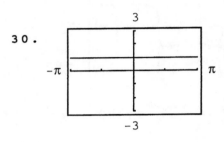

61. Not an identity 62. Not an identity 63. An identity

64. An identity 65. Not an identity 66. Not an identity

67. An identity 68. An identity 69. An identity

70. An identity 71. Not an identity 72. Not an identity

79. $g(x) = \cot x$ 80. $g(x) = \tan x$

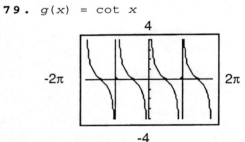 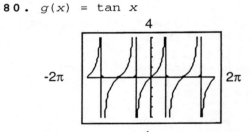

81. $g(x) = -1 + \csc x$ 82. $g(x) = 1 + \sec x$

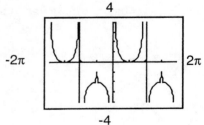 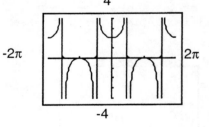

83. $g(x) = 3 \cos x$

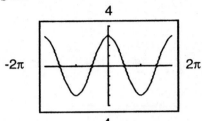

84. $g(x) = 2 \sin x$

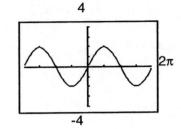

85. III, IV

86. QI or QIV

87. I, II

88. QII or QIII

89. All quadrants

90. QI, II, III, IV

91. I, IV

92. QII, III

93. $a \cos x$

94. $a \sin x$

95. $a \sec x$

96. $a \csc x$

Exercise 6-2

13. $\frac{1}{2}(\cos x - \sqrt{3} \sin x)$

14. $\frac{\sqrt{2}}{2}(\sin x - \cos x)$

15. $\sin x$

16. $-\cos x$

17. $\frac{\tan x + \sqrt{3}}{1 - \sqrt{3} \tan x}$

18. $\frac{1 - \tan x}{1 + \tan x}$

19. $\frac{2\sqrt{2}}{\sqrt{3} - 1}$

20. $\frac{\sqrt{3} + 1}{2\sqrt{2}}$

21. $\frac{\sqrt{3} + 1}{2\sqrt{2}}$

22. $\frac{\sqrt{6} + \sqrt{2}}{4}$

23. $\frac{\sqrt{3}}{2}$

24. $\frac{\sqrt{3}}{2}$

25. 1

26. $\sqrt{3}$

27. $\sin(x - y) = \frac{-3 - 4\sqrt{8}}{15}$; $\tan(x + y) = \frac{4\sqrt{8} - 3}{4 + 3\sqrt{8}}$

28. $\sin(x - y) = \frac{-2 - 5\sqrt{3}}{12}$; $\tan(x + y) = \frac{-2 + 5\sqrt{3}}{\sqrt{5} + 2\sqrt{15}}$

29. $\sin(x - y) = \frac{-2}{\sqrt{5}}$; $\tan(x + y) = \frac{2}{11}$

30. $\sin(x - y) = \frac{-4\sqrt{2} - 1}{3\sqrt{5}}$; $\tan(x + y) = \frac{1 - 4\sqrt{2}}{2 + 2\sqrt{2}}$

44. $\frac{\sin(x + h) - \sin x}{h} = \sin x\left(\frac{\cos h - 1}{h}\right) + \cos x\left(\frac{\sin h}{h}\right)$

45. $-0.3685, -0.3685; 0.9771, 0.9771$

46. $0.6115, 0.6115, -1.155, -1.155$

47. $-0.4429, -0.4429; -2.682, -2.682$

48. $0.9756, 0.9756, -0.4895, -0.4895$

49. Evaluate each side for a particular set of values of x and y for which each side is defined. If the left side is not equal to the right side, then the equation is not an identity. For example, for $x = 2$ and $y = 1$, both sides are defined, but are not equal.

50. Evaluate each side for a particular set of values of x and y for which each side is defined. If the left side is not equal to the right side, then the equation is not an identity. For example, for $x = 2$ and $y = 1$, both sides are defined, but are not equal.

51. $y_1 = \sin(x + \pi/6)$

$y_2 = \dfrac{\sqrt{3}}{2} \sin x + \dfrac{1}{2} \cos x$

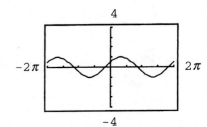

52. $y_1 = \sin(x - \pi/3)$

$y_2 = \dfrac{1}{2} \sin x - \dfrac{\sqrt{3}}{2} \cos x$

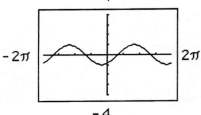

53. $y_1 = \cos(x - 3\pi/4)$

$y_2 = -\dfrac{\sqrt{2}}{2} \cos x + \dfrac{\sqrt{2}}{2} \sin x$

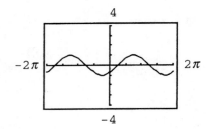

54. $y_1 = \cos(x + 5\pi/6)$

$y_2 = -\dfrac{\sqrt{3}}{2} \cos x - \dfrac{1}{2} \sin x$

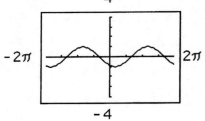

55. $y_1 = \tan(x + 2\pi/3)$

$y_2 = \dfrac{\tan x - \sqrt{3}}{1 + \sqrt{3} \tan x}$

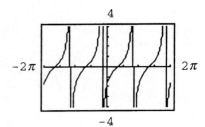

56. $y_1 = \tan(x - \pi/4)$

$y_2 = \dfrac{\tan x - 1}{1 + \tan x}$

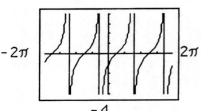

57. $\dfrac{24}{25}$

58. 1

59. $-\dfrac{1}{2}$

60. -1

61. $xy + \sqrt{1 - x^2}\sqrt{1 - y^2}$

62. $y\sqrt{1 - x^2} + x\sqrt{1 - y^2}$

65. $y_1 = \cos 1.2x \cos 0.8x -$
$\qquad \sin 1.2x \sin 0.8x$

$\quad y_2 = \cos 2x$

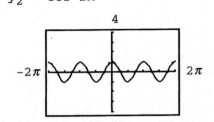

66. $y_1 = \sin 0.8x \cos 0.3x -$
$\qquad \cos 0.8x \sin 0.3x$

$\quad y_2 = \sin 0.5x$

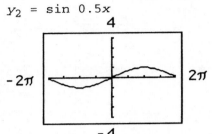

68. $45°$ **70.** $18°$ **71.** (C) 3,510 ft

Exercise 6-3

1. $\dfrac{1}{2} = \dfrac{1}{2}$ **2.** $1 = 1$ **3.** $-\sqrt{3} = -\sqrt{3}$ **4.** $\sqrt{3} = \sqrt{3}$

5. $1 = 1$ **6.** $\dfrac{\sqrt{2}}{2} = \dfrac{\sqrt{2}}{2}$ **7.** $\dfrac{\sqrt{2 - \sqrt{2}}}{2}$ **8.** $2 + \sqrt{3}$

9. $\dfrac{\sqrt{2 - \sqrt{2}}}{2}$ **10.** $2 - \sqrt{3}$

11.

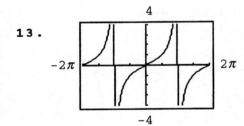

12.

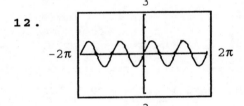

13.

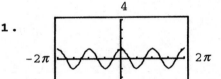

14.

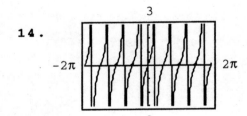

33. $\sin 2x = -\dfrac{24}{25}$, $\cos 2x = \dfrac{7}{25}$, $\tan 2x = -\dfrac{24}{7}$

34. $\sin 2x = -\dfrac{24}{25}$, $\cos 2x = \dfrac{7}{25}$, $\tan 2x = -\dfrac{24}{7}$

35. $\sin 2x = -\dfrac{120}{169}$, $\cos 2x = \dfrac{119}{169}$, $\tan 2x = -\dfrac{120}{119}$

36. $\sin 2x = -\dfrac{120}{169}$, $\cos 2x = \dfrac{-119}{169}$, $\tan 2x = \dfrac{120}{119}$

37. $\sin \frac{1}{2}x = \sqrt{\dfrac{3 + 2\sqrt{2}}{6}}$, $\cos \frac{1}{2}x = -\sqrt{\dfrac{3 - 2\sqrt{2}}{6}}$, $\tan \frac{1}{2}x = -3 - 2\sqrt{2}$

38. $\sin \dfrac{x}{2} = \dfrac{\sqrt{10}}{4}$, $\cos \dfrac{x}{2} = \dfrac{-\sqrt{6}}{4}$, $\tan \dfrac{x}{2} = -\dfrac{\sqrt{15}}{3}$

39. $\sin \frac{1}{2}x = -\dfrac{2\sqrt{5}}{5}$, $\cos \frac{1}{2}x = \dfrac{\sqrt{5}}{5}$, $\tan \frac{1}{2}x = -2$

40. $\sin \dfrac{x}{2} = \dfrac{-3\sqrt{10}}{10}$, $\cos \dfrac{x}{2} = \dfrac{\sqrt{10}}{10}$, $\tan \dfrac{x}{2} = -3$

41. (A) 2θ is a second quadrant angle, since θ is a first quadrant angle and $\tan 2\theta$ is negative for 2θ in the second quadrant and not for 2θ in the first.

(B) Construct a reference triangle for 2θ in the second quadrant with $(a, b) = (-3, 4)$. Use the pythagorean theorem to find $r = 5$. Thus, $\sin 2\theta = 4/5$ and $\cos 2\theta = -3/5$.

(C) The double angle identities $\cos 2\theta = 1 - 2 \sin^2 \theta$ and $\cos 2\theta = 2 \cos^2 \theta - 1$.

(D) Use the identities in part (C) in the form
$$\sin \theta = \sqrt{\dfrac{1 - \cos 2\theta}{2}} \quad \text{and} \quad \cos \theta = \sqrt{\dfrac{1 + \cos 2\theta}{2}}$$
The positive radicals are used because θ is in quadrant one.

(E) $\sin \theta = 2\sqrt{5}/5$; $\cos \theta = \sqrt{5}/5$

42. (A) 2θ is a second quadrant angle, since θ is a first quadrant angle and $\sec 2\theta$ is negative for 2θ in the second quadrant and not for 2θ in the first.

(B) Construct a reference triangle for 2θ in the second quadrant with $a = -4$ and $r = 5$. Use the pythagorean theorem to find $b = 3$. Thus, $\sin 2\theta = 3/5$ and $\cos 2\theta = -4/5$.

(C) The double angle identities $\cos 2\theta = 1 - 2 \sin^2 \theta$ and $\cos 2\theta = 2 \cos^2 \theta - 1$.

(D) Use the identities in part (C) in the form
$$\sin \theta = \sqrt{\dfrac{1 - \cos 2\theta}{2}} \quad \text{and} \quad \cos \theta = \sqrt{\dfrac{1 + \cos 2\theta}{2}}$$
The positive radicals are used because θ is in quadrant one.

(E) $\sin \theta = 3\sqrt{10}/10$; $\cos \theta = \sqrt{10}/10$

43. (A) $-0.72335 = -0.72335$ (B) $-0.58821 = -0.58821$

44. (A) $-0.70762 = -0.70762$ (B) $0.80718 = 0.80718$

45. (A) $-3.2518 = -3.2518$ (B) $0.89279 = 0.89279$

46. (A) $-6.7997 = -6.7997$ (B) $-0.41615 = -0.41615$

47. $y_1 = y_2$ for $[-\pi, \pi]$

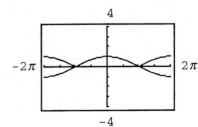

48. $y_1 = y_2$ for $[-2\pi, -\pi]$ and $[\pi, 2\pi]$

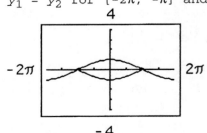

49. $y_1 = y_2$ for $[-2\pi, 0]$

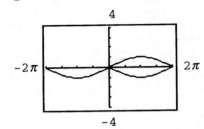

50. $y_1 = y_2$ for $[0, 2\pi]$

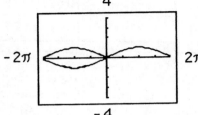

55. $-\dfrac{7}{25}$ **56.** $\dfrac{24}{25}$ **57.** $-\dfrac{24}{7}$ **58.** $-\dfrac{24}{7}$ **59.** $\dfrac{\sqrt{5}}{5}$ **60.** $-\dfrac{\sqrt{5}}{5}$

61. $\tan \dfrac{x}{2}$

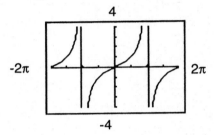

62. $\cot \dfrac{x}{2}$

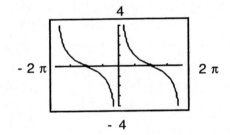

63. $1 + 2 \sin x$

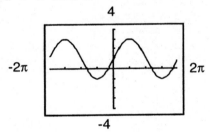

64. $-1 + 2 \cos x$

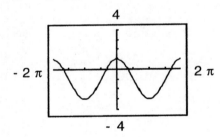

65. $\sec 2x$

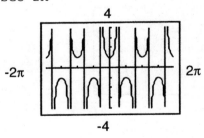

66. $\csc 2x$

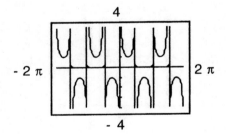

67. $x = \dfrac{224}{17} \approx 13.176$ m; $\theta = 28.955°$

68. $x = 2\sqrt{3} \approx 3.464$ ft, $\theta = 30.000°$

69. (A) $d = \dfrac{v_0^2 \sin 2\theta}{32 \text{ ft/sec}^2}$ (B) $\theta = 45°$

70. $\dfrac{4}{5}$

71. (B) TABLE 1

n	10	100	1,000	10,000
A_n	2.93893	3.13953	3.14157	3.14159

(C) A_n appears to approach π, the area of the circle with radius 1.

(D) A_n will not exactly equal the area of the circumscribing circle for any n no matter how large n is chosen; however, A_n can be made as close to the area of the circumscribing circle as we like by making n sufficiently large.

Exercise 6-4

1. $\frac{1}{2} \sin 4m + \frac{1}{2} \sin 2m$ **2.** $\frac{1}{2} \cos 12A + \frac{1}{2} \cos 2A$ **3.** $\frac{1}{2} \cos 2u - \frac{1}{2} \cos 4u$

4. $\frac{1}{2} \sin 5\theta + \frac{1}{2} \sin \theta$ **5.** $2 \sin 2t \cos t$ **6.** $2 \cos 6\theta \cos \theta$

7. $2 \sin 7w \sin 2w$ **8.** $-2 \cos 3u \sin 2u$ **9.** $\frac{\sqrt{3} - 2}{4}$

10. $\frac{2 - \sqrt{3}}{4}$ **11.** $\frac{1}{4}$ **12.** $\frac{1}{4}$ **13.** $-\frac{\sqrt{2}}{2}$ **14.** $\frac{\sqrt{2}}{2}$ **15.** $\frac{\sqrt{6}}{2}$ **16.** $\frac{\sqrt{2}}{2}$

19. Let $x = u + v$ and $y = u - v$ and solve the resulting system for u and v in terms of x and y, then substitute the results into the first identity. The second identity will result after a small amount of algebraic manipulation.

20. Let $x = u - v$ and $y = u + v$ and solve the resulting system for u and v in terms of x and y, then substitute the results into the first identity. The second identity will result after a small amount of algebraic manipulation.

29. (A) $-0.34207 = -0.34207$ (B) $-0.05311 = -0.05311$

30. (A) $0.19853 = 0.19853$ (B) $1.5918 = 1.5918$

31. (A) $-0.19115 = -0.19115$ (B) $-0.46541 = -0.46541$

32. (A) $0.57285 = 0.57285$ (B) $1.8186 = 1.8186$

33. $y_2 = 2 \sin \frac{3x}{2} \cos \frac{x}{2}$

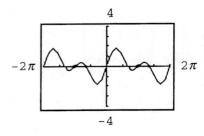

34. $y_2 = 2 \cos 2x \cos x$

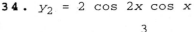
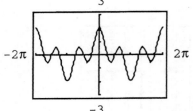

35. $y_2 = -2 \sin x \sin 0.7x$

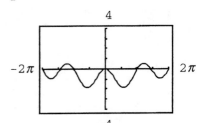

36. $y_2 = 2 \cos 1.3x \sin 0.8x$

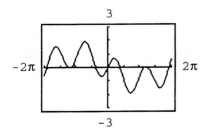

37. $y_2 = \frac{1}{2}(\sin 4x + \sin 2x)$

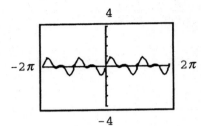

38. $y_2 = \frac{1}{2}[\cos 8x + \cos 2x]$

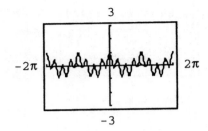

39. $y_2 = \frac{1}{2}(\cos 1.6x - \cos 3x)$

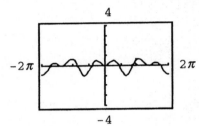

40. $y_2 = \frac{1}{2}[\sin 2.4x - \sin 1.4x]$

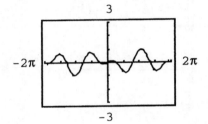

43. (A)

(B) $y_1 = \cos(30\pi x) + \cos(26\pi x)$
Graph same as part (A)

44. (A)

(B) $y_1 = \cos(22\pi x) - \cos(26\pi x)$
Graph same as part (A)

45. (A)

(B) $y_1 = \sin(22\pi x) + \sin(18\pi x)$
Graph same as part (A)

46. (A)

(B) $Y_1 = \sin(18\pi x) - \sin(14\pi x)$
Graph same as part (A)

47. (B)

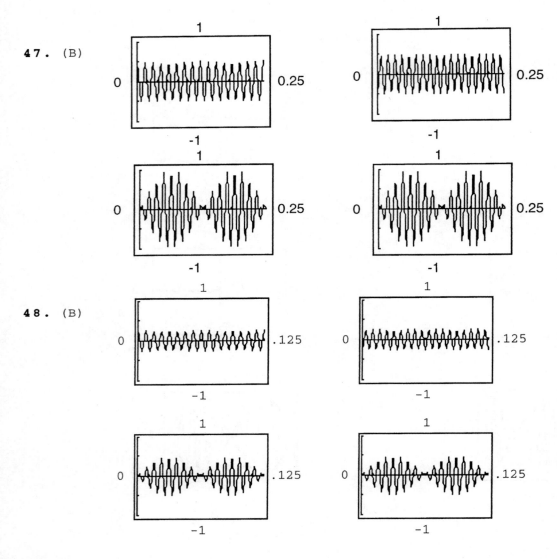

48. (B)

Exercise 6-5

1. $7\pi/6$, $11\pi/6$ **2.** $2\pi/3$, $4\pi/3$ **3.** $7\pi/6 + 2k\pi$, $11\pi/6 + 2k\pi$, k any integer

4. $2\pi/3 + 2k\pi$, $4\pi/3 + 2k\pi$, k any integer   **5.** $2\pi/3$ **6.** $5\pi/6$

7. $2\pi/3 + k\pi$, k any integer   **8.** $5\pi/6 + k\pi$, k any integer

9. $30°$, $330°$ **10.** $45°$, $135°$ **11.** $30° + k(360°)$, $330° + k(360°)$, k any integer

12. $45° + k(360)°$, $135° + k(360)°$, k any integer   **13.** 1.1279, 5.1553

14. 1.1593, 5.1239   **15.** 74.0546°   **16.** 104.9314°

17. $3.5075 + 2k\pi$, $5.9172 + 2k\pi$, k any integer

18. $0.6696 + 2\pi k$, $2.4720 + 2\pi k$, k any integer

19. 0.3376   **20.** 0.4502   **21.** 2.7642   **22.** 0.6167

23. $k(180°)$, $135° + k(180°)$, k any integer

24. $90° + k180°$, $45° + k180°$, k any integer

25. 0, $2\pi/3$, π, $4\pi/3$ **26.** $\dfrac{\pi}{2}$, $\dfrac{3\pi}{2}$ **27.** $4\pi/3$ **28.** $\dfrac{\pi}{2}$

29. 210°, 330°   **30.** 180°   **31.** 60°, 180°, 300°   **32.** 90°, 270°

33. $\pi/3$, π, $5\pi/3$ **34.** $\dfrac{\pi}{6}$, $\dfrac{5\pi}{6}$, $\dfrac{7\pi}{6}$, $\dfrac{11\pi}{6}$ **35.** 41.81°   **36.** 104.5°

37. 1.911   **38.** 0.2527   **39.** 0.3747, 2.767   **40.** 0.9987, 5.284

41. $0.3747 + 2k\pi$, $2.767 + 2k\pi$,   **42.** $0.9987 + 2\pi k$, $5.2845 + 2\pi k$,
 k any integer k any integer

43. 0.3747, 2.7669   **44.** 0.9987, 5.2845

45. $0.3747 + 2k\pi$, $2.7669 + 2k\pi$, k any integer

46. $0.9987 + 2\pi k$, $5.2845 + 2\pi k$, k any integer

47. (-1.1530, 1.1530)   **48.** (-1.5099, 1.8281)

49. [3.5424, 5.3778], [5.9227, ∞)   **50.** [0.4204, 1.2346], [2.9752, ∞)

51. 1.8183   **52.** 2.4652

53. $\tan^{-1}(-5.377)$ has exactly one value, -1.387; the equation $\tan x = -5.377$ has infinitely many solutions, which are found by adding $k\pi$, k any integer, to each solution in one period of $\tan x$.

54. Evaluating $\cos^{-1}(-0.7334)$ gives a unique number, ≈ 2.3941, the value of the inverse cosine function at -0.7334, while solving $\cos x = -0.7334$ involves finding an infinite number of x values whose cosine is -0.7334 by adding $2\pi k$, k any integer, to each solution in one period of $\cos x$.

55. 0, $3\pi/2$ **56.** 0, $\dfrac{\pi}{2}$ **57.** π **58.** 0

59. 0.1204, 0.1384   **60.** 0.006104, 0.006137

61. (A) The largest zero for f is 0.3183. As x increases without bound, $1/x$ tends to 0 through positive numbers, and $\sin(1/x)$ tends to 0 through positive numbers. $y = 0$ is a horizontal asymptote for the graph of f.

(B) Infinitely many zeros exist between 0 and b, for any b, however small. The exploration graphs suggest this conclusion, which is reinforced by the following reasoning. Note that for each interval (0, b], however small, as x tends to zero through positive numbers, $1/x$ increases without bound, and as $1/x$ increases without bound, $\sin(1/x)$ will cross the x axis an unlimited number of times. The function f does not have a smallest zero, because, between 0 and b, no matter how small b is, there is always an unlimited number of zeros.

62. (A) 0.6366 is the largest zero. As $x \to \infty$, $1/x \to 0 \Rightarrow \cos\left(\dfrac{1}{x}\right) \to 1$ so $y = 1$ is a horizontal asymptote for the graph of g.

(B) Infinitely many zeros exist between 0 and b, for any b, however small. The exploration graphs suggest this conclusion, which is reinforced by the following reasoning: Note that for each interval (0, b], however small, as x tends to zero through positive numbers, $1/x$ increases without bound, and as $1/x$ increases without bound, $\cos(1/x)$ will cross the x axis an unlimited number of times. The function g does not have a smallest zero, because, between 0 and b, no matter how small b is, there is always an unlimited number of zeros.

63. 0.009235 sec   **64.** 0.002613 sec   **65.** 50.77°   **66.** 33.21°

67. 123°   **68.** 64.1°   **69.** 2.267 rad   **70.** 1.779 rad

71. (A) 12.4575 mm   (B) 2.6496 mm   **72.** (A) 12.1703 mm   (B) 2.2318 mm

73. $(r, \theta) = (0, 0°)$, $(0, 180°)$, $(0, 360°)$ **74.** $(r, \theta) = (1, 30°)$, $(1, 150°)$

75. $\theta = 45°$ **76.** $\theta = 45°$

CHAPTER 6 REVIEW

5. $\frac{1}{2} \sin 8\alpha + \frac{1}{2} \sin 2\alpha$ (6-4)   **6.** $-2 \sin 6x \sin x$ (6-4)

7. $\cos x$ (6-2)   **8.** $135° + k360°$, $225° + k360°$, k any integer   (6-5)

9. $k\pi$ or $\frac{\pi}{4} + k\pi$, k any integer   (6-5) **10.** $x = \begin{cases} 0.7878 + 2k\pi \\ 2.3538 + 2k\pi \end{cases}$ k any integer   (6-5)

11. $x = \begin{cases} 75.1849° + k360° \\ 284.8151° + k360° \end{cases}$ k any integer   (6-5) **12.** -1.4032 (6-5)

13. 3.1855 (6-5)   **14.** (A) Not an identity (B) An identity   (6-1)

24. $\frac{-2 - \sqrt{3}}{4}$ (6-4, 5-4) **25.** $-\frac{\sqrt{6}}{2}$ (6-4, 5-4)

26. $\frac{\pi}{3}, \frac{2\pi}{3}, \frac{4\pi}{3}, \frac{5\pi}{3}$ (6-5) **27.** $0°, 120°$ (6-5)

28. $x = 0 + 2k\pi$, $x = \pi + 2k\pi$, $x = \frac{\pi}{6} + 2k\pi$, $x = \frac{5\pi}{6} + 2k\pi$, k any integer.
The first two can also be written together as $x = k\pi$, k any integer.   (6-5)

29. $x = 0 + 2k\pi$, $x = \pi + 2k\pi$, $x = \frac{\pi}{6} + 2k\pi$, $x = \frac{11\pi}{6} + 2k\pi$, k any integer.
The first two can also be written together as $x = k\pi$, k any integer.   (6-5)

30. $120° + k360°$, $240° + k360°$, k any integer   (6-5)

31. $14.34° + k180°$ (6-5) **32.** $x = \begin{cases} 0.6259 + 2k\pi \\ 2.516 + 2k\pi \end{cases}$ k any integer   (6-5)

33. $1.178, 2.749$ (6-5) **34.** 1.4903 (6-5) **35.** $(-\infty, 1.4903)$ (6-5)

36. $-0.6716, 0.6716$ (6-5) **37.** $[-0.6716, 0.6716]$ (6-5)

38. (A) Yes
(B) Conditional equation, since the equation is false for $x = 1$ and $y = 1$, for example, and both sides are defined at $x = 1$ and $y = 1$.   (6-1)

39. $\sin^{-1} 0.3351$ has exactly one value, while the equation $\sin x = 0.3351$ has infinitely many solutions.   (5-9, 6-5)

40. (A) Not an identity (B) An identity   (6-1)

41. $y2 = \frac{1}{2} \cos x + \frac{\sqrt{3}}{2} \sin x$

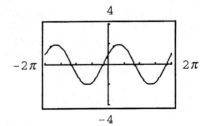

(6-2)

42. (A) $0, \frac{2\pi}{3}, \frac{4\pi}{3}$
(B) $0, 2.0944$ and 4.1888 (6-5)

43. 0.149 and -2.233 (6-5)

44. (A) $\frac{3}{\sqrt{10}}$ or $\frac{3\sqrt{10}}{10}$
(B) $\frac{7}{25}$ (6-3)

45. $-\dfrac{24}{25}$ (6-3)   **46.** $\dfrac{24}{25}$ (6-2)   **47.** (A) $0, \dfrac{\pi}{3}, \dfrac{2\pi}{3}$ (B) 0, 1.0472, 2.0944 (6-5)

48. (A) 0.6817, 1.3183

(B) As x increases without bound, $\dfrac{1}{x-1}$ tends to 0 through positive numbers and $\sin\dfrac{1}{x-1}$ tends to 0 through positive numbers. $y = 0$ is a horizontal asymptote for the graph of f.

(C) The exploratory graphs are left to the student. There are infinitely many zeros in any interval containing $x = 1$. The number $x = 1$ is not a zero because $\sin\dfrac{1}{x-1}$ is not defined at $x = 1$. (6-5)

49. $x = \sqrt{27}$; $x = 5.196$ cm, $\theta = 30.000°$ (6-3)   **50.** 0.00346 sec (6-5)

51. (B) $y = 0.6\cos 184\pi t$ $y = -0.6\cos 208\pi t$

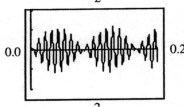   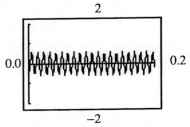

$y = 0.6\cos 184\pi t - 0.6\cos 208\pi t$ $y = 1.2\sin 12\pi t \sin 196\pi t$

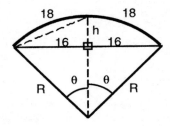   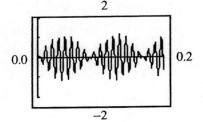

(6-4)

52. Height = 7.057 ft, raduis = 21.668 ft

From the figure, $R\theta = 18$ and $\sin\theta = \dfrac{16}{R}$. From these two equations, solving each for R in terms of θ and setting the results equal to each other, we obtain the desired trigonometric equation. (6-5)

CHAPTER 7

Exercise 7-1

1. $\gamma = 79°$, $a = 41$ ft, $b = 20$ ft

2. $\gamma = 106°$, $a = 14$ cm, $b = 12$ cm

3. $\beta = 40°$, $a = 16$ km, $c = 5.8$ km

4. $\alpha = 101°$, $b = 64$ mm, $c = 55$ mm

5. $\alpha = 49°$, $a = 53$ yd, $b = 66$ yd

6. $\beta = 23°$, $a = 38$ m, $b = 19$ m

7. $\beta = 81°$, $b = 16$ cm, $c = 12$ cm

8. $\alpha = 20°$, $b = 25$ mi, $a = 8.8$ mi

9. 1 triangle; the case where α is acute and $a = 2 = h$

10. 1 triangle; the case where α is acute and $a = 3 = h$

11. 1 triangle; the case where α is acute and $a \geq b$ ($a = 6$, $b = 4$)

12. 1 triangle; the case where α is acute and $a \geq b$ ($a = 8$, $b = 6$)

13. 0 triangles; the case where α is acute and $0 < a < h$ ($a = 1$, $h = 2$)

14. 0 triangles; the case where α is acute and $0 < a < h$ ($a = 2$, $h = 3$)

15. 2 triangles; the case where α is acute and $h < a < b$ ($h = 2$, $a = 3$, $b = 4$)

16. 2 triangles; the case where α is acute and $h < a < b$ ($h = 3$, $a = 5$, $b = 6$)

17. $\beta = 49.5°$, $a = 20.0$ ft, $c = 4.81$ ft

18. $\alpha = 98°$, $b = 4.32$ in, $c = 7.62$ in

19. $\gamma = 58.1°$, $a = 140$ m, $c = 129$ m

20. $\gamma = 22.9°$, $a = 27.3$ km, $c = 12.6$ km

21. no solution   22. no solution

23. $\alpha = 63.4°$, $\gamma = 77.7°$, $c = 46.7$ in

24. $\alpha = 56.0°$, $c = 292$ cm, $\gamma = 96.7°$

25. $\alpha = 116.6°$, $\gamma = 24.5°$, $c = 19.8$ in

26. $\alpha = 124°$, $c = 141$ cm, $\gamma = 28.7°$

27. no solution   28. no solution

29. $\alpha = 22°10'$, $\gamma = 128°20'$, $c = 89.9$ mm

30. $\alpha = 17°40'$, $c = 1740$ m, $\gamma = 128°30'$

31. $k = 25.2 \sin 42.3° = 17.0$

32. $k = 42.8 \sin 37.3° = 25.9$

33. Left side: 16.204; right side: 16.073

34. (B) Right side: 0.3415; Left side: 0.3443

35. 4.06 mi, 2.47 mi

36. 8.08 mi, 4.82 mi

37. 353 ft   38. 14,490 ft

39. 5.8 in, 3.1 in   40. 7.4", 5.0"

41. 4.42×10^7 km, 2.39×10^8 km

42. 46.5°

43. 159 ft   44. 109 ft

45. $R = 7.76$ mm, $s = 13.4$ mm

46. $R = 9.73$ mm, $s = 10.7$ mm

Exercise 7-2

1. Angle γ is acute. A triangle can have at most one obtuse angle. Since α is acute, then, if the triangle has an obtuse angle it must be the angle opposite the longer of the two sides, b and c. Thus, γ, the angle opposite the shorter of the two sides, c, must be acute.

2. A triangle can have at most one obtuse angle. Since α is obtuse, both β and γ must be acute.

3. $a = 6.03$ yd, $\beta = 56.6°$, $\gamma = 52.2°$

4. $b = 5.48$ cm, $\alpha = 69.0°$, $\gamma = 53.7°$

5. $c = 14.0$ mm, $\alpha = 20°40'$, $\beta = 39°0'$

6. $a = 27.0$ in, $\beta = 12°30'$, $\gamma = 31°40'$

7. If the triangle has an obtuse angle, then it must be the angle opposite the longest side; in this case, β.

8. Sides *a* and *c* are not long enough to construct a triangle (*a* + *c* < *b*).

9. α = 23.0°, β = 94.9°, γ = 62.1°

10. α = 22.4°, β = 131.4°, γ = 26.2°

11. α = 67.3°, β = 54.6°, γ = 58.1°

12. α = 59.4°, β = 53.5°, γ = 67.1°

13. No solution, since α + γ > 180°

14. β + γ > 180° $\Rightarrow$ no solution

15. *b* = 23.1 in, α = 46.1°, γ = 29.4°

16. *b* = 10.1 yd, γ = 114.2°, α = 38.5°

17. β = 10.8°, *a* = 22.5 m, *b* = 5.01 m

18. α = 30.3°, *a* = 46.2 km, *c* = 27.2 km

19. α = 30.7°, γ = 110.9°, *c* = 21.0 in

20. β = 66.4°, α = 47.2°, *a* = 20.4 yd

21. α = 49.1°, β = 102.9°, γ = 28.0°

22. α = 95°, β = 29.7°, γ = 55.3°

23. Triangle I: β = 109.7°, α = 11.9°, *a* = 1.58 m
Triangle II: β = 70.3°, α = 51.3°, *a* = 5.99 m

24. β = 65.3° $\Rightarrow$ γ = 68° $\Rightarrow$ *c* = 23.1 m
β' = 114.7° $\Rightarrow$ γ' = 18.6° $\Rightarrow$ *c'* = 7.93 m

25. no solution   **26.** no solution   **31.** 120 yd   **32.** 130 m

33. 100.6°   **34.** 113.3°   **35.** 5.81 ft   **36.** 10.6 ft

37. 121 mi   **38.** 713 mi   **39.** 74.1 m   **40.** 43.6 cm

41. 0.284 radian   **42.** 0.446 radian   **43.** α = 31°50', β = 50°10', γ = 98°0'

44. α = 32°10', β = 49°40', γ = 98°10'   **45.** $\angle CAB$ = 33°   **46.** $\angle ACB$ = 80°

47. 24,800 mi   **48.** 638 mi

Exercise 7-3

1. |**u** + **v**| = 58 mi/hr, θ = 51°

2. |**u** + **v**| = 71 mph, θ = 29°

3. |**u** + **v**| = 65 kg, θ = 54°

4. |**u** + **v**| = 57 kg, θ = 33°

5. |**u** + **v**| = 447 km/hr, θ = 13.6°

6. |**u** + **v**| = 154 km/hr, θ = 21.9°

7. |**u**| = 30 lb, |**v**| = 12 lb

8. |**u**| = 110 lb., |**v**| = 230 lb.

9. |**u**| = 71 mi/hr, |**v**| = 220 mi/hr

10. |**u**| = 27 mph, |**v**| = 5.8 mph

11. No. Two vectors are equal if and only if they have the same magnitude and direction.

12. The magnitude of a vector is a length and therefore cannot be negative.

13. |**u** + **v**| = 77g, α = 15°

14. |**u** + **v**| = 190 gm, α = 18°

15. |**u** + **v**| = 23 knots, α = 6°

16. |**u** + **v**| = 9.1 knots, α = 11°

17. |**u**| = 12 kg, |**v**| = 6.0 kg

18. |**v**| = 14 kg, |**u**| = 21 kg

19. |**u**| = 109 mi/hr, |**v**| = 160 mi/hr

20. |**v**| = 173 mph and |**u**| = 306 mph

21. Since the zero vector has an arbitrary direction, it can be perpendicular to any vector.

22. Since the zero vector has an arbitrary direction, it can be parallel (or perpendicular) to any vector.

23. 260 mph at 282°   **24.** 14 mph at 40°

25. 288°, 7.6 knots   **26.** 251 mph at 349.6°

27. 3,900 lbs @ 72°   **28.** 6300 kg @ 178°

29. (A) 388 lb (B) 4,030 lb   **30.** (A) 650 lb (B) 2400 lb

31. to the right   **32.** slide left

Exercise 7-4

1. ⟨-3, -3⟩   **2.** ⟨2, -8⟩   **3.** ⟨-6, 7⟩   **4.** ⟨-2, 1⟩

5. ⟨3, 5⟩   **6.** ⟨-2, -1⟩   **7.** 5   **8.** 5

9. $\sqrt{34}$ **10.** $\sqrt{29}$ **11.** 25   **12.** 67

13. Two algebraic vectors, ⟨a, b⟩ and ⟨c, d⟩, are equal if and only if a = b and c = d.

14. Two geometric vectors are equal if and only if they have the same magnitude and direction.

15. (A) ⟨1, 4⟩ (B) ⟨3, -2⟩ (C) ⟨14, -1⟩   **16.** (A) ⟨2, 0⟩ (B) ⟨-4, 4⟩ (C) ⟨-5, 0⟩

17. (A) ⟨-2, 1⟩ (B) ⟨-6, -3⟩ (C) ⟨-10, -1⟩   **18.** (A) ⟨-5, 4⟩ (B) ⟨-1, 0⟩ (C) ⟨-13, 2⟩

19. $v = -3i + 4j$ **20.** $2i - 5j$ **21.** $v = 3i$ **22.** $-27j$

23. $v = -5i - 2j$ **24.** $2i + 3j$ **25.** $5i + 2j$ **26.** $i - 6j$

27. $-16j$ **28.** $13i + 2j$ **29.** $-8j$ **30.** $i - 14j$

31. $u = \left\langle -\frac{3}{5}, \frac{4}{5} \right\rangle$ **32.** $u = \left\langle \frac{4}{5}, -\frac{3}{5} \right\rangle$ **33.** $u = \left\langle \frac{-5}{\sqrt{34}}, \frac{3}{\sqrt{34}} \right\rangle$ **34.** $u = \left\langle \frac{2}{\sqrt{13}}, \frac{-3}{\sqrt{13}} \right\rangle$

35. Any one of the force vectors must have the same magnitude as the sum vector of the other two and be oppositely directed as the sum vector.

36. The two vectors are equal in magnitude and opposite in direction.

45. 760 lb to the left; 761 lb to the right

46. $T_L = 676$ lb, $T_R = 677$ lb

47. 897 lb to the left; 732 lb to the right

48. $T_L = 518$ lb, $T_R = 390$ lb

49. This corresponds to a tension force of 462 lb in member CB.
This corresponds to a compression force of 231 lb in member AB.

50. BC = 2000 kg, tension; AB = 1730 kg, compression

51. AB = a compression of 2,360 lb; BC = a tension of 2,000 lb

52. AB = 9040 kg, compression; BC = 7530 kg, tension

Exercise 7-5

1.

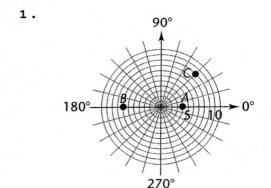

2.

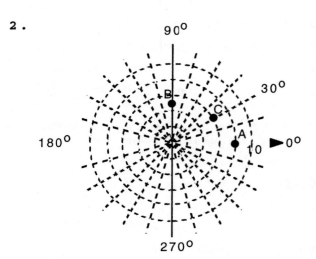

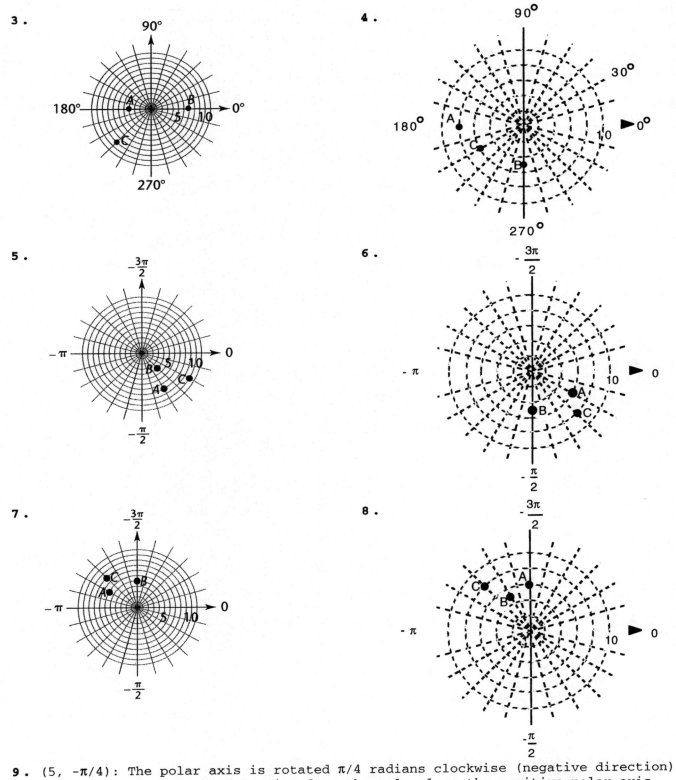

9. (5, -π/4): The polar axis is rotated π/4 radians clockwise (negative direction) and the point is located 5 units from the pole along the positive polar axis. (5, 7π/4): The polar axis is rotated 7π/4 radians counterclockwise (positive direction) and the point is located 5 units from the pole along the positive polar axis. (-5, -5π/4): The polar axis is rotated 5π/4 radians clockwise (negative direction) and the point is located 5 units from the pole along the negative polar axis.

10. (-6, -210°): The polar axis is rotated 210° clockwise (negative direction) and the point is located 6 units from the pole along the negative polar axis. (-6, 150°): The polar axis is rotated 150° counterclockwise (positive direction) and the point is located 6 units from the pole along the negative polar axis. (6, 330°): The polar axis is rotated 330° counterclockwise (positive direction) and the point is located 6 units along the positive polar axis.

11.

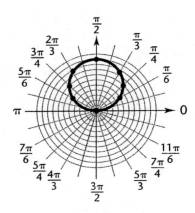

12.

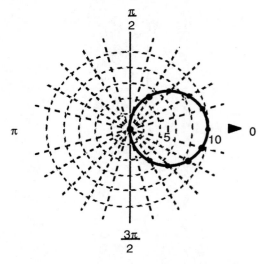

13.

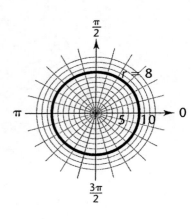

14.

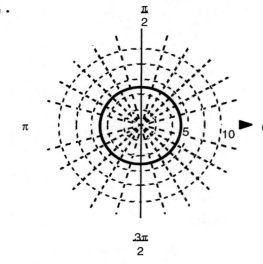

15.

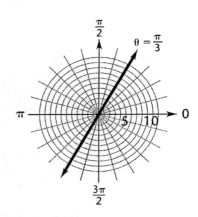

16.

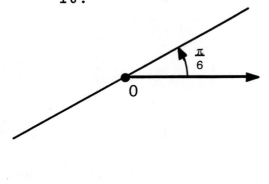

17. (5.196, 3.000)   **18.** (-3.500, 6.062)   **19.** (1.848, -0.765)

20. (0.668, -2.925)   **21.** (2.078, 3.688)   **22.** (-7.115, 5.557)

23. (7.9, 64°)   **24.** (8.3, 34°)   **25.** (26, -32°)

26. (31, -59°)   **27.** (7.61, -164.4°)   **28.** (9.37, 152.8°)

29.

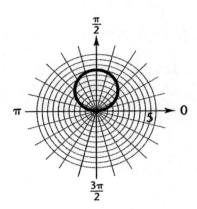

30.

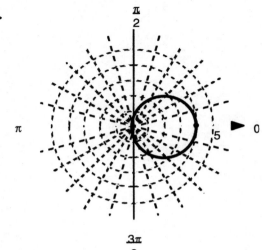

31.

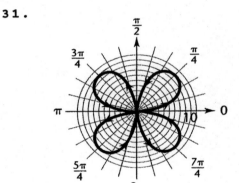

32.

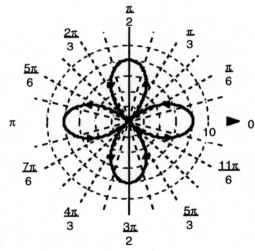

33.

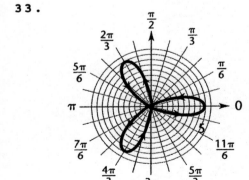

34.

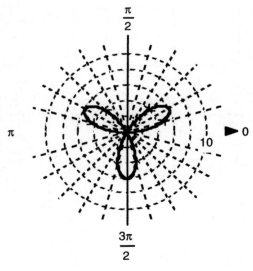

35.

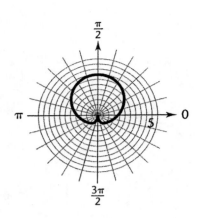

36.

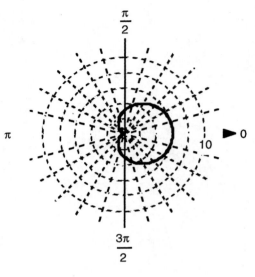

37.

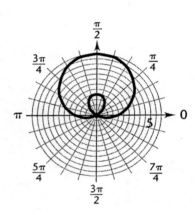

38.

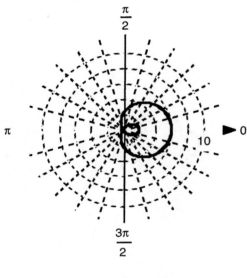

39.

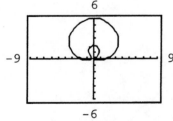

40.

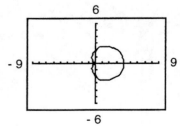
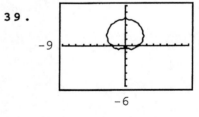
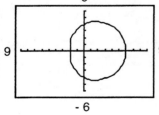

41. (A)

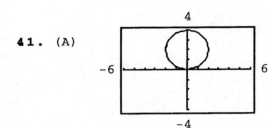 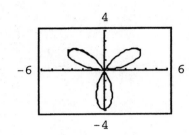 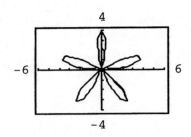

(B) 7 (C) n

42. (A)

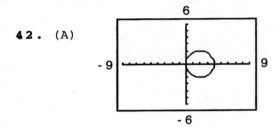 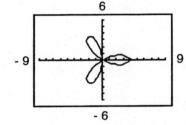 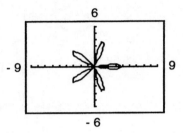

(B) 7 (C) n

43. (A)

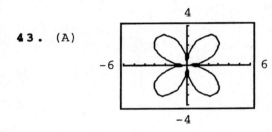 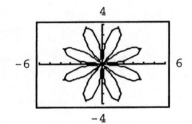 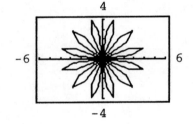

(B) 16 (C) $2n$

44. (A)

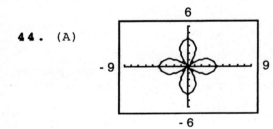 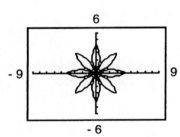 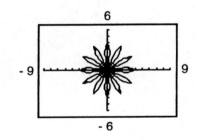

(B) 16 (C) $2n$

45. $r = 5 \sin \theta$ **46.** $r = 6 \cos \theta$ **47.** $\tan \theta = 1$ or $\theta = \dfrac{\pi}{4}$

48. $r^2 = 9$, $r = \pm 3$ **49.** $r = \dfrac{4 \cos \theta}{\sin^2 \theta} = 4 \cot \theta \csc \theta$

50. $r^2 = \dfrac{1}{\sin 2\theta} = \csc 2\theta$ **51.** $3x - 4y = -1$ **52.** $2x + y = 4$

53. $x^2 + y^2 = -2y$ **54.** $x^2 + y^2 = 8x$

55. $y = x$ **56.** $x^2 + y^2 = 16$

57. For each n, there are n large petals and n small petals. For n odd, the small petals are within the large petals; for n even, the small petals are between the large petals.

58. For each *n*, there are *n* large petals and *n* small petals. For *n* odd, the small petals are within the large petals; for *n* even, the small petals are between the large petals.

59.

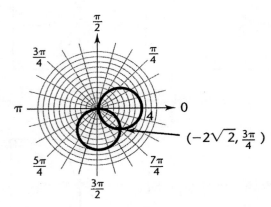

$(r, \theta) = \left(-2\sqrt{2}, \dfrac{3\pi}{4}\right)$ [Note: (0, 0) is not a solution of the system even though the graphs cross at the origin.]

60.

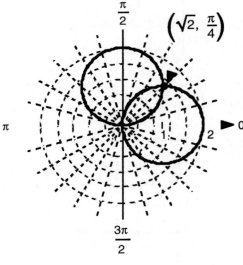

$(r, \theta) = \left(\sqrt{2}, \dfrac{\pi}{4}\right)$

[Note: (0, 0) is not a solution to this system even though the graphs cross at the origin.]

61.

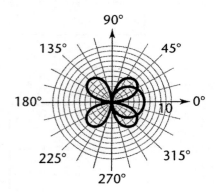

$(r, \theta) = (0, 90°), (0, 270°), (3\sqrt{3}, 30°),$
$(-3\sqrt{3}, 150°)$
[Note: (0, 0) is not a solution of the system even though the graphs cross at the origin.]

62.

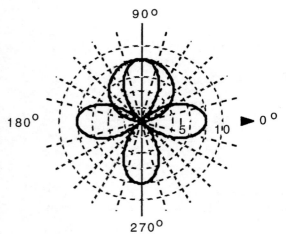

$(r, \theta) = (4, 30°), (4, 150°), (-8, 270°)$
[Note: (0, 0) is not a solution to the system even though the graphs cross at the origin.]

63. 3.368 units   **64.** 1.615   **65.** 6 k, 13 k, 12 k, 9 k

66. at 45°: 9k, at 90°: 14k, at 120°: 13k, at 150°: 11k

67. (A) Ellipse   (B) Parabola   (C) Hyperbola

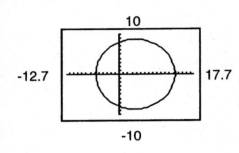 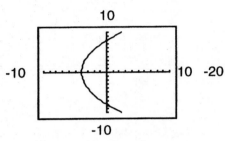 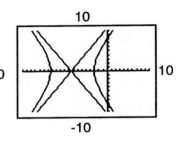

68. (A) Ellipse   (B) Parabola   (C) Hyperbola

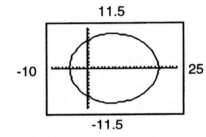 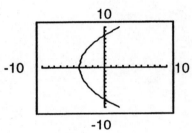 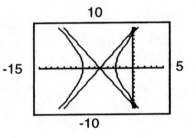

69. (A) Aphelion: 4.34×10^7 mi; Perihelion: 2.85×10^7 mi

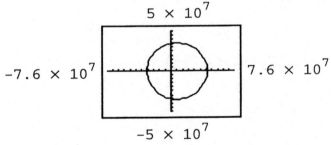

(B) Faster at perihelion. Since the distance from the sun to Mercury is less at perihelion than at aphelion, the planet must move faster near perihelion in order for the line joining Mercury to the sun to sweep out equal areas in equal intervals of time.

Exercise 7-6

1.

2.

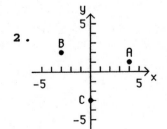

3.

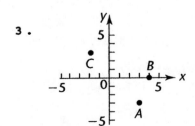

4.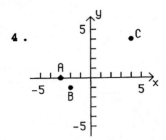

5.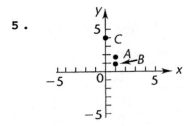

6.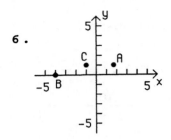

7.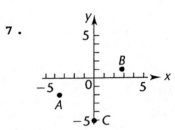

8.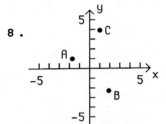

9. (A) $2e^{30°i}$ (B) $\sqrt{2}e^{(-135°)i}$ (C) $7.81e^{(-50.19°)i}$

10. (A) $2e^{120°i}$ (B) $3e^{(-90°)i}$ (C) $8.06e^{(-150.26°)i}$

11. (A) $\sqrt{3}e^{(-\pi/2)i}$ (B) $2e^{(-5\pi/6)i}$ (C) $9.43e^{2.58i}$

12. (A) $2e^{-(\pi/6)i}$ (B) $2\sqrt{2}e^{(3\pi/4)i}$ (C) $7.81e^{-0.69i}$

13. (A) $1 + i\sqrt{3}$ (B) $1 - i$ (C) $-2.35 + 1.99i$

14. (A) $\sqrt{3} + i$ (B) $-1 - i$ (C) $5.06 - 2.64i$

15. (A) $3\sqrt{3} + 3i$ (B) $-i\sqrt{7}$ (C) $-2.22 - 3.43i$

16. (A) $-i\sqrt{3}$ (B) $-1 + i$ (C) $-2.20 - 6.46i$

17. $14e^{113°i}$; $3.5e^{51°i}$ **18.** $18e^{225°i}$; $2e^{39°i}$ **19.** $10e^{135°i}$; $2.5e^{(-31°)i}$

20. $6e^{164°i}$; $1.5e^{(-30°)i}$ **21.** $36.42e^{4.35i}$; $0.26e^{-0.83i}$

22. $18.91e^{1.86i}$; $2.67e^{(-0.28)i}$ **23.** $-2i$; $2e^{-90°i}$

24. $2i$; $2e^{90°i}$ **25.** -2; $2e^{180°i}$ **26.** $4i$; $4e^{90°i}$ **27.** $-2 - 2i$, $2\sqrt{2}e^{(-135°)i}$

28. $-2 + 2i$, $2\sqrt{2}e^{135°i}$ **31.** $z^n = r^n e^{n\theta i}$ **32.** $\dfrac{z_1}{z_2} = \dfrac{r_1}{r_2} e^{i(\theta_1 - \theta_2)}$

33. (A) $(20 + 0i) + (5 + 5i\sqrt{3}) = 25 + 5i\sqrt{3}$ (B) $26.5e^{19.1°i}$
      (C) 26.5 pounds at an angle of 19.1°

34. (A) $(8 + 0i) + (3\sqrt{3} + 3i) = (8 + 3\sqrt{3}) + 3i$ (B) $13.5e^{12.8°i}$
      (C) 13.5 lb at 12.8°

Exercise 7-7

1. $8e^{90°i}$ **2.** $125e^{45°i}$ **3.** $8e^{60°i}$ **4.** $16e^{120°i}$ **5.** $8e^{180°i}$

6. $256e^{240°i}$ **7.** $-8 + 8i\sqrt{3}$ **8.** -4 **9.** 16 **10.** $16\sqrt{3} + 16i$

11. 1 **12.** 1 **13.** $w_1 = 2e^{10°i}$, $w_2 = 2e^{130°i}$, $w_3 = 2e^{250°i}$

14. $w_1 = 2e^{15°i}$, $w_2 = 2e^{135°i}$, $w_3 = 2e^{255°i}$

15. $w_1 = 3e^{15°i}$, $w_2 = 3e^{105°i}$, $w_3 = 3e^{195°i}$, $w_4 = 3e^{285°i}$

16. $w_1 = 2e^{22.5°i}$, $w_2 = 2e^{112.5°i}$, $w_3 = 2e^{202.5°i}$, $w_4 = 2e^{292.5°i}$

17. $w_1 = 2^{1/10}e^{(-9°)i}$, $w_2 = 2^{1/10}e^{63°i}$, $w_3 = 2^{1/10}e^{135°i}$, $w_4 = 2^{1/10}e^{207°i}$, $w_4 = 2^{1/10}e^{279°i}$

18. $w_1 = 2^{1/6}e^{45°i}$, $w_2 = 2^{1/6}e^{165°i}$, $w_3 = 2^{1/6}e^{285°i}$

19. $w_1 = 2e^{0°i}$, $w_2 = 2e^{120°i}$, $w_3 = 2e^{240°i}$

20. $w_1 = 1e^{0°i}$, $w_2 = 1e^{90°i}$, $w_3 = 1e^{180°i}$, $w_4 = 1e^{270°i}$

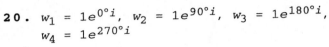

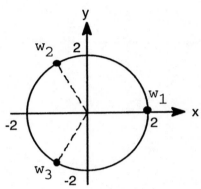
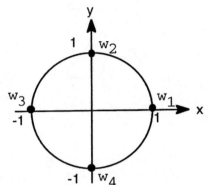

21. $w_1 = 2e^{45°i}$, $w_2 = 2e^{135°i}$, $w_3 = 2e^{225°i}$, $w_4 = 2e^{315°i}$

22. $w_1 = 2e^{60°i}$, $w_2 = 2e^{180°i}$, $w_3 = 2e^{300°i}$

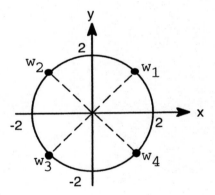
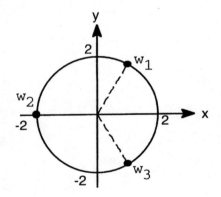

23. $w_1 = 1e^{15°i}$, $w_2 = 1e^{75°i}$, $w_3 = 1e^{135°i}$, $w_4 = 1e^{195°i}$, $w_5 = 1e^{255°i}$, $w_6 = 1e^{315°i}$

24. $w_1 = 1e^{(-18°)i}$, $w_2 = 1e^{54°i}$, $w_3 = 1e^{126°i}$, $w_4 = 1e^{198°i}$, $w_5 = 1e^{270°i}$

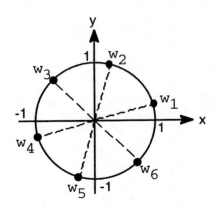
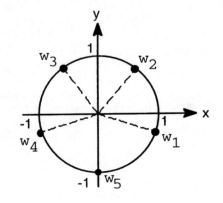

25. (A) $(1 + i)^4 + 4 = -4 + 4 = 0$
There are three other roots.

(B) The four roots are equally spaced around the circle. Since there are 4 roots, the angle between successive roots on the circle is $360°/4 = 90°$.

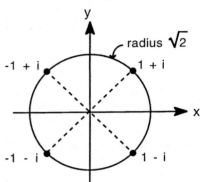

(C) $(-1 + i)^4 + 4 = -4 + 4 = 0$;
$(-1 - i)^4 + 4 = -4 + 4 = 0$;
$(1 - i)^4 + 4 = -4 + 4 = 0$

26. (A) $(-2)^3 + 8 = -8 + 8 = 0$; There are two other roots.

(B) The three roots are equally spaced around a circle of radius 2. The angle between successive roots on the circle is $360°/3 = 120°$.

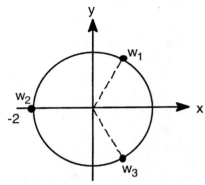

(C) $(1 + i\sqrt{3})^3 + 8 = -8 + 8 = 0$;
$(1 - i\sqrt{3})^3 + 8 = -8 + 8 = 0$

27. $w_1 = 4e^{60°i} = 2 + 2i\sqrt{3}$, $w_2 = 4e^{180°i} = -4$, $w_3 = 4e^{300°i} = 2 - 2i\sqrt{3}$

28. $x_1 = 4e^{0°i} = 4$, $x_2 = 4e^{120°i} = -2 + 2\sqrt{3}\,i$, $x_3 = 4e^{240°i} = -2 - 2\sqrt{3}\,i$

29. $w_1 = 3e^{0°i} = 3$, $w_2 = 3e^{120°i} = -\dfrac{3}{2} + \dfrac{3\sqrt{3}}{2}\,i$, $w_3 = 3e^{240°i} = -\dfrac{3}{2} - \dfrac{3\sqrt{3}}{2}\,i$

30. $x_1 = 3e^{60°i} = \dfrac{3}{2} + \dfrac{3\sqrt{3}}{2}\,i$, $x_2 = 3e^{180°i} = -3$, $x_3 = 3e^{300°i} = \dfrac{3}{2} - \dfrac{3\sqrt{3}}{2}\,i$

33. $w_1 = 2e^{0°i}$, $w_2 = 2e^{72°i}$, $w_3 = 2e^{144°i}$, $w_4 = 2e^{216°i}$, $w_5 = 2e^{288°i}$

34. $x_1 = 1e^{30°i}$, $x_2 = 1e^{90°i}$, $x_3 = 1e^{150°i}$, $x_4 = 1e^{210°i}$, $x_5 = 1e^{270°i}$, $x_6 = 1e^{330°i}$

35. $w_1 = e^{36°i}$, $w_2 = e^{108°i}$, $w_3 = e^{180°i}$, $w_4 = e^{252°i}$, $w_5 = e^{324°i}$

36. $x_1 = 1e^{30°i}$, $x_2 = 1e^{150°i}$, $x_3 = 1e^{270°i}$

37. $P(x) = (x - 2i)(x + 2i)[x - (-\sqrt{3} + i)][x - (-\sqrt{3} - i)]$

$$[x - (\sqrt{3} + i)][x - (\sqrt{3} - i)]$$

38. $(x - 1)(x + 1)\left(x - \left(\dfrac{1}{2} + \dfrac{\sqrt{3}}{2}\,i\right)\right)\left(x - \left(-\dfrac{1}{2} - \dfrac{\sqrt{3}}{2}\,i\right)\right) \cdot \left(x - \left(-\dfrac{1}{2} + \dfrac{\sqrt{3}}{2}\,i\right)\right)\left(x - \left(\dfrac{1}{2} - \dfrac{\sqrt{3}}{2}\,i\right)\right)$

CHAPTER 7 REVIEW

1. 1   *(7-1)*   **2.** 0   *(7-1)*   **3.** 2   *(7-1)*

4. Angle β is acute. A triangle can have at most one obtuse angle. Since α is acute, then, if the triangle has an obtuse angle it must be the angle opposite the longer of the two sides, b and c. Thus, β, the angle opposite the shorter of the two sides, b, must be acute.   *(7-2)*

5. $\gamma = 75°$, $a = 47$ m, $b = 31$ m   *(7-1)*

6. $a = 4.00$ ft, $\beta = 36°$, $\gamma = 129°$ *(7-1, 7-2)*

7. $\beta = 19°$, $\alpha = 40°$, $a = 8.2$ cm *(7-1)*

8. $|\mathbf{u} + \mathbf{v}| = 170$ mi/hr, $\theta = 19°$ *(7-3)* **9.** $\langle 3, -7 \rangle$ *(7-4)* **10.** $\sqrt{34}$ *(7-4)*

11.   **12.**   **13.**

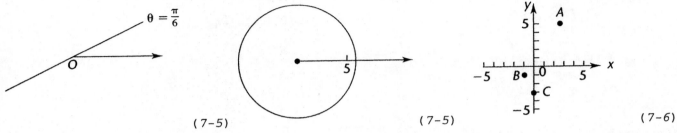

            (7-5)   *(7-5)*   *(7-6)*

14. (-10, -210°): The polar axis is rotated 210° clockwise (negative direction) and the point is located 10 units from the pole along the negative polar axis. (-10, 150°): The polar axis is rotated 150° counterclockwise (positive direction) and the point is located 10 units from the pole along the negative polar axis. (10, 330°): The polar axis is rotated 330° counterclockwise and the point is located 10 units from the pole along the positive polar axis. *(7-5)*

15.

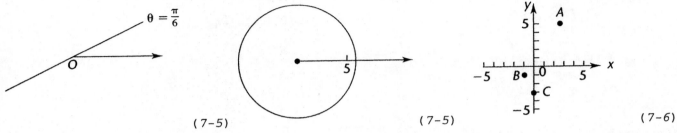

            (7-6)

16. (A) $2e^{(-60°)i}$ (B) $2\sqrt{3} - 2i$ *(7-6)*

17. (A) 1 *(7-7)*   **18.** $8 + i\,8\sqrt{3}$ *(7-7)*

19. If the triangle has an obtuse angle, then it must be the angle opposite the longest side; in this case, α. *(7-2)*

20. $b = 10.5$ cm, $\alpha = 27.2°$, $\gamma = 37.4°$ *(7-2)*

21. No solution *(7-1)*

22. Two solutions. Obtuse case: $\beta = 133.9°$, $\gamma = 19.7°$, $c = 39.6$ km *(7-1)*

23. $\alpha = 41.1°$, $\beta = 74.2°$, $\gamma = 64.7°$ *(7-1, 7-2)*

24. The sum of all of the force vectors must be the zero vector for the object to remain at rest. *(7-4)*

25. $|\mathbf{u} + \mathbf{v}| = 98.0$ kg, $\alpha = 17.1°$ *(7-3)*

26. (A) $\mathbf{u} = -3\mathbf{i} + 9\mathbf{j}$ (B) $\mathbf{v} = -2\mathbf{j}$ *(7-4)* **27.** (A) $\langle -4, 7 \rangle$ (B) $\langle -14, 13 \rangle$ *(7-4)*

28. (A) $-2\mathbf{i} - 4\mathbf{j}$ (B) $-10\mathbf{j}$ *(7-4)* **29.** $\mathbf{u} = \left\langle \dfrac{-1}{\sqrt{10}}, \dfrac{-3}{\sqrt{10}} \right\rangle$ *(7-4)*

30.

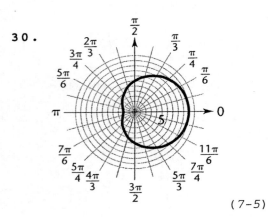

(7-5)

31.

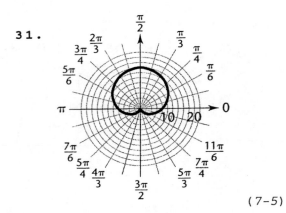

(7-5)

32.

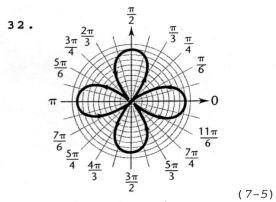

(7-5)

33.

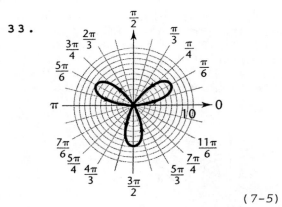

(7-5)

34.

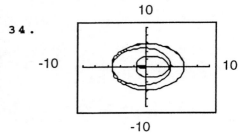

(7-5)

35.

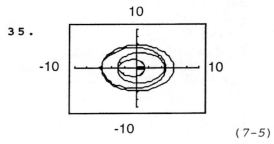

(7-5)

36. *n* = 1   *n* = 2   *n* = 3

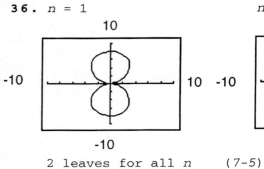

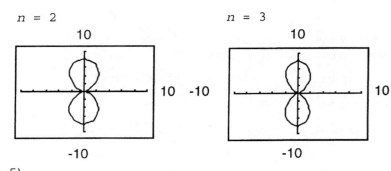

2 leaves for all *n*   (7-5)

37. (A) Ellipse

10

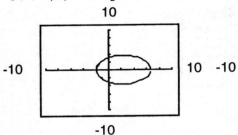

-10   10

-10

(B) Parabola

10

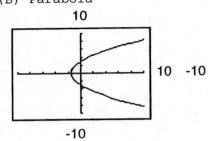

-10   10

-10

(C) Hyperbola

10

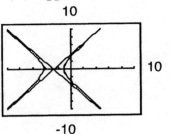

-10   10

-10   *(7-5)*

38. $r^2 = 6r \cos \theta$ or $r = 6 \cos \theta$ *(7-5)*   **39.** $x^2 + y^2 = 5x$ *(7-5)*

40. $z_1 = \sqrt{2}\, e^{135°i}$, $z_2 = 2\, e^{(-120°)i}$, $z_3 = 5\, e^{0°i}$ *(7-6)*

41. $z_1 = 1 + i$, $z_2 = (-3\sqrt{3}/2) - (3/2)i$, $z_3 = -1 - i\sqrt{3}$ *(7-6)*

42. (A) $32\, e^{44°i}$ (B) $2\, e^{6°i}$ *(7-6)*

43. (A) $-8 - 8i\sqrt{3}$ (B) $-8 - 13.86i$ *(7-7)*

44. $w_1 = e^{30°i}$
$w_2 = e^{150°i}$
$w_3 = e^{270°i}$

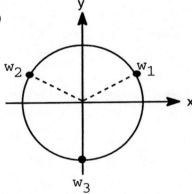

(7-7)

45. $2\, e^{50°i}$, $2\, e^{170°i}$, $2\, e^{290°i}$ *(7-7)*   **46.** $(4\, e^{15°i})^2 = 16\, e^{30°i} = 8\sqrt{3} + 8i$ *(7-7)*

47. $(5.76, -26.08°)$ *(7-5)*   **48.** $(-5.30, -2.38)$ *(7-5)*

49. $5.26e^{127.20°i}$ *(7-6)*   **50.** $-7.27 - 2.32i$ *(7-6)*

51. (A) There are a total of three cube roots and they are spaced equally around a circle of radius 2.

(B) $w_2 = -\sqrt{3} - i$, $w_3 = \sqrt{3} - i$

(C) The cube of each cube root is $-8i$.

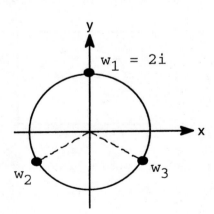

(7-7)

52. $k = 44.6 \sin 23.4°$ *(7-1)*

55. (A)

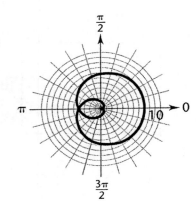

(B)

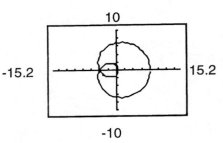

(7-5)

56. (A) The coordinates of P represent a simultaneous solution.

(B) $r = -4\sqrt{2}$, $\theta = 3\pi/4$

(C) The two graphs go through the pole at different values of θ.

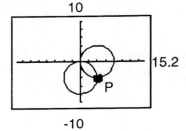

(7-5)

57. 1, -1, i, $-i$, $\dfrac{\sqrt{2}}{2} + i\dfrac{\sqrt{2}}{2}$, $\dfrac{\sqrt{2}}{2} - i\dfrac{\sqrt{2}}{2}$, $-\dfrac{\sqrt{2}}{2} + i\dfrac{\sqrt{2}}{2}$, $-\dfrac{\sqrt{2}}{2} - i\dfrac{\sqrt{2}}{2}$ (7-7)

58. $P(x) = [x - (\sqrt{3} + i)][x - (-\sqrt{3} + i)](x + 2i)$ (7-7)

59. 438 miles   (7-3)   **60.** 438 miles per hour at 83°   (7-3)

61. 86°, 464 miles per hour   (7-3)   **62.** 0.6 miles   (7-3)

63. 177 pounds at 15.2° relative to **v**   (7-3)

64. 19 kg at 204° relative to **u**   (7-4)   **65.** 5,740 lb   (7-4)

66. (A) Distance at aphelion: 1.56×10^8 miles
Distance at perihelion: 1.29×10^8 miles

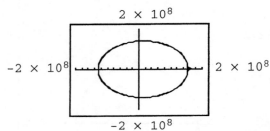

(B) Distance at aphelion: 1.56×10^8 miles
Distance at perihelion: 1.29×10^8 miles   (7-5)

CUMULATIVE REVIEW EXERCISE (Chapters 5, 6 and 7)

1. 1.86 meters   *(5-1)*   **2.** $\theta = 57.3°$, 14.5 cm, 7.83 cm   *(5-2)*

3. (A) I, II   (B) I, IV   (C) I, III   *(5-3)*

4. (A) $-\dfrac{3}{5}$ (B) $\dfrac{5}{4}$ (C) $-\dfrac{4}{3}$ *(5-3)*   **5.** (A) $\dfrac{\pi}{4}$ (B) 65°   (C) 30°   *(5-4)*

6. (A) Domain: all real numbers; Range: $-1 \leq y \leq 1$; Period: 2π

   (B) Domain: all real numbers; Range: $-1 \leq y \leq 1$; Period: 2π

   (C) Domain: all real numbers except $x = \dfrac{\pi}{2} + k\pi$, k an integer;

   Range: all real numbers; Period: π *(5-6)*

7.

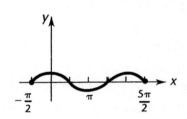

(5-6)

8.

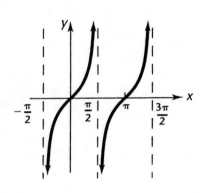

(5-6)

9. The central angle of a circle subtended by an arc of twice the length of the radius.   *(5-1)*

10. If the graph of $y = \cos x$ is shifted $\pi/2$ units to the right, the result will be the graph of $y = \sin x$.   *(5-6, 5-7)*

15. (A) Not an identity   (B) An identity   *(6-1)*

16. Angle α is acute. A triangle can have at most one obtuse angle. Since β is acute, then, if the triangle has an obtuse angle it must be the angle opposite the longer of the two sides, a and c. Thus, α, the angle opposite the shorter of the two sides, a, must be acute.   *(7-2)*

17. 0.3245, 2.8171   *(6-5)*   **18.** -76.2154°   *(6-5)*

19. $b = 22$ ft, $\alpha = 28°$, $\gamma = 31°$ *(7-2, 7-1)*   **20.** $\langle 6, -3 \rangle$ *(7-4)*

21. (5, -30°): The polar axis is rotated 30° clockwise (negative direction) and the point is located 5 units from the pole along the positive polar axis.
(-5, -210°): The polar axis is rotated 210° clockwise (negative direction) and the point is located 5 units from the pole along the negative polar axis.
(5, 330°): The polar axis is rotated 330° counterclockwise (positive direction) and the point is located 5 units from the pole along the positive polar axis.   *(7-5)*

22.

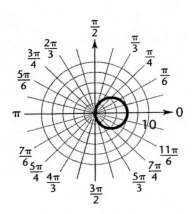

(7-5)

23.

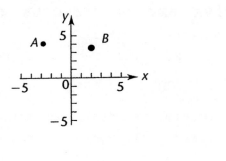

(7-7)

24. $4\sqrt{3} + 4i$ (7-7)

25. $-\frac{7\pi}{6}$, 870°   (5-1)

26. 75.06°   (5-1)

27. (A) and (C)   (5-3, 5-5)

28. $-\frac{1}{2}$ (5-4)

29. Not defined   (5-3, 5-4, 5-5)

30. -1 (5-4)

31. $\frac{2}{\sqrt{3}}$ (5-4)

32. π (5-4, 5-9)

33. not defined   (5-9)

34. $\frac{2\pi}{3}$ (5-9)

35. 0.55   (5-9)

36. $\frac{3}{5}$ (5-3, 5-9)

37. $\frac{1}{\sqrt{5}}$ (5-9, 5-3)

38. (A) 9.871   (B) -3.748   (C) -1.559   (D) not defined   (5-3, 5-5, 5-9)

39.

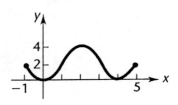

(5-7)

40. (A) 150°   (5-9)

41. $\sin^{-1}(\sin 3) = 0.142$. For the identity $\sin^{-1}(\sin x) = x$ to hold, x must be in the restricted domain of the sine function; that is , $-\pi/2 \leq x \leq \pi/2$. The number 3 is not in the restricted domain.   (5-9)

42. Since the coordinates of a point on a unit circle are given by $P(a, b) = P(\cos x, \sin x)$, we evaluate $P(\cos(11.205), \sin(11.205))$--using a calculator set in radian mode--to obtain $P(0.208, -0.978)$. The quadrant in which $P(a, b)$ lies can be determined by the signs of a and b. In this case P is in the fourth quadrant, since a is positive and b is negative. *(5-5)*

43. The equation has infinitely many solutions $[x = \tan^{-1}(-24.5) + k\pi$, k any integer]; $\tan^{-1}(-24.5)$ has a unique value (-1.530 to three decimal places). *(5-9, 6-5)*

44. $y = 3 + 2 \sin \pi x$ *(5-7)*

45. $A = 3$, $P = \pi$, $P.S. = \dfrac{\pi}{2}$

46. Phase shift = 1, Period = 2

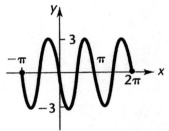

(5-7)

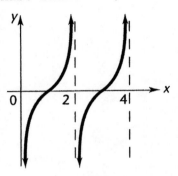

(5-8)

47.

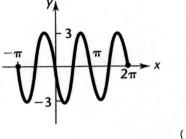

(5-6)

48. If the graph of $y = \cot x$ is shifted to the left $\pi/2$ units and reflected in the x axis, the result will be the graph of $y = \tan x$. *(5-6, 5-7)*

49. $y = \dfrac{1}{2} - \dfrac{1}{2} \cos 2x$ *(5-7)*

50. $y = \cot x$ *(5-7, 5-8)*

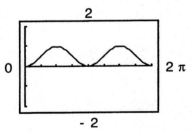

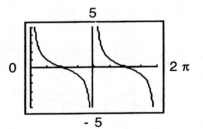

51. (A) Yes

(B) Conditional, since both sides are defined at $x = \pi/2$, for example, but $\pi/2$ is not a solution. *(6-1)*

58. (A) Not an identity   (B) An identity   *(6-1)*   **59.** 0   *(6-2)*

60. $\sin 2x = \dfrac{-24}{25}$, $\cos \dfrac{x}{2} = \sqrt{\dfrac{1}{10}}$ or $\dfrac{\sqrt{10}}{10}$ *(5-4, 6-3)*

61. 30°, 150°, 270°   *(6-5)*

62. $x = k\pi,\ \frac{\pi}{3} + 2k\pi,\ -\frac{\pi}{3} + 2k\pi,\ k$ any integer *(6-5)*

63. (A) $\pi/2,\ 3\pi/2,\ 7\pi/6,\ 11\pi/6$ (B) 1.571, 3.665, 4.712, 5.760   *(6-5)*

64. $x = 0.926$ *(6-5)*   **65.** $\gamma = 107.2°,\ \alpha = 25.0°,\ \beta = 47.8°$ *(7-1, 7-2)*

66. No solution   *(7-1)*   **67.** $\beta = 120.7°,\ \gamma = 6.4°\ c = 4.81$ in   *(7-1)*

68. β must be acute. A triangle can have at most one obtuse angle, and since γ is acute, the obtuse angle, if present, must be opposite the longer of the two sides a and b.   *(7-2)*

69. $|\mathbf{u} + \mathbf{v}| = 35.6$ lb, $\alpha = 16.3°$ *(7-1, 7-2, 7-3)*

70. (A) $\langle 1,\ 3 \rangle$ (B) $3\mathbf{i} + \mathbf{j}$ *(7-4)*   **71.** $r = 8 \sin \theta$ *(7-5)*

72. $x^2 + y^2 = -4x$ *(7-5)*

73. 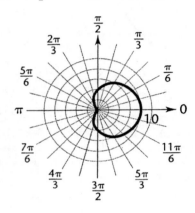   *(7-5)*   **74.** 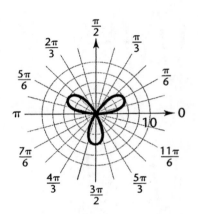   *(7-5)*

75. $n = 1$ $n = 2$ $n = 3$

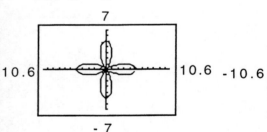   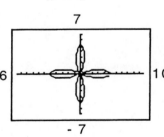   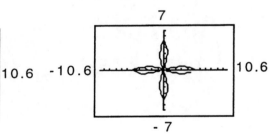

4 leaves for all n *(7-5)*

76. 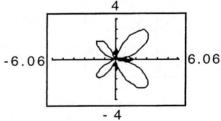   *(7-5)*

77. $(4.23,\ -131.07°)$ *(7-5)*   **78.** $(-3.68,\ 5.02)$ *(7-5)*

79. $\sqrt{3} - i$ *(7-6)*   **80.** $z = 2e^{120°i}$ *(7-6)*

81. $64 + 0i = 64$ *(7-7)*

82. $w_1 = \dfrac{\sqrt{3}}{2} - i\dfrac{1}{2}$,

$w_2 = i$,

$w_3 = -\dfrac{\sqrt{3}}{2} - i\dfrac{1}{2}$

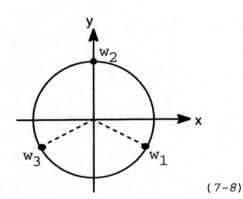

(7-8)

83. $5.82e^{(-146.99°)i}$ (7-6)

84. $-6.70 + 1.94i$ (7-6)

85. (A) There are a total of four fourth roots and they are spaced equally around a circle of radius $\sqrt{2}$.

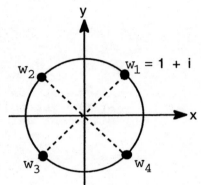

(B) $w_2 = -1 + i$,
$\quad w_3 = -1 - i$,
$\quad w_4 = 1 - i$

(C) The fourth power of each fourth root is -4.

(7-7)

86. $a = \cos 1.2 = 0.362$
$b = \sin 1.2 = 0.932$ (5-5)

87.

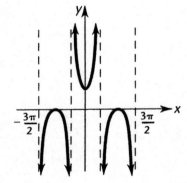

(5-8)

88. $y = 3\cos(2\pi x - \pi/4)$; Amplitude = 3, Period = 1, P.S. = 1/8   (5-7)

89. $y = 2\sin(2x - 0.644)$

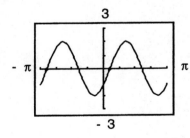

(5-7)

90. $\dfrac{1}{\sqrt{1 - x^2}}$ (5-9)

91. $\dfrac{24}{25}$ (5-9, 6-3)

92. (A) $\dfrac{2}{\sqrt{5}}$ or $\dfrac{2\sqrt{5}}{5}$ (B) $-\dfrac{7}{25}$ (6-3)

93. (A) $\pi/3$, $5\pi/3$ (B) 1.0472, 5.2360   (6-5)

94. (A)

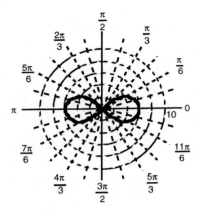

(B)

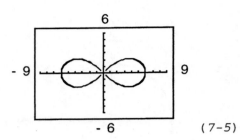

(7-5)

95. (A)

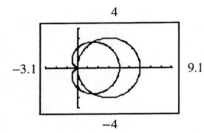

(B) 6

(C) (3, π/3), (3, 5π/3)

(D) The points on r2 and r1 arrive at the intersection points for different values of θ, except for the two found in part (C).

(7-5)

96. $P(x) = (x - i)[x - (\sqrt{3}/2 - i/2)][x - (-\sqrt{3}/2 - i/2)]$ (7-7)

97. $\frac{2\pi}{73}$ radians   (5-1)

98. 1,088 m   (5-2)

99. 5.88 in   (7-2)

100. 76°   (7-2)

101. $I = 50 \cos 220\pi t$ (5-7)

102. 274 miles per hour at 117°   (7-3)

103. Both have a tension of 234 lb   (7-4)

104. (A) Add the perpendicular bisector of the chord as shown in the figure. Then, sin θ = 4/R and θ = 5/R. Substituting the second into the first, we obtain sin 5/R = 4/R.

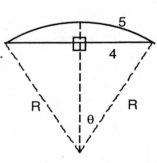

(B) R cannot be isolated on one side of the equation.

(C) Plot $y_1 = \sin 5/R$ and $y_2 = 4/R$ in the same viewing window and solve for R at the point of intersection using a built-in routine (see figure).
$R = 4.420$ cm.

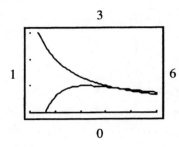

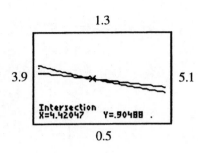

(6-5)

105. (A)

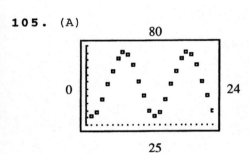

(C)

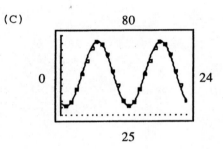

(B) $y = 53.5 + 22.5 \sin(\pi x/6 - 2.1)$

(5-7)

CHAPTER 8

Exercise 8-1

1. B, no solution   **2.** a, (2, 1)   **3.** D, (1, -3)

4. c, infinitely many solutions: for any real number s, $x = s$, $y = 2s - 5$

5. (5, 2)   **6.** (3, 1)   **7.** (2, -3)   **8.** (2, 4)

9. No solution (parallel lines)   **10.** parallel lines, no solution

11. $x = 8$, $y = 19$ **12.** $x = 3$, $y = 7$ **13.** $x = 6$, $y = 2$ **14.** $x = 4$, $y = 5$

15. $x = 2$, $y = -1$ **16.** $x = 1$, $y = 4$ **17.** $x = 5$, $y = 2$ **18.** $x = 1$, $y = -5$

19. $m = 1$, $n = -2/3$ **20.** $x = -4/3$, $y = 1$ **21.** $x = 2,500$, $y = 200$

22. $x = 4,000$, $y = 280$ **23.** $u = 1.1$ and $v = 0.3$ **24.** $s = 1.2$, $t = 0.3$

25. $x = -5/4$, $y = 5/3$ **26.** $x = \dfrac{11}{3}$, $y = \dfrac{17}{5}$ **27.** (1.12, 2.41)

28. (2.21, -1.52)   **29.** (-2.24, -3.31)   **30.** (-3.35, 1.23)

31. The system has no solution.

32. The system has an infinite number of solutions.

33. $q = x + y - 5$, $p = 3x + 2y - 12$ **34.** $p = x + y - 3$, $q = x + 2y - 7$

35. $x = \dfrac{dh - bk}{ad - bc}$, $y = \dfrac{ak - ch}{ad - bc}$, $ad - bc \neq 0$

36. If $ad - bc = 0$, there may be no solutions or an infinite number of solutions.

37. airspeed = 330 mph; wind rate = 90 mph   **38.** 1,440 miles

39. 2.475 km   **40.** 5/3 mph

41. 40 milliliters of 50% solution and 60 milliliters of 80% solution

42. $6\frac{2}{3}$ grams of 12-carat gold; $3\frac{1}{3}$ grams of 18-carat gold

43. $7,200 invested at 10% and $4,800 invested at 15%

44. $5,000 at 8% and $15,000 at 12%

45. Mexico plant: 75 hours; Taiwan plant: 50 hours

46. Green Bay plant: 60 hrs; Sheboygan plant: 28.5 hrs

47. Mix A: 60 g; Mix B: 80 g

48. 55 bags of Brand A and 40 bags of Brand B

49. (A) Supply: 143 T-shirts; demand: 611 T-shirts

(B) Supply: 714 T-shirts; demand: 389 T-shirts

(C) Equilibrium price: $6.36; equilibrium quantity: 480 T-shirts

(D)

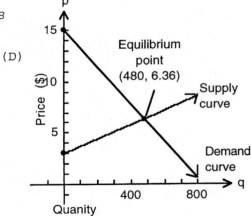

50. (A) Supply: 33,333 baseball caps; demand: 64,286 baseball caps

(B) Supply: 100,000 baseball caps; demand: 35,714 baseball caps

(C) Equilibrium price: $5.30; equilibrium quantity: 55,000 baseball caps

(D)

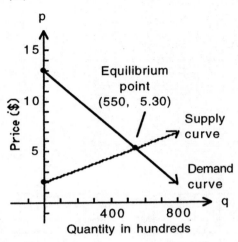

51. (A) $p = 0.001q + 0.15$ (B) $p = -0.002q + 1.89$
(C) Equilibrium price = $0.73; equilibrium quantity = 580 bushels

52. (A) $p = 0.0004x + 0.97$ (B) $p = -0.0005x + 1.69$
(C) Equilibrium price = $1.29; equilibrium quantity = 800 bushels

53. (A) $a = 196$, $b = -16$ (B) 196 feet   (C) 3.5 seconds

54. (A) $a = 256$, $b = -16$ (B) 256 ft   (C) 4 sec, fall time of object

55. 40 seconds, 24 seconds, 120 mi

56. $t = 1\frac{9}{13}$ sec, $t + 6 = 7\frac{9}{13}$ sec; $d = 8{,}462$ ft

Exercise 8-2

1. (2, −1)   **2.** (8, 6)   **3.** (3, −1)   **4.** (−1, 3)

5. 2 × 3, 1 × 3   **6.** 3 × 3, 2 × 1   **7.** C   **8.** D

9. B **10.** 1   **11.** −2, −6   **12.** 4, 0

13. −2, 6, 0   **14.** 3, 1   **15.** $\begin{bmatrix} 4 & -6 & | & -8 \\ 1 & -3 & | & 2 \end{bmatrix}$ **16.** $\begin{bmatrix} 1 & -3 & | & 2 \\ 2 & -3 & | & -4 \end{bmatrix}$

17. $\begin{bmatrix} -4 & 12 & | & -8 \\ 4 & -6 & | & -8 \end{bmatrix}$ **18.** $\begin{bmatrix} -2 & 6 & | & -4 \\ 4 & -6 & | & -8 \end{bmatrix}$ **19.** $\begin{bmatrix} 1 & -3 & | & 2 \\ 8 & -12 & | & -16 \end{bmatrix}$ **20.** $\begin{bmatrix} 1 & -3 & | & 2 \\ -4 & 6 & | & 8 \end{bmatrix}$

21. $\begin{bmatrix} 1 & -3 & | & 2 \\ 0 & 6 & | & -16 \end{bmatrix}$ **22.** $\begin{bmatrix} -1 & 0 & | & 6 \\ 4 & -6 & | & -8 \end{bmatrix}$ **23.** $\begin{bmatrix} 1 & -3 & | & 2 \\ 2 & 0 & | & -12 \end{bmatrix}$ **24.** $\begin{bmatrix} 1 & -3 & | & 2 \\ 1 & 3 & | & -14 \end{bmatrix}$

25. $\begin{bmatrix} 1 & -3 & | & 2 \\ 3 & -3 & | & -10 \end{bmatrix}$ **26.** $\begin{bmatrix} 1 & -3 & | & 2 \\ 5 & -9 & | & -6 \end{bmatrix}$

27. $\frac{1}{3} R_2 \rightarrow R_2$ **28.** $2R_1 \rightarrow R_1$ **29.** $6R_1 + R_2 \rightarrow R_2$

30. $\frac{2}{3} R_2 + R_1 \rightarrow R_1$ **31.** $\frac{1}{3} R_2 + R_1 \rightarrow R_1$ **32.** $4R_1 + R_2 \rightarrow R_2$

33. $x_1 = 4$, $x_2 = 3$; each pair of lines has the same intersection point.

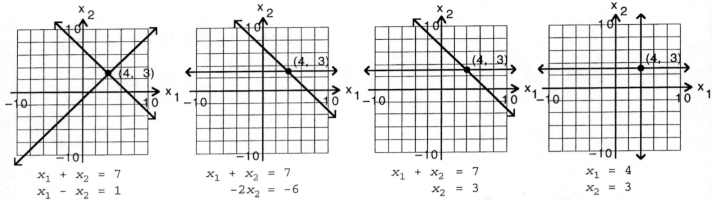

$$x_1 + x_2 = 7$$
$$x_1 - x_2 = 1$$

$$x_1 + x_2 = 7$$
$$-2x_2 = -6$$

$$x_1 + x_2 = 7$$
$$x_2 = 3$$

$$x_1 = 4$$
$$x_2 = 3$$

34. $x_1 = 1$, $x_2 = 4$; each pair of lines has the same intersection point.

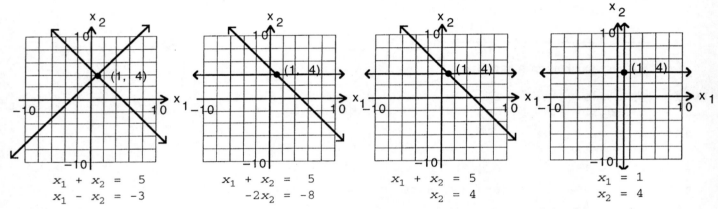

$$x_1 + x_2 = 5$$
$$x_1 - x_2 = -3$$

$$x_1 + x_2 = 5$$
$$-2x_2 = -8$$

$$x_1 + x_2 = 5$$
$$x_2 = 4$$

$$x_1 = 1$$
$$x_2 = 4$$

35. $x_1 = 2$ and $x_2 = 1$ **36.** $x_1 = -2$, $x_2 = 1$ **37.** $x_1 = 2$ and $x_2 = 4$

38. $x_1 = -1$, $x_2 = 2$ **39.** no solution   **40.** no solution

41. $x_1 = 1$ and $x_2 = 4$ **42.** $x_1 = -1$, $x_2 = 2$

43. Infinitely many solutions for any real number s, $x_2 = s$, $x_1 = 2s - 3$

44. Infinitely many solutions for $x_2 = s$, $x_1 = 2s - 1$ for any real number s

45. Infinitely many solutions for any real number s, $x_2 = s$, $x_1 = \frac{1}{2}s + \frac{1}{2}$

46. Infinitely many solutions for $x_2 = s$, $x_1 = \frac{1}{3}s - \frac{2}{3}$ for any real number s

47. (A) $(-24, 20)$ (B) $(6, -4)$ (C) No solution

48. (A) $(10, 10)$ (B) $(-2, 0)$ (C) Infinite number of solutions

49. $(-23.125, 7.8125)$ **50.** $(1.25, -1.5625)$ **51.** $(3.225, -6.9375)$

52. $(6.2625, 8.375)$ **53.** 25 32-cent stamps, 50 23-cent stamps

54. 57 nickels, 32 dimes   **55.** $107,500 in bond A and $92,500 in bond B

56. 25% in fund A and 75% in fund B

57. 30 liters of 20% solution and 70 liters of 80% solution

58. 56 liters of 40% solution and 24 liters of 70% solution

59. 200 grams of mix A and 80 grams of mix B

60. 50 bags of brand A and 40 bags of brand B

61. Base price = \$17.95, surcharge = \$2.45 per pound

62. (A) Base price = \$22.15, surcharge = \$1.95

(B) Ship packages under 10 pounds with United Express and all others with Federated Shipping.

63. 5,720 pounds of the robust blend and 6,160 pounds of the mild blend.

64. (A) The company can produce 8,448 pounds of the mild blend by blending 3,168 pounds of Columbian beans with 5,280 pounds of Brazilian beans. There will be 3,432 pounds of Columbian beans that are not used.

(B) The company can produce 8,800 pounds of the robust blend by blending 6,600 pounds of Columbian beans with 2,200 pounds of Brazilian beans. There will be 3,080 pounds of Brazilian beans that are not used.

Exercise 8-3

1. Reduced form

2. Not reduced form; $R_1 \leftrightarrow R_2$

3. Not reduced form; $R_2 \leftrightarrow R_3$

4. Reduced form

5. Not reduced form; $\frac{1}{3} R_2 \to R_2$

6. Not reduced form; $3R_2 + R_1 \to R_1$

7. Reduced form

8. Not reduced form; $\frac{1}{2} R_2 \to R_2$

9. Not reduced form; $3R_2 + R_1 \to R_1$

10. Reduced form

11. $x_1 = -2$, $x_2 = 3$, $x_3 = 0$

12. $x_1 = -2$, $x_2 = 0$, $x_3 = 1$, $x_4 = 3$

13. $x_1 = 2t + 3$, $x_2 = -t - 5$, $x_3 = t$ is the solution for t any real number

14. $x_1 = 2t - 3$, $x_2 = t$, $x_3 = 5$, t any real number

15. No solution

16. $x_1 = 5$, $x_2 = -3$

17. $x_1 = 2s + 3t - 5$, $x_2 = s$, $x_3 = -3t + 2$, $x_4 = t$ is the solution, for s and t any real numbers

18. $x_1 - 2x_3 + 3x_4 = 4$, $x_2 - x_3 + 2x_4 = -1$; $x_1 = 2s - 3t + 4$, $x_2 = s - 2t - 1$, $x_3 = s$, $x_4 = t$, s and t = any real number

19. $\begin{bmatrix} 1 & 0 & | & -7 \\ 0 & 1 & | & 3 \end{bmatrix}$

20. $\begin{bmatrix} 1 & 0 & | & 7 \\ 0 & 1 & | & -2 \end{bmatrix}$

21. $\begin{bmatrix} 1 & 0 & 0 & | & -5 \\ 0 & 1 & 0 & | & 4 \\ 0 & 0 & 1 & | & -2 \end{bmatrix}$

22. $\begin{bmatrix} 1 & 0 & 0 & | & 4 \\ 0 & 1 & 0 & | & -4 \\ 0 & 0 & 1 & | & -1 \end{bmatrix}$

23. $\begin{bmatrix} 1 & 0 & 2 & | & -\frac{5}{3} \\ 0 & 1 & -2 & | & \frac{1}{3} \\ 0 & 0 & 0 & | & 0 \end{bmatrix}$

24. $\begin{bmatrix} 1 & 0 & -1 & | & -\frac{5}{2} \\ 0 & 1 & -4 & | & -\frac{1}{2} \\ 0 & 0 & 0 & | & 0 \end{bmatrix}$

25. $x_1 = -2$, $x_2 = 3$, and $x_3 = 1$

26. $x_1 = -2$, $x_2 = 0$, $x_3 = 1$

27. $x_1 = 0$, $x_2 = -2$, and $x_3 = 2$

28. $x_1 = 1$, $x_2 = -2$, $x_3 = 0$

29. $x_1 = 2t + 3$, $x_2 = t - 2$, $x_3 = t$, t any real number

30. $x_3 = t$, $x_1 = -t - 1$, $x_2 = 3 + 2t$, t any real number

31. $x_1 = 1$, $x_2 = 2$

32. No solution

458 CHAPTER 8 SYSTEMS; MATRICES

33. No solution   **34.** No solution

35. $x_1 = 2t + 4$, $x_2 = t + 1$, $x_3 = t$, t any real number

36. $x_1 = 3t - 1$, $x_2 = -2t - 1$, $x_3 = t$, t any real number

37. $x_1 = s + 2t - 1$, $x_2 = s$, $x_3 = t$, s and t any real numbers

38. $x_2 = s$ and $x_3 = t$, $x_1 = -4s + 3t + 2$, s, t any real numbers

39. No solution   **40.** No solution

41. $x_1 = 2.5t - 4$, $x_2 = t$, $x_3 = -5$ for t any real number

42. $x_1 = 1.5t - 2.5$, $x_2 = -0.5t - 2$, $x_3 = t$ for t any real number

43. $x_1 = 1$, $x_2 = -2$, $x_3 = 1$ **44.** $x_1 = -1$, $x_2 = 1$, $x_3 = 3$

45. (A) Dependent with two parameters   (B) Dependent with one parameter
(C) Independent   (D) Impossible

46. (A) $\begin{bmatrix} 1 & 0 & m & | & a \\ 0 & 1 & n & | & b \\ 0 & 0 & 0 & | & 0 \end{bmatrix}$, $\begin{bmatrix} 1 & m & 0 & | & a \\ 0 & 0 & 1 & | & b \\ 0 & 0 & 0 & | & 0 \end{bmatrix}$, $\begin{bmatrix} 1 & m & n & | & a \\ 0 & 0 & 0 & | & 0 \\ 0 & 0 & 0 & | & 0 \end{bmatrix}$

(B) $\begin{bmatrix} 1 & 0 & m & | & 0 \\ 0 & 1 & n & | & 0 \\ 0 & 0 & 0 & | & 1 \end{bmatrix}$, $\begin{bmatrix} 1 & m & n & | & 0 \\ 0 & 0 & 0 & | & 1 \\ 0 & 0 & 0 & | & 0 \end{bmatrix}$

51. $x_1 = 2s - 3t + 3$, $x_2 = s + 2t + 2$, $x_3 = s$, $x_4 = t$, s and t any real numbers

52. $x_1 = -2s + 3t - 1$, $x_2 = s$ and $x_3 = -2t + 2$, $x_4 = t$; s, t any real numbers

53. $x_1 = -0.5$, $x_2 = 0.2$, $x_3 = 0.3$, $x_4 = -0.4$

54. $x_1 = -1.2$, $x_2 = 0.6$, $x_3 = 0.7$, $x_4 = -0.9$

55. $x_1 = 2s - 1.5t + 1$, $x_2 = s$, $x_3 = -t + 1.5$, $x_4 = 0.5t - 0.5$, $x_5 = t$ for s and t any real numbers

56. $x_1 = -5.5s + 3.5t + 10.5$, $x_2 = -1.5s + 1.5t + 2.5$, $x_3 = s$, $x_4 = -t - 1$, $x_5 = t$ for s and t any real numbers

57. $x_1 = 4$, $x_2 = 1$ **58.** $x_1 = 2$, $x_2 = -1$

59. $x_1 = -1.4$, $x_2 = 4.8$, $x_3 = 4$ **60.** $x_1 = 4$, $x_2 = -3$, $x_3 = 2$

63. $x_1 = (3t - 100)$ 15-cent stamps, $x_2 = (145 - 4t)$ 20-cent stamps, $x_3 = t$ 35-cent stamps, where $t = 34$, 35, or 36

64. if $Q = t = 24$, 25, 26 then $N = 3t - 72$ and $D = 104 - 4t$

65. $x_1 = (6t - 24)$, 500-cc containers of 10% solution
$x_2 = (48 - 8t)$, 500-cc containers of 20% solution
$x_3 = t$, 1000-cc containers of 50% solution
where $t = 4$, 5, or 6

66. $x = 9t - 24$, 10% containers; $y = 48 - 12t$, 20% containers;
$z = t$, 50% containers, where $t = 3$, 4

67. $a = 3$, $b = 2$, $c = 1$ **68.** $a = 8$, $b = -7$, $c = 2$

69. $a = -2$, $b = -4$, and $c = -20$ **70.** $a = 2$, $b = 6$, $c = -15$

71. (A) $x_1 = 20$ one-person boats, $x_2 = 220$ two-person boats,
$x_3 = 100$ four-person boats

(B) $x_1 = (t - 80)$ one-person boats, $x_2 = (-2t + 420)$ two-person boats, $x_3 = t$ four-person boats $80 \leq t \leq 210$, t an integer

(C) No solution; no production schedule will use all the work-hours in all departments.

72. (A) 150 one-person boats, 200 two-person boats, 50 four-person boats

(B) $x_1 = 100 + t$, one-person; $x_2 = 300 - 2t$, two-person; $x_3 = t$, four-person, $0 \leq t \leq 150$, t = integer

(C) No production schedule will use all work hours in all departments.

73. (A) $x_1 = 8$ ounces food A, $x_2 = 2$ ounces food B, $x_3 = 4$ ounces food C

(B) No solution

(C) $x_1 = 8$ ounces food A, $x_2 = -2t + 10$ ounces food B, $x_3 = t$ ounces food C, $0 \leq t \leq 5$

74. (A) 12 oz. food A, 4 oz. food B, 0 oz. food C

(B) 12 oz. food A, 4 oz. food B

(C) 12 oz. food A, $4 - 2t$ oz. of food B, t oz. of food C where $0 \leq t \leq 2$

75. $10 - t$ barrels of mix A, $t - 5$ barrels of mix B, $25 - 2t$ barrels of mix C, and t barrels of mix D, where t is an integer satisfying $5 \leq t \leq 10$

76. 2 of b and 3 of d; or 1 of a, 1 of c, and 3 of d; or 1 of b, 2 of c, and 2 of d; or 4 of c and 1 of d

77. $x_1 = 10$ hours company A, $x_2 = 15$ hours company B

78. 15 hours company A, 10 hours company B

Exercise 8-4

1. $\begin{bmatrix} 0 & 2 \\ 2 & -1 \end{bmatrix}$ **2.** $\begin{bmatrix} -1 & 0 \\ 5 & -3 \end{bmatrix}$ **3.** $\begin{bmatrix} -1 & 6 \\ -4 & 3 \\ 1 & -1 \end{bmatrix}$ **4.** $\begin{bmatrix} 2 & 0 & 3 \\ 7 & 7 & -5 \end{bmatrix}$

5. Not defined   **6.** Not defined   **7.** $\begin{bmatrix} 2 & 3 & -5 \\ 5 & -5 & 7 \end{bmatrix}$ **8.** $\begin{bmatrix} 5 & -7 \\ -5 & 2 \\ 0 & 4 \end{bmatrix}$

9. $\begin{bmatrix} 20 & -10 & 30 \\ 0 & -40 & 50 \end{bmatrix}$ **10.** $\begin{bmatrix} 5 & -10 & 0 & 20 \\ -15 & 10 & -5 & 30 \end{bmatrix}$ **11.** $[10]$ **12.** $[16]$

13. $\begin{bmatrix} 5 \\ -3 \end{bmatrix}$ **14.** $\begin{bmatrix} -6 \\ 14 \end{bmatrix}$ **15.** $\begin{bmatrix} 2 & 4 \\ 1 & -5 \end{bmatrix}$ **16.** $\begin{bmatrix} 4 & -9 \\ -7 & 17 \end{bmatrix}$

17. $\begin{bmatrix} 1 & -5 \\ -2 & -4 \end{bmatrix}$ **18.** $\begin{bmatrix} 26 & -9 \\ 15 & -5 \end{bmatrix}$ **19.** $[-14]$ **20.** $[10]$

21. $\begin{bmatrix} -20 & 10 \\ -12 & 6 \end{bmatrix}$ **22.** $\begin{bmatrix} 6 & -3 \\ -8 & 4 \end{bmatrix}$ **23.** $[11]$ **24.** $[6]$

25. $\begin{bmatrix} 3 & -2 & -4 \\ 6 & -4 & -8 \\ -9 & 6 & 12 \end{bmatrix}$ **26.** $\begin{bmatrix} 2 & -4 & 4 \\ -1 & 2 & -2 \\ 1 & -2 & 2 \end{bmatrix}$ **27.** Not defined   **28.** $\begin{bmatrix} -12 & 12 & 18 \\ 20 & -18 & -6 \end{bmatrix}$

29. $\begin{bmatrix} -6 & 7 & -11 \\ 4 & 18 & -4 \end{bmatrix}$ **30.** Not defined   **31.** $\begin{bmatrix} -3 & 6 & 8 \\ -18 & 12 & 10 \\ 4 & 6 & 24 \end{bmatrix}$ **32.** $\begin{bmatrix} 11 & 2 \\ 4 & 27 \end{bmatrix}$

33. $\begin{bmatrix} 5 & -11 & 15 \\ 4 & -7 & 3 \\ 0 & 10 & 4 \end{bmatrix}$ **34.** $\begin{bmatrix} 6 & 4 \\ 0 & -3 \end{bmatrix}$ **35.** $\begin{bmatrix} -0.2 & 1.2 \\ 2.6 & -0.6 \\ -0.2 & 2.2 \end{bmatrix}$ **36.** $\begin{bmatrix} -1.3 & -0.7 \\ -0.2 & -0.5 \\ 0.1 & 1.1 \end{bmatrix}$

37. $\begin{bmatrix} -31 & 16 \\ 61 & -25 \\ -3 & 77 \end{bmatrix}$ **38.** $\begin{bmatrix} -66 & 69 & 39 \\ 92 & -18 & -36 \end{bmatrix}$ **39.** Not defined   **40.** Not defined

41. $\begin{bmatrix} -2 & 25 & -15 \\ 26 & -25 & 45 \\ -2 & 45 & -25 \end{bmatrix}$ **42.** $\begin{bmatrix} -18 & 48 \\ 54 & -34 \end{bmatrix}$ **43.** $\begin{bmatrix} -26 & -15 & -25 \\ -4 & -18 & 4 \\ 2 & 43 & -19 \end{bmatrix}$ **44.** $\begin{bmatrix} -29 & -17 \\ 8 & -34 \end{bmatrix}$

45. $B^n \to \begin{bmatrix} 0.25 & 0.75 \\ 0.25 & 0.75 \end{bmatrix}$, $AB^n \to \begin{bmatrix} 0.25 & 0.75 \end{bmatrix}$

46. $B^n \to \begin{bmatrix} 0.75 & 0.25 \\ 0.75 & 0.25 \end{bmatrix}$, $AB^n \to \begin{bmatrix} 0.75 & 0.25 \end{bmatrix}$

47. $a = -1$, $b = 1$, $c = 3$, $d = -5$ **48.** $w = -2$, $x = -1$, $y = 3$, $z = 5$

49. $x = 1$, $y = 2$ **50.** $x = -4$, $y = -3$ **51.** $x = -5$, $y = 4$

52. $x = 3$, $y = 2$ **53.** $a = 3$, $b = 1$, $c = 1$, $d = -2$

54. $a = 3$, $b = 4$, $c = 1$, $d = 2$ **55.** All are true

56. A, B, and C are true; D is false

57. Guitar Banjo $\begin{bmatrix} \$33 & \$26 \\ \$57 & \$77 \end{bmatrix}$ Materials / Labor   **58.** Guitar Banjo $\begin{bmatrix} \$36 & \$28.5 \\ \$63 & \$85 \end{bmatrix}$ Materials / Labor

59.

	Basic Car	Markup Air	AM/FM radio	Cruise control
Model A	$3,330	$77	$42	$27
Model B	$2,125	$93	$95	$50
Model C	$1,270	$113	$121	$52

60.

	Basic Car	Markup Air	AM/FM radio	Cruise control
Model A	$3,505	$82	$44	$29
Model B	$2,250	$99	$100	$53
Model C	$1,365	$120	$127	$55

61. (A) $11.80 (B) $30.30   (C) MN gives the labor costs per boat at each plant.

(D)

	Plant I	Plant II	
$MN = $	$11.80	$13.80	One-person
	$18.50	$21.60	Two-person
	$26.00	$30.30	Four-person

62. (A) $48,480   (B) $39,300

(C) *MN* gives the total wholesale and retail values of each store.

(D)
$$
\begin{array}{cc}
W & R \\
\end{array}
$$

$$
\begin{bmatrix}
\$33,400 & \$42,160 \\
\$35,600 & \$48,480 \\
\$39,300 & \$50,700
\end{bmatrix}
\begin{array}{l}
S1 \\
S2 \\
S3
\end{array}
$$

(E) $[1 \quad 1 \quad 1]M = [16 \quad 9 \quad 11 \quad 11 \quad 10]$ (F) $M\begin{bmatrix}1\\1\\1\\1\\1\end{bmatrix} = \begin{bmatrix}17\\16\\24\end{bmatrix}$

63. (A) $A^2 = \begin{bmatrix} 0 & 0 & 2 & 0 & 0 \\ 1 & 0 & 0 & 0 & 1 \\ 0 & 1 & 0 & 2 & 0 \\ 1 & 0 & 0 & 0 & 1 \\ 0 & 0 & 1 & 0 & 0 \end{bmatrix}$

There is one way to travel from Baltimore to Atlanta with one intermediate connection; there are two ways to travel from Atlanta to Chicago with one intermediate connection. In general, the elements in A^2 indicate the number of different ways to travel from the ith city to the jth city with one intermediate connection.

(B) $A^3 = \begin{bmatrix} 2 & 0 & 0 & 0 & 2 \\ 0 & 1 & 0 & 2 & 0 \\ 0 & 0 & 3 & 0 & 0 \\ 0 & 1 & 0 & 2 & 0 \\ 1 & 0 & 0 & 0 & 1 \end{bmatrix}$

There is one way to travel from Denver to Baltimore with two intermediate connections; there are two ways to travel from Atlanta to El Paso with two intermediate connections. In general, the elements in A^3 indicate the number of different ways to travel from the ith city to the jth city with two intermediate connections.

(C) $A + A^2 + A^3 + A^4 = \begin{bmatrix} 2 & 3 & 2 & 5 & 2 \\ 1 & 1 & 4 & 2 & 1 \\ 4 & 1 & 3 & 2 & 4 \\ 1 & 1 & 4 & 2 & 1 \\ 1 & 1 & 1 & 3 & 1 \end{bmatrix}$

It is possible to travel from any origin to any destination with at most 3 intermediate connections

64. $A = \begin{bmatrix} 0 & 0 & 0 & 1 & 1 \\ 1 & 0 & 0 & 1 & 0 \\ 0 & 1 & 0 & 0 & 0 \\ 1 & 0 & 0 & 0 & 1 \\ 0 & 1 & 1 & 0 & 0 \end{bmatrix}$; $A + A^2 + A^3 = \begin{bmatrix} 2 & 3 & 2 & 3 & 3 \\ 3 & 2 & 2 & 3 & 4 \\ 2 & 1 & 0 & 2 & 2 \\ 3 & 3 & 2 & 2 & 3 \\ 3 & 2 & 1 & 3 & 2 \end{bmatrix}$;

It is possible to travel from any origin to any destination with at most 2 intermediate connections.

65. (A) $3,550   (B) $6,000   (C) NM gives the total cost per town.

               Cost/town

(D) $NM = \begin{bmatrix} \$3{,}550 \\ \$6{,}000 \end{bmatrix}$ Berkeley
   Oakland

               Telephone   House
               call   call   Letter

(E) $[1 \quad 1]N = [3{,}000 \qquad 1{,}300 \qquad 13{,}000]$

               Total
               contacts

(F) $N\begin{bmatrix} 1 \\ 1 \\ 1 \end{bmatrix} = \begin{bmatrix} 6{,}500 \\ 10{,}800 \end{bmatrix}$ Berkeley
   Oakland

66. (A) 70 g   (B) 30 g

(C) MN gives total amounts in grams of protein, carbohydrates, and fat in 20 ounces of each mix.

(D) X Y Z

$\begin{bmatrix} 70g & 60g & 50g \\ 380g & 360g & 340g \\ 50g & 40g & 30g \end{bmatrix}$ protein
   carbohydrates
   fat

67. (A)

$$\begin{bmatrix} 0 & 0 & 1 & 1 & 1 & 0 \\ 1 & 0 & 0 & 1 & 1 & 0 \\ 0 & 1 & 0 & 1 & 0 & 0 \\ 0 & 0 & 0 & 0 & 0 & 1 \\ 0 & 0 & 1 & 1 & 0 & 1 \\ 1 & 1 & 1 & 0 & 0 & 0 \end{bmatrix}$$

(B)

$$\begin{bmatrix} 0 & 1 & 2 & 3 & 1 & 2 \\ 1 & 0 & 2 & 3 & 2 & 2 \\ 1 & 1 & 0 & 2 & 1 & 1 \\ 1 & 1 & 1 & 0 & 0 & 1 \\ 1 & 2 & 2 & 2 & 0 & 2 \\ 2 & 2 & 2 & 3 & 2 & 0 \end{bmatrix}$$

(C) $BC = \begin{bmatrix} 9 \\ 10 \\ 6 \\ 4 \\ 9 \\ 11 \end{bmatrix}$ where $C = \begin{bmatrix} 1 \\ 1 \\ 1 \\ 1 \\ 1 \\ 1 \end{bmatrix}$

(D) Frank, Bart, Aaron and Elvis (tie), Charles, Dan

68. (A)

$$\begin{bmatrix} 0 & 0 & 0 & 1 & 0 \\ 1 & 0 & 1 & 1 & 0 \\ 1 & 0 & 0 & 0 & 0 \\ 0 & 0 & 1 & 0 & 1 \\ 1 & 1 & 1 & 0 & 0 \end{bmatrix}$$

(B)

$$\begin{bmatrix} 0 & 0 & 1 & 1 & 1 \\ 2 & 0 & 2 & 2 & 1 \\ 1 & 0 & 0 & 1 & 0 \\ 2 & 1 & 2 & 0 & 1 \\ 3 & 1 & 2 & 2 & 0 \end{bmatrix}$$

(C) $BC = \begin{bmatrix} 3 \\ 7 \\ 2 \\ 6 \\ 8 \end{bmatrix}$ where $C = \begin{bmatrix} 1 \\ 1 \\ 1 \\ 1 \\ 1 \end{bmatrix}$

(D) Erlene, Bridget, Diane, Anne, Carol

Exercise 8-5

1. $\begin{bmatrix} 2 & -3 \\ 4 & 5 \end{bmatrix}$ **2.** $\begin{bmatrix} 4 & -3 \\ 0 & 2 \end{bmatrix}$ **3.** $\begin{bmatrix} 2 & -3 \\ 4 & 5 \end{bmatrix}$ **4.** $\begin{bmatrix} 4 & -3 \\ 0 & 2 \end{bmatrix}$

5. $\begin{bmatrix} -2 & 1 & 3 \\ 2 & 4 & -2 \\ 5 & 1 & 0 \end{bmatrix}$ **6.** $\begin{bmatrix} -3 & 0 & 2 \\ 1 & 1 & 5 \\ 2 & -1 & 7 \end{bmatrix}$ **7.** $\begin{bmatrix} -2 & 1 & 3 \\ 2 & 4 & -2 \\ 5 & 1 & 0 \end{bmatrix}$ **8.** $\begin{bmatrix} -3 & 0 & 2 \\ 1 & 1 & 5 \\ 2 & -1 & 7 \end{bmatrix}$

9. Yes   **10.** No   **11.** No   **12.** Yes   **13.** Yes   **14.** Yes   **15.** No

16. Yes   **17.** Yes   **18.** No

19. $\begin{bmatrix} 4 & 1 \\ -1 & 0 \end{bmatrix}$ **20.** $\begin{bmatrix} -1 & -5 \\ 0 & -1 \end{bmatrix}$ **21.** $\begin{bmatrix} 3 & -2 \\ -1 & 1 \end{bmatrix}$ **22.** $\begin{bmatrix} 3 & -1 \\ -5 & 2 \end{bmatrix}$

23. $\begin{bmatrix} 7 & -3 \\ -2 & 1 \end{bmatrix}$ **24.** $\begin{bmatrix} 1 & -1 \\ -1 & 2 \end{bmatrix}$

25. $\begin{bmatrix} -3 & -4 & 2 \\ -2 & -2 & 1 \\ 2 & 3 & -1 \end{bmatrix}$ **26.** $\begin{bmatrix} 7 & -6 & 9 \\ -2 & 2 & -3 \\ -1 & 1 & -1 \end{bmatrix}$ **27.** $\begin{bmatrix} 2 & -1 & -1 \\ -1 & 1 & 1 \\ -2 & 1 & 2 \end{bmatrix}$ **28.** $\begin{bmatrix} 4 & -1 & -1 \\ 8 & -3 & -2 \\ 3 & -1 & -1 \end{bmatrix}$

29. does not exist   **30.** inverse does not exist   **31.** $\begin{bmatrix} 5 & -3 \\ -3 & 2 \end{bmatrix}$

32. $\begin{bmatrix} 3 & 4 \\ 4 & 5 \end{bmatrix}$ **33.** $\begin{bmatrix} 1 & 0 & 1 \\ \frac{1}{2} & \frac{1}{2} & 1 \\ 2 & 1 & 4 \end{bmatrix}$ **34.** $\begin{bmatrix} 0 & -\frac{1}{2} & -\frac{1}{2} \\ 1 & \frac{1}{2} & \frac{3}{2} \\ 1 & -1 & 1 \end{bmatrix}$

35. does not exist   **36.** inverse does not exist   **37.** $\begin{bmatrix} -9 & -15 & 10 \\ 4 & 5 & -4 \\ -1 & -1 & 1 \end{bmatrix}$

38. $\begin{bmatrix} 21 & 25 & -20 \\ 6 & 7 & -6 \\ -1 & -1 & 1 \end{bmatrix}$

39. M^{-1} exists if and only if all the elements on the main diagonal are nonzero.

40. M^{-1} exists if and only if all the elements on the main diagonal are nonzero.

41. In both parts, $A^{-1} = A$ and $A^2 = I$

43. In both parts, $(A^{-1})^{-1} = A$.

45. (A) $(AB)^{-1} = \begin{bmatrix} 29 & -41 \\ -12 & 17 \end{bmatrix}$, $A^{-1}B^{-1} = \begin{bmatrix} 23 & -33 \\ -16 & 23 \end{bmatrix}$, $B^{-1}A^{-1} = \begin{bmatrix} 29 & -41 \\ -12 & 17 \end{bmatrix}$

(B) $(AB)^{-1} = \begin{bmatrix} 0.7 & -0.1 \\ -1.8 & 0.4 \end{bmatrix}$, $A^{-1}B^{-1} = \begin{bmatrix} 0.1 & 0 \\ -0.4 & 1 \end{bmatrix}$, $B^{-1}A^{-1} = \begin{bmatrix} 0.7 & -0.1 \\ -1.8 & 0.4 \end{bmatrix}$

47. 14 5 195 74 97 37 181 67 49 18 121 43 103 41

48. 93 36 207 78 97 37 176 65 60 21 128 49

49. GREEN EGGS AND HAM   **50.** HORTON HEARS A WHO

51. 21 56 55 25 58 46 97 94 48 75 45 58 63 45 59 48 64 80 44 69 68 104 123 72 127

52. 45 104 84 62 88 33 50 74 34 94 10 31 45 9 52 46 58 98 33 85 57 110 93 79 115

53. LYNDON BAINES JOHNSON   **54.** RICHARD MILHOUS NIXON

Exercise 8-6

1. $2x_1 - x_2 = 3$
   $x_1 + 3x_2 = -2$

2. $-3x_1 + x_2 = -2$
   $-x_1 + 2x_2 = 5$

3. $\begin{aligned} -2x_1 \qquad\quad + x_3 &= 3 \\ x_1 + 2x_2 + x_3 &= -4 \\ x_2 - x_3 &= 2 \end{aligned}$

4. $\begin{aligned} x_1 - 2x_2 + 0x_3 &= 3 \\ -3x_1 + x_2 - x_3 &= -2 \\ 2x_1 + 0x_2 + 4x_3 &= 5 \end{aligned}$

5. $\begin{bmatrix} 4 & -3 \\ 1 & 2 \end{bmatrix}\begin{bmatrix} x_1 \\ x_2 \end{bmatrix} = \begin{bmatrix} 2 \\ 1 \end{bmatrix}$

6. $\begin{bmatrix} 1 & 2 \\ -3 & 1 \end{bmatrix}\begin{bmatrix} x_1 \\ x_2 \end{bmatrix} = \begin{bmatrix} 7 \\ -3 \end{bmatrix}$

7. $\begin{bmatrix} 1 & -2 & 1 \\ -1 & 1 & 0 \\ 2 & 3 & 1 \end{bmatrix}\begin{bmatrix} x_1 \\ x_2 \\ x_3 \end{bmatrix} = \begin{bmatrix} -1 \\ 2 \\ -3 \end{bmatrix}$

8. $\begin{bmatrix} 2 & 0 & 3 \\ 1 & -2 & 1 \\ -1 & 3 & 0 \end{bmatrix}\begin{bmatrix} x_1 \\ x_2 \\ x_3 \end{bmatrix} = \begin{bmatrix} 5 \\ -4 \\ 2 \end{bmatrix}$

9. $x_1 = -8$ and $x_2 = 2$

10. $x_1 = -8$, $x_2 = -7$

11. $x_1 = 0$ and $x_2 = 4$

12. $x_1 = -7$, $x_2 = 2$

13. $x_1 = 3$, $x_2 = -2$

14. $x_1 = 18$, $x_2 = -3$

15. $x_1 = 11$, $x_2 = 4$

16. $x_1 = 8$, $x_2 = 2$

17. (A) $x_1 = -3$, $x_2 = 2$ (B) $x_1 = -1$, $x_2 = 2$ (C) $x_1 = -8$, $x_2 = 3$

18. (A) $\begin{bmatrix} x_1 \\ x_2 \end{bmatrix} = \begin{bmatrix} -7 \\ 16 \end{bmatrix}$ (B) $\begin{bmatrix} x_1 \\ x_2 \end{bmatrix} = \begin{bmatrix} -10 \\ 18 \end{bmatrix}$ (C) $\begin{bmatrix} x_1 \\ x_2 \end{bmatrix} = \begin{bmatrix} 6 \\ -11 \end{bmatrix}$

19. (A) $x_1 = 17$, $x_2 = -5$ (B) $x_1 = 7$, $x_2 = -2$ (C) $x_1 = 24$, $x_2 = -7$

20. (A) $\begin{bmatrix} x_1 \\ x_2 \end{bmatrix} = \begin{bmatrix} 1 \\ -3 \end{bmatrix}$ (B) $\begin{bmatrix} x_1 \\ x_2 \end{bmatrix} = \begin{bmatrix} -1 \\ 4 \end{bmatrix}$ (C) $\begin{bmatrix} x_1 \\ x_2 \end{bmatrix} = \begin{bmatrix} 2 \\ -2 \end{bmatrix}$

21. (A) $x_1 = 1$, $x_2 = 0$, $x_3 = 0$
(B) $x_1 = -1$, $x_2 = 0$, $x_3 = 1$
(C) $x_1 = 4$, $x_2 = 1$, $x_3 = -3$

22. (A) $x_1 = -3$, $x_2 = 1$, $x_3 = 1$
(B) $x_1 = -5$, $x_2 = 1$, $x_3 = 1$
(C) $x_1 = 15$, $x_2 = -4$, $x_3 = -2$

23. (A) $x_1 = 0$, $x_2 = 2$, $x_3 = 4$
(B) $x_1 = -2$, $x_2 = 2$, $x_3 = 0$
(C) $x_1 = 6$, $x_2 = -2$, $x_3 = -6$

24. (A) $x_1 = 8$, $x_2 = 8$, $x_3 = 4$
(B) $x_1 = 20$, $x_2 = 40$, $x_3 = 16$
(C) $x_1 = 0$, $x_2 = -8$, $x_3 = 0$

25. $x_1 = 2.5 + 2t$, $x_2 = t$, t any real number

26. No solution

27. No solution

28. $x_1 = 5t + 2$, $x_2 = t + 1$, $x_3 = t$, t any real number

29. $x_1 = 13t + 3$, $x_2 = 8t + 1$, $x_3 = t$, t any real number

30. No solution

31. $X = (A - B)^{-1}C$ $[X \neq C(A - B)^{-1}]$

32. $X = (A + B)^{-1}C$ $[X \neq C(A + B)^{-1}]$

33. $X = (A + I)^{-1}C$

34. $X = (A - I)^{-1}C$

35. $X = (A + B)^{-1}(C + D)$

36. $X = (A - B)^{-1}(D - C)$

37. (A) $x_1 = 1$, $x_2 = 0$
(B) $x_1 = -2{,}000$, $x_2 = 1{,}000$
(C) $x_1 = 2{,}001$, $x_2 = -1{,}000$

38. (A) $x_1 = 1$, $x_2 = 0$
(B) $x_1 = -3{,}000$, $x_2 = -1{,}000$
(C) $x_1 = 3{,}001$, $x_2 = 1{,}000$

39. (A) Concert 1: 6,000 $4 tickets and 4,000 $8 tickets; Concert 2: 5,000 $4 tickets and 5,000 $8 tickets; Concert 3: 3,000 $4 tickets and 7,000 $8 tickets

(B) No (C) Between $40,000 and $80,000

40. (A) Allocation 1: $\begin{bmatrix} A \\ B \end{bmatrix} = \begin{bmatrix} 60 \\ 0 \end{bmatrix}$; Allocation 2: $\begin{bmatrix} A \\ B \end{bmatrix} = \begin{bmatrix} 25 \\ 25 \end{bmatrix}$; Allocation 3: $\begin{bmatrix} A \\ B \end{bmatrix} = \begin{bmatrix} 4 \\ 40 \end{bmatrix}$

　　　(B) No

41. (A) $I_1 = 4$, $I_2 = 6$, $I_3 = 2$　　　(B) $I_1 = 3$, $I_2 = 7$, $I_3 = 4$
　　　(C) $I_1 = 7$, $I_2 = 8$, $I_3 = 1$

42. (A) $\begin{bmatrix} I_1 \\ I_2 \\ I_3 \end{bmatrix} = \begin{bmatrix} \frac{5}{2} \\ \frac{15}{4} \\ \frac{5}{4} \end{bmatrix}$　　(B) $\begin{bmatrix} I_1 \\ I_2 \\ I_3 \end{bmatrix} = \begin{bmatrix} \frac{5}{4} \\ \frac{35}{8} \\ \frac{25}{8} \end{bmatrix}$　　(C) $\begin{bmatrix} I_1 \\ I_2 \\ I_3 \end{bmatrix} = \begin{bmatrix} 5 \\ 5 \\ 0 \end{bmatrix}$

43. (A) $a = 1$, $b = 0$, $c = -3$　　　(B) $a = -2$, $b = 5$, $c = 1$
　　　(C) $a = 11$, $b = -46$, $c = 43$

44. (A) $\begin{bmatrix} a \\ b \\ c \end{bmatrix} = \begin{bmatrix} 1 \\ 4 \\ 1 \end{bmatrix}$　　(B) $\begin{bmatrix} a \\ b \\ c \end{bmatrix} = \begin{bmatrix} -2 \\ -3 \\ 3 \end{bmatrix}$　　(C) $\begin{bmatrix} a \\ b \\ c \end{bmatrix} = \begin{bmatrix} 11 \\ -2 \\ -5 \end{bmatrix}$

45. (A) Diet 1: 60 ounces Mix *A* and 80 ounces Mix *B*; Diet 2: 20 ounces Mix *A* and 60
　　　ounces Mix *B*; Diet 3: 0 ounces Mix *A* and 100 ounces Mix *B*

　　　(B) No

Exercise 8-7

1.
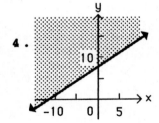

2.
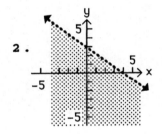

3.
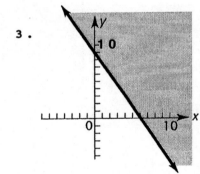

4.
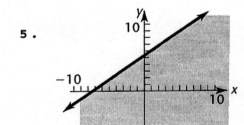

5.

6.
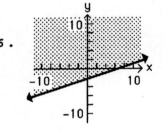

7.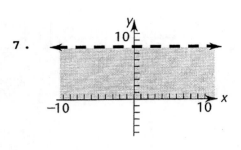

8.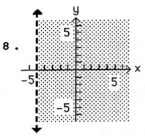

9.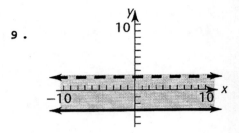

10.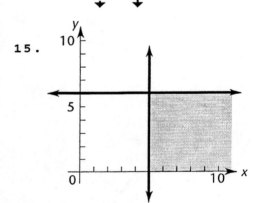

11. region IV

12. II

13. region I

14. III

15.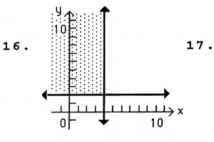

16.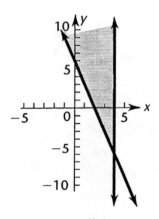

17.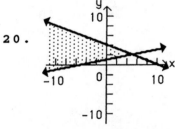

18.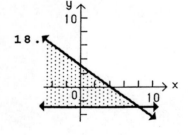

19.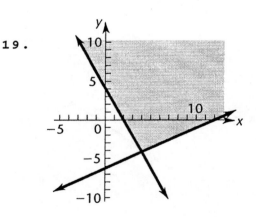

20.

21. (A) Solution region is the double-shaded region.

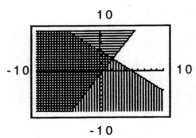

(B) Solution region is the unshaded region.

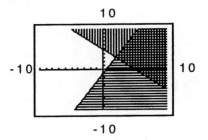

22. (A) Solution region is the double-shaded region.

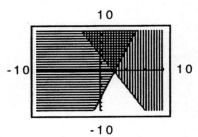

(B) Solution region is the unshaded region.

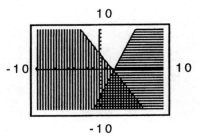

23. (A) Solution region is the double-shaded region.

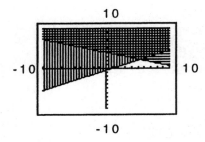

(B) Solution region is the unshaded region.

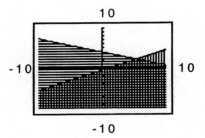

24. (A) Solution region is the double-shaded region.

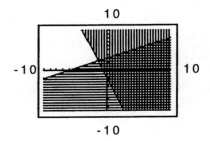

(B) Solution region is the unshaded region.

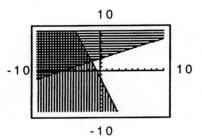

25. Region IV; corner points are (6, 4), (8, 0), and (18, 0)

26. Region III; corner points: (0, 0), (0, 6), (6, 4), (8, 0)

27. Region I; corner points are (0, 16), (6, 4), and (18, 0)

28. Region II; corner points: (6, 4), (0, 6), (0, 16)

29.

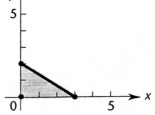

corner points: (0, 0), (0, 2), (3, 0); bounded

30.

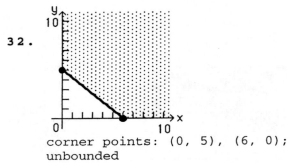

corner points: (0, 0), (0, 4), (3, 0); bounded

31.

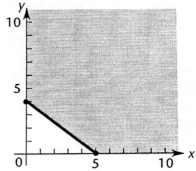

corner points: (0, 4) and (5, 0); unbounded

32.

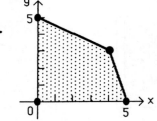

corner points: (0, 5), (6, 0); unbounded

33.

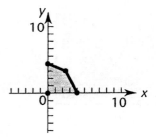

corner points: (0, 4), (0, 0), $\left(\dfrac{12}{5}, \dfrac{16}{5}\right)$, (4, 0); bounded

34.

corner points: (0, 0), (0, 5), (4, 3), (5, 0); bounded

35.

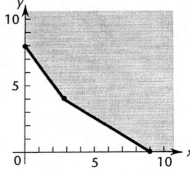

corner points: (9, 0), (0, 8), and (3, 4); unbounded

36.

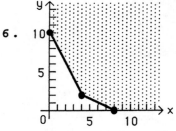

corner points: (8, 0), (4, 2), (0, 10); unbounded

37.

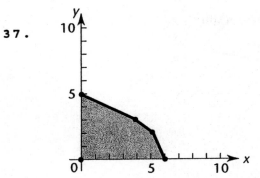

corner points: (6, 0), (4, 3),
(5, 2), (0, 0), and (0, 5);
bounded

38.

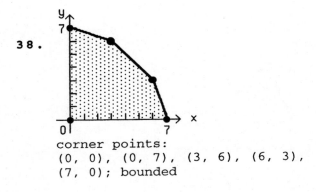

corner points:
(0, 0), (0, 7), (3, 6), (6, 3),
(7, 0); bounded

39.

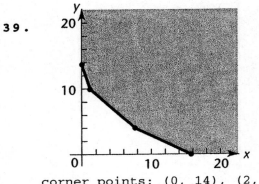

corner points: (0, 14), (2, 10),
(8, 4), (16, 0); unbounded

40.

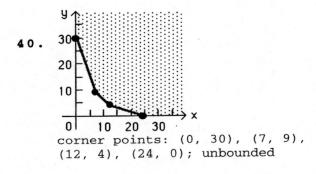

corner points: (0, 30), (7, 9),
(12, 4), (24, 0); unbounded

41.

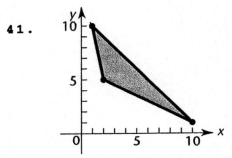

corner points: (2, 5), (10, 1),
(1, 10); bounded

42.

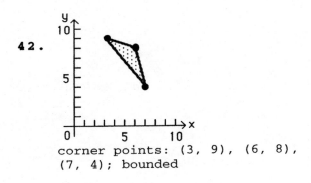

corner points: (3, 9), (6, 8),
(7, 4); bounded

43. The feasible region is empty.

44. The feasible region is empty.

45.

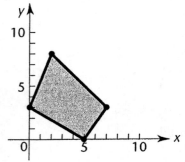

corner points: (0, 3), (5, 0), (7, 3), (2, 8); bounded

46.

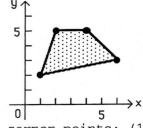

corner points: (1, 2), (2, 5), (4, 5), (6, 3); bounded

47.

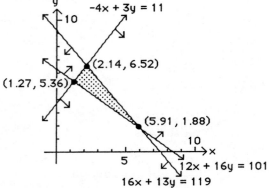

corner points: (1.27, 5.36), (2.14, 6.52), (5.91, 1.88); bounded

48.

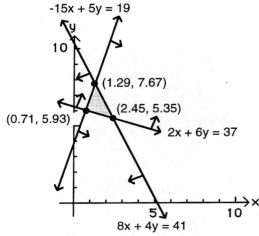

corner points: (0.71, 5.93), (1.29, 7.67), (2.45, 5.35); bounded

49. $6x + 4y \leq 108$
$\quad\;\; x + \;\; y \leq 24$
$\quad\qquad x \geq 0$
$\quad\qquad y \geq 0$

50. $8x + 2y \leq 400$
$\quad 2x + \;\; y \leq 120$
$\quad\qquad x \geq 0$
$\quad\qquad y \geq 0$

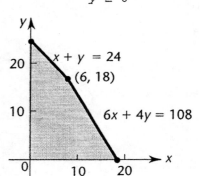

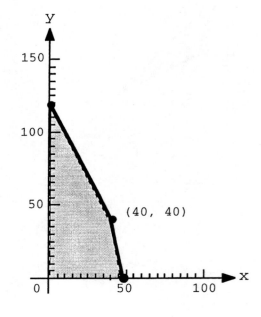

51. (A) All production schedules in the feasible region that are on the graph of $50x + 60y = 1{,}100$ will result in a profit of \$1,100.

(B) There are many possible choices. For example, producing 5 trick and 15 slalom skies will produce a profit of \$1,150. The graph of the line $50x + 60y = 1{,}150$ includes all the production schedules in the feasible region that result in a profit of \$1,150.

52. (A) All production schedules in the feasible region that are on the graph of $50x + 15y = 1{,}300$ will result in a profit of \$1,300.

(B) There are many possible choices. For example, producing 30 tables and 30 chairs will produce a profit of \$1,950. The graph of the line $50x + 15y = 1{,}950$ includes all the production schedules in the feasible region that result in a profit of \$1,950.

53. $20x + 10y \geq 460$
$30x + 30y \geq 960$
$5x + 10y \geq 220$
$x \geq 0$
$y \geq 0$

54. $30x + 10y \geq 360$
$10x + 10y \geq 160$
$10x + 30y \geq 240$
$x \geq 0$
$y \geq 0$

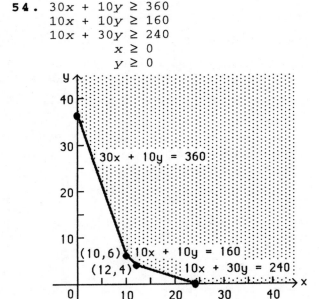

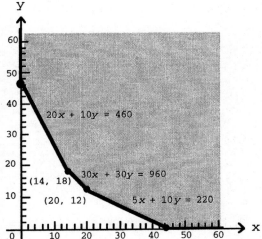

55. $10x + 30y \geq 280$
$30x + 10y \geq 360$
$x \geq 0$
$y \geq 0$

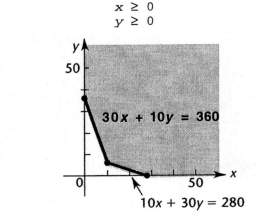

56. $10x + 20y \leq 800$
$20x + 10y \leq 640$
$x \geq 0$
$y \geq 0$

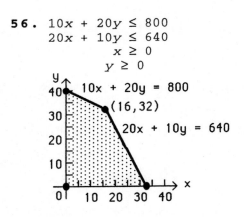

Exercise 8-8

1. maximum value of z on S is 16 at $(7, 9)$ **2.** $z_{max} = 40$ at $(10, 0)$

3. maximum value of z on S is 84 at both $(0, 12)$ and $(7, 9)$

4. $z_{max} = 90$ at $(7, 9)$ and $(10, 0)$ (multiple optimal solutions)

5. minimum value of z on S is 32 at $(0, 8)$ **6.** $z_{min} = 55$ at $(4, 3)$

7. minimum value of z on S is 36 at both $(12, 0)$ and $(4, 3)$

8. $z_{min} = 32$ at $(0, 8)$ and $(4, 3)$ (multiple optimal solutions)

9. maximum value of z on S is 18 at $(4, 3)$ **10.** $z_{max} = 42$ at $(3, 6)$

11. minimum value of z on S is 12 at $(4, 0)$ **12.** $z_{min} = 8$ at $(0, 8)$

13. maximum value of z on S is 52 at $(4, 10)$ **14.** $z_{max} = 44$ at $(7, 3)$

15. minimum value of z on S is 44 at $(4, 4)$ **16.** $z_{min} = 15$ at $(15, 0)$

17. The minimum value of z on S is 1,500 at $(60, 0)$. The maximum value of z on S is 3,000 at $(60, 30)$ and $(120, 0)$ (multiple optimal solutions).

18. $z_{max} = 6000$ at $(0, 200)$; $z_{min} = 1500$ at $(0, 50)$ and $(20, 40)$ (multiple optimal solutions)

19. The minimum value of z on S is 300 at $(0, 20)$. The maximum value of z on S is 1,725 at $(60, 15)$.

20. $z_{min} = 1200$ at $(0, 40)$; $z_{max} = 4600$ at $(40, 120)$

21. Max $P = 5,507$ at $x_1 = 6.62$ and $x_2 = 4.25$

22. Max $P = 4,484$ at $x_1 = 4.52$ and $x_2 = 6.8$

23. (A) $a > 2b$ (B) $\frac{1}{3}b < a < 2b$ (C) $a < \frac{1}{3}b$ or $b > 3a$ (D) $a = 2b$ (E) $b = 3a$

24. (A) $2a < b$ (B) $\frac{1}{2}b < a < b$ (C) $a > b$ (D) $b = 2a$ (E) $b = a$

25. (A) 6 trick skis, 18 slalom skis; $780

(B) The maximum profit decreases to $720 when 18 trick and no slalom skis are produced.

(C) The maximum profit increases to $1,080 when no trick and 24 slalom skis are produced.

26. 48; 16 mice, 32 rats

27. 9 model A trucks and 6 model B trucks to realize the minimum cost of $279,000

28. 7 buses, 15 vans; $9,900

29. (A) 40 tables, 40 chairs; $4,600

(B) The maximum profit decreases to $3,800 when 20 tables and 80 chairs are produced.

30. (A) 72 (all portable)

(B) Profit on 72 portable computers is $15,840. Maximum profit is $16,640 when 30 desktop and 32 portable computers are manufactured.

31. (A) Max $P = \$450$ when 750 gallons are produced using the old process exclusively.

(B) The maximum profit decreases to $380 when 400 gallons are produced using the old process and 700 gallons using the new process.

(C) The maximum profit decreases to $288 when 1,440 gallons are produced using the new process exclusively.

32. (A) 10 sociologists, 6 research assistants; $6,800

(B) The minimum cost will increase to $7,200 when 9 sociologists and 9 research assistants are hired.

33. The nitrogen will range from a minimum of 940 pounds when 40 bags of brand A and 100 bags of brand B are used to a maximum of 1,190 pounds when 140 bags of brand A and 50 bags of brand B are used.

34. The amount of vitamin A will range from a minimum of 200 units when 15 ounces of food M and 20 ounces of food N are used to a maximum of 380 units when 40 ounces of food M and 15 ounces of food N are used.

CHAPTER 8 REVIEW

1. $x = 3,\ y = 3$ *(8-1)*

2. $x = 3,\ y = -2$ *(8-1)*

3.
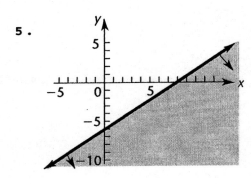
(8-1)

4. $x = 1.1875,\ y = 1.625$
(8-1)

5.
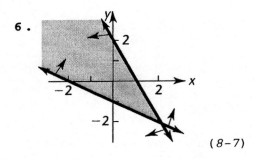
(8-7)

6.

(8-7)

7. $\begin{bmatrix} 3 & -6 & | & 12 \\ 1 & -4 & | & 5 \end{bmatrix}$ *(8-2)* **8.** $\begin{bmatrix} 1 & -4 & | & 5 \\ 1 & -2 & | & 4 \end{bmatrix}$ *(8-2)* **9.** $\begin{bmatrix} 1 & -4 & | & 5 \\ 0 & 6 & | & -3 \end{bmatrix}$ *(8-2)*

10. $x_1 = 4$
$x_2 = -7$
The solution is $(4, -7)$ *(8-3)*

11. $x_1 - x_2 = 4$
$0 = 1$
No solution *(8-3)*

12. $x_1 - x_2 = 4$
$x_1 = t + 4,\ x_2 = t$ is the solution, for t any real number *(8-3)*

13. $\begin{bmatrix} 3 & 3 \\ 4 & 2 \end{bmatrix}$ $(8-4)$ **14.** not defined $(8-4)$

15. $\begin{bmatrix} -3 & 0 \\ 1 & -1 \end{bmatrix}$ $(8-4)$ **16.** $\begin{bmatrix} 4 & 3 \\ 7 & 4 \end{bmatrix}$ $(8-4)$

17. Not defined $(8-4)$ **18.** $\begin{bmatrix} 5 \\ 5 \end{bmatrix}$ $(8-4)$

19. $\begin{bmatrix} 2 & 3 \\ 4 & 6 \end{bmatrix}$ $(8-4)$ **20.** $[8]$ $(8-4)$

21. Not defined $(8-4)$ **22.** $\begin{bmatrix} 3 & -2 \\ -4 & 3 \end{bmatrix}$ $(8-5)$

23. (A) $x_1 = -1$, $x_2 = 3$ (B) $x_1 = 1$, $x_2 = 2$ (C) $x_1 = 8$, $x_2 = -10$ $(8-6)$

24. The maximum value of z on S is 42 at $(6, 4)$. The minimum value of z on S is 18 at $(0, 6)$. $(8-8)$

25. $x_1 = 2$, $x_2 = -2$; each pair of lines has the same intersection point.

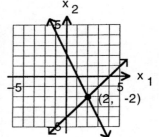 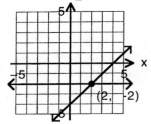 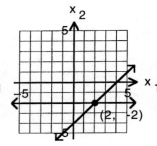 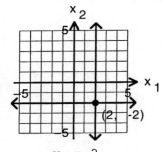

$$x_1 - x_2 = 4 \qquad\qquad x_1 - x_2 = 4 \qquad\qquad x_1 - x_2 = 4 \qquad\qquad x_1 = 2$$
$$2x_1 + x_2 = 2 \qquad\qquad 3x_2 = -6 \qquad\qquad x_2 = -2 \qquad\qquad x_2 = -2 \quad (8-3)$$

26. $x_1 = -1$, $x_2 = 3$ $(8-3)$

27. $x_1 = -1$, $x_2 = 2$, $x_3 = 1$ $(8-3)$

28. $x_1 = 2$, $x_2 = 1$, $x_3 = -1$ $(8-3)$

29. $x_1 = -5t - 12$, $x_2 = 3t + 7$, $x_3 = t$ is a solution for every real number t. There are infinitely many solutions. $(8-3)$

30. no solution $(8-3)$

31. $x_1 = -\frac{3}{7}t - \frac{4}{7}$, $x_2 = \frac{5}{7}t + \frac{9}{7}$, $x_3 = t$ is a solution for every real number t. There are infinitely many solutions. $(8-3)$

32. not defined $(8-4)$

33. $\begin{bmatrix} 10 & -8 \\ 4 & 6 \end{bmatrix}$ $(8-4)$ **34.** $\begin{bmatrix} -2 & 8 \\ 8 & 6 \end{bmatrix}$ $(8-4)$

35. Not defined $(8-4)$ **36.** $[9]$ $(8-4)$

37. $\begin{bmatrix} 10 & -5 & 1 \\ -1 & -4 & -5 \\ 1 & -7 & -2 \end{bmatrix}$ $(8-4)$

38. $\begin{bmatrix} -\frac{5}{2} & 2 & -\frac{1}{2} \\ 1 & -1 & 1 \\ \frac{1}{2} & 0 & -\frac{1}{2} \end{bmatrix}$ or $\frac{1}{2}\begin{bmatrix} -5 & 4 & -1 \\ 2 & -2 & 2 \\ 1 & 0 & -1 \end{bmatrix}$ *(8-5)*

39. (A) $x_1 = 2$, $x_2 = 1$, $x_3 = -1$ (B) $x_1 = 1$, $x_2 = -2$, $x_3 = 1$
(C) $x_1 = -1$, $x_2 = 2$, $x_3 = -2$ *(8-6)*

40. (A) A unique solution
(B) Either no solution or an infinite number   *(8-6)*

41. No   *(8-5)*

42. corners: (0, 4), (0, 0),(4, 0), and   **43.** corners: (0, 8), (12, 0),
(3, 2); bounded   and $\left(\frac{12}{5}, \frac{16}{5}\right)$; unbounded

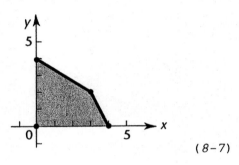

(8-7)

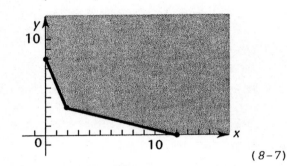

(8-7)

44. corners: (4, 4), (10, 10), (20, 0)
bounded

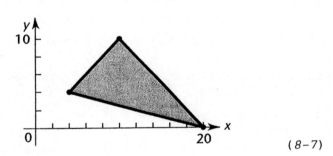

(8-7)

45. The maximum value of z on S is 46 at (4, 2).   *(8-8)*

46. The minimum value of z on S is 75 at (3, 6) and (15, 0) (multiple optimal
solutions).   *(8-8)*

47. The minimum value of z on S is 44 at (4, 3). The maximum value of z on S is 82
at (2, 9).   *(8-8)*

48. $X = (A - C)^{-1}B$ *(8-6)*

49. $\begin{bmatrix} -\frac{11}{12} & -\frac{1}{12} & 5 \\ \frac{10}{12} & \frac{2}{12} & -4 \\ \frac{1}{12} & -\frac{1}{12} & 0 \end{bmatrix}$ or $\frac{1}{12}\begin{bmatrix} -11 & -1 & 60 \\ 10 & 2 & -48 \\ 1 & -1 & 0 \end{bmatrix}$ *(8-5)*

50. $x_1 = 1,000$, $x_2 = 4,000$, $x_3 = 2,000$ *(8-6)*

51. $x_1 = 1000$, $x_2 = 4000$, $x_3 = 2000$ *(8-3)*

52. The maximum value of z on S is 26,000 at (600, 400).   *(8-8)*

53. (A) A unique solution   (B) No solution
(C) An infinite number of solutions   *(8-3)*

54. 48 $\frac{1}{2}$-pound packages and 72 $\frac{1}{3}$-pound packages   *(8-1)*

55. 6 meters by 8 meters   *(8-1)*

56. $x_1 = 40$ grams Mix A, $x_2 = 60$ grams Mix B, $x_3 = 30$ grams Mix C *(8-3)*

57. (A) $x_1 = 22$ nickels, $x_2 = 8$ dimes

(B) $x_1 = 3t + 22$ nickels, $x_2 = 8 - 4t$ dimes, $x_3 = t$ quarters, $t = 0$, 1, or 2
     (8-3)

58. (A) $27

(B) Elements in LH give the total cost of manufacturing each product at each plant.

(C)
$$LH = \begin{bmatrix} \$46.35 & \$41.00 \\ \$30.45 & \$27.00 \end{bmatrix} \begin{matrix} \text{Desk} \\ \text{Stands} \end{matrix}$$
with N.C. and S.C. columns   *(8-4)*

59. (A) $\begin{bmatrix} 1,600 & 1,730 \\ 890 & 720 \end{bmatrix}$ (B) $\begin{bmatrix} 200 & 160 \\ 80 & 40 \end{bmatrix}$

(C) $\begin{bmatrix} 3,150 \\ 1,550 \end{bmatrix} \begin{matrix} \text{Desks} \\ \text{Stands} \end{matrix}$

This matrix represents the total production of each item in January.   *(8-4)*

60. GRAPHING UTILITY   *(8-5)*

61. (A) 60 tons of ore must be produced at Big Bend, 20 tons of ore at Saw Pit.

(B) 30 tons of ore must be produced at Big Bend, 50 tons of ore at Saw Pit.

(C) 40 tons of ore must be produced at Big Bend, 40 tons of ore at Saw Pit.
     (8-6)

62. (A) Maximum profit is $P = \$7,800$ when 80 regular and 30 competition sails are produced.

(B) The maximum profit increases to $8,750 when 70 competition and no regular sails are produced.

(C) The maximum profit decreases to $7,200 when no competition and 120 regular sails are produced.   *(8-8)*

63. (A) The minimum cost is $C = \$13$ when 100 grams of mix A and 150 grams of mix B are used.

(B) The minimum cost decreases to $9 when 50 grams of mix A and 275 grams of mix B are used.

(C) The minimum cost increases to $28.75 when 250 grams of mix A and 75 grams of mix B are used.   *(8-8)*

CHAPTER 9

Exercise 9-1

1. -1, 0, 1, 2

2. 4, 5, 6, 7

3. 0, $\dfrac{1}{3}$, $\dfrac{1}{2}$, $\dfrac{3}{5}$

4. 2, $\left(\dfrac{3}{2}\right)^2 = \dfrac{9}{4}$, $\left(\dfrac{4}{3}\right)^3 = \dfrac{64}{27}$, $\left(\dfrac{5}{4}\right)^4 = \dfrac{625}{256}$

5. 4, -8, 16, -32

6. 1, $-\dfrac{1}{4}$, $\dfrac{1}{9}$, $-\dfrac{1}{16}$

7. 6

8. 13

9. $\dfrac{99}{101}$

10. $\left(\dfrac{201}{200}\right)^{200}$

11. 1 + 2 + 3 + 4 + 5

12. 1 + 4 + 9 + 16

13. $\dfrac{1}{10} + \dfrac{1}{100} + \dfrac{1}{1000}$

14. $\dfrac{1}{3} + \dfrac{1}{9} + \dfrac{1}{27} + \dfrac{1}{81} + \dfrac{1}{243}$

15. -1 + 1 - 1 + 1

16. 1 - 2 + 3 - 4 + 5 - 6

17. 1, -4, 9, -16, 25

18. $\dfrac{1}{2}$, $-\dfrac{1}{4}$, $\dfrac{1}{8}$, $-\dfrac{1}{16}$, $\dfrac{1}{32}$

19. 0.3, 0.33, 0.333, 0.3333, 0.33333

20. 2, 0, 6, 0, 10

21. 1, $-\dfrac{1}{2}$, $\dfrac{1}{4}$, $-\dfrac{1}{8}$, $\dfrac{1}{16}$

22. 1, $-\dfrac{3}{2}$, $\dfrac{9}{4}$, $-\dfrac{27}{8}$, $\dfrac{81}{16}$

23. 7, 3, -1, -5, -9

24. 1, 1, 2, 3, 5

25. 4, 1, $\dfrac{1}{4}$, $\dfrac{1}{16}$, $\dfrac{1}{64}$

26. 2, 4, 8, 16, 32

27. $a_n = n + 3$

28. $a_n = n - 3$

29. $a_n = 3n$

30. $a_n = -2n$

31. $a_n = \dfrac{n}{n + 1}$

32. $a_n = \dfrac{2n - 1}{2n}$

33. $a_n = (-1)^{n+1}$

34. $a_n = (-1)^{n+1} n$

35. $a_n = (-2)^n$

36. $a_n = (-1)^{n+1}(2n - 1)$

37. $a_n = \dfrac{x^n}{n}$

38. $a_n = (-1)^{n+1} x^{2n-1}$

39.

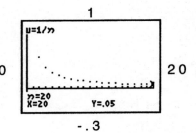

40.

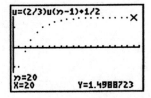

41.

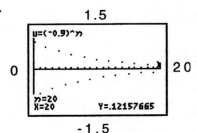

42.

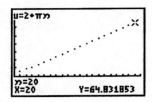

43. $\frac{4}{1} - \frac{8}{2} + \frac{16}{3} - \frac{32}{4}$

44. $1^2 - 3^2 + 5^2 - 7^2 + 9^2$

45. $x^2 + \frac{x^3}{2} + \frac{x^4}{3}$

46. $1 + x + x^2 + x^3 + x^4$

47. $x - \frac{x^2}{2} + \frac{x^3}{3} - \frac{x^4}{4} + \frac{x^5}{5}$

48. $x - \frac{x^3}{3} + \frac{x^5}{5} - \frac{x^7}{7} + \frac{x^9}{9}$

49. $\sum_{k=1}^{4} k^2$

50. $\sum_{k=1}^{5} (k + 1)$

51. $\sum_{k=1}^{5} \frac{1}{2^k}$

52. $\sum_{k=1}^{4} \frac{(-1)^{k+1}}{k}$

53. $\sum_{k=1}^{n} \frac{1}{k^2}$

54. $\sum_{k=1}^{n} \frac{k + 1}{k}$

55. $\sum_{k=1}^{n} (-1)^{k+1} k^2$

56. $\sum_{k=1}^{n} \frac{(-1)^{k+1}}{2^k}$

57. (A) 3, 1.83, 1.46, 1.415   (B) Calculator $\sqrt{2} = 1.4142135\ldots$
(C) $a_1 = 1$; 1, 1.5, 1.417, 1.414

58. (A) 2, 2.25, 2.236$\bar{1}$, 2.236067978   (B) $\sqrt{5} = 2.236067978$
(C) 3, 2.$\bar{3}$, 2.238095238, 2.236068896, 2.2360679775

59. The values of c_n are approximately 2.236 (i.e., $\sqrt{5}$) for large values of n.

60. $\{u_n\}$ is the Fibonacci sequence, $\{v_n\}$ is the Fibonacci sequence preceded by 0.

61. $e^{0.2} = 1.2214000$; $e^{0.2} = 1.2214028$ (calculator—direct evaluation)

62. $e^{-0.5} \approx 0.6067708333$; $e^{-0.5} = 0.6065306597$, calculator

Exercise 9-2

1. Fails at $n = 2$

2. 10 is the first positive integer which fails

3. Fails at $n = 3$

4. 4 is first positive integer which fails

5. P_1: $2 = 2 \cdot 1^2$; P_2: $2 + 6 = 2 \cdot 2^2$; P_3: $2 + 6 + 10 = 2 \cdot 3^2$

6. $4 = 2(1)(1 + 1)$; $4 + 8 = 2(2)(2 + 1)$; $4 + 8 + 12 = 2(3)(3 + 1)$

7. P_1: $a^5 a^1 = a^{5+1}$; P_2: $a^5 a^2 = a^5 (a^1 a) = (a^5 a) a = a^6 a = a^7 = a^{5+2}$;
P_3: $a^5 a^3 = a^5 (a^2 a) = a^5 (a^1 a) a = [(a^5 a) a] a = a^8 = a^{5+3}$

8. $(a^5)^1 = a^{5 \cdot 1} = a^5$; $(a^5)^2 = a^{5 \cdot 2} = a^{10}$; $(a^5)^3 = a^{5 \cdot 3} = a^{15}$

9. P_1: $9^1 - 1 = 8$ is divisible by 4; P_2: $9^2 - 1 = 80$ is divisible by 4;
P_3: $9^3 - 1 = 728$ is divisible by 4

10. P_1: $4^1 - 1 = 3$ which is divisible by 3; P_2: $4^2 - 1 = 15$ which is divisible by 3;
P_3: $4^3 - 1 = 63$ which is divisible by 3

11. P_k: $2 + 6 + 10 + \cdots + (4k - 2) = 2k^2$
P_{k+1}: $2 + 6 + 10 + \cdots + (4k - 2) + (4k + 2) = 2(k + 1)^2$

12. P_k: $4 + 8 + 12 + \cdots + 4k = 2k(k + 1)$;
P_{k+1}: $4 + 8 + 12 + \cdots + 4k + 4(k + 1) = 2(k + 1)(k + 2)$

13. P_k: $a^5 a^k = a^{5+k}$; P_{k+1}: $a^5 a^{k+1}$

14. P_k: $(a^5)^k = a^{5k}$; P_{k+1}: $(a^5)^{k+1} = a^{5(k+1)}$

15. P_k: $9^k - 1 = 4r$ for some integer r; P_{k+1}: $9^{k+1} - 1 = 4s$ for some integer s

16. P_k: $4^k - 1 = 3r$, $r \in N$; P_{k+1}: $4^{(k+1)} - 1 = 3s$, $s \in N$

23. $n = 4$, $p(x) = x^4 + 1$ **24.** $n = 15$

25. $n = 23$ **26.** $a = 1$, $b = 7$, $c = 5$, $d = 5$

43. P_n: $2 + 4 + 6 + \cdots + 2n = n(n + 1)$

44. $\dfrac{1}{1 \cdot 2} + \dfrac{1}{2 \cdot 3} + \dfrac{1}{3 \cdot 4} + \cdots + \dfrac{1}{n(n + 1)} = \dfrac{n}{n + 1}$

45. $1 + 2 + 3 + \cdots + (n - 1) = \dfrac{n(n - 1)}{2}$, $n \geq 2$

46. $2 + 3 + 4 + \cdots + (n - 2) = \dfrac{n(n - 3)}{2}$, $n > 3$

51. $3^4 + 4^4 + 5^4 + 6^4 \neq 7^4$ **52.** Prime up to $n = 17$; fails at $n = 18$

Exercise 9-3

1. (A) Arithmetic with $d = -5$; -26, -31 (B) Geometric with $r = -2$; -16, 32
     (C) Neither   (D) Geometric with $r = \frac{1}{3}$; $\frac{1}{54}$, $\frac{1}{162}$

2. (A) Neither   (B) Both with $d = 0$, $r = 1$; -5, -5
     (C) Arithmetic with $d = -0.5$; 5.5, 5 (D) Geometric with $r = \frac{1}{2}$; 64, 32

3. $a_2 = -1$; $a_3 = 3$; $a_4 = 7$ **4.** $a_2 = -15$; $a_3 = -12$; $a_4 = -9$

5. $a_{15} = 67$; $S_{11} = 242$ **6.** $a_{22} = 87$; $S_{21} = 903$

7. $S_{21} = 861$ **8.** $S_{11} = 385$ **9.** $a_{15} = -21$

10. $a_{10} = -39$ **11.** $a_2 = 3$; $a_3 = -\frac{3}{2}$; $a_4 = \frac{3}{4}$

12. $a_2 = 8$; $a_3 = \frac{16}{3}$; $a_4 = \frac{32}{9}$ **13.** $a_{10} = \frac{1}{243}$ **14.** $a_{13} = \frac{1}{64}$

15. $S_7 = 3,279$ **16.** $S_7 = 547$ **17.** $d = 6$; $a_{101} = 603$

18. $d = 3$; $a_{25} = 79$ **19.** $S_{40} = 200$ **20.** $S_{24} = -48$

21. $a_{11} = 2$; $S_{11} = \frac{77}{6}$ **22.** $a_{19} = \frac{5}{3}$; $S_{19} = \frac{209}{12}$ **23.** $a_1 = 1$

24. $a_1 = -42$ **25.** $r = 0.398$ **26.** $r \approx 1.13$

27. $S_{10} = -1,705$ **28.** $S_{10} = 3069$ **29.** $a_2 = 6$; $a_3 = 4$

30. $a_2 = -4$; $a_3 = \frac{4}{3}$ **31.** $S_{51} = 4,131$ **32.** $S_{40} = 1520$

33. $S_7 = 547$ **34.** $S_7 = 3279$ **35.** $-1,071$

36. 320 **37.** $\dfrac{1,023}{1,024}$ **38.** 2046

39. $4,446$ **40.** $60,000$ **43.** $x = 2\sqrt{3}$

44. $x = 4\sqrt{3}$ **45.** $a_n = -3 + (n - 1)3$ or $3n - 6$

46. $S_n = \frac{n}{2}[-6 + 3(n - 1)]$ **47.** 66 **48.** 11

49. 133

50. 122

51. $S_\infty = \dfrac{9}{2}$

52. $\dfrac{64}{3}$

53. no sum

54. no sum

55. $S_\infty = \dfrac{8}{5}$

56. $\dfrac{147}{8}$

57. $\dfrac{7}{9}$

58. $\dfrac{5}{9}$

59. $\dfrac{6}{11}$

60. $\dfrac{3}{11}$

61. $3\frac{8}{37}$ or $\frac{119}{37}$

62. $5 + \dfrac{7}{11} = \dfrac{62}{11}$

65. $a_n = (-2)(-3)^{n-1}$

66. $S_n = \dfrac{-2 - (-2)(-3)^n}{1 - (-3)} = \dfrac{(-3)^n - 1}{2}$

67. *Hint:* $y = x + d$, $z = x + 2d$

68. 25

71. $x = -1$, $y = 2$

72. 40; -24

73. Firm A: \$501,000; Firm B: \$504,000

74. Firm A: \$35,800; Firm B: \$35,200

75. \$4,000,000

76. \$1400

77. $P(1 + r)^n$; approximately 12 yr

78. $A_0(1 + r)^t$; 35 years

79. \$700 per year; \$115,500

80. (A) arithmetic sequence   (B) $T_n = 80 + (n)(-5)$

81. 900

82. 100 inches

83. 1,250,000

84. $2^{20} = 1,048,576$

85. (A) 336 ft   (B) 1,936 ft   (C) $16t^2$ ft

86. 624 feet; $a_t = 32t - 16$

87. $A = A_0 2^{2t}$

88. 15th day

89. $r = 10^{-0.4} = 0.398$

90. (A) 1.065   (B) 483 cps

91. 9.22×10^{16} dollars; 1.845×10^{17} dollars

92. 68 miles

93. 0.0015 pounds per square inch

94. 1 min

95. 2

96. $\dfrac{1}{2}$, 1.4

97. 3,420°

Exercise 9-4

1. 362,880

2. 3,628,800

3. 39,916,800

4. 479,001,600

5. 990

6. 182

7. 10

8. 15

9. 35

10. 56

11. 1

12. 1

13. 60

14. 12

15. 6,497,400

16. 2652

17. 10

18. 6

19. 270,725

20. 1326

23. $5 \cdot 3 \cdot 4 \cdot 2 = 120$

24. $3 \cdot 5 \cdot 2 = 30$

25. $P_{10,3} = 10 \cdot 9 \cdot 8 = 720$

26. $P_{50,5} = 254,251,200$

27. $C_{7,3} = 35$ subcommittees; $P_{7,3} = 210$

28. (A) $P_{9,3} = 504$ (B) $C_{9,3} = 84$

29. $C_{10,2} = 45$

30. $C_{7,2} = 21$

31. No repeats: $6 \cdot 5 \cdot 4 \cdot 3 = 360$; with repeats: $6 \cdot 6 \cdot 6 \cdot 6 = 1,296$

32. No repeats: $P_{7,5}$ = 2520; with repeats: $7 \cdot 7 \cdot 7 \cdot 7 \cdot 7$ = 16,807

33. No repeats: $10 \cdot 9 \cdot 8 \cdot 7 \cdot 6$ = 30,240; with repeats: $10 \cdot 10 \cdot 10 \cdot 10 \cdot 10$ = 100,000

34. No repeats: $P_{10,3}$ = 720; with repeats: 10^3 = 1000

35. $C_{13,5}$ = 1,287   **36.** $C_{12,5}$ = 792, $C_{8,5}$ = 56

37. $26 \cdot 26 \cdot 26 \cdot 10 \cdot 10 \cdot 10$ = 17,576,000 possible license plates;
no repeats: $26 \cdot 25 \cdot 24 \cdot 10 \cdot 9 \cdot 8$ = 11,232,000

38. 10^5 = 100,000; $P_{10,5}$ = 30,240   **39.** $C_{13,5} \cdot C_{13,2}$ = 100,386

40. $C_{13,2} \cdot C_{13,3}$ = 22,308   **41.** $C_{8,3} \cdot C_{10,4} \cdot C_{7,2}$ = 246,960

42. $P_{12,2} \cdot P_{15,2} \cdot P_{18,2}$ = 8,482,320

43. (B) r = 0, 10
(C) Each is the product of r consecutive integers, the largest of which is n for $P_{n,r}$ and r for $r!$.

44. (A) They are equal.   (B) They are equal.

45. $12 \cdot 11$ = 132

46. $6 \cdot 5$ = 30   **47.** (A) $C_{8,2}$ = 28   (B) $C_{8,3}$ = 56   (C) $C_{8,4}$ = 70

48. (A) $C_{5,2}$ = 10   (B) $C_{5,3}$ = 10

49. two people: $5 \cdot 4$ = 20; three people: $5 \cdot 4 \cdot 3$ = 60; four people: $5 \cdot 4 \cdot 3 \cdot 2$ = 120;
five people: $5 \cdot 4 \cdot 3 \cdot 2 \cdot 1$ = 120

50. 28,800   **51.** (A) $P_{8,5}$ = 6,720   (B) $C_{8,5}$ = 56   (C) $C_{2,1} \cdot C_{6,4}$ = 30

52. (A) $C_{9,4}$ = 126   (B) $C_{7,2}$ = 21   (C) $2C_{7,3}$ = 70

53. There are $C_{4,1} \cdot C_{48,4}$ = 778,320 hands which contain exactly one king, and
$C_{39,5}$ = 575,757 hands containing no hearts, so the former is more likely.

54. There are $C_{26,10}$ = 5,311,735 hands whose cards are all red and $C_{48,6}$ = 12,271,512
hands containing all four aces, so the hand with four aces is more likely.

Exercise 9-5

1. occurrence of E is certain   **2.** E cannot happen

3. (A) no probability can be negative   (B) $P(R) + P(G) + P(Y) + P(B) \neq 1$
(C) Is an acceptable probability assignment.

4. $P(R) + P(G) + P(Y)$ = 0.7   **5.** $P(R) + P(Y)$ = .56

6. P(not R or not Y) = $P(G) + P(B)$ = 0.14 + 0.30 = 0.44

7. .1   **8.** 0.14   **9.** .45   **10.** 0.8

11. $P(E) = \dfrac{n(E)}{n(S)} = \dfrac{1}{720} \approx .0014$ **12.** $\dfrac{1}{P_{10,5}} \approx 0.000033$

13. $\dfrac{C_{26,5}}{C_{52,5}} \approx .025$ **14.** $\dfrac{C_{13,5}}{C_{52,5}} \approx 0.000495$ **15.** $\dfrac{C_{16,5}}{C_{52,5}} \approx .0017$

16. $\dfrac{C_{40,5}}{C_{52,5}} \approx 0.25$ **17.** $P(E) = \dfrac{n(E)}{n(S)} = \dfrac{50}{250} = .2$ **18.** $\dfrac{4^4}{6^4} \approx 0.198$

19. $P(E) = \dfrac{n(E)}{n(S)} = \dfrac{1}{120} \approx .008$ **20.** $\dfrac{1}{P_{6,6}} = \dfrac{1}{6!} = 0.00139$

21. $\dfrac{1}{36}$ **22.** $\dfrac{1}{12}$ **23.** $\dfrac{5}{36}$ **24.** $\dfrac{5}{36}$

25. $\dfrac{1}{6}$ **26.** $\dfrac{5}{18}$ **27.** $\dfrac{7}{9}$ **28.** $\dfrac{3}{4}$

29. 0   **30.** 1   **31.** $\dfrac{1}{3}$ **32.** $\dfrac{1}{4}$

33. $\dfrac{2}{9}$ **34.** $\dfrac{1}{9}$ **35.** $\dfrac{2}{3}$ **36.** $\dfrac{1}{6}$

37. $S = \{1, 2, 3, \ldots, 365\}$; $P(e_i) = 1/365$

38. $S = \{C_1, C_2, C_3\}$ where C_i represents candidate i;
$P(C_1) = P(C_2) = 2/5$, $P(C_3) = 1/5$

39. (A) $P(2) = .022$, $P(3) = .07$, $P(4) = .088$, $P(5) = .1$, $P(6) = .142$, $P(7) = .178$,
$P(8) = .144$, $P(9) = .104$, $P(10) = .072$, $P(11) = .052$, $P(12) = .028$

(B) $P(2) = \dfrac{1}{36}$, $P(3) = \dfrac{2}{36}$, $P(4) = \dfrac{3}{36}$, $P(5) = \dfrac{4}{36}$, $P(6) = \dfrac{5}{36}$, $P(7) = \dfrac{6}{36}$,

$P(8) = \dfrac{5}{36}$, $P(9) = \dfrac{4}{36}$, $P(10) = \dfrac{3}{36}$, $P(11) = \dfrac{2}{36}$, $P(12) = \dfrac{1}{36}$

(C)
Sum	2	3	4	5	6	7	8	9	10	11	12
Expected frequency	13.9	27.8	41.7	55.6	69.4	83.3	69.4	55.6	41.7	27.8	13.9

40. (A) $P(3 \text{ heads}) = 0.116$, $P(2 \text{ heads}) = 0.396$, $P(1 \text{ head}) = 0.38$,
$P(0 \text{ heads}) = 0.108$

(B) $P(3 \text{ heads}) = \dfrac{1}{8}$, $P(2 \text{ heads}) = \dfrac{3}{8}$, $P(1 \text{ head}) = \dfrac{3}{8}$, $P(0 \text{ heads}) = \dfrac{1}{8}$

(C) 3 heads: 62.5; 2 heads: 187.5; 1 head: 187.5, 0 heads: 62.5

43. $\dfrac{1}{4}$ **44.** $\dfrac{1}{2}$ **45.** $\dfrac{1}{4}$ **46.** 0

47. $\dfrac{3}{4}$ **48.** $\dfrac{1}{4}$ **49.** $\dfrac{1}{9}$ **50.** $\dfrac{2}{9}$

51. $\dfrac{1}{3}$ **52.** $\dfrac{2}{9}$ **53.** $\dfrac{1}{9}$ **54.** 0

55. $\dfrac{4}{9}$ **56.** $\dfrac{5}{9}$ **57.** $\dfrac{C_{16,5}}{C_{52,5}} \approx .00168$ **58.** $\dfrac{C_{36,5}}{C_{52,5}} \approx 0.145$

59. $\dfrac{48}{C_{52,5}} \approx .000\ 0185$ **60.** $\dfrac{(13)(48)}{C_{52,5}} \approx 0.00024$

61. $\dfrac{4}{C_{52,5}} \approx .000\ 0015$ **62.** $\dfrac{4}{C_{52,5}} \approx 0.0000015$

63. $\dfrac{C_{4,2} \cdot C_{4,3}}{C_{52,5}} \approx .000\ 009$ **64.** $\dfrac{C_{4,2} C_{4,3}}{C_{52,5}} \approx 0.000009$

65. (A) .015   (B) .222   (C) .169   (D) .958

66. (A) 0.01   (B) 0.108   (C) 0.506   (D) 0.946

Exercise 9-6

1. 10   **2.** 15   **3.** 6   **4.** 21   **5.** 20   **6.** 10

7. 35   **8.** 4   **9.** 84   **10.** 210   **11.** 66   **12.** 1,287

13. 2,380   **14.** 4845   **15.** 230,300   **16.** 2,118,760

17. $m^3 + 3m^2n + 3mn^2 + n^3$ **18.** $x^3 + 6x^2 + 12x + 8$

19. $8x^3 - 36x^2y + 54xy^2 - 27y^3$ **20.** $27u^3 + 54u^2v + 36uv^2 + 8v^3$

21. $x^4 - 8x^3 + 24x^2 - 32x + 16$ **22.** $x^4 - 4x^3y + 6x^2y^2 - 4xy^3 + y^4$

23. $m^4 + 12m^3n + 54m^2n^2 + 108mn^3 + 81n^4$ **24.** $81p^4 - 108p^3q + 54p^2q^2 - 12pq^3 + q^4$

25. $32x^5 - 80x^4y + 80x^3y^2 - 40x^2y^3 + 10xy^4 - y^5$

26. $32x^5 - 80x^4 + 80x^3 - 40x^2 + 10x - 1$

27. $m^6 + 12m^5n + 60m^4n^2 + 160m^3n^3 + 240m^2n^4 + 192mn^5 + 64n^6$

28. $64x^6 - 192x^5y + 240x^4y^2 - 160x^3y^3 + 60x^2y^4 - 12xy^5 + y^6$

29. $35x^4$ **30.** $56x^5$ **31.** $-29,568x^6$ **32.** $1,732,104x^7$

33. $4,060,938,240x^{14}$ **34.** $6,159,089,664x^5$ **35.** $15x^8$ **36.** Does not exist

37. Does not exist   **38.** $120x^{14}$ **39.** $5,005u^9v^6$ **40.** $495a^8b^4$

41. $264m^2n^{10}$ **42.** $760x^{18}y^2$ **43.** $924w^6$ **44.** $-3240x^7$

45. $-48,384x^3y^5$ **46.** $-15,120p^4q^3$ **47.** $3x^2 + 3xh + h^2$; approaches $3x^2$

48. $4x^3 + 6x^2h + 4xh^2 + h^3$; approaches $4x^3$

49. $5x^4 + 10x^3h + 10x^2h^2 + 5xh^3 + h^4$; approaches $5x^4$

50. $6x^5 + 15x^4h + 20x^3h^2 + 15x^2h^3 + 6xh^4 + h^5$; approaches $6x^5$

51. 5   **52.** 7   **53.** (A) $a_4 = 0.2508$ (B) 1

54. (A) $a_7 \approx 0.267$ (B) 1   **55.** 1.1046   **56.** 0.9415

CHAPTER 9 REVIEW

1. (A) geometric   (B) arithmetic   (C) arithmetic
(D) neither   (E) geometric   *(9-1, 9-3)*

2. (A) 5, 7, 9, 11   (B) $a_{10} = 23$ (C) $S_{10} = 140$ *(9-1, 9-3)*

3. (A) 16, 8, 4, 2   (B) $a_{10} = \frac{1}{32}$ (C) $S_{10} = 31\frac{31}{32}$ *(9-1, 9-3)*

4. (A) -8, -5, -2, 1   (B) $a_{10} = 19$ (C) $S_{10} = 55$ *(9-1, 9-3)*

5. (A) -1, 2, -4, 8   (B) $a_{10} = 512$ (C) $S_{10} = 341$ *(9-1, 9-3)*

6. $S_\infty = 32$ *(9-3)*   **7.** 720   *(9-4)*   **8.** $\dfrac{22 \cdot 21 \cdot 20 \cdot 19!}{19!} = 9,240$ *(9-4)*

9. 21   *(9-4)*   **10.** $C_{6,2} = 15$; $P_{6,2} = 30$ *(9-5)*

11. (A) 12 combined outcomes: (B) $6 \cdot 2 = 12$

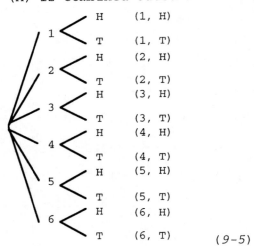

1	H	(1, H)
	T	(1, T)
2	H	(2, H)
	T	(2, T)
3	H	(3, H)
	T	(3, T)
4	H	(4, H)
	T	(4, T)
5	H	(5, H)
	T	(5, T)
6	H	(6, H)
	T	(6, T)

(9-5)

12. $6 \cdot 5 \cdot 4 \cdot 3 \cdot 2 \cdot 1 = 720$ *(9-5)*   **13.** $P_{6,6} = 6! = 720$ *(9-5)*

14. $\dfrac{C_{13,5}}{C_{52,5}} \approx .0005$ *(9-5)*   **15.** $\dfrac{1}{P_{15,2}} \approx .005$ *(9-5)*   **16.** .05 *(9-5)*

17. P_1: $5 = 1^2 + 4 \cdot 1 = 5$; P_2: $5 + 7 = 2^2 + 4 \cdot 2$; P_3: $5 + 7 + 9 = 3^2 + 4 \cdot 3$ *(9-2)*

18. P_1: $2 = 2^{1+1} - 2$; P_2: $2 + 4 = 2^{2+1} - 2$; P_3: $2 + 4 + 8 = 2^{3+1} - 2$ *(9-2)*

19. P_1: $49^1 - 1 = 48$ is divisible by 6; P_2: $49^2 - 1 = 2,400$ is divisible by 6;
P_3: $49^3 - 1 = 117,648$ is divisible by 6   *(9-2)*

20. P_k: $5 + 7 + 9 + \cdots + (2k + 3) = k^2 + 4k$
P_{k+1}: $5 + 7 + 9 + \cdots + (2k + 3) + (2k + 5) = (k + 1)^2 + 4(k + 1)$ *(9-2)*

21. P_k: $2 + 4 + 8 + \cdots + 2^k = 2^{k+1} - 2$
P_{k+1}: $2 + 4 + 8 + \cdots + 2^k + 2^{k+1} = 2^{k+2} - 2$ *(9-2)*

22. P_k: $49^k - 1 = 6r$ for some integer r
P_{k+1}: $49^{k+1} - 1 = 6s$ for some integer s *(9-2)*

23. $n = 31$ is a counterexample   *(9-2)*

24. $S_{10} = (-6) + (-4) + (-2) + 0 + 2 + 4 + 6 + 8 + 10 + 12 = 30$ *(9-3)*

25. $S_7 = 8 + 4 + 2 + 1 + \dfrac{1}{2} + \dfrac{1}{4} + \dfrac{1}{8} = 15\dfrac{7}{8}$ *(9-3)*

26. $S_\infty = \dfrac{81}{5}$ *(9-3)*   **27.** $S_n = \displaystyle\sum_{k=1}^{n} \dfrac{(-1)^{k+1}}{3^k}$; $S_\infty = \dfrac{1}{4}$ *(9-3)*

28. The probability of an event cannot be negative, but $P(e_2)$ is given as negative. The sum of the probabilities of the simple events must be 1, but it is given as 2.5. The probability of an event cannot be greater than 1, but $P(e_4)$ is given as 2.   *(9-5)*

29. $C_{6,3} = 20$ *(9-5)*   **30.** $d = 3$, $a_5 = 25$ *(9-3)*

31. 336; 512; 392   *(9-4)*

32. (A) $P(2\text{ heads}) = .21$; $P(1\text{ head}) = .48$; $P(0\text{ heads}) = .31$

(B) $P(E_1) = .25$; $P(E_2) = .5$; $P(E_3) = .25$

(C) 2 heads = 250; 1 head = 500; 0 heads = 250   (9-5)

33. (A) $\dfrac{C_{13,5}}{C_{52,5}}$ (B) $\dfrac{C_{13,3} \cdot C_{13,2}}{C_{52,5}}$ (9-5)   **34.** $\dfrac{C_{8,2}}{C_{10,4}} = \dfrac{2}{15}$ (9-5)

35. (A) $\dfrac{1}{3}$ (B) $\dfrac{2}{9}$ (9-5)   **36.** $\dfrac{8}{11}$ (9-3)

37. (A) $P_{6,3} = 120$ (B) $C_{5,2} = 10$ (9-4)   **38.** 190   (9-6)

39. 1,820   (9-6)   **40.** 1   (9-6)

41. $x^5 - 5x^4y + 10x^3y^2 - 10x^2y^3 + 5xy^4 - y^5$ (9-6)   **42.** $672x^6$ (9-6)

43. $-1760x^3y^9$ (9-6)

47. 29   (9-6)

48. 26   (9-1)   **49.** $2 \cdot 2 \cdot 2 \cdot 2 \cdot 2 = 32$; 6   (9-4)

50. $\dfrac{49g}{2}$ feet; $\dfrac{625g}{2}$ feet   (9-3)   **51.** 12   (9-4)

52. $x^6 + 6ix^5 - 15x^4 - 20ix^3 + 15x^2 + 6ix - 1$ (9-6)

53. $1 - \dfrac{C_{7,3}}{C_{10,3}} = \dfrac{17}{24}$ (9-5)   **54.** (A) .350   (B) $\dfrac{3}{8} = .375$ (C) 375   (9-5)

60. \$900 (9-3)   **61.** \$7,200 (9-3)

62. \$895.42; \$1,603.57   (9-3)   **63.** $P_{5,5} = 120$ (9-4)

64. (A) .04   (B) .16   (C) .54   (9-5)

65. $1 - \dfrac{C_{10,4}}{C_{12,4}} \approx .576$ (9-5)

CHAPTER 10

Exercise 10-1

1.
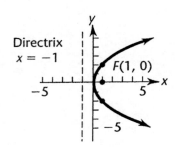

2.
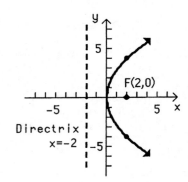

3.
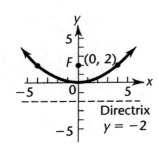

4.
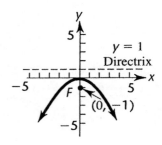

5.
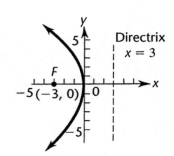

6.
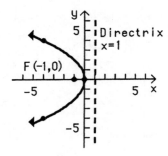

7.
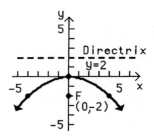

8.
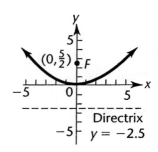

9.
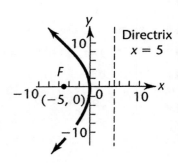

10.
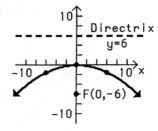

11.
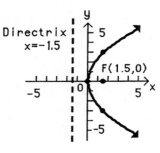

12.

13. $(9.75, 0)$

14. $F(0, 14.5)$

15. $(0, -26.25)$

16. $F(-23.25, 0)$

17. $(-19.25, 0)$

18. $F(0, -51.25)$

19. $x^2 = 12y$

20. $x^2 = -16y$

21. $x^2 = -28y$

22. $x^2 = 20y$

23. $y^2 = -24x$

24. $y^2 = 36x$

25. $y^2 = 8x$

26. $y^2 = -16x$

27. $x^2 = 8y$

28. $y^2 = 16x$

29. $y^2 = -12x$

30. $x^2 = 2.5y$

31. $x^2 = -4y$

32. $y^2 = -24x$

33.

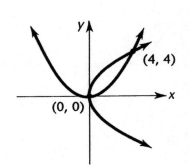

34.

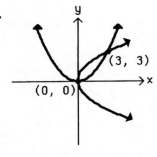

35.

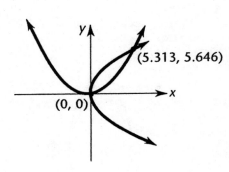

36.

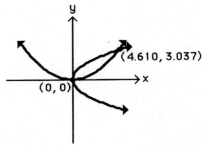

37. (A) 2; $x = 0$ and $y = 0$ (B) $(0, 0)$, $(4am, 4am^2)$

38. $(0, 0)$, $(4\sqrt[3]{a^2 b}, 4\sqrt[3]{ab^2})$

39. $A(-2a, a)$, $B(2a, a)$

40. $A(a, -2a)$, $B(a, 2a)$

41. $x^2 - 4x - 12y - 8 = 0$

42. $x^2 + 6x - 8y + 41 = 0$

43. $y^2 + 8y - 8x + 48 = 0$

44. $y^2 - 8y - 8x + 8 = 0$

45. $(-0.78, 0.08)$, $(40.78, 207.92)$

46. $(-6.52, 14.15)$, $(1.27, 0.53)$

47. $(-6.84, -5.85)$, $(0,0)$

48. $(0.31, -1.37)$, $(134.19, 28.37)$

49. $x^2 = -200y$

50. (A) $x^2 = 60y$ (B) 15 inches

51. (A) $y = 0.0025x^2$, $-100 \le x \le 100$ (B) 25 ft

52. (A) $y^2 = 6x$, $0 \le x \le 6$ (B) depth = 6 inches

Exercise 10-2

1. Foci: $F'(-\sqrt{21}, 0)$, $F(\sqrt{21}, 0)$
Major axis length = 10
Minor axis length = 4

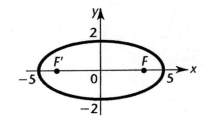

2. Foci: $F(\sqrt{5}, 0)$, $F'(-\sqrt{5}, 0)$
major axis length = 6
minor axis length = 4

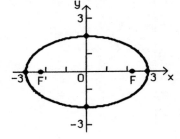

3. Foci: $F'(0, -\sqrt{21})$, $F(0, \sqrt{21})$
   Major axis length = 10
   Minor axis length = 4

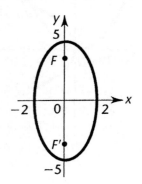

4. Foci: $F(0, \sqrt{5})$, $F'(0, -\sqrt{5})$
   major axis length = 6
   minor axis length = 4

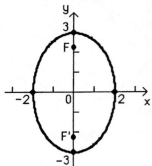

5. Foci: $F'(-\sqrt{8}, 0)$, $F(\sqrt{8}, 0)$
   Major axis length = 6
   Minor axis length = 2

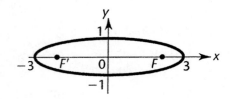

6. Foci: $F(0, \sqrt{3})$, $F'(0, -\sqrt{3})$
   major axis length = 4
   minor axis length = 2

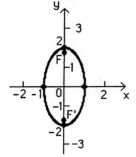

7. (b)   **8.** (d)   **9.** (a)   **10.** (c)

11. Foci: $F'(0, -4)$, $F(0, 4)$
   Major axis length = 10
   Minor axis length = 6

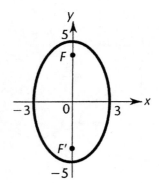

12. Foci: $F(3, 0)$, $F'(-3, 0)$
   major axis length = 10
   minor axis length = 8

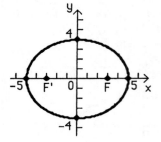

13. Foci: $F'(0, -\sqrt{6})$, $F(0, \sqrt{6})$

Major axis length $= 2\sqrt{12} \approx 6.93$

Minor axis length $= 2\sqrt{6} \approx 4.90$

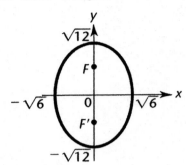

14. Foci: $F(0, \sqrt{2})$, $F'(0, -\sqrt{2})$

major axis length $= 2\sqrt{8}$

minor axis length $= 2\sqrt{6}$

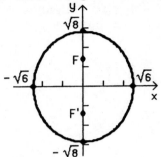

15. Foci: $F'(-\sqrt{3}, 0)$, $F(\sqrt{3}, 0)$

Major axis length $= 2\sqrt{7} \approx 5.29$

Minor axis length $= 4$

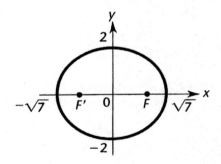

16. Foci: $F(0, 2)$, $F'(0, -2)$

major axis length $= 2\sqrt{12}$

minor axis length $= 2\sqrt{8}$

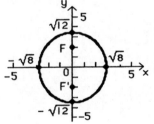

17. $\dfrac{x^2}{25} + \dfrac{y^2}{16} = 1$ **18.** $\dfrac{x^2}{36} + \dfrac{y^2}{9} = 1$ **19.** $\dfrac{x^2}{9} + \dfrac{y^2}{36} = 1$ **20.** $\dfrac{x^2}{16} + \dfrac{y^2}{25} = 1$

21. $\dfrac{x^2}{25} + \dfrac{y^2}{9} = 1$ **22.** $\dfrac{x^2}{49} + \dfrac{y^2}{25} = 1$ **23.** $\dfrac{x^2}{64} + \dfrac{y^2}{121} = 1$ **24.** $\dfrac{x^2}{81} + \dfrac{y^2}{144} = 1$

25. $\dfrac{x^2}{64} + \dfrac{y^2}{28} = 1$ **26.** $\dfrac{x^2}{144} + \dfrac{y^2}{44} = 1$ **27.** $\dfrac{x^2}{100} + \dfrac{y^2}{170} = 1$ **28.** $\dfrac{x^2}{49} + \dfrac{y^2}{249} = 1$

29. It does not pass the vertical line test.

30. An ellipse having $(0, \pm 1)$ as the ends of the minor axis is almost circular when the foci are close to the origin and becomes more elongated as the distance of the foci from the origin increases.

31. $(5, 0)$, $(-3, -3.2)$ **32.** $(4, 0)$, $(-2.4, 4)$ **33.** $(-2.4, 4)$, $(2.4, 4)$

34. $(-4. 2.4)$, $(4, 2.4)$ **35.** $(2.201, 4.402)$, $(-2.201, -4.402)$

36. $(3.775, 1.887)$, $(-3.775, -1.887)$ **37.** $(3.565, 1.589)$, $(-3.565, 1.589)$

38. $(3.673, 1.124)$, $(-3.673, 1.124)$ **39.** $\dfrac{x^2}{16} + \dfrac{y^2}{12} = 1$: ellipse

40. $\dfrac{x^2}{63} + \dfrac{y^2}{144} = 1$: ellipse   **41.** $(-0.46, 2.57)$, $(4.08, -1.06)$

42. (-13.86, -7.68), (13.86, -7.68)   **43.** (±3.64, ±9.50)

44. No points of intersection   **45.** $\dfrac{x^2}{400} + \dfrac{y^2}{144} = 1$; 7.94 feet approximately

46. $4 - \sqrt{12} \approx 0.54$, distance from edge to focus
length of string = 8 ft

47. (A) $\dfrac{x^2}{576} + \dfrac{y^2}{15.9} = 1$ (B) 5.13 ft   **48.** (A) $\dfrac{x^2}{36} + \dfrac{y^2}{6.26} = 1$ (B) 2.38 ft

Exercise 10-3

1. (d)   **2.** (a)   **3.** (c)   **4.** (b)

5. Foci: $F'(-\sqrt{13}, 0)$, $F(\sqrt{13}, 0)$
Transverse axis length = 6
Conjugate axis length = 4

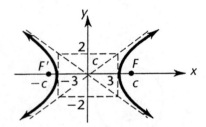

6. Foci: $F'(-\sqrt{34}, 0)$, $F(\sqrt{34}, 0)$
conjugate axis length = 10
transverse axis length = 6

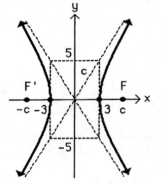

7. Foci: $F'(0, -\sqrt{13})$, $F(0, \sqrt{13})$
Transverse axis length = 4
Conjugate axis length = 6

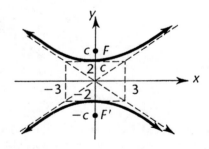

8. Foci: $F'(0, -\sqrt{34})$, $F(0, \sqrt{34})$
transverse axis length = 10
conjugate axis length = 6

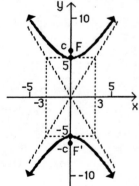

9. Foci: $F'(-\sqrt{20}, 0)$, $F(\sqrt{20}, 0)$
Transverse axis length = 4
Conjugate axis length = 8

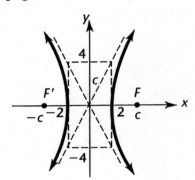

10. Foci: $F'(-\sqrt{10}, 0)$, $F(\sqrt{10}, 0)$
transverse axis length = 6
conjugate axis length = 2

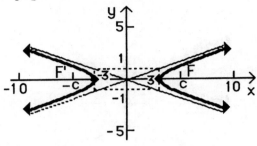

11. Foci: $F'(0, -5)$, $F(0, 5)$
Transverse axis length = 8
Conjugate axis length = 6

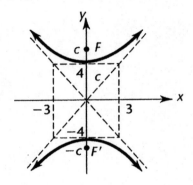

12. Foci: $F'(0, -\sqrt{29})$, $F(0, \sqrt{29})$
transverse axis length = 10
conjugate axis length = 4

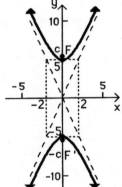

13. Foci: $F'(-\sqrt{10}, 0)$, $F(\sqrt{10}, 0)$
Transverse axis length = 4
Conjugate axis length = $2\sqrt{6} \approx 4.90$

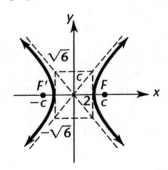

14. Foci: $F'(-\sqrt{14}, 0)$, $F(\sqrt{14}, 0)$
transverse axis length = $2\sqrt{8} \approx 5.66$
conjugate axis length = $2\sqrt{6} \approx 4.90$

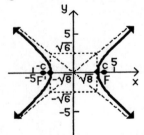

15. Foci: $F'(0, -\sqrt{11})$, $F(0, \sqrt{11})$
Transverse axis length = 4
Conjugate axis length = $2\sqrt{7} \approx 5.29$

16. Foci: $F'(0, -\sqrt{20})$, $F(0, \sqrt{20})$
transverse axis length = $2\sqrt{8} \approx 5.66$
conjugate axis length = $2\sqrt{12} \approx 6.93$

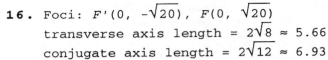

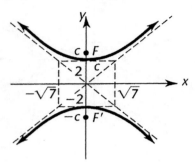

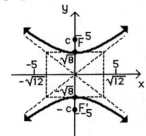

17. $\dfrac{x^2}{9} - \dfrac{y^2}{9} = 1$ **18.** $\dfrac{y^2}{9} - \dfrac{x^2}{9} = 1$ **19.** $\dfrac{y^2}{16} - \dfrac{x^2}{16} = 1$ **20.** $\dfrac{x^2}{16} - \dfrac{y^2}{16} = 1$

21. $\dfrac{x^2}{49} - \dfrac{y^2}{25} = 1$ **22.** $\dfrac{x^2}{16} - \dfrac{y^2}{9} = 1$ **23.** $\dfrac{y^2}{144} - \dfrac{x^2}{81} = 1$ **24.** $\dfrac{y^2}{64} - \dfrac{x^2}{121} = 1$

25. $\dfrac{x^2}{81} - \dfrac{y^2}{40} = 1$ **26.** $\dfrac{x^2}{64} - \dfrac{y^2}{36} = 1$ **27.** $\dfrac{y^2}{151} - \dfrac{x^2}{49} = 1$ **28.** $\dfrac{y^2}{45} - \dfrac{x^2}{25} = 1$

29. (A) Infinitely many; $\dfrac{x^2}{a^2} - \dfrac{y^2}{1 - a^2} = 1$ $(0 < a < 1)$

(B) Infinitely many; $\dfrac{x^2}{a^2} + \dfrac{y^2}{a^2 - 1} = 1$ $(a > 1)$

(C) One; $y^2 = 4x$

30. Infinitely many; $\dfrac{x^2}{a^2} - \dfrac{y^2}{4a^2} = 1$, $\dfrac{y^2}{a^2} - \dfrac{4x^2}{a^2} = 1$ $(a > 0)$

31. $(-3, -4)$, $(-3, 4)$, $(3, -4)$, $(3, 4)$

32. $(-1, -2)$, $(-1, 2)$, $(1, -2)$, $(1, 2)$

33. $(-2, -4)$, $(-2, 4)$, $(2, -4)$, $(2, 4)$

34. $(-2, -3)$, $(-2, 3)$, $(2, -3)$, $(2, 3)$

35. $(-1.389, 3.306)$, $(6.722, 7.361)$

36. $(-2.667, 3.333)$

37. $(3.266, 3.830)$, $(-3.266, 3.830)$, $(-3.266, -3.830)$, $(3.266, -3.830)$

38. $(2.160, 2.380)$, $(-2.160, 2.380)$, $(-2.160, -2.380)$, $(-2.160, 2.380)$

39. $\dfrac{x^2}{4} - \dfrac{y^2}{5} = 1$; hyperbola   **40.** $\dfrac{y^2}{9} - \dfrac{x^2}{7} = 1$; hyperbola

41. $(-4.73, 2.88)$, $(3.35, -0.90)$ **42.** $(-1.06, -3.37)$, $(1.06, -3.37)$

43. $(\pm 1.39, \pm 2.96)$ **44.** No points of intersection

45. $\dfrac{y^2}{16} - \dfrac{x^2}{8} = 1$; 5.38 ft above vertex

46. 141 ft, top radius; 254 ft, base radius; 100 ft, radius of smallest circular cross section

47. $y = \frac{4}{3}\sqrt{x^2 + 30^2}$

Exercise 10-4

1. (A) $x' = x - 3;\ y' = y - 5$ (B) $x'^2 + y'^2 = 81$ (C) Circle

2. (A) $x' = x - 3,\ y' = y + 2$ (B) $x'^2 = 8y'$ (C) parabola

3. (A) $x' = x + 7,\ y' = y - 4$ (B) $\dfrac{x'^2}{9} + \dfrac{y'^2}{16} = 1$ (C) Ellipse

4. (A) $x' = x + 2,\ y' = y + 6$ (B) $x'^2 + y'^2 = 36$ (C) circle

5. (A) $x' = x - 4,\ y' = y + 9$ (B) $y'^2 = 16x'$ (C) Parabola

6. (A) $x' = x + 5,\ y' = y - 9$ (B) $\dfrac{y'^2}{10} - \dfrac{x'^2}{6} = 1$ (C) hyperbola

7. (A) $x' = x + 8,\ y' = y + 3$ (B) $\dfrac{x'^2}{12} + \dfrac{y'^2}{8} = 1$ (C) Ellipse

8. (A) $x' = x + 7,\ y' = y - 8$ (B) $\dfrac{x'^2}{25} - \dfrac{y'^2}{50} = 1$ (C) hyperbola

9. (A) $\dfrac{(x - 3)^2}{9} - \dfrac{(y + 2)^2}{16} = 1$ (B) hyperbola

10. (A) $(y + 2)^2 = 12(x - 3)$ (B) parabola

11. (A) $\dfrac{(x + 5)^2}{5} + \dfrac{(y + 7)^2}{6} = 1$ (B) ellipse

12. (A) $\dfrac{(y - 5)^2}{2} - \dfrac{(x - 3)^2}{3} = 1$ (B) hyperbola

13. (A) $(x + 6)^2 = -24(y - 4)$ (B) parabola

14. (A) $\dfrac{(x - 7)^2}{7} + \dfrac{(y - 3)^2}{4} = 1$ (B) ellipse

15. $\dfrac{(x - 2)^2}{9} + \dfrac{(y - 2)^2}{4} = 1$; ellipse

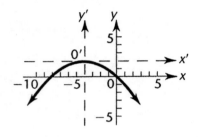

16. $\dfrac{(x + 2)^2}{9} + \dfrac{(y + 3)^2}{16} = 1$: ellipse

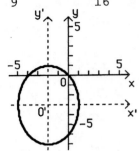

17. $(x + 4)^2 = -8(y - 2)$; parabola

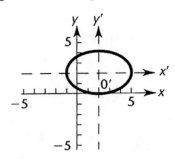

18. $(y + 2)^2 = -12(x - 3)$: parabola

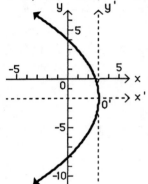

19. $(x + 6)^2 + (y + 5)^2 = 16$; circle

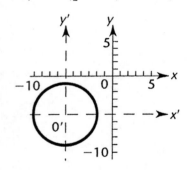

20. $(x - 4)^2 + (y - 3)^2 = 25$: circle

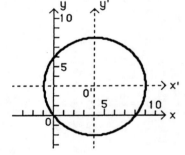

21. $\dfrac{(y - 3)^2}{9} - \dfrac{(x + 4)^2}{16} = 1$; hyperbola

22. $\dfrac{(x - 5)^2}{25} - \dfrac{y^2}{16} = 1$: hyperbola

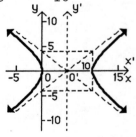

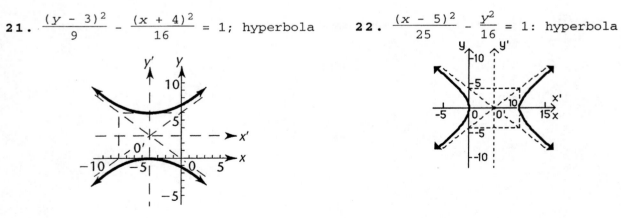

23. $h = -\dfrac{D}{2A}$, $k = \dfrac{D^2 - 4AF}{4AE}$

24. $h = \dfrac{E^2 - 4CF}{4CD}$, $k = \dfrac{-E}{2C}$

25. $x^2 - 4x + 4y - 16 = 0$

26. $y^2 + 8x + 2y - 31 = 0$

27. $x^2 + 4y^2 + 4x + 24y + 24 = 0$

28. $4x^2 + y^2 + 32x - 2y + 61 = 0$

29. $25x^2 + 9y^2 - 200x + 36y + 211 = 0$

30. $16x^2 + 25y^2 - 64x - 50y - 311 = 0$

31. $4x^2 - y^2 - 16x + 6y + 11 = 0$

32. $x^2 - y^2 - 4x - 10y - 30 = 0$

33. $9x^2 + y^2 + 36x - 2y + 28 = 0$

34. $x^2 + 4y^2 + 6x + 16y + 21 = 0$

35. $x^2 - 2y^2 - 2x + 8y - 8 = 0$

36. $3x^2 - y^2 - 12x - 2y + 12 = 0$

37. $F'(-\sqrt{5} + 2, 2)$ and $F(\sqrt{5} + 2, 2)$

38. $F(-2, \sqrt{7} - 3)$, $F'(-2, -\sqrt{7} - 3)$

39. $F(-4, 0)$

40. $F(0, -2)$

41. $F'(-4, -2)$, $F(-4, 8)$

42. $F(\sqrt{41} + 5, 0)$, $F'(-\sqrt{41} + 5, 0)$

43. $(1.18, 1.98)$, $(6.85, -6.52)$

44. $(-2.06, -3.03)$, $(3.45, -0.52)$

45. $(-1.72, -1.87)$, $(-0.99, 2.06)$

46. $(1.30, 2.40)$, $(2.39, -2.23)$, $(3.43, -1.86)$, $(4.19, 1.38)$

Exercise 10-5

3. $y = -2x - 2$; straight line

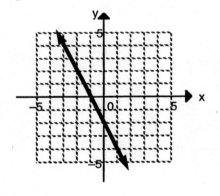

4. $y = x + 1$, straight line

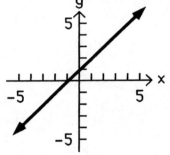

5. $y = -2x - 2$, $x \le 0$
   a ray (part of a straight line)

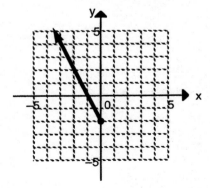

6. $y = x + 1$, $x \ge 0$
   a ray (part of a straight line)

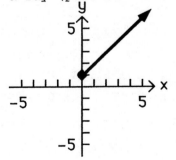

7. $y = -\frac{2}{3}x$; straight line

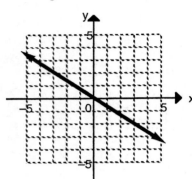

8. $y = \frac{1}{2}x$, straight line

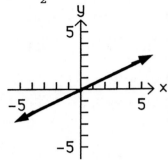

9. $y^2 = 4x$; parabola

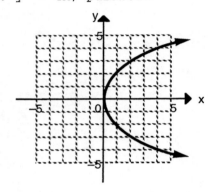

10. $x^2 = 4y$; parabola

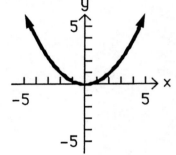

11. $y^2 = 4x$, $y \geq 0$; parabola (upper half)

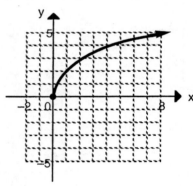

12. $x^2 = 4y$, $x \geq 0$; parabola (right half)

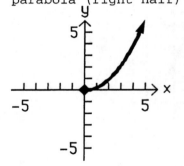

13. $y = -2x$; line

14. $y = 2x + 4$; line

15. $y^2 = x + 1$, $y \geq 0$, $x \geq -1$; parabola (upper half)

16. $y = x^2 + 1$, $x \geq 0$, $y \geq 1$; parabola (right half)

17. $4x^2 + y^2 = 64$, $0 \leq x \leq 4$, $0 \leq y \leq 8$; ellipse (first quadrant portion)

18. $x^2 + 9y^2 = 225$, $-15 \leq x \leq 0$, $0 \leq y \leq 5$; ellipse (second quadrant portion)

19. $x^2 - y^2 = 2$, $x \leq -\sqrt{2}$, $y \leq 0$; hyperbola (third quadrant portion)

20. $y^2 - x^2 = 2$, $x \geq 0$, $y \leq -\sqrt{2}$; hyperbola (fourth quadrant portion)

21. $\frac{x^2}{9} + \frac{y^2}{16} = 1$; ellipse

22. $x^2 + y^2 = 9$; circle

23. $(x - 2)^2 + (y - 3)^2 = 4$; circle

24. $\dfrac{(x - 3)^2}{16} + \dfrac{(y - 2)^2}{4} = 1$; ellipse

25. $x = t$, $y = \dfrac{At^2 + Dt + F}{-E}$, $-\infty < t < \infty$; parabola

26. $x = \dfrac{-(Ct^2 + Et + F)}{D}$, $y = t$; $t \in (-\infty, \infty)$

27. $\dfrac{(x - 3)^2}{36} + \dfrac{(y - 2)^2}{16} = 1$; ellipse with center $(3, 2)$

28. $\dfrac{(x - 1)^2}{9} - \dfrac{(y + 2)^2}{4} = 1$; hyperbola with center $(1, -2)$

29. $\dfrac{(y + 1)^2}{25} - \dfrac{(x + 3)^2}{4} = 1$; hyperbola with center $(-3, -1)$

30. $\dfrac{(x + 4)^2}{25} + \dfrac{(y - 1)^2}{64} = 1$; ellipse with center $(-4, 1)$

31. $y^2 - x^2 = 8$ for $x \geq 1$ and $y \geq 3$; part of a hyperbola

32. $x^2 - y^2 = 3$; part of a hyperbola

33. $x^2 + y^2 = 4$, $0 < x \leq 2$, $-2 < y < 2$; semicircle (excluding the end points)

34. $x^2 + y^2 = 9$, $-3 < x < 3$, $0 < y \leq 3$; semicircle (excluding the end points)

35. $x^2 + y^2 = 2x$, $x \neq 0$ or $(x - 1)^2 + y^2 = 1$, $x \neq 0$; circle (note hole at origin)

36. $x^2 + y^2 = 4y$, $y \neq 4$ or $x^2 + (y - 2)^2 = 4$; circle [note hole at $(0, 4)$]

37. $\dfrac{(y + 1)^2}{25} - \dfrac{(x - 4)^2}{9} = 1$; hyperbola with center $(4, -1)$; $x = 4 + 3 \tan t$,
$y = -1 + 5 \sec t$, $0 \leq t \leq 2\pi$, $t \neq \dfrac{\pi}{2}, \dfrac{3\pi}{2}$

38. $\dfrac{(x + 5)^2}{4} + \dfrac{(y - 1)^2}{36} = 1$; ellipse with center $(-5, 1)$; $x = -5 + 2 \cos t$,
$y = 1 + 6 \sin t$, $0 \leq t \leq 2\pi$

39. $\dfrac{(x - 3)^2}{49} + \dfrac{(y + 4)^2}{4} = 1$; ellipse with center $(3, -4)$; $x = 3 + 7 \cos t$,
$y = -4 + 2 \sin t$, $0 \leq t \leq 2\pi$

40. $\dfrac{(x + 1)^2}{9} - \dfrac{(y + 2)^2}{16} = 1$; hyperbola with center $(-1, -2)$; $x = -1 + 3 \sec t$,
$y = -2 + 4 \tan t$, $0 < t < 2\pi$, $t \neq \dfrac{\pi}{2}, \dfrac{3\pi}{2}$

43. 1,786 m

44. 85.7 m

45. (A) 43.292 sec   (B) 9,183.620 m, 9.184 km   (c) 2,295.918 m

46. (A) 39.354 sec   (B) 9,044.153 m, 9.044 km   (C) 1,897.236 m

CHAPTER 10 REVIEW

1. Foci: $F'(-4, 0)$, $F(4, 0)$
Major axis length = 10
Minor axis length = 6

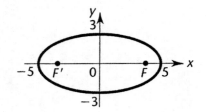

2.

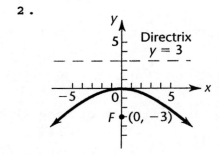

$(10\text{-}2)$

$(10\text{-}1)$

3. Foci: $F'(0, -\sqrt{34})$, $F(0, \sqrt{34})$
Transverse axis length = 6
Conjugate axis length = 10

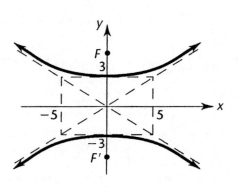

$(10\text{-}3)$

4. (A) $\dfrac{(y + 2)^2}{25} - \dfrac{(x - 4)^2}{4} = 1$ (B) hyperbola $(10\text{-}4)$

5. (A) $(x + 5)^2 = -12(y + 4)$ (B) parabola $(10\text{-}4)$

6. (A) $\dfrac{(x - 6)^2}{9} + \dfrac{(y - 4)^2}{16} = 1$ (B) ellipse $(10\text{-}4)$

8. $y^2 = -x$ $(10\text{-}1)$ **9.** $\dfrac{x^2}{9} + \dfrac{y^2}{25} = 1$ $(10\text{-}2)$

10. $\dfrac{y^2}{9} - \dfrac{x^2}{16} = 1$ $(10\text{-}3)$

11. $y = \dfrac{1}{2}x + 1$, $x \leq 0$; a ray (part of a straight line)

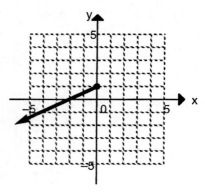

$(10\text{-}5)$

12.

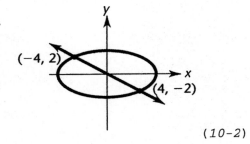

(10-2)

13.

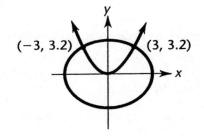

(10-1, 10-2)

14.

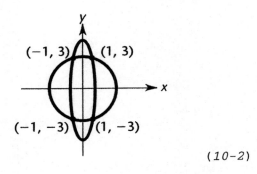

(10-2)

15. $\dfrac{(x+3)^2}{4} + \dfrac{(y-2)^2}{16} = 1$; ellipse

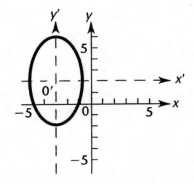

(10-4)

16. $(x-2)^2 = 4(2)(y+3)$; parabola

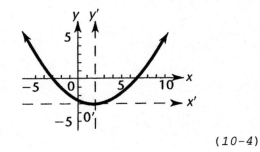

(10-4)

17. $\dfrac{(x+3)^2}{9} - \dfrac{(y+2)^2}{4} = 1$; hyperbola

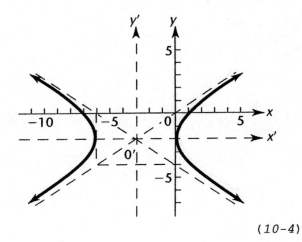

(10-4)

18. $\dfrac{(x+2)^2}{4} + \dfrac{(y-3)^2}{16} = 1$; ellipse

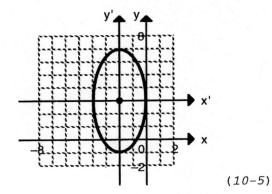

(10-5)

19. $m = 0.2$; $x^2 = 50y$ is a magnification by a factor 50 of $x^2 = y$ *(10-1)*

20. $x = -3 + 2 \sin \theta$, $y = 2 + 4 \cos \theta$, $0 \le \theta \le 2\pi$ *(10-5)*

21. $x = -3 + 3 \sec \theta$, $y = -2 + 2 \tan \theta$, $0 \le \theta \le 2\pi$, $\theta \ne \dfrac{\pi}{2}, \dfrac{3\pi}{2}$ *(10-5)*

22. $(y - 4)^2 = -8(x - 4)$ or $y^2 - 8y + 8x - 16 = 0$ *(10-1, 10-4)*

23. $\dfrac{x^2}{4} - \dfrac{y^2}{12} = 1$; hyperbola   *(10-3, 10-4)*

24. $\dfrac{x^2}{36} + \dfrac{y^2}{20} = 1$; ellipse   *(10-2, 10-4)*

25. $F'(-3, -\sqrt{12} + 2)$ and $F(-3, \sqrt{12} + 2)$ *(10-4)*

26. $F(2, -1)$ *(10-4)*

27. $F'(-\sqrt{13} - 3, -2)$ and $F(\sqrt{13} - 3, -2)$ *(10-4)*

28. $y = \dfrac{1}{x}$, $x > 0$; $y > 0$; hyperbola (one branch)   *(10-5)*

29. $4x^2 + 9y^2 = 36$, $-3 < x < 3$, $0 < y \le 2$; ellipse (upper half, excluding the end points)   *(10-5)*

31. $(2.09, 2.50)$, $(3.67, -1.92)$ *(10-4)*

32. 4 feet   *(10-1)*   **33.** $\dfrac{x^2}{5^2} + \dfrac{y^2}{3^2} = 1$ *(10-2)*

34. 4.72 feet deep   *(10-3)*   **35.** 404 m   *(10-5)*

CUMULATIVE REVIEW EXERCISE (Chapters 8, 9, and 10)

1. $(2, -1)$ $(8-1, 8-2)$ **2.** $(-1, 2)$ $(8-1)$

3. $\left(-\dfrac{1}{5}, -\dfrac{7}{5}\right)$, $(1, 1)$ $(8-1, 8-2)$

4.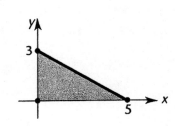

$(8-2)$

5. The minimum value of z on S is 10 at $(5, 0)$.
The maximum value of z on S is 33 at $(6, 7)$. $(8-7)$

6. (A) $\begin{bmatrix} 0 & -3 \\ 3 & -9 \end{bmatrix}$ (B) not defined (C) $[3]$ (D) $\begin{bmatrix} 1 & 7 \\ 4 & -7 \end{bmatrix}$ (E) $[-1 \quad 8]$
(F) not defined $(8-4)$

7. (A) $x_1 = 3$, $x_2 = -4$
(B) $x_1 = 2t + 3$, $x_2 = t$ is a solution for every real number t
(C) No solution. $(8-2)$

8. (A) $\begin{bmatrix} 1 & 1 & | & 3 \\ -1 & 1 & | & 5 \end{bmatrix}$ (B) $\begin{bmatrix} 1 & 0 & | & -1 \\ 0 & 1 & | & 4 \end{bmatrix}$ (C) $x_1 = -1$, $x_2 = 4$ $(8-2, 8-3)$

9. (A) $\begin{bmatrix} 1 & -3 \\ 2 & -5 \end{bmatrix}\begin{bmatrix} x_1 \\ x_2 \end{bmatrix} = \begin{bmatrix} k_1 \\ k_2 \end{bmatrix}$ (B) $A^{-1} = \begin{bmatrix} -5 & 3 \\ -2 & 1 \end{bmatrix}$ (C) $x_1 = 13$, $x_2 = 5$

(D) $x_1 = -11$, $x_2 = -4$ $(8-6)$

10. $x_1 = 1$, $x_2 = 3$; each pair of lines has the same intersection point.

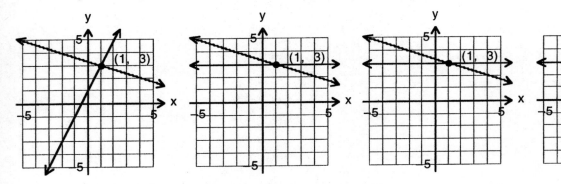

$$x_1 + 3x_2 = 10$$
$$2x_1 - x_2 = -1$$

$$x_1 + 3x_2 = 10$$
$$-7x_2 = -21$$

$$x_1 + 3x_2 = 10$$
$$x_2 = 3$$

$$x_1 = 1$$
$$x_2 = 3$$
   $(8-1, 8-3)$

11. $(1.53, 3.35)$ $(8-1)$

12. (A) arithmetic (B) geometric (C) neither (D) geometric (E) arithmetic $(9-3)$

13. (A) $10, 50, 250, 1,250$ (B) $a_8 = 781,250$ (C) $S_8 = 976,560$ $(9-3)$

14. (A) 2, 5, 8, 11   (B) $a_8 = 23$ (C) $S_8 = 100$ (*9-3*)

15. (A) 100, 94, 88, 82   (B) $a_8 = 58$ (C) $S_8 = 632$ (*9-3*)

16. (A) 40,320   (B) 992   (C) 84   (*9-4*)   **17.** (A) 21   (B) 21   (C) 42   (*9-4, 9-5*)

18. Foci: $F'(-\sqrt{61}, 0)$, $F(\sqrt{61}, 0)$ **19.** Foci: $F'(-\sqrt{11}, 0)$, $F(\sqrt{11}, 0)$
Transverse axis length = 12   Major axis length = 12
Conjugate axis length = 10   Minor axis length = 10

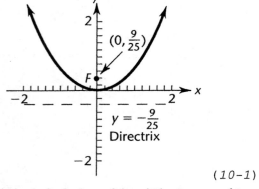

(*10-3*)

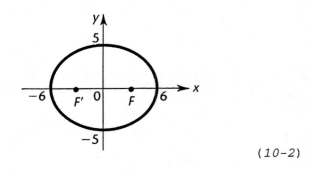

(*10-2*)

20.

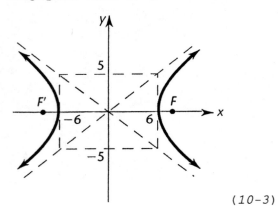

(*10-1*)

21. (A) 8 combined outcomes:

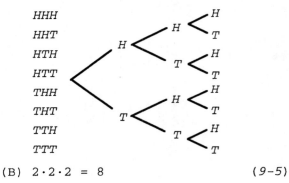

HHH
HHT
HTH
HTT
THH
THT
TTH
TTT

(B) $2 \cdot 2 \cdot 2 = 8$ (*9-5*)

22. (A) $4 \cdot 3 \cdot 2 \cdot 1 = 24$ (B) $P_{4,4} = 4! = 24$ (*9-5*)

23. $\dfrac{C_{13,3}}{C_{52,3}} \approx .0129$ (*9-5*)   **24.** $\dfrac{1}{P_{10,4}} \approx .0002$; $\dfrac{1}{C_{10,4}} \approx .0048$ (*9-5*)

25. .62   (*9-5*)

26. $y = 2x - 1$; straight line

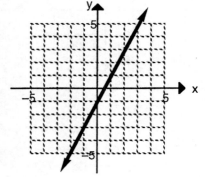

(*10-5*)

27. P_1: $1 = 1(2 \cdot 1 - 1)$;
P_2: $1 + 5 = 2(2 \cdot 2 - 1)$;
P_3: $1 + 5 + 9 = 3(2 \cdot 3 - 1)$ (*9-2*)

28. P_1: $1^2 + 1 + 2 = 4$ is divisible by 2;
P_2: $2^2 + 2 + 2 = 8$ is divisible by 2;
P_3: $3^2 + 3 + 2 = 14$ is divisible by 2
(*9-2*)

29. P_k: $1 + 5 + 9 + \cdots + (4k - 3) = k(2k - 1)$
P_{k+1}: $1 + 5 + 9 + \cdots + (4k - 3) + (4k + 1)$
$= (k + 1)(2k + 1)$ (*9-2*)

30. P_k: $k^2 + k + 2 = 2r$ for some integer r
P_{k+1}: $(k + 1)^2 + (k + 1) + 2 = 2s$ for some integer s *(9-2)*

31. $x_1 = 1$, $x_2 = 0$, $x_3 = -2$ *(8-3)*   **32.** no solution   *(8-3)*

33. $x_1 = t - 3$, $x_2 = t - 2$, $x_3 = t$ is a solution for every real number t *(8-3)*

34. (A) $[-3]$ (B) $\begin{bmatrix} 1 & 2 & -1 \\ -1 & -2 & 1 \\ 2 & 4 & -2 \end{bmatrix}$ *(8-4)*

35. (A) $\begin{bmatrix} -1 & 2 \\ 2 & 3 \end{bmatrix}$ (B) not defined   *(8-4)*

36.

(8-7)

37. 63   *(8-8)*

38. (A) $\begin{bmatrix} 1 & 4 & 2 \\ 2 & 6 & 3 \\ 2 & 5 & 2 \end{bmatrix} \begin{bmatrix} x_1 \\ x_2 \\ x_3 \end{bmatrix} = \begin{bmatrix} k_1 \\ k_2 \\ k_3 \end{bmatrix}$ (B) $A^{-1} = \begin{bmatrix} -3 & 2 & 0 \\ 2 & -2 & 1 \\ -2 & 3 & -2 \end{bmatrix}$

    (C) $x_1 = 7$, $x_2 = -5$, $x_3 = 6$ (D) $x_1 = -6$, $x_2 = 3$, $x_3 = -2$ *(8-6)*

39. $y = -2x^2$ *(10-1)*   **40.** $\dfrac{x^2}{25} + \dfrac{y^2}{16} = 1$ *(10-2)*

41. $\dfrac{x^2}{64} - \dfrac{y^2}{25} = 1$ *(10-3)*   **42.** $1 + 4 + 27 + 256 + 3{,}125 = 3{,}413$ *(9-1)*

43. $\displaystyle\sum_{k=1}^{6} (-1)^{k+1} \dfrac{2^k}{(k + 1)!}$ *(9-1)*   **44.** 81   *(9-3)*

45. 360; 1,296; 750   *(9-4)*   **46.** $\dfrac{C_{10,3}}{C_{12,5}} = \dfrac{5}{33} = .\overline{15}$ *(9-5)*

47. (A) .365   (B) $\dfrac{1}{3}$ *(9-5)*   **48.** $n = 22$ *(9-3)*

49. $\dfrac{(x - 2)^2}{49} + \dfrac{(y + 3)^2}{25} = 1$; ellipse   *(10-5)*

50. (A) 6,375,600 (B) 53,130 (C) 53,130   *(9-4, 9-6)*

51. $a^6 + 3a^5b + \dfrac{15}{4}a^4b^2 + \dfrac{5}{2}a^3b^3 + \dfrac{15}{16}a^2b^4 + \dfrac{3}{16}ab^5 + \dfrac{1}{64}b^6$ *(9-6)*

52. $153{,}090x^6y^4$; $-3{,}240x^3y^7$ *(9-6)*

55. 61,875   *(9-3)*

56. $\dfrac{27}{11}$ *(9-3)*

57. $a_{27} = 0.236088$; 8 terms *(9-6)*

58. $4(x + 3) = (y - 2)^2$; parabola

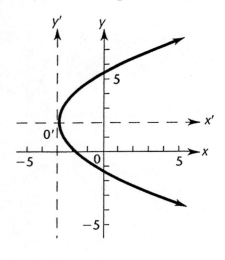

(10-1)

59. $\dfrac{(y + 2)^2}{4} - \dfrac{(x + 1)^2}{16} = 1$; hyperbola

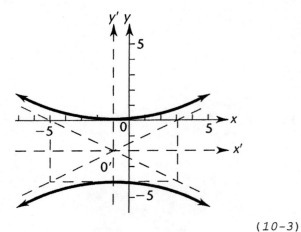

(10-3)

60. $\dfrac{(x - 2)^2}{9} + \dfrac{(y + 3)^2}{4} = 1$; ellipse

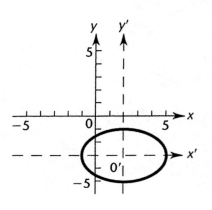

(10-2)

61. 10^9; 3,628,800 zip codes *(9-1)*

62. $(-2.26, -4.72)$, $(1.85, 3.09)$ *(10-4)*

64. $\dfrac{2}{5}$; $\dfrac{2}{5}$ *(9-5)*

65. $x^6 - 12ix^5 - 60x^4 + 160ix^3 + 240x^2 - 192ix - 64$ *(9-6)*

66. $x^2 - 12x + 4y + 28 = 0$ *(10-1)*

67. $\pm 2\sqrt{3}$ *(10-2)*

68. 8 *(10-2)*

69. (A) Infinite number of solutions (B) No solution (C) Unique solution *(8-3)*

70. $A = I$, the $n \times n$ identity *(8-5)*

71. L, M, and P *(8-3)*

72. $C_{7,3} = 35$ *(9-4)*

73. $x + 4 = (y - 1)^2$, $y < 1$; lower half of a parabola (excluding the vertex) *(10-5)*

76. $x^2 - 2x - 8y^2 - 8y + 17 = 0$; hyperbola *(10-3)*

77. $1 - \dfrac{C_{8,3}}{C_{12,3}} = \dfrac{41}{55} = .7\overline{45}$ *(9-5)*

78. $8,000 at 8% and $4,000 at 14% *(8-1, 8-2)*

79. $6,000,000 *(9-3)*

80. $x_1 = 60g$ Mix A, $x_2 = 50g$ Mix B, $x_3 = 40g$ Mix C *(8-3)*

81. 1 model A truck, 6 model B trucks, and 5 model C trucks; or 3 model A trucks, 3 model B trucks, and 6 model C trucks; or 5 model A trucks and 7 model C trucks. *(8-3)*

82. 4 in. *(10-1)*   **83.** 32 ft, 14.4 ft *(10-2)*

84. (A) Manufacturing 400 standard and 200 deluxe day packs produces a maxmimum weekly profit of $5,600.

(B) The maximum weekly profit increases to $6,000 when 0 standard and 400 deluxe day packs are manufactured.

(C) The maximum weekly profit increases to $6,600 when 600 standard and 0 deluxe day packs are manufactured. *(8-8)*

85. (A) $M\begin{bmatrix} 0.25 \\ 0.25 \\ 0.25 \\ 0.25 \end{bmatrix} = \begin{bmatrix} 82.25 \\ 83 \\ 92 \\ 83.75 \\ 82 \end{bmatrix}\begin{matrix} \text{Ann} \\ \text{Bob} \\ \text{Carol} \\ \text{Dan} \\ \text{Eric} \end{matrix}$ (B) $M\begin{bmatrix} 0.2 \\ 0.2 \\ 0.2 \\ 0.4 \end{bmatrix} = \begin{bmatrix} 83 \\ 84.8 \\ 91.8 \\ 85.2 \\ 80.8 \end{bmatrix}\begin{matrix} \text{Ann} \\ \text{Bob} \\ \text{Carol} \\ \text{Dan} \\ \text{Eric} \end{matrix}$

Class averages
Test 1   Test 2   Test 3   Test 4
(C) $[0.2 \quad 0.2 \quad 0.2 \quad 0.2 \quad 0.2]M = [84.4 \quad 81.8 \quad 85 \quad 87.2]$ *(8-4)*

86. (A) .13 (B) .17 (C) .32 *(9-5)*

APPENDIX A

Exercise A-1

1. True **2.** True **3.** False **4.** True **5.** False **6.** True

7. True **8.** True **9.** $7 + x$ **10.** vu **11.** $(xy)z$ **12.** $(3 + 7) + y$

13. $9m$ **14.** $u + v$ **15.** Commutative$(\cdot)$ **16.** Associative$(\cdot)$

17. Distributive **18.** Negatives **19.** Inverse$(\cdot)$ **20.** Subtraction

21. Inverse $(+)$ **22.** Division **23.** Identity $(+)$

24. Distributive **25.** Negatives **26.** Zero **27.** $\{-2, 0, 2, 4\}$

28. $\{-3, -1, 1, 3, 5\}$ **29.** $\{a, s, t, u\}$ **30.** $\{c, o, n, s, e, u\}$

31. $\varnothing$ **32.** $\varnothing$ **33.** Commutative $(+)$ **34.** Associative

35. Associative $(+)$ **36.** Distributive **37.** Distributive **38.** Negatives

39. Zero **40.** Zero **41.** Yes **42.** No **43.** (A) True (B) False (C) True

44. (A) False (B) True (C) True

45. $\frac{3}{5}$ and -1.43 are two examples of infinitely many

46. $\sqrt{2}$ and π are two examples of infinitely many

47. (A) Z, Q, R (B) Q, R (C) R (D) Q, R

48. (A) N, Z, Q, R (B) R (C) Q, R (D) Q, R

49. (A) $0.88888888\ldots$ (B) $0.27272727\ldots$ (C) $2.23606797\ldots$ (D) $1.37500000\ldots$

50. (A) $2.1666\ldots = 2.1\overline{6}$ (B) $4.582575695\ldots$ (C) $0.437500\ldots = 0.4375$

(D) $0.261261261\ldots = 0.\overline{261}$

51. (A) True (B) False; for example $3 - 5 \neq 5 - 3$.
(C) True (D) False; for example $9 \div 3 \neq 3 \div 9$.

52. (A) True (B) False, since, for example, $(8 - 4) - 2 \neq 8 - (4 - 2)$
(C) True (D) False, since, for example, $(8 \div 4) \div 2 \neq 8 \div (4 \div 2)$

53. (A) $\{1, 2, 3, 4, 6\}$ (B) $\{2, 4\}$ **54.** (A) $\{-2, -1, 0, 1, 2\}$ (B) $\{0, 2\}$

55. $\frac{1}{11}$ **56.** $\frac{2}{11}$ **57.**

$$
\begin{array}{rl}
23 & \\
\underline{12} & \\
46 & 23 \cdot 2 \\
\underline{230} & 23 \cdot 10 \\
276 &
\end{array}
$$

$$
\begin{aligned}
23 \cdot 12 &= 23(2 + 10) \\
&= 23 \cdot 2 + 23 \cdot 10 \\
&= 46 + 230 \\
&= 276
\end{aligned}
$$

58. (1) Commutative (2) Associative (3) Inverse (4) Identity

Exercise A-2

1. 3 **2.** 2 **3.** $2x^3 - x^2 + 2x + 4$ **4.** $2x^2 + 4x - 3$

5. $2x^3 - 5x^2 + 6$ **6.** $2x^2 - 2x + 1$ **7.** $6x^4 - 13x^3 + 9x^2 + 13x - 10$

8. $6x^3 - x^2 - 5x + 2$ **9.** $4x - 6$ **10.** $-5u + 2$ **11.** $6y^2 - 16y$

12. $6a^2 + 6a$ **13.** $m^2 - n^2$ **14.** $a^2 - b^2$

15. $4t^2 - 11t + 6$ **16.** $6x^2 - 7x - 5$ **17.** $3x^2 - 7xy - 6y^2$

18. $2x^2 + xy - 6y^2$ **19.** $4m^2 - 49$ **20.** $9y^2 - 4$

21. $30x^2 - 2xy - 12y^2$ **22.** $6m^2 - mn - 35n^2$ **23.** $9x^2 - 4y^2$ **24.** $16m^2 - 9n^2$

25. $16x^2 - 8xy + y^2$ **26.** $9u^2 + 24uv + 16v^2$ **27.** $a^3 + b^3$ **28.** $a^3 - b^3$

29. $-x + 27$ **30.** 1 **31.** $32a - 34$ **32.** $-b + 6$

33. $2x^4 - 5x^3 + 5x^2 + 11x - 10$ **34.** $x^4 - 2x^2y^2 + y^4$

35. $h^4 + h^2k^2 + k^4$ **36.** $n^4 - 2n^3 - 10n^2 - 10n - 3$ **37.** $-5x^2 - 4x + 5$

38. $5a^2 + 12ab - 10b^2$ **39.** $2m^2 + 15mn$ **40.** $2y^2 - 14$

41. $8m^3 - 12m^2n + 6mn^2 - n^3$ **42.** $27a^3 + 54a^2b + 36ab^2 + 8b^3$

43. $5h$ **44.** $6h$ **45.** $6xh + 3h^2 + 2h$

46. $8xh + 4h^2 - 5h$ **47.** $-4xh - 2h^2 - 3h$ **48.** $-2xh - h^2 + 4h$

49. $3x^2h + 3xh^2 + h^3$ **50.** $4xh + 2h^2 + 3h$ **51.** $m^3 - 3m^2 - 5$

52. $2x^2 - 2xy + 3y^2$ **53.** $2x^3 - 13x^2 + 25x - 18$ **54.** $8x^3 - 20x^2 + 20x + 1$

55. $9x^3 - 9x^2 - 18x$ **56.** $4x^3 - 14x^2 + 8x - 6$

57. $(1 + 1)^2 \neq 1^2 + 1^2$; either a or b must be zero

58. Unless $b = 0$ or $a = b$, $(a - b)^2 = a^2 - b^2$ will not be true.
In general, $(a - b)^2 \neq a^2 - b^2$.

59. m **60.** $m + n$

61. Now the degree is less than or equal to m.   **62.** It doesn't change.

63. Perimeter $= 4x - 10$ **64.** Area $= x^2 + 8x$

65. Value $= 40x - 125$ **66.** Value $= 35x + 40$

67. Volume $= 1.2\pi x^2 + 0.36\pi x + 0.036\pi$ **68.** Volume $= 12x^2 + 48x + 64$

Exercise A-3

1. $2x^2(3x^2 - 4x - 1)$ **2.** $3m^2(2m^2 - 3m - 1)$ **3.** $5xy(2x^2 + 4xy - 3y^2)$

4. $2uv(4u^2 - 3uv + 2v^2)$ **5.** $(x + 1)(5x - 3)$ **6.** $(2m - 3)(7m + 5)$

7. $(y - 2z)(2w - x)$ **8.** $(3c + d)(a - 4b)$ **9.** $(x - 2)(x + 3)$

10. $(y - 3)(2y + 5)$ **11.** $(3m + 5)(2m - 1)$ **12.** $(x - 8)(5x - 1)$

13. $(x - 2y)(2x - 3y)$ **14.** $(a - 4b)(3a - 2b)$ **15.** $(2c - d)(4a - 3b)$

16. $(3p - q)(r + 2s)$ **17.** $(2x - 1)(x + 3)$ **18.** $(3y + 2)(y - 1)$

19. $(x - 6y)(x + 2y)$ **20.** $(u - 5v)(u + 3v)$ **21.** Prime   **22.** Prime

23. $(5m + 4n)(5m - 4n)$ **24.** $(wx - y)(wx + y)$ **25.** $(x + 5y)^2$

26. $(3m - n)^2$ **27.** Prime   **28.** Prime

29. $6(x + 2)(x + 6)$ **30.** $4(z - 3)(z - 4)$ **31.** $2y(y - 3)(y - 8)$

32. $2x^2(x - 10)(x - 2)$ **33.** $y(4x - 1)^2$ **34.** $x(2y - 3)^2$

35. $(3s - t)(2s + 3t)$ **36.** $(2m - 3n)(3m + 4n)$

37. $xy(x - 3y)(x + 3y)$ **38.** $uv(2u - v)(2u + v)$

39. $3m(m^2 - 2m + 5)$ **40.** $2x(x^2 - x + 4)$ **41.** $(m + n)(m^2 - mn + n^2)$

42. $(r - t)(r^2 + rt + t^2)$ **43.** $(c - 1)(c^2 + c + 1)$

44. $(a + 1)(a^2 - a + 1)$ **45.** $2(3x - 5)(2x - 3)(12x - 19)$

46. $2(x - 3)(4x + 7)(8x - 5)$ **47.** $9x^4(9 - x)^3(5 - x)$

48. $7x^3(x - 7)^2(x - 4)$ **49.** $2(x + 1)(x^2 - 5)(3x + 5)(x - 1)$

50. $2(x - 3)^3(x^2 + 2)^2(5x - 4)(x - 1)$

51. $[(a - b) - 2(c - d)][(a - b) + 2(c - d)]$

52. $(x + 3y + 2)(x - 3y + 2)$ **53.** $(2m - 3n)(a + b)$ **54.** $(3c - 4d)(5a + b)$

55. Prime   **56.** Prime   **57.** $(x - 3)^2(x + 3)$ **58.** $(x + 1)(x - 1)^2$

59. $(a - 2)(a + 1)(a - 1)$ **60.** $(t - 2)(t^2 + 1)$

61. $[4(A + B) + 3][(A + B) - 2]$ **62.** $(x - y + 4)(6x - 6y - 1)$

63. $(m - n)(m + n)(m^2 + n^2)$ **64.** $(y - 2)(y + 2)(y^2 + 1)$

65. $st(st - 2)[s^2t^2 + 2st + 4]$ **66.** $a^2(3 + ab)(9 - 3ab + a^2b^2)$

67. $(m + n)(m + n - 1)$ **68.** $(y - x)(y - x - 1)$

69. $2a[3a - 2(x + 4)][3a + 2(x + 4)]$ **70.** $[10x - 15y + 3ab][10x - 15y - 3ab]$

71. $(x^2 - x + 1)(x^2 + x + 1)$ **72.** $(a^2 + b^2 - ab)(a^2 + b^2 + ab)$

73. (A) $4(10 - x)(10 + x) = 400 - 4x^2$ (B) $4x(10 - x)^2 = 400x - 80x^2 + 4x^3$

74. (A) $4(6 - x)(6 + x) = 144 - 4x^2$ (B) $2x(8 - x)(9 - 2x) = 144x - 50x^2 + 4x^3$

Exercise A-4

1. $\dfrac{a^2}{2}$ **2.** $8d^6$ **3.** $\dfrac{22y + 9}{252}$ **4.** $\dfrac{15x^2 + 10x - 6}{180}$ **5.** $\dfrac{x^2 + 8}{8x^3}$

6. $\dfrac{15m^2 + 14m - 6}{36m^3}$ **7.** $\dfrac{1}{2x - 1}$ **8.** $\dfrac{1}{x(x - 4)}$ **9.** $\dfrac{1}{m}$

10. $\dfrac{x}{x + 5}$ **11.** $\dfrac{2a}{(a + b)^2(a - b)}$ **12.** $\dfrac{x - 5}{(x - 1)^2(x + 1)}$ **13.** $\dfrac{m^2 - 6m + 7}{m - 2}$

14. $\dfrac{2}{x - 1}$ **15.** $\dfrac{7}{x - 3}$ **16.** $\dfrac{5}{a - 1}$ **17.** $\dfrac{3}{y + 3}$

18. $\dfrac{2}{x + y}$ **19.** $\dfrac{x + y}{x}$ **20.** $\dfrac{1}{x - 3}$

21. $\dfrac{4(x^2 + 2)^2(x + 1)(x - 1)}{x^3}$ **22.** $\dfrac{(x + 3)(x - 3)(x^2 + 3)}{x^4}$

23. $\dfrac{x(2 + 3x)}{(1 - 3x)^4}$ **24.** $\dfrac{2x(3 - 2x)}{(2x + 3)^5}$ **25.** $\dfrac{(x + 1)(x - 9)}{(x + 4)^4}$

26. $\dfrac{3(x + 2)(x - 2)}{(x + 1)^4}$ **27.** $\dfrac{y + 3}{(y - 2)(y + 7)}$ **28.** $\dfrac{7x^2 - 2x - 3}{6(x + 1)^2}$ **29.** -1

30. $-\dfrac{1}{x}$ **31.** $\dfrac{7y - 9x}{xy(a - b)}$ **32.** $\dfrac{-17c + 16}{15(c - 1)}$ **33.** $\dfrac{x^2 - x + 1}{2(x - 9)}$

34. 1 **35.** $\dfrac{(x - y)^2}{y^2(x + y)}$ **36.** $\dfrac{x^2(x + y)}{(x - y)^2}$ **37.** $\dfrac{1}{x - 4}$

38. $\dfrac{2x + 5}{(x + 1)(x + 4)}$ **39.** $\dfrac{x - 3}{x - 1}$ **40.** $\dfrac{x - y}{x + y}$ **41.** $\dfrac{-1}{x(x + h)}$

42. $\dfrac{-2x - h}{x^2(x + h)^2}$ **43.** $\dfrac{x^2 + hx + 4x + 2h}{(x + h + 2)(x + 2)}$ **44.** $\dfrac{-3}{x(x + h)}$

45. (A) Incorrect (B) $x + 1$ **46.** (A) Incorrect (B) $x + 1$

47. (A) Incorrect (B) $2x + h$ **48.** (A) Incorrect (B) $3x^2 + 3xh + h^2$

49. (A) Incorrect (B) $\dfrac{x^2 - 2}{x + 1}$ **50.** (A) Correct **51.** (A) (B) Correct

52. (A) Incorrect (B) $\dfrac{x^2 - x + 1}{x - 1}$ **53.** $\dfrac{-x(x + y)}{y}$ **54.** 1 **55.** $\dfrac{a - 2}{a}$ **56.** x

Exercise A-5

1. 1 **2.** 1 **3.** $6x^9$ **4.** $24x^{14}$ **5.** $\dfrac{9x^6}{y^4}$ **6.** $\dfrac{1}{8c^3d^6}$ **7.** $\dfrac{a^4b^{12}}{c^8d^4}$

8. $\dfrac{x^6y^3}{8w^6}$ **9.** 10^{17} **10.** 10 **11.** $\dfrac{2x}{y^2}$ **12.** $\dfrac{a^9}{8b^4}$ **13.** n^2

14. $\dfrac{1}{x^7}$ **15.** 4×10^8 **16.** 3×10^{16} **17.** 3.225×10^7

18. 4.93×10^3 **19.** 8.5×10^{-2} **20.** 1.7×10^{-2}

21. 7.29×10^{-8} **22.** 5.92×10^{-4} **23.** 0.005 **24.** 0.0004

25. 26,900,000 **26.** 6,500,000,000 **27.** 0.000 00000059

28. 0.0000063 **29.** $\dfrac{3y^4}{2}$ **30.** $\dfrac{4}{3n^3}$ **31.** $\dfrac{x^{12}}{y^8}$ **32.** $\dfrac{n^8}{m^{12}}$ **33.** $\dfrac{4x^8}{y^6}$

34. $\dfrac{n^{12}}{8m^6}$ **35.** $\dfrac{w^{12}}{u^{20}v^4}$ **36.** $\dfrac{t^2}{x^2y^{10}}$ **37.** $\dfrac{1}{(x + y)^2}$ **38.** $\dfrac{1}{a^2 - b^2}$ **39.** $\dfrac{x}{x - 1}$

40. x **41.** $\dfrac{-1}{xy}$ **42.** uv **43.** $\dfrac{-9x^2}{(x^3 + 3)^4}$ **44.** $\dfrac{-2(2x + 3)}{(x^2 + 3x)^3}$ **45.** 64

46. $2^{(3^2)} = 2^9 = 512$ while $(2^3)^2 = 8^2 = 64$ which is the calculator result.

49. $2x - 6x^{-1}$ **50.** $2 + 3x^{-2}$ **51.** $\dfrac{5}{3}x - \dfrac{2}{3}x^{-2}$ **52.** $\dfrac{7}{4} - \dfrac{1}{4}x^{-3}$

53. $x - \dfrac{3}{2} + \dfrac{1}{2}x^{-1}$ **54.** $\dfrac{3}{4}x - x^{-1} - \dfrac{1}{4}x^{-3}$ **55.** 6.65×10^{-17} **56.** 5.74×10^{-21}

57. 1.54×10^{12} **58.** 1.77×10^{-18} **59.** 1.0295×10^{11} **60.** -2.2911×10^{17}

61. -4.3647×10^{-18} **62.** 9.7137×10^{-12} **63.** 9.4697×10^{29} **64.** 1.8527×10^{37}

65. $2(a + 2b)^5$ **66.** $\dfrac{1}{2(x - 3)^2}$ **67.** $\dfrac{x^2 + xy + y^2}{xy}$ **68.** $\dfrac{bc(c + b)}{c^2 + bc + b^2}$

69. $\dfrac{y - x}{y}$ **70.** $\dfrac{v - u}{v + u}$ **71.** 1.3×10^{25} lb **72.** 3.3×10^{18} lb

73. 10^{10} or 10 billion, 6×10^{11} or 600 billion

74. 1.86×10^{-5} mi, 9.82×10^{-2} ft, 1.18 in

75. 1.44×10^3 dollars per person; $1,440 per person

76. $17,500 per person

Exercise A-6

1. 4   **2.** 4   **3.** 64   **4.** 8   **5.** −6   **6.** 8

7. $(-36)^{1/2}$ is not a real number   **8.** −8   **9.** $\dfrac{8}{125}$ **10.** $\dfrac{4}{9}$ **11.** $\dfrac{1}{27}$

12. $\dfrac{1}{4}$ **13.** $y^{3/5}$ **14.** x **15.** $d^{1/3}$ **16.** $\dfrac{1}{x^{1/2}}$ **17.** $\dfrac{1}{y^{1/2}}$ **18.** x^4

19. $\dfrac{2x}{y^2}$ **20.** $\dfrac{2v^2}{u}$ **21.** $\dfrac{1}{a^{1/4}b^{1/3}}$ **22.** $\dfrac{m^4}{n^3}$ **23.** $\dfrac{xy^2}{2}$ **24.** $\dfrac{3}{xw^2}$

25. $\dfrac{2b^2}{3a^2}$ **26.** $\dfrac{5}{4}x^4y^2$ **27.** $\dfrac{2}{3x^{7/12}}$ **28.** $\dfrac{2}{5}a^{13/12}$ **29.** $\dfrac{a^{1/3}}{b^2}$ **30.** $\dfrac{y}{x^{1/2}}$

31. $6m - 2m^{19/3}$ **32.** $12x - 6x^{35/4}$ **33.** $a - a^{1/2}b^{1/2} - 6b$

34. $3u - 13u^{1/2}v^{1/2} + 4v$ **35.** $4x - 9y$ **36.** $25m - n$

37. $x + 4x^{1/2}y^{1/2} + 4y$ **38.** $9x - 6x^{1/2}y^{1/2} + y$ **39.** 29.52   **40.** 103.2

41. 0.03093   **42.** 0.08053   **43.** 5.421   **44.** 4588   **45.** 107.6

46. 2.883×10^{20} **47.** $x = y = 1$ is one of many choices

48. $x = y = 1$ is one of many choices.   **49.** $x = y = 1$ is one of many choices.

50. $x = y = 1$ is one of many choices.   **51.** $3 - \dfrac{3}{4}x^{-1/2}$ **52.** $\dfrac{1}{2}x^{1/3} + x^{-1/3}$

53. $\dfrac{3}{5}x^{-1/3} + \dfrac{1}{5}x^{-1/2}$ **54.** $\dfrac{2}{3}x^{-1/4} + x^{-2/3}$ **55.** $\dfrac{1}{2}x^{5/3} - 2x^{1/6}$ **56.** $\dfrac{1}{2}x^{-1/6} - \dfrac{1}{4}$

57. $a^{1/n}b^{1/m}$ **58.** $a^{1/2}b^{1/3}$ **59.** $\dfrac{1}{x^{3m}y^{4n}}$ **60.** $\dfrac{1}{a^{2m}b^{3n}}$

61. (A) $x = -2$, for example (B) $x = 2$, for example (C) Not possible

62. (A) $x = 1$, for example (B) $x = -1$, for example (C) $x = 0$ is the only choice

63. No   **64.** No   **65.** $\dfrac{x - 3}{(2x - 1)^{3/2}}$ **66.** $\dfrac{x - 2}{2(x - 1)^{3/2}}$

67. $\dfrac{4x - 3}{(3x - 1)^{4/3}}$ **68.** $\dfrac{x + 6}{3(x + 2)^{5/3}}$ **69.** 1,920 units   **70.** 9600 units

71. 428 feet   **72.** 195 feet

Exercise A-7

1. $\sqrt[3]{m^2}$ or $(\sqrt[3]{m})^2$ (first preferred)   **2.** $\sqrt[5]{n^4}$ **3.** $6\sqrt[5]{x^3}$ **4.** $7\sqrt[5]{y^2}$

5. $\sqrt[5]{(4xy^3)^2}$ **6.** $\sqrt[7]{(7x^2y)^5}$ **7.** $\sqrt{x + y}$ **8.** $\sqrt{x} + \sqrt{y}$

9. $b^{1/5}$ **10.** $c^{1/2}$ **11.** $5x^{3/4}$ **12.** $7mn^{2/5}$ **13.** $(2x^2y)^{3/5}$ **14.** $(3m^4n)^{2/9}$

15. $x^{1/3} + y^{1/3}$ **16.** $(x + y)^{1/3}$ **17.** −2   **18.** −3   **19.** $3x^4y^2$

20. $4m^2y^4$ **21.** $2mn^2$ **22.** $2a^3b^2$ **23.** $2ab^2\sqrt{2ab}$ **24.** $3mn^3\sqrt{3n}$

25. $2xy^2\sqrt[3]{2xy}$ **26.** $2xy^2\sqrt[4]{x}$ **27.** $\sqrt{m}$ **28.** $\sqrt[5]{n^3}$ **29.** $\sqrt[15]{xy}$

30. $\sqrt[8]{5x}$ **31.** $3x\sqrt[3]{3}$ **32.** $4x\sqrt{y}$ **33.** $\dfrac{\sqrt{5}}{5}$ **34.** $\dfrac{\sqrt{7}}{7}$

35. $2\sqrt{3x}$ **36.** $2y\sqrt{6y}$ **37.** $2\sqrt{2} + 2$ **38.** $2\sqrt{6} + 4$

39. $\sqrt{3} - \sqrt{2}$ **40.** $\dfrac{\sqrt{5} + \sqrt{2}}{3}$ **41.** $3x^2y^2\sqrt[5]{3x^2y}$ **42.** $4a^3b^4\sqrt[3]{a^2b}$

43. $n\sqrt[4]{2m^3n}$ **44.** $2u\sqrt[5]{u^2v^3}$ **45.** $\sqrt[3]{a^2(b-a)}$ **46.** $\sqrt[4]{3^3(u+v)^3}$

47. $\sqrt[4]{a^3b}$ **48.** $\sqrt[6]{x^4y^3}$ **49.** $x^2y\sqrt[3]{6xy^2}$ **50.** $m^2n\sqrt[4]{24n}$

51. In simplified form   **52.** In simplified form   **53.** $\dfrac{\sqrt{2}}{2}$ or $\dfrac{1}{2}\sqrt{2}$

54. $\dfrac{2\sqrt{6}}{3}$ **55.** $2a^2b\sqrt[3]{4a^2b}$ **56.** $4x^2y^4\sqrt[3]{2xy^2}$ **57.** $\dfrac{\sqrt[4]{12xy^3}}{2x}$ or $\dfrac{1}{2x}\sqrt[4]{12xy^3}$

58. $\dfrac{\sqrt[5]{8x^2y^2}}{2y}$ **59.** $\dfrac{6y + 9\sqrt{y}}{4y - 9}$ **60.** $\dfrac{15\sqrt{x} + 10x}{9 - 4x}$ **61.** $\dfrac{38 + 11\sqrt{10}}{117}$

62. $\dfrac{5\sqrt{6} - 6}{19}$ **63.** $\sqrt{x^2 + 9} + 3$ **64.** $2 + \sqrt{y^2 + 4}$ **65.** $\dfrac{1}{\sqrt{t} + \sqrt{x}}$

66. $\dfrac{x - y}{x + 2\sqrt{xy} + y}$ **67.** $\dfrac{1}{\sqrt{x+h} + \sqrt{x}}$ **68.** $\dfrac{1}{\sqrt{2+h} - \sqrt{2}}$ **69.** 0.2222

70. 17.51 using calculator   **71.** 1.934 **72.** 0.7174 using calculator

73. $0.069\ 79$ **74.** 11.68 using calculator   **75.** 2.073

76. 1.397 using calculator   **77.** Both are 1.059 **78.** 1.308 using calculator

79. Both are 0.6300 **80.** 0.5848 using calculator **81.** $x \leq 0$ **82.** $x \geq 0$

83. All real numbers   **84.** $x = 0$ **85.** A and E, B and F, C and D

86. A and F, B and D, C and E   **87.** $\dfrac{\sqrt[3]{a^2} + \sqrt[3]{ab} + \sqrt[3]{b^2}}{a - b}$ **88.** $\dfrac{\sqrt[3]{m^2} - \sqrt[3]{mn} + \sqrt[3]{n^2}}{m + n}$

89. $\dfrac{(\sqrt{x} - \sqrt{y} - \sqrt{z})[(x + y - z) + 2\sqrt{xy}]}{(x + y - z)^2 - 4xy}$ **90.** $\dfrac{(\sqrt{x} + \sqrt{y} + \sqrt{z})(x + y - z - 2\sqrt{xy})}{(x + y - z)^2 - 4xy}$

91. $\dfrac{1}{\sqrt[3]{(x+h)^2} + \sqrt[3]{x(x+h)} + \sqrt[3]{x^2}}$ **92.** $\dfrac{1}{\sqrt[3]{t^2} + \sqrt[3]{tx} + \sqrt[3]{x^2}}$

93. $\sqrt[kn]{x^{km}} = (x^{km})^{1/kn} = x^{km/kn} = x^{m/n} = \sqrt[n]{x^m}$

Exercise A-8

1. $x = 7$ **2.** $x = 7$ **3.** $s = 2.5$ **4.** $t = 2$

5. $m = 5$ **6.** $y = 5$

7. $-8 \leq x \leq 7$; x

8. $-4 < x < 8$; x

9. $-6 \leq x < 6$;

10. $-3 < x \leq 3$;

11. $x \geq -6$;

12. $x < 7$;

13. $(-2, 6]$;

14. $[-5, 5]$;

15. $(-7, 8)$;

16. $[-4, 5)$;

17. $(-\infty, -2]$;

18. $(3, \infty)$;

19. $[-7, 2)$; $-7 \leq x < 2$

20. $[5, 6]$; $-5 \leq x \leq 6$

21. $(-\infty, 0]$; $x \leq 0$

22. $(1, \infty)$; $x > 1$

23. $x < 5$ or $(-\infty, 5)$;

24. $x \geq -3$; $[-3, \infty)$;

25. $x \geq 3$ or $[3, \infty)$;

26. $x < 2$; $(-\infty, 2)$;

27. $N < -8$ or $(-\infty, -8)$;

28. $m \geq 6$; $[6, \infty)$;

29. $m > 3$ or $(3, \infty)$;

30. $u \leq \frac{2}{7}$; $\left(-\infty, \frac{2}{7}\right]$;

31. $B \geq -4$ or $[-4, \infty)$;

32. $y < -7$; $(-\infty, -7)$;

33. 9   **34.** $-\frac{7}{4}$ **35.** 10   **36.** 150   **37.** 8   **38.** -9

39. $-5 < x \leq 7$;

40. $4 \leq x < 5$;

41. $2 < x < 4$;

42. $-1 \leq x \leq 6$;

43. $-\infty < x < \infty$;

44. $\varnothing$, the empty set

45. $x < -1$ or $3 \leq x < 7$;

46. $1 < x \leq 6$ or $x \geq 9$

47. $1 < x < 5$;

48. $2 \leq x \leq 3$;

49. $x \leq 6$;

50. $x > -3$;

51. $q < -14$ or $(-\infty, -14)$;

52. $p \geq 12$; $[12, \infty)$

53. $x \geq 4.5$ or $[4.5, \infty)$;

54. $x > -4\frac{2}{9}$ or $(-4\frac{2}{9}, \infty)$;

55. $-20 \leq x \leq 20$ or $[-20, 20]$;

56. $-9 \leq A \leq 9$ or $[-9, 9]$

57. $-8 \leq x < -3$ or $[-8, -3)$;

58. $2 < x \leq 5$ or $(2, 5]$

59. $-14 < x \leq 11$ or $(-14, 11]$;

60. $-35 \leq x \leq -20$ or $[-35, -20]$

61. (A) False (B) True (C) True

62. When both sides are divided by $n - m$ the order of the inequality should be changed, because $n - m$ is negative.

APPENDIX A REVIEW

1. (A) True (B) True (C) False (D) True (E) False (F) False (A-1)

2. (A) $(y + z)x$ (B) $(2 + x) + y$ (C) $2x + 3x$ (A-1)

3. $x^3 + 3x^2 + 5x - 2$ (A-2)   **4.** $x^3 - 3x^2 - 3x + 22$ (A-2)

5. $3x^5 + x^4 - 8x^3 + 24x^2 + 8x - 64$ (A-2)   **6.** 3 (A-2)   **7.** 1 (A-2)

8. $14x^2 - 30x$ (A-2)   **9.** $9m^2 - 25n^2$ (A-2) **10.** $6x^2 - 5xy - 4y^2$ (A-2)

11. $4a^2 - 12ab + 9b^2$ (A-2)   **12.** $(3x - 2)^2$ (A-3)   **13.** Prime (A-3)

14. $3n(2n - 5)(n + 1)$ (A-3)   **15.** $\dfrac{12a^3b - 40b^2 - 5a}{30a^3b^2}$ (A-4)

16. $\dfrac{7x - 4}{6x(x - 4)}$ (A-4) **17.** $\dfrac{y + 2}{y(y - 2)}$ (A-4) **18.** u (A-4) **19.** $6x^5y^{15}$ (A-5)

20. $\dfrac{3u^4}{v^2}$ (A-5)   **21.** 6×10^2 (A-5)   **22.** $\dfrac{x^6}{y^4}$ (A-5)   **23.** $u^{7/3}$ (A-6)

24. $\dfrac{3a^2}{b}$ (A-6)   **25.** $3\sqrt[5]{x^2}$ (A-7)   **26.** $-3(xy)^{2/3}$ (A-7)

27. $3x^2y\sqrt[3]{x^2y}$ (A-7)   **28.** $6x^2y^3\sqrt{xy}$ (A-7)   **29.** $2b\sqrt{3a}$ (A-7)   **30.** $\dfrac{3\sqrt{5} + 5}{4}$ (A-7)

31. $\sqrt[4]{y^3}$ (*A–7*)

32. $x = 4$ (*A–8*)

33. $x < 6$ or $(-\infty, 6)$ (*A–8*)

34. $\{-3, -1, 1\}$ (*A–1*)   **35.** Subtraction   (*A–1*)

36. Commutative (+)   (*A–1*)   **37.** Distributive   (*A–1*)

38. Associative (·)   (*A–1*)   **39.** Negatives   (*A–1*)

40. Identity (+)   (*A–1*)   **41.** (A) T   (B) F   (*A–1*)

42. 0 and –3 are two examples of infinitely many   (*A–1*)

43. (A) a and d   (B) None   (*A–2*) **44.** $4xy - 2y^2$ (*A–2*)   **45.** $m^4 - 6m^2n^2 + n^4$ (*A–2*)

46. $10xh + 5h^2 - 7h$ (*A–2*)   **47.** $2x^3 - 4x^2 + 12x$ (*A–2*)

48. $x^3 - 6x^2y + 12xy^2 - 8y^3$ (*A–2*) **49.** $(x - y)(7x - y)$ (*A–3*)   **50.** Prime   (*A–3*)

51. $3xy(2x^2 + 4xy - 5y^2)$ (*A–3*)   **52.** $(y - b)(y - b - 1)$ (*A–3*)

53. $3(x + 2y)(x^2 - 2xy + 4y^2)$ (*A–3*)   **54.** $(y - 2)(y + 2)^2$ (*A–3*)

55. $x(x - 4)^2(5x - 8)$ (*A–3*)   **56.** $\dfrac{(x + 2)^2(x - 4)}{x^3}$ (*A–4*)

57. $\dfrac{2m}{(m - 2)^2(m + 2)}$ (*A–4*)   **58.** $\dfrac{y^2}{x}$ (*A–4*)   **59.** $\dfrac{x - y}{x + y}$ (*A–4*)

60. $\dfrac{-ab}{a^2 + ab + b^2}$ (*A–4, A–5*)

61. Incorrect; correct final form is $\dfrac{x^2 + 2x - 2}{x - 1}$ (*A–4*)   **62.** $\dfrac{1}{4}$ (*A–5*)

63. $\dfrac{5}{9}$ (*A–5*)   **64.** $\dfrac{3x^2}{2y^2}$ (*A–6*)   **65.** $\dfrac{27a^{1/6}}{b^{1/2}}$ (*A–6*)

66. $x + 2x^{1/2}y^{1/2} + y$ (*A–6*)   **67.** $6x + 7x^{1/2}y^{1/2} - 3y$ (*A–6*)

68. 2×10^{-7} (*A–5*)   **69.** 3.213×10^6 (*A–5*)   **70.** 4.434×10^{-5} (*A–5*)

71. -4.541×10^{-6} (*A–5*)   **72.** $128,800$ (*A–6*)   **73.** 0.01507 (*A–6*)

74. 0.3664 (*A–7*)   **75.** 1.640 (*A–7*)   **76.** 0.08726 (*A–6*)

77. $-6x^2y^2 \sqrt[5]{3x^2y}$ *(A-7)*   **78.** $x\sqrt[3]{2x^2}$ *(A-7)*   **79.** $\dfrac{\sqrt[5]{12x^3y^2}}{2x}$ *(A-7)*

80. $y\sqrt[3]{2x^2y}$ *(A-7)*   **81.** $\sqrt[3]{2x^2}$ *(A-7)*   **82.** $2x - 3\sqrt{xy} - 5y$ *(A-7)*

83. $\dfrac{6x + 3\sqrt{xy}}{4x - y}$ *(A-7)* **84.** $\dfrac{4u - 12\sqrt{uv} + 9v}{4u - 9v}$ *(A-7)*   **85.** $\sqrt{y^2 + 4} + 2$ *(A-7)*

86. $\dfrac{1}{\sqrt{t} + \sqrt{5}}$ *(A-7)*   **87.** $2 - \dfrac{3}{2}x^{-1/2}$ *(A-7)*

88. $x = 0.\overline{36}$ *(A-8)*

89. $-2 < x \le 4$ or $(-2, 4]$ *(A-8)*

90. $\dfrac{6}{11}$; rational *(A-1)*

91. (A) $\{-4, -3, 0, 2\}$ (B) $\{-3, 2\}$ *(A-1)*   **92.** 0 *(A-7)*

93. $x^3 + 8x^2 - 6x + 1$ *(A-2)*   **94.** $x(2a + 3x - 4)(2a - 3x - 4)$ *(A-3)*

95. All three have the same value. *(A-7)*

96. $\dfrac{2}{3}(x - 2)(x + 3)^4$ *(A-5)*   **97.** $\dfrac{a^2b^2}{a^3 + b^3}$ *(A-5)*

98. $x - y$ *(A-6)*   **99.** x^{m-1} *(A-6)*   **100.** $\dfrac{1 + \sqrt[3]{x} + \sqrt[3]{x^2}}{1 - x}$ *(A-7)*

101. $\dfrac{1}{\sqrt[3]{t^2} + \sqrt[3]{5t} + \sqrt[3]{25}}$ *(A-7)*   **102.** x^{n+1} *(A-7)*

103. Volume $= 12\pi x + 12\pi$ ft^3 *(A-2)*

104. $9.60 \times 10^3 = 9,600$ kg per person *(A-5)*

105. (A) 24,000 units   (B) Production doubles to 48,000 units

   (C) At any production level, doubling the units of capital and labor
       doubles production.   *(A-6)*

106. $R = \dfrac{R_1R_2R_3}{R_2R_3 + R_1R_3 + R_1R_2}$ *(A-4)*

107. (A) $A = 480 - 6x^2 = 6(80 - x^2)$
   (B) $V = x(16 - 2x)(15 - 1.5x) = 240x - 54x^2 + 3x^3$ *(A-3)*

APPENDIX B

Exercise B-1

1. $A = 2$, $B = 5$ **2.** $B = 6$, $A = 3$ **3.** $A = 7$, $B = -2$ **4.** $B = -3$, $A = 5$

5. $A = 1$, $B = 2$, $C = 3$ **6.** $A = 2$, $C = 1$, $B = -1$

7. $A = 2$, $B = 1$, $C = 3$ **8.** $A = 3$, $B = 2$, $C = -1$

9. $A = 0$, $B = 2$, $C = 2$, $D = -3$ **10.** $B = 0$, $D = -4$, $A = 3$, $C = 1$

11. $\dfrac{-4}{x + 2} + \dfrac{3}{x - 4}$ **12.** $\dfrac{-3}{x - 3} + \dfrac{2}{x + 5}$ **13.** $\dfrac{3}{3x + 4} - \dfrac{1}{2x - 3}$

14. $\dfrac{5}{2x + 3} + \dfrac{-2}{3x - 1}$ **15.** $\dfrac{2}{x} - \dfrac{1}{x - 3} - \dfrac{3}{(x - 3)^2}$

16. $\dfrac{3}{x} + \dfrac{2}{x - 4} + \dfrac{-4}{(x - 4)^2}$ **17.** $\dfrac{2}{x} + \dfrac{3x - 1}{x^2 + 2x + 3}$

18. $\dfrac{4}{x} + \dfrac{2x - 3}{x^2 - 3x + 4}$ **19.** $\dfrac{2x}{x^2 + 2} + \dfrac{3x + 5}{(x^2 + 2)^2}$

20. $\dfrac{-5}{x^2 + 3} + \dfrac{7x - 3}{(x^2 + 3)^2}$ **21.** $x - 2 + \dfrac{3}{x - 2} - \dfrac{2}{x - 3}$

22. $x - 1 + \dfrac{3}{x + 5} + \dfrac{1}{x - 3}$ **23.** $\dfrac{2}{x - 3} + \dfrac{2x + 5}{x^2 + 3x + 3}$

24. $\dfrac{3}{x + 2} + \dfrac{x - 4}{x^2 - 2x + 3}$ **25.** $\dfrac{2}{x - 4} - \dfrac{1}{x + 3} + \dfrac{3}{(x + 3)^2}$

26. $\dfrac{4}{x + 3} + \dfrac{1}{x - 2} + \dfrac{-3}{(x - 2)^2}$ **27.** $\dfrac{2}{x - 2} - \dfrac{3}{(x - 2)^2} - \dfrac{2x}{x^2 - x + 1}$

28. $\dfrac{1}{x - 3} + \dfrac{-2}{(x - 3)^2} + \dfrac{-3x}{x^2 - x + 2}$ **29.** $x + 2 - \dfrac{2}{x + 2} + \dfrac{1}{2x - 1} + \dfrac{x - 1}{2x^2 - x + 1}$

30. $x - 1 + \dfrac{1}{2x + 1} + \dfrac{-2}{x - 1} + \dfrac{x - 2}{3x^2 - 2x + 1}$